CHILDREN ARE IN DANGER IN THE NINETEEN-EIGHTIES. IT COULD GET WORSE IN THE NINETEEN-NINETIES. YOU COULD PREVENT IT.

CHILDREN IN DANGER CAMPAIGN

For the last three years we have reported back to the nation on the state of the country's children. We have spoken out about youth unemployment, about the poverty that affects a growing number of families with children, and about drug problems. It has mostly been bad news we have brought and it is getting worse.

That is why we have launched a Children in Danger campaign. For we are fearful about what is happening to children in this country and concerned that the crisis could deepen in the next decade.

A legacy to National Children's Home could be your stake in making that future a little less grim. Whatever you can bequest now can only aid our work in the future. We invite you to find out more about the Children in Danger campaign and about why we are worried. More positively, we want to tell you how those dangers can be prevented and how we spend the income we receive from legacies.

Write to:
Viscount Tonypandy,
Children in Danger Campaign,
National Children's Home,
85 Highbury Park, London N5 1UD.

NATIONAL CHILDREN'S HOME

NCH Plaza Tower
East Kilbride G74 1LW
Tel: 03552 35925

If you care, commit yourself.

What you can do with the best Will in the world.

Half the people in the Third World have no secure home.

More than half the Third World's farmers are landless.

Easily preventable diseases leave millions of children chronically sick.

Christian Aid is working together with the poor through local churches and communities in more than 70 countries to right these wrongs.

Ask for our free booklet on How to make a Will and read what your legacy or Covenant can do.

It is time to right wrongs.

Christian Aid

CHURCHES IN ACTION WITH THE WORLD'S POOR.
P.O. Box 11, Edinburgh.

YOUR NEW CHURCH or HALL:

BUILT BY THE SPECIALISTS WITH THE EXPERIENCE

- Economy of construction

- Low maintenance costs

- Full insulation for energy conservation

- Realistic completion dates

- Confidence of 25 years' experience

- Free consultancy service

- Nationwide design and build service

STOCKS

Springburn Parish Church, Springburn, Glasgow

DESIGN BUILD

Please send coupon for special literature on church buildings to:
**Stocks Bros (Buildings) Ltd.,
5 Ninelands Lane, Garforth,
Leeds LS25 1NT.**
Tel: (0532) 868011

Name_____

Position_____

Organisation_____

Address_____

_____

Telephone No._____

St. Andrew's Trinity Church, Johnstone, Renfrewshire

In writing to advertisers please mention the "Year-Book"

The Church of Scotland, Board of Social Responsibility, 121 George Street, Edinburgh EH2 4YN.

Photograph by ANNE H. MAXWELL

THE RIGHT REVEREND JAMES A. WHYTE, MA, LLD
MODERATOR

THE
Church of Scotland

YEAR BOOK
1989
(HUNDRED AND FOURTH YEAR OF ISSUE)

Edited by
The Very Rev. ANDREW HERRON, DD, LLD
and
Rev. ROY M. TUTON, MA

Published for
THE CHURCH OF SCOTLAND
DEPARTMENT OF COMMUNICATION
by

THE SAINT ANDREW PRESS
121 George Street, Edinburgh EH2 4YN

ISBN 0 86153 107 8

CALENDAR FOR 1989

JANUARY
```
S  1  8 15 22 29
M  2  9 16 23 30
T  3 10 17 24 31
W  4 11 18 25 —
T  5 12 19 26 —
F  6 13 20 27 —
S  7 14 21 28 —
```

FEBRUARY
```
S  —  5 12 19 26
M  —  6 13 20 27
T  —  7 14 21 28
W  1  8 15 22 —
T  2  9 16 23 —
F  3 10 17 24 —
S  4 11 18 25 —
```

MARCH
```
S  —  5 12 19 26
M  —  6 13 20 27
T  —  7 14 21 28
W  1  8 15 22 29
T  2  9 16 23 30
F  3 10 17 24 31
S  4 11 18 25 —
```

APRIL
```
S    2  9 16 23 30
M    3 10 17 24 —
T    4 11 18 25 —
W    5 12 19 26 —
T    6 13 20 27 —
F    7 14 21 28 —
S  1 8 15 22 29 —
```

MAY
```
S  —  7 14 21 28
M  1  8 15 22 29
T  2  9 16 23 30
W  3 10 17 24 31
T  4 11 18 25 —
F  5 12 19 26 —
S  6 13 20 27 —
```

JUNE
```
S  —  4 11 18 25
M  —  5 12 19 26
T  —  6 13 20 27
W  —  7 14 21 28
T  1  8 15 22 29
F  2  9 16 23 30
S  3 10 17 24 —
```

JULY
```
S    2  9 16 23 30
M    3 10 17 24 31
T    4 11 18 25 —
W    5 12 19 26 —
T    6 13 20 27 —
F    7 14 21 28 —
S  1 8 15 22 29 —
```

AUGUST
```
S  —  6 13 20 27
M  —  7 14 21 28
T  1  8 15 22 29
W  2  9 16 23 30
T  3 10 17 24 31
F  4 11 18 25 —
S  5 12 19 26 —
```

SEPTEMBER
```
S  —  3 10 17 24
M  —  4 11 18 25
T  —  5 12 19 26
W  —  6 13 20 27
T  —  7 14 21 28
F  1  8 15 22 29
S  2  9 16 23 30
```

OCTOBER
```
S  1  8 15 22 29
M  2  9 16 23 30
T  3 10 17 24 31
W  4 11 18 25 —
T  5 12 19 26 —
F  6 13 20 27 —
S  7 14 21 28 —
```

NOVEMBER
```
S  —  5 12 19 26
M  —  6 13 20 27
T  —  7 14 21 28
W  1  8 15 22 29
T  2  9 16 23 30
F  3 10 17 24 —
S  4 11 18 25 —
```

DECEMBER
```
S    3 10 17 24 31
M    4 11 18 25 —
T    5 12 19 26 —
W    6 13 20 27 —
T    7 14 21 28 —
F  1 8 15 22 29 —
S  2 9 16 23 30 —
```

CALENDAR FOR 1990

JANUARY
```
S  —  7 14 21 28
M  1  8 15 22 29
T  2  9 16 23 30
W  3 10 17 24 31
T  4 11 18 25 —
F  5 12 19 26 —
S  6 13 20 27 —
```

FEBRUARY
```
S  —  4 11 18 25
M  —  5 12 19 26
T  —  6 13 20 27
W  —  7 14 21 28
T  1  8 15 22 —
F  2  9 16 23 —
S  3 10 17 24 —
```

MARCH
```
S  —  4 11 18 25
M  —  5 12 19 26
T  —  6 13 20 27
W  —  7 14 21 28
T  1  8 15 22 29
F  2  9 16 23 30
S  3 10 17 24 31
```

APRIL
```
S  1  8 15 22 29
M  2  9 16 23 30
T  3 10 17 24 —
W  4 11 18 25 —
T  5 12 19 26 —
F  6 13 20 27 —
S  7 14 21 28 —
```

MAY
```
S  —  6 13 20 27
M  —  7 14 21 28
T  1  8 15 22 29
W  2  9 16 23 30
T  3 10 17 24 31
F  4 11 18 25 —
S  5 12 19 26 —
```

JUNE
```
S  —  3 10 17 24
M  —  4 11 18 25
T  —  5 12 19 26
W  —  6 13 20 27
T  —  7 14 21 28
F  1  8 15 22 29
S  2  9 16 23 30
```

JULY
```
S  1  8 15 22 29
M  2  9 16 23 30
T  3 10 17 24 31
W  4 11 18 25 —
T  5 12 19 26 —
F  6 13 20 27 —
S  7 14 21 28 —
```

AUGUST
```
S  —  5 12 19 26
M  —  6 13 20 27
T  —  7 14 21 28
W  1  8 15 22 29
T  2  9 16 23 30
F  3 10 17 24 31
S  4 11 18 25 —
```

SEPTEMBER
```
S    2  9 16 23 30
M    3 10 17 24 —
T    4 11 18 25 —
W    5 12 19 26 —
T    6 13 20 27 —
F    7 14 21 28 —
S  1 8 15 22 29 —
```

OCTOBER
```
S  —  7 14 21 28
M  1  8 15 22 29
T  2  9 16 23 30
W  3 10 17 24 31
T  4 11 18 25 —
F  5 12 19 26 —
S  6 13 20 27 —
```

NOVEMBER
```
S  —  4 11 18 25
M  —  5 12 19 26
T  —  6 13 20 27
W  —  7 14 21 28
T  1  8 15 22 29
F  2  9 16 23 30
S  3 10 17 24 —
```

DECEMBER
```
S    2  9 16 23 30
M    3 10 17 24 31
T    4 11 18 25 —
W    5 12 19 26 —
T    6 13 20 27 —
F    7 14 21 28 —
S  1 8 15 22 29 —
```

FESTIVALS, ANNIVERSARIES, Etc., in 1990

Jan.	6.	Epiphany.
Apr.	20.	Good Friday.
Apr.	22.	Easter Sunday.
May	31.	Ascension Day.
June	10.	Whitsunday or Pentecost.
June	17.	Trinity Sunday.
Nov.	11.	Remembrance Day.
Dec.	2.	Advent Sunday.
Nov.	30.	St. Andrew's Day.
Dec.	25.	Christmas Day.

Contents

PREFACE

To guild refined gold, To paint the lily—these, and a number of similar operations, were classified by Shakespeare as "wasteful and ridiculous excess".

I wonder what he would have said about writing a Preface to commend the Church of Scotland Year-Book to its readers. No book requires it less. Everyone who has used it knows its value.

It is hard to think that the Church could ever have managed without it, but in fact it is only one hundred and four years old, which is relatively young by ecclesiastical standards.

The Year Book is the indispensable work of reference for everyone concerned with the work of the Church and its parishes, ministries, and agencies. The task of keeping it up-to-date and accurate must be a formidable one, but the Editors somehow manage to keep abreast not only of the many changes in personnel and in statistics, but also of the changes in the Church's structure and administration.

In my youth we used to call it affectionately "The Probationers' Bible", but it is of interest not only to probationers and ministers.

It is a mine of useful information for anyone whose vision goes beyond the limits of a single congregation—and that should be everyone.

Dr Herron and his helpers deserve the support and the thanks of the Church.

JAMES A. WHYTE
Moderator

EDITOR'S PREFACE

Some fairly minor changes have been made in the Book this year, two of them calling for comment.

First the occasion of the transfer of all but two of the Lay Missionaries to the ranks of the Diaconate necessitated alterations. List I (Deaconesses) has disappeared completely, List H now containing particulars of the Diaconate of both sexes, of the remaining Lay Missionaries (as well as retired members of both), and of Agents, a category of which we can find no specific Assembly recognition but of which there are now sixteen in active service.

So far as we know no title has been officially adopted for male members of the Diaconate. While aware of the possibility of confusion we have called them "Deacons".

Secondly we have included in the List of Ministers, etc at the end of the book the names of retired overseas staff as well as of deaconesses and lay missionaries. This list began as the Alphabetical List of Ministers and has been regularly expanded to include more and more groups. It seemed appropriate to adopt the simple heading, "Index of Personnel".

Once again we are much indebted to Secretaries and Presbytery Clerks and to the staff of Messrs M'Corquodale for unfailing courtesy and help, and this year we have been encouraged and greatly assisted by the Assistant Editor, our good friend Roy Tuton.

ANDREW HERRON
Editor

DATES TO BE NOTED IN 1989

Jan. 1. Petitions for Admission to the Ministry of the Church to be lodged with the Secretary of the Admission Committee.

Jan. 6. Epiphany.

Jan. 14. Woman's Guild Schedules to be returned to Presbyterial Council Treasurers.

Jan. 15. Statistical Returns from Congregations to be in hands of Presbytery Clerks.

Jan. 18–25. Week of Prayer for Christian Unity.

Jan. 31. Finance Schedules to be returned to General Treasurer.

Jan. 31. Statistical Returns to be sent by Presbyteries to the Clerks of General Assembly.

Jan. 31. Last day for application for recognition by Committee on Education for the Ministry as a student for the Ministry.

Jan. 31. Woman's Guild Financial Schedules to be returned to Presbyterial Council Treasurers.

Feb. 21–22. Stated Committee Meetings.

Feb. 22. Thinking Day (Girl Guides).

Feb. 23. Commission of Assembly (if called).

Mar. 3. World Day of Prayer.

Mar. 15. Returns from Presbyteries to Nomination Committee due.

Mar. 19. Palm Sunday.

Mar. 19. Day of Intercession for Jewry and Jewish Missions.

Mar. 19–26. Week of Prayer, Thank-offering and Self-denial.

Mar. 24. Good Friday.

Mar. 26. Easter Sunday.

Mar. 26. Summer Time begins.

Mar. 31. Commissions to General Assembly to be transmitted by Presbytery Clerks to Clerk of Assembly.

Mar. 31. List of Ministers without charge to be sent by Clerks of Presbyteries to the Clerks of General Assembly and to the Secretary of the Probationers and Transference and Admission of Ministers Committee.

April 18-19. Stated Committee Meetings.

April 21. Queen Elizabeth born, 1926.

April 24. Overtures, Commissions, Appeals, Complaints, Memorials, Petitions, References, etc., to be in hands of Clerks of Assembly.

April 25. Woman's Guild Annual Meeting.

April 30. Woman's Guild Branch/Group Schedules to be returned to Guild Office.

May 4. Ascension Day.

May 8. Woman's Guild Presbyterial Council Schedules to be returned to Guild Office.

May 14. Whitsunday or Pentecost.

May 20–26. General Assembly.

May 21. Trinity Sunday.

May 22–28. Christian Aid Week.

May 28. Christian Life-Style Sunday.

June 20–21. Stated Committee Meetings.

July 25. Report of Committee on work of students to be sent to Presbyteries.

Aug. 4. Queen Elizabeth, the Queen Mother, born, 1900.

Sept. 1. Applications for Bursaries to be returned to Secretary of Education for the Ministry Committee.

Sept. 17. Presbyteries to inform Committee of nomination of Candidates for the Ministry.

Sept. 25. Presbyteries to report to Assembly Committee on work of students.

Oct. 3. Reports on Intersessional Work of Students to be forwarded to Secretary of Education for the Ministry Committee.

Oct. 17–18. Stated Committee Meetings.

Oct. 19. Commission of Assembly (if called).

Oct. 22. Summer Time ends.

Oct. 24. United Nations Day.

Oct. 31. Last day for application to Committee to be taken on Trials for Licence.

Nov. 1. All Saints' Day.

Nov. 12. Remembrance Day.

Nov. 30. St. Andrew's Day.

Nov. 30. Candidates to intimate to Presbytery that they wish to be taken on trials for licence.

Dec. 3. Advent Sunday.

Dec. 25. Christmas Day.

THE MODERATOR 1988

The Right Reverend JAMES A. WHYTE MA LLD

By The Revd George D. Wilkie OBE BD

James Aitken Whyte grew up in the years between the wars in the Trinity district of Edinburgh. Along with his brothers (one older, one younger) he was educated at Daniel Stewart's College where he was Dux in 1937. During his school years a major influence in his life was the Scottish Schoolboys Club, which sought through Easter Camps and Sunday Discussion Groups to help boys "to discover for themselves and for the world the full meaning of the Christian Faith."

By the time he went to Edinburgh University the idea of entering the ministry of the Church of Scotland was very much in his mind. He studied Philosophy under the twin giants of that day, Professors Kemp Smith and A.E. Taylor, obtaining in 1942 a First Class Honours degree. He was a keen member of the Student Christian Movement, and much of his understanding of the faith was hammered out in S.C.M. conferences, meetings and study groups. Indeed this contact with S.C.M. has been maintained throughout the years, in particular through the Presidency of the Christian Education Movement—the schools offshoot of the S.C.M.

After three years' study in New College, where he was President of the Theological Society, Professor Whyte became a chaplain in the Scots Guards and was stationed with the 1st Battalion in Italy. In 1948 he was called to Christ's Church Dunollie in Oban, moving in 1952 to Mayfield (then Mayfield North) Church in Edinburgh. In 1958 he was appointed to the chair of Christian Ethics and Practical Theology in St Mary's College, St Andrews. He was Principal of the College from 1978 to 1982, and in 1981 received the honoray degree of LL.D. from the University of Dundee.

James Whyte is no cloistered academic. He sees theology as essentially practical and, while properly to be studied within the discipline of a university course, it must at the same time be firmly related to the needs of ordinary Christians and of the Christian Church. As well as fulfilling his pastoral responsibilities within the student community in St Andrews Professor Whyte has always found time to address elders' meetings, lead Bible study, and speak at numerous conferences where lay people are to be found struggling with the issues of life and faith. He has also served on numerous Church committees and was Convener of the Inter-Church Relations Commttee from 1974 to 1978.

The Moderatorial Year has been overshadowed by the tragic death of Mrs Whyte a few short weeks after the close of the Assembly. Although she had undergone major surgery in the months leading up to the Assembly, Mrs Whyte carried out all her duties —including the generous hospitality of the Moderator's flat—with characteristic courage, cheerfulness and goodwill. In this she was surrounded and supported by her daughter and two sons and their own young families. Mrs Whyte also played her part in the visit to the Irish Assembly immediately following our own, and indeed was actively supporting her husband a few days before her death.

In spite of this very great loss Professor Whyte has continued to fulfil all his major engagements with the graciousness, wisdom and friendliness which are the hallmark of the man. The Church expects a great deal from its Moderators nowadays and James Whyte has a quiet determination to fulfil all the duties of the office to which the Church has called him.

THE GENERAL ASSEMBLY 1988

Certainly the liveliest scenes to characterise the Assembly of 1988 were inspired by something which strictly was no part of Assembly business. There is a tradition of long standing that when the Lord High Commissioner has among his guests at Holyroodhouse some person of peculiar importance in the national life the Convener of the Business Committee draws the attention of the Moderator to the presence of a stranger and suggests that the Assembly may wish to welcome and hear that person. This year on, resuming after Saturday's Garden Party, Mrs Margaret Thatcher was to be seen seated in the Lord High's Gallery and the usual formula was pronounced. Exception was taken to hearing the lady and when the Assembly vociferously rejected the protest five commissioners registered their dissent. The net result, so far as we could judge, was that the Prime Minister received a welcome much more tumultuous than might otherwise have been the case. Ourselves we found it difficult to understand the objection to hearing the lady—nothing she could say had any significance so far as the business of the Court was concerned, the whole thing being no more than a courtesy to the holder of a unique office—both Harold Wilson and James Callaghan were welcomed and listened to by many in the Assembly to whom their policies were anathema.

For the fourth year in succession the subject of Abortion engendered a long and heated debate. In the end agreement was reached on the Board's recommendation that the time limit should be reduced, and regret was expressed that Mr David Alton's Bill had been denied a free vote in the House of Commons, the Government being called upon to make time for such a vote.

Considerable opposition was forthcoming to a proposal by the Youth Education Committee that Kirk Sessions should be instructed to maintain a Young Persons Roll containing the names and addresses of all childen under the age of sixteen who are in any way connected with the congregation, the Roll to be revised annually and to be submitted for inspection by the Presbytery. It was agreed that the proposal be framed as an Overture and be sent down to Presbyteries under the Barrier Act.

The report on the Inter-Church Process instigated at the recent Swanwick Conference and the news of the Roman Catholic commitment thereto was responsible for a great wave of enthusiasm—we heard the word "ecuphoria" used—and it will be interesting to see how the report fares in Presbyteries and Kirk Sessions.

A decision of no small constitutional moment was the agreement reported as having been given by Presbyteries to changes in the Act anent the Judicial Commission so as to give it finality of judgment. The Assembly have always been reluctant to delegate their ultimate authority to any body however distinguished or representative. Of recent years, however, it has become increasingly apparent that either the Judicial Commission must be given the last word or the Assembly themselves must deal with these cases from start to finish. The former alternative has been accepted.

The future of the Manse at Iona (requiring repairs to the tune of £123,000) provided material for a long debate—which might more advantageously have been conducted in Gaelic! It was remitted to the General Trustees with powers to decide what is a highly complicated issue.

Notice was taken of the fact that 1988 marks the 350th anniversary of the signing of the National Covenant and of the famous Glasgow Assembly that did so much to restore Presbyterianism. Sunday 20th November was appointed for the celebration of the occasion.

The Assembly also approved the sale of the painting, "The Assuaging of the Waters", the proceeds to be used by the Board of Practice and Procedure in its care of the Assembly Hall and of the Church's portraits and paintings generally.

Once the heat of the Thatcher controversy had died down it was never a very exciting, and rarely even a very interesting Assembly. But it got through a lot of necessary business and that, after all, is what it exists to do.

THE GENERAL ASSEMBLY — OFFICIALS

The General Assembly is appointed to meet on Saturday, 20th May, 1989

The Commission of Assembly will be held at Edinburgh when called at the instance of the Board of Practice and Procedure.

The Lord High Commissioner (1988)
His Grace Sir IAIN MARK TENNANT, KT, FRSA

Moderator (1988)
The Right Rev. JAMES A. WHYTE, MA, LLD
St. Andrews

Chaplains to the Moderator
Rev. GEORGE D. WILKIE, CBE, BL, Edinburgh
Rev. BARBARA D. QUIGLEY, MTheol, ThM, DPSS, New Stevenson

Moderator-Designate (1989)
The Rev. WILLIAM J. G. M'DONALD, MA, BD, DD
Edinburgh Mayfield

Principal Clerk and Secretary to the Moderator
The Rev. JAMES L. WEATHERHEAD, MA, LLB
121 George Street, Edinburgh EH2 4YN *031–225 5722*

Depute Clerk
The Rev. A. GORDON M'GILLIVRAY, MA, BD, STM
Clerk to the Presbytery of Edinburgh *031–225 9137*

Procurator
Mr. GEORGE W. PENROSE, QC

Solicitor, Law Agent and Custodier of Titles
Mr. R. A. PATERSON, MA, LLB, 121 George Street, Edinburgh EH2 4YN
031–225 5722

Convener of Business Committee
The Rev. W. B. R. MACMILLAN, MA, BD, Dundee

Vice-Convener of Business Committee
The Rev. FINLAY A. J. MACDONALD, MA, BD, PhD, Glasgow

Precentor
The Rev. WILLIAM HENNEY, MA, St. Andrews

Officer
Mr. GEORGE STEPHENSON

General Treasurer Mr. W. G. P. COLLEDGE, CA

Parliamentary Solicitor
Mr. IAN M'CULLOCH, Martin & Co., 1 Dean Farrar Street, Westminster, London SW1H 0DY

Auditor Mr. ROBERT GORDON, CA

ASSEMBLY STANDING COMMITTEES

I. ADMINISTRATION AND SPECIAL INTERESTS DEPARTMENT
Administration

Board of Practice and Procedure
Membership 38 (32 Assembly appointed direct plus Moderator, Moderator Designate, Clerks, Procurator and Law Agent *ex officiis*).
Convener—Rev. FINLAY A. J. MACDONALD, MA, BD, PhD, Glasgow.
Vice-Convener—Mr. JAMES H. F. SMITH
Secretary—Rev. JAMES L. WEATHERHEAD, MA, LLB. *031–225 5722.*

Assembly Council
Membership 23 (16 appointed by Assembly with Conveners of Departments).
Convener—Rev. HUGH R. WYLLIE, MA, Hamilton.
Vice-Convener—Rev. DAVID P. MUNRO, MA, BD, STM, Bearsden.
Secretary—Rev. RONALD S. BLAKEY, MA, BD, MTh. *031–225 5722*

Committee to Nominate the Moderator
Membership 61 (Seven ex Moderators plus seven elders and one member from each UK Presbytery).
Meets on Tuesday, 17th October, 1989.
Chairman—Earliest serving ex-Moderator present.
Secretary—Rev. JAMES L. WEATHERHEAD, MA, LLB.

Judicial Commission of the General Assembly
Chairman—Very Rev. W. B. JOHNSTON, MA, BD, DD, Colinton
Vice-Chairman—Very Rev. Prof. JOHN M'INTYRE, CVO, DLitt, DD, DUNIV, FRSE, Edinburgh
Secretaries—The CLERKS OF ASSEMBLY.

General Trustees
Chairman—Very Rev. PETER P. BRODIE, MA, BD, LLB, DD, Stirling
Vice-Chairman—Mr. R. M. MARTIN, MA, LLB, WS, Edinburgh.
Secretary and Clerk—ALAN W. COWE, MA, LLB. *031–225 5722.*
Depute Secretary and Clerk—T. R. W. PARKER, LLB.

Nomination Committee
Membership 44 (20 appointed by Assembly direct and 24 nominated by Synods).
Convener—Rev. R. CAMPBELL ROBERTSON, Glasgow.
Vice-Convener—Rev. W. PETER GRAHAM, MA, BD, Chirnside.
Secretary—Rev. JAMES L. WEATHERHEAD, MA, LLB. *031–225 5722.*

Special Interests

The Woman's Guild
President—Mrs. MARGARET BROWN, MA.
Vice-Presidents—Mrs. ELIZABETH GALBRAITH, Mrs. M. RUTH FORBES, RGN, SCM, and Mrs. DIANA LAMB.
General Secretary—Mrs. LORNA M. PATERSON, MA. *031–225 5722.*

Church and Nation Committee
Membership 57 (36—at least eight of them women—appointed direct by the General Assembly, one from each Synod and 7 representatives of Boards etc.).
Convener—Rev. NORMAN J. SHANKS, MA, BD, Glasgow
Vice-Convener—Rev. GEORGE D. WILKIE, OBE, BL, Edinburgh
Office Secretary—Miss CHRIS BROWN, MBE, BA, 121 George Street Edinburgh EH2 4YN. *031–225 5722.*

Panel on Doctrine

Membership 19 (12 appointed direct by the Assembly, 4 from the Faculties and others *ex officiis)*.
Convener—Rev. DOUGLAS M. MURRAY, MA, BD, PhD, Edinburgh.
Vice-Convener—Rev. A. STEWART TODD, MA, BD, DD, Aberdeen
Secretary—Rev. DAVID M. BECKETT, BA, BD, Edinburgh. *031–667 8671.*

Panel on Worship

Membership 30 (all appointed direct by the Assembly).
Convener—Rev. ANDREW J. SCOBIE, MA, BD, Cardross.
Vice-Convener—Rev. DAVID C. MACFARLANE, MA, Peebles.
Secretary—Rev. CHARLES ROBERTSON, MA, Manse of Canongate, Edinburgh EH8 8BN. *031–556 3515.*

II. DEPARTMENT OF STEWARDSHIP AND FINANCE

Board of Stewardship and Finance

Membership 73 (26 Assembly-appointed, 47 from Presbyteries).
Convener—Rev. W. JACK BEAUMONT, MA, BD, Cadder.
Vice-Convener—Mr. JOHN F. WILSON, FIB(Scot), North Berwick.
Secretary—Rev. GEORGE ELLIOT, MA, BD, STM. *031–225 5722*
General Treasurer—Mr. W. G. P. COLLEDGE, CA. *031–225 5722.*

Church of Scotland Trust

Chairman—Mr. T. Y. DARLING, MA, FICE, ACII.
Vice-Chairman—Mr. D. D. M'KINNON, BSc, FFA.
Secretary—Mr. D. F. ROSS, MA, CA. *031–225 5722.*

Personnel Committee for Staff in the Church Offices

Membership 14 (8 Assembly appointed).
Convener—Mr. J. G. G. LEES.
Secretary—Mr. W. G. P. COLLEDGE, CA. *031–225 5722.*

III. DEPARTMENT OF MINISTRY AND MISSION

Joint Secretaries—Rev. IAN B. DOYLE, MA, BD, PhD.
Rev. SANDY M'DONALD, BA, CMIWSc.
Joint Secretaries Depute—Rev. DUNCAN C. M'PHEE, MA, BD.
Rev. DAVID P. L. CUMMING, MA
Assistant Secretary and Accountant—Mr. ALEX F. GEMMILL, BAcc, CA.
Assistant Secretary—Miss ALISON E. L. BROWNE, DA.

Board of Ministry and Mission

Membership 26.
Joint Conveners—Rev. JEAN B. MONTGOMERIE, MA, BD, Peterculter.
Rev. DOUGLAS A. O. NICOL, MA, BD, Kilmacolm.
Vice-Conveners—Rev. RODERICK D. M. CAMPBELL, BD, FSAScot., Mearns.
Rev. JOHN RUSSELL, MA, Tillicoultry.
Mrs. ELIZABETH B. CORMACK, Bearsden.

Committees—(1) Personnel and Finance

Maintenance of the Ministry

Membership 75 (one from each Presbytery and 28 from membership of Board).
Convener—Rev. JEAN B. MONTGOMERIE, MA, BD, Peterculter.
Vice-Conveners—Rev. JAMES P. WILSON, MA, Lanark.
Dr. A. PRENTICE, FALKIRK.

Probationers and Transference and Admission of Ministers

Membership 25 (with teachers of Practical Theology, Secretary of Education Department and Assembly Clerks *ex-officiis*).
Convener—Rev. A. DOUGLAS STIRLING, BSc, Rhu.
Vice-Convener—Rev. CALLUM T. O'DONNELL, MA, BD, Anwoth.

Retirement Scheme

Membership 29.
Comvener—Rev. MATTHEW A. RODGER, BD, Ellon.
Vice-Convener—Mr. TOM HARRISON.

Committees—(2) Forward Planning

Unions and Readjustments

Membership 48.
Convener—Rev. JOHN RUSSELL, MA, Tillicoultry.
Vice-Conveners—Mr. A ROSS, Aberdeen.
Rev. FRANK J. GARDNER, MA, Gourock.

National Church Extension

Membership 38.
Convener—Rev. RODERICK D. M. CAMPBELL, BD, FSA(Scot), Mearns.
Vice-Convener—Rev. DONALD PIRIE, LTh, Lenzie.

Committees—(3) Mission

Mission

Membership 61 (one from each Presbytery and 14 from membership of Board).
These are the Committee on Evangelism, the Committee on Chaplaincies, the Society, Religion and Technology Project, and the Women's Council.
Convener—Rev. DOUGLAS A. O. NICOL, MA, BD, Kilmacolm

Associated Committees

Chaplains to Her Majesty's Forces

Membership 20 (all Assembly appointed).
Convener—Rev. DONALD M. STEPHEN, TD, MA, BD, ThM, Edinburgh.
Vice-Convener—Mr. JOHN WIGHTMAN.
Secretary—Mr. THOMAS M. HUNTER, WS, 42 Melville Street, Edinburgh EH2 7HA. *031–225 6502.*

Advisory Committee on Artistic Matters

Membership 18 (8 ministers and of remainder at least 5 with professional qualifications).
Convener—Sir ILAY M. CAMPBELL, Bart, Crarae.
Vice-Convener—Rev. WILLIAM NIVEN, LTh, Lesmahagow.
Hon. Secretary—Mr. DAVID H. MAXWELL, ACIS, AIB(Scot), 121 George Street, Edinburgh EH2 4YN. *031–225 5722.*

Diaconate Committee

Membership 15 (4 ministers, 4 members,—Assembly appointed; President, Vice-President and Secretary of Diaconate Council; three other members of Diaconate).
Convener—Rev. MARY I. LEVISON, BA, BD, Edinburgh.
Vice-Convener—Mrs. JEAN MORRISON, DCS, Currie.
Secretary—Mrs. YVONNE TEAGUE, DCS.

Prison Chaplaincies Board

Convener—Rev. JOHN JOLLY, BA, Glasgow.
Secretary—Rev. IAN B. DOYLE, MA, BD, PhD, Edinburgh

Iona Community Board
Membership 24.
Convener—Rev. W. U. MacDONALD, MA, JP, Perth.
Secretary—Rev. COLIN R. DOUGLAS, MA, BD, STM, Livingston.

IV. BOARD OF WORLD MISSION AND UNITY

Convener—Rev. D. HUGH DAVIDSON, MA, Edinburgh.
Vice-Conveners—Mrs CATHERINE LAIDLAW, Broughty Ferry.
Rev. MARGARET R. FORRESTER (Mrs.) MA, BD, Edinburgh.
General Secretary—Rev. J. CHRISTOPHER WIGGLESWORTH, MBE, BSc, PhD, BD, *031–225 5722.*
Deputy General Secretary—Rev. ANDREW R. MORTON, MA, BD.

Committees

Executive
Convener—Rev. D. HUGH DAVIDSON, MA, Edinburgh.

Finance
Convener—Rev. COLIN G. F. BROCKIE, BSc, BD, Kilmarnock.

Global
Convener—Rev. GILLIAN M. MORTON (Mrs.) MA, BD, Melrose.

Local Involvement
Convener—Rev. D. ROSS MITCHELL, BA, BD, West Kilbride.

Personnel
Convener—Mrs. MARGARET BARBOUR, Pitlochry.

Africa (Sub-Saharan), Latin America, and the Carribean
Convener—Rev. IAIN A. WHYTE, MA, BD, STM, Coatbridge.

Middle East and North Africa
Convener—Rev. JOHN M. SPIERS, LTh, Giffnock.

Asia
Convener—Rev. W. EWING SMITH, BSc, Livingston.

Europe
Convener—Mrs. NANSIE BLACKIE, MA, Edinburgh.

United Kingdom and Eire
Convener—Rev. MALCOLM MACLEOD, BA, BD, Arbroath.

Women's Business Committee
Convener—Mrs. CATHERINE LAIDLAW, Broughty Ferry.

V. DEPARTMENT OF SOCIAL RESPONSIBILITY

Board of Social Responsibility
Membership 91 (44 Assembly appointed and one from each Home Presbytery).
Convener—Rev. ROBERT M'GHEE, DD, Falkirk.
Vice-Conveners—Rev. ANDREW T. MacLEAN, BA, BD, Glasgow and Mrs. HELEN MacLEOD, Forfar.
Director of Social Work—Rev. F. S. GIBSON, BL, BD, STM, DSWA.
031–225 5722.

VI. DEPARTMENT OF EDUCATION

General Secretary—Rev. ALASDAIR J. MORTON, MA, BD, DipEd, FEIS.
Deputy Secretary—Rev. GORDON F. C. JENKINS, MA, BD.

Board of Education

Membership 43.

Convener—Rev. HENRY R. SEFTON, MA, BD, STM, PhD, Aberdeen.
Vice-Convener—Rev. IAN G. SCOTT, BSc, BD, STM, Edinburgh.

Committees

Education Committee
Membership 22.

Convener—Rev. J. IAN H. M'DONALD, MA, BD, MTh, PhD, FEIS, Edinburgh.
Vice-Convener—Mr. JOHN A. DONALD, MA, BD.

Education for the Ministry Committee
Membership 41.

Convener—Rev. ANGUS W. MORRISON, MA, BD, Edinburgh.
Joint Vice-Conveners—Rev. DAVID J. H. HARBISON, MA, BD, Beith.
Rev. A. DAVID K. ARNOTT, MA, BD, Netherlee.
Rev. JAMES W. M'LEOD, MA, Bellshill.
Rev. EVELYN M. YOUNG, (Mrs.) BD, Larbert.

Youth Education Committee
Membership 34.

Convener—Rev. W. HAISLEY MOORE, BA, Jedburgh.

Adult Education Committee
Membership 34.

Convener—Rev. A. ANN WINNING, MA, BD, Morvern.

Church Representatives on the University Boards of Nomination
Chairman—The Right Reverend THE MODERATOR.
Vice-Chairman—Rev. COLIN R. MARTIN, MA, BD, Edinburgh.

VII. DEPARTMENT OF COMMUNICATION

Board of Communication

Membership 42 (all Assembly appointed).
Convener—Rev. DOUGLAS N. ALEXANDER, MA, BD, Bishopton.
Vice-Convener—Rev. WILLIAM SUTHERLAND, Bo'ness.
Secretary—Mr. D. BRUCE CANNON. *031–225 5722.*

Committees

Publicity Services
Convener—Rev. LAURENCE H. TWADDLE, MA, BD, Dunbar.
Secretary—Mr. W. A. MORRISON. *031–225 5722.*

Media
Convener—Mr. A. ROSS ANDERSON, Edinburgh.
Secretary—Mrs. ANN DAVIES. *031–226 3405.*

Audio-Visual Production
> *Convener*—Rev. J. WALTER M'GINTY, BA, Alloway.
> *Secretary*—Rev. RALPH C. P. SMITH, MA, STM. *031–447 3531.*

Life and Work
> *Convener*—Mr. P. BRYCE GRANT, Aberdeen.
> *Secretary*—Mr. R. D. KERNOHAN, MA. *031–225 5722.*

The Saint Andrew Press
> *Convener*—Rev. IAN R. FISHER, MA, Glasgow.
> *Secretary*—Miss LESLEY A. TAYLOR, MA

Bookshops
> *Convener*—Rev. ANDREW F. ANDERSON, MA, BD, Edinburgh.
> *Secretary*—Mr. IAIN G. CAMERON. *031–225 5722.*

AD HOC COMMITTEES

(*a*) **Delegation of General Assembly**—*Chairman*—Rev. JAMES L. WEATHER-HEAD, MA, LL B. *Secretary*—Mr. R. A. PATERSON, MA, LL B.

(*b*) **Committee on the James M'Kechnie Bequest**—*Convener*—Mr. CHARLES R. BLACK, WS, Edinburgh. *Clerk*—

REPRESENTATIVES TO OTHER ORGANISATIONS

The General Assembly has also appointed representatives to the following organisations:—

The British Council of Churches (8).

The World Alliance of Reformed Churches (5).

Central Committee of the World Council of Churches (2).

Scottish Churches' Council (8).

Scottish Religious Advisory Committee of the British Broadcasting Corporation (7).

United Society for Christian Literature (6).

Society for the Sons and Daughters of the Clergy (3).

Highlands and Islands Trust (1).

Scottish Savings Committee (1).

Scottish National Council of the Y.M.C.A. (4).

Board of the Dean Orphanage and Cauvin's Institution (1).

Esdaile Trust (2).

Central Committee of the Woman's Guild (4).

Pollock Memorial Missionary Trust (1).

Scottish Reformation Society (5).

National Bible Society of Scotland (6).

Churches' Council for Health and Healing (4).

LORD HIGH COMMISSIONERS SINCE 1959

1959–60	Francis David, Earl of Wemyss and March, DL, LLD.
1961–62	Mungo David Malcolm Murray, Earl of Mansfield and Mansfield.
1963	HRH Henry William Frederick Albert, Duke of Gloucester, KG, KT, KP, GCB, GCMG, GCVO.
1964	General Sir Richard Nugent O'Connor, GCB, DSO, MC.
1965–66	Lord Birsay, CBE, QC, TD.
1967–68	The Right Hon Lord Reith of Stonehaven, GCVO, GBE, CB, TD.
1969	Her Majesty the Queen attended in person.
1970	The Right Hon Margaret Herbison, PC.
1971–72	The Right Hon Lord Clydesmuir of Braidwood, CB, MBE, TD.
1973–74	The Right Hon Lord Ballantrae of Auchairne and the Bay of Islands, GCMG, GCVO, DSO, OBE.
1975–76	Sir Hector MacLennan, KT, FRCP Glas, FRCOG.
1977	Francis David, Earl of Wemyss and March, KT, LLD.
1978–79	The Right Hon William Ross, MBE, LLD.
1980–81	Andrew Douglas Alexander Thomas, Earl of Elgin and Kincardine, DL, JP.
1982–83	Colonel Sir John Edward Gilmour, Bt., DSO, TD.
1984–85	Charles Hector Fitzroy Maclean, Baron Maclean of Duart and Morvern, KT, GCVO, KBE.
1986–87	John Campbell Arbuthnott, Viscount of Arbuthnott, CBE, DSC, FRSE, FRSA.
1988	Sir Iain Mark Tennant, KT, FRSA.

MODERATORS OF ASSEMBLY SINCE 1957

1957	George F. MacLeod, MC, DD, Glasgow.
1958	John A. Fraser, MBE, TD, DD, Hamilton Old and Auchingramont.
1959	R. H. W. Shephard, DD, DLitt, Lovedale.
1960	John H. S. Burleigh, DD, BLitt, Principal of New College, Edinburgh.
1961	A. C. Craig, MC, DD, Glasgow.
1962	Nevile Davidson, DD, Glasgow Cathedral.
1963	James S. Stewart, DD, Professor of New Testament, New College.
1964	Duncan Fraser, DD, PhD, Invergordon.
1965	Archibald Watt, DD, STM, Edzell and Lethnot.
1966	R. Leonard Small, OBE, DD, Edinburgh St. Cuthbert's.
1967	W. Roy Sanderson, DD, Stenton *with* Whittingehame.
1968	J. B. Longmuir, TD, DD, Principal Clerk of Assembly.
1969	T. M. Murchison, MA, DD, Glasgow St. Columba's Summertown.
1970	Hugh O. Douglas, CBE, DD, LLD, Dundee St. Mary's.
1971	Andrew Herron, MA, BD, LLB, Clerk to the Presbytery of Glasgow.
1972	R. W. V. Selby Wright, CVO, TD, DD, FRSE, JP, Edinburgh Canongate.
1973	George T. H. Reid, MC, MA, BD, DD, Aberdeen Langstane.
1974	David Steel, MA, BD, DD, Linlithgow St. Michael's.
1975	James G. Matheson, MA, BD, DD, Portree.
1976	Thomas F. Torrance, MBE, DLitt, DD, DrTheol, DTheol, DrTeol, University of Edinburgh.
1977	John R. Gray, VRD, MA, BD, ThM, Dunblane Cathedral.
1978	Peter P. Brodie, MA, BD, LLB, DD, Alloa St. Mungo's.
1979	Robert A. S. Barbour, MC, BD, STM, DD, University of Aberdeen.
1980	William B. Johnston, MA, BD, DD, Edinburgh Colinton.
1981	Andrew B. Doig, DD, BD, STM, National Bible Society of Scotland
1982	John M'Intyre, CVO, DD, DLitt, FRSE, University of Edinburgh.
1983	J. Fraser M'Luskey, MC, DD, London St. Columba's.
1984	John M. K. Paterson, MA, ACII, BD, Milngavie St. Paul's.
1985	David M. B. A. Smith, MA, BD, DUNIV, Logie
1986	Robert Craig, CBE, DLitt, LLD, DD, Emeritus of Jerusalem.
1987	Duncan Shaw, Bundesverdienstkreuz, PhD, ThDr, JP, Edinburgh, Craigentinny St Christopher's.
1988	James A. Whyte, MA, LLD, University of St. Andrews.

HER MAJESTY'S HOUSEHOLD IN SCOTLAND—ECCLESIASTICAL

Dean of the Chapel Royal
Very Rev. Professor Robert A. S. Barbour, MC, BD, STM, DD.

Dean of the Order of the Thistle
Very Rev. Prof. John M'Intyre, CVO, DD, DLitt, FRSE.

Domestic Chaplain
Rev. J. A. Keith Angus, TD, MA.

Chaplains in Ordinary

Rev. W. J. Morris, DD, PhD, LLD.

Rev. H. W. M. Cant, BD, STM.

Rev. Kenneth MacVicar,
MBE, DFC, TD, MA, JP.

Rev. Alwyn J. C. Macfarlane, MA.

Rev. John MacLeod, MA.

Rev. Gilleasbuig I. Macmillan, BD.

Very Rev. William B. Johnston, DD.

Rev. Maxwell D. Craig, BD, ThM

Rev. William B. R. Macmillan, BD.

Extra Chaplains
Very Rev. The Lord MacLeod of Fuinary, MC, DD.
Very Rev. James S. Stewart, DD.
Rev. Edgar P. Dickie, MC, DD, LLD.
Very Rev. R. Leonard Small, CBE, DD.
Very Rev. W. Roy Sanderson, DD.
Very Rev. Ronald W. V. Selby Wright, CVO, TD, DD, FRSE, JP.
Rev. T. J. T. Nicol, MVO, MBE, MC, DD.
Very Rev. George T. H. Reid, MC, DD.
Very Rev. Prof. John M'Intyre, CVO, DD, DLitt, FRSE.
Rev. Colin Forrester-Paton, BD

MATTER OF PRECEDENCE

"Rank and Precedence in Scotland"—The Lord High Commissioner to the General Assembly of the Church of Scotland (while the Assembly is sitting) ranks next to the Sovereign, the Duke of Edinburgh and the Duke of Rothesay, and before the rest of the Royal Family; and the Moderator of the General Assembly of the Church of Scotland next to the Lord Chancellor of Great Britain and before the Prime Minister and the Dukes.

LONG SERVICE CERTIFICATE

A suitable scroll bearing the crest of the Church in colour and signed by the Moderator of the General Assembly is available for presentation to elders and others who have given particularly long and distinguished service within their own congregations. Application should be made in the first instance, giving full particulars, by the minister of the congregation concerned, to the Principal Clerk of Assembly at 121 George Street, Edinburgh EH2 4YN. The certificate is awarded after not less than thirty years' service. In the case of Sunday School teachers and Bible Class leaders it is awarded after twenty-one years' service.

THE OFFICES OF THE CHURCH

Office Hours—9 a.m. to 5 p.m.
Closed all day Saturday

121 GEORGE STREET, EDINBURGH EH2 4YN

Telegraphic Address—"Free, Edinburgh"

Telephone Nos.—
Offices—031–225 5722
Book Shop—031–225 2229

NOTE: During the present period of reconstruction etc. there is of necessity considerable upheaval and upset in the arrangements generally within the Offices, and any indication of locality given herewith must be taken with considerable reservation.

General Interests Department (*Fourth Floor*).—*Secretary*—Rev. James L. Weatherhead, MA, LLB; *Administrative Assistant*—Miss Chris Brown, MBE, BA.

Assembly Council (*Fourth Floor*).—*Secretary*—Rev. Ronald S. Blakey, MA, BD, MTh.

Department of Stewardship and Finance (*First Floor*).—1. General Treasurer's Department. *General Treasurer*—W. G. P. Colledge, CA; *Deputy General Treasurer*—D. F. Ross, MA, CA; *Assistant Treasurer*—G. Reid, CA; *Accountant*—Mrs. J. E. E. Beer, CA. 2. Stewardship Department. *Secretary*—Rev. George Elliot, MA, BD, STM; *Assistant Secretary* —William J. Farrell; *Field Representatives*—William H. Mackay [*0250 83*] *Meikleour 316* and Thomas J. Kinvig (*0236 821400*).

Law (*First Floor*).—*Solicitor of the Church and of the General Trustees*—R. A. Paterson, MA, LLB; *Depute Solicitor*—Mrs. J. S. Wilson, LLB, NP; *Assistant Solicitors*—Mrs. J. A. L. Drummond, LLB; I. K. Johnstone, MA, LLB; and D. G. Smart, LLB.

General Trustees (*First Floor*).—*Secretary and Clerk*—Alan W. Cowe, MA, LLB; *Depute Secretary and Clerk*—T. R. W. Parker, LLB; *Assistants*—Miss D. A. Laing, BL (Ecclesiastical Buildings) and Mrs. M. J. Grant, LLB, (Glebes); *Assistant Treasurer*—Mrs. J. E. E. Beer, CA.

Department of Ministry and Mission (*Second Floor*).—*Joint Secretaries*—Rev. Ian B. Doyle, MA, BD, PhD, and Rev. Sandy M'Donald, BA, CMIWSc; *Joint Secretaries Depute*—Rev. Duncan C. M'Phee, MA, BD, and Rev. D. P. L. Cumming, MA; *Assistant Secretary and Accountant*—Mr. A. F. Gemmill, BAcc, CA; *Assistant Secretary*—Miss A. E. L. Browne, DA; *Industrial Mission Organiser*—Rev. D. M. Ross, MA; *Director Science, Religion and Technology Project*—Dr. D. J. Pullinger; *National Organiser for Evangelism*—Rev. Peter Neilson, MA, BD.

Department of World Mission and Unity (*Third Floor*).—*Telegrams* "Evangel, Edinburgh." *General Secretary*—Rev. J. Christopher Wigglesworth, MBE, BSc, PhD, BD; *Deputy General Secretary*—Rev. Andrew R. Morton, MA, BD; *Secretaries*—Rev. William G. Murison; Mrs. Sue Pattison, BA, CertEd; Mr. R. Macleod Robertson; Rev. Robin Ross, MA, BD; Miss Elma C. Sloan, DCS; and Rev. James L. Wilkie, MA, BD; *Field Officers*—Rev. Robert S. Anderson; Mr. Peter Bell; *China Liaison Officer*—Miss Jill Hughes, BA, MTh; *Medical Officers*—Dr. Alexander G. Reid, MB, ChB, DRCOG, DCH, MRCGP; Dr. Irene A. Wilkie, MB, ChB.

Department of Communication (*123, First Floor*).—*Secretary and Director*—D. Bruce Cannon; (10 Young Street Lane) *Depute Secretary*—W. A. Morrison.

Press Office (*121, Ground Floor*)—Senior Press Officer—Mrs. Ann Davies.

Publicity Services(10 Young Street Lane)—*Director*—W. A. Morrison.

"Life and Work" *(121, Ground Floor)—Editor*—R. D. Kernohan, MA; *Assistant Editor*—Alison Buckley; *Advertisement Manager*—David M. Carson, 55 Belford Road, Edinburgh.

The Saint Andrew Press *(123, Ground Floor)—Publishing Manager—Lesley A. Taylor, MA.*

Bookshops *(121, Ground Floor)—General Manager*— Iain G. Cameron.

Audio-Visual Production (22 Colinton Road). *Director*—Rev. Ralph C. P. Smith, MA, STM.

"The Church of Scotland Year-Book"—Communications for Editor should be addressed to Very Rev. Andrew Herron, DD, LLD, 36 Darnley Road, Glasgow G41 4NE *(041–423 6422).*

Department of Social Responsibility *(Second Floor).—Director of Social Work*—Rev. F. S. Gibson, BL, BD, STM, DSWA; *Deputy Director (Elderly)*—Miss J. M. Carswell, BA, DSW; *Deputy Director (Community)*—Mr A. MacLullich, BSc, MEd, ABPS; *Deputy Director (Field Administration)*—Mr. J. Maguire, ASCA, AFA; *Secretary of Women's Council*—Mrs. Marilyn Davie; *Training Officer*— Mrs. M. Rainey; *Social Interests Secretary*—Miss K. J. Gibb; *Master of Works*—Mr. H. R. Kennedy; *Technical Officer*—Mr. R. Law; *Publicity Officer*—Mr. J. R. H. Thompson.

Woman's Guild *(Third Floor).—General Secretary*—Mrs. Lorna M. Paterson, MA.

Department of Education *(Fourth Floor).—General Secretary*—Rev. Alasdair J. Morton, MA, BD, DipEd, FEIS; *Deputy Secretary*—Rev. Gordon F. C. Jenkins, MA, BD; *Curriculum Officer*—Rev. David G. Hamilton, MA, BD; *Curriculum Assistant*—Miss Ionwen Roberts, BA; *Research and Development Officer in Special Educational Needs*—Rev. Stewart M. M'Pherson, BD, DipMin.

Diaconate Committee *(Third Floor).—Secretary*—Mrs. Yvonne Teague; *Office Secretary*—Mrs. Catherine Jameson, DCS.

59 ELMBANK STREET, GLASGOW G2 4PQ

Department of Ministry and Mission—Representatives of the Secretariat attend at this office by appointment.

The Industrial Chaplain for the Glasgow area, Rev. Norman B. Orr, operates from this office.

Telephone—041–332 4458.

260 BATH STREET, GLASGOW G2 4JP

Department of Education—The Youth Adviser for the Presbytery of Glasgow, Mr. Graham D. Aitken, MA, operates from this office.

Telephone—041–333 9374

THE LIBRARIES OF THE CHURCH

General Assembly Library and Record Room.—Most of the books contained in the General Assembly Library have been transferred to New College Library. Records of the General Assembly, Synods, Presbyteries and Kirk Sessions are now in H.M. Register House, Edinburgh. All records more than fifty years old and not in current use should be sent to the Principal Clerk of Assembly, 121 George Street, Edinburgh EH2 4YN.

College Libraries.—New College, Edinburgh and Christ's College, Aberdeen. Membership of these well-equipped theological libraries is open to students free of charge and to others on payment of a subscription.

Church Music.—The Library of New College contains a selection of works on Church music.

SONGS OF GOD'S PEOPLE

**THE CHURCH OF SCOTLAND
SUPPLEMENT TO
THE CHURCH HYMNARY THIRD EDITION**

Words only edition   *£1.25*
Full Music edition   *£6.50*

published by
OXFORD UNIVERSITY PRESS

Administration and Special Interests

The Committees here grouped together do not represent a Department in the ordinary sense. They are divided into two groups, the former (Administration) comprising the Board of Practice and Procedure, the Assembly Council, the Committee to Nominate the Moderator, Judicial Commission, General Trustees, Nomination Committee; while the latter (Special Interests) comprises Church and Nation Committee, Panel on Doctrine, Panel on Worship, and the Woman's Guild.

BOARD OF PRACTICE AND PROCEDURE

The Board of Church Law, Procedure and Practice, now to be designated "The Board of Practice and Procedure" is the successor to the General Administration Committee whose work it will continue and in particular will have the following remit:

(*a*) To advise the General Assembly on questions of Church Law and of Constitutional Law affecting the relationship between Church and State.

(*b*) To advise and assist Committees of the General Assembly in the preparation of proposed legislation and on questions of interpretation.

(*c*) To make all necessary arrangements for the General Assembly each year.

(*d*) To advise the Moderator anent his official duties, if so required.

(*e*) To be responsible to the General Assembly for the care and maintenance of all Assembly buildings and other property.

(*f*) To compile the statistics of the Church, except Youth and Finance; and to supervise on behalf of the General Assembly all arrangements for care of Church Records and for Quinquennial Visitations.

(*g*) To act for the General Assembly in connection with proposals to sell surplus Communion Plate.

(*h*) To attend to the general interests of the Church in matters which are not covered by the remit of any other Committee; and to perform such other duties as may be assigned to it by Act or Deliverance of the General Assembly.

THE ASSEMBLY COUNCIL

The remit of the Assembly Council as set forth in Act VI 1980, as amended by Act VIII 1981, is as follows—

(i) To establish a system of operating and servicing boards as described in the Report, and to review periodically the structure by which the General Assembly delegates responsibility for those functions it determines shall be controlled centrally.

(ii) To keep under review the size and organisation of the staff at the Church offices.

(iii) To establish a management committee to co-ordinate the work of the central organisation.

(iv) To appoint a Secretary to the Council, and to approve the proposals for appointment of secretaries and senior officials by the boards.

(v) To co-ordinate the policies of the boards.

(vi) To advise the General Assembly on the relative importance of work in various fields.

(vii) To advise the General Assembly on those matters which can effectively be devolved from the central organisation to Presbyteries.

(viii) To check that resources are, or can be expected to be, available to support proposals before the General Assembly.

(ix) To evaluate the progress and effectiveness of the work of the boards.

(x) To deal with urgent issues arising between meetings of the General Assembly or the Commission of Assembly which do not fall within the remit of any Board, provided that:

    (*a*) It shall not be competent for the Council to take or authorise any action which is:

        (i) of such a nature that it would have been *ultra vires* of the Commission of Assembly, or

        (ii) of a legislative or judicial nature, or

        (iii) an order or instruction to any Court or Courts of the Church.

    (*b*) Any action taken in terms of this Clause shall be reported by the Council to the next meeting of the General Assembly or the Commission of Assembly, whichever is the sooner.

THE GENERAL TRUSTEES

The General Trustees are a property corporation created and incorporated under the Church of Scotland (General Trustees) Order Confirmation Act 1921. Their duties, powers and responsibilities were greatly extended by the Church of Scotland (Property & Endowments) Acts 1925 to 1978 and the General Assembly of 1979 also charged them with the administration of the Central Fabric Fund and of all fabric monies controlled centrally for individual congregations.

The scope of the work of the Trustees is broad, covering all facets of property administration, but particular reference is made to the following matters:

1. *Ecclesiastical Buildings*—The Trustees' Fabric Committee (which normally meets on the third or fourth Tuesday of each month except August) considers proposals for extraordinary repairs, improvements and material alterations to buildings vested in the General Trustees and plans for new buildings to be vested in them. Details of all such works should be submitted to the Committee for approval before work is commenced. The Committee also deals with applications for the release of fabric monies held by the General Trustees for individual congregations.

The Committee also considers applications for assistance from the Central Fabric Fund from which grants and/or loans may be given to assist congregations faced with expenditure on fabric. Application forms are obtainable from the Secretary to the Trustees and require to be submitted through Presbytery with its approval.

2. *Sale, Purchase and Letting of Properties*—All sales or lets of properties vested in the General Trustees fall to be carried out by them in consultation with the Financial Board of the congregation concerned, and no steps should be taken towards any sale or let without prior consultation with the Secretary of the Trustees. Where property to be purchased is to be vested in the General Trustees it is essential that contact be made at the earliest possible stage with the Solicitor to the Trustees who is responsible for the lodging of offers for such properties and all subsequent legal procedure.

3. *Glebes*—The Trustees are responsible for the administration of Glebes vested in their ownership. All lets fall to be granted by them in consultation with the Minister concerned. It should be noted that neither Ministers nor Kirk Sessions may grant lets of Glebe land vested in the General Trustees. As part of their Glebe administration the Trustees review regularly all Glebe rents.

4. *Insurance*—Properties vested in the General Trustees are insured with the Church of Scotland Insurance Co. Ltd, a company wholly owned by the Church of Scotland, whose profits are applied for Church purposes. Insurance enquiries should be sent directly to the Company at 1 Royal Terrace, Edinburgh EH7 5AD.

CHURCH AND NATION COMMITTEE

The function of the Committee may be stated generally as being "to watch over developments of the Nation's life in which moral and spiritual considerations specially arise, and to consider what action the Church from time to time may be advised to take to further the highest interests of the people."

The extent of the Committee's responsibilities is indicated by the list of its Sub-Committees, viz.:—International Interests, Economic Interests, Social Interests, Commonwealth Interests, Scottish Interests, Church Interests, and Mass Means of Communication.

PANEL ON DOCTRINE

The Panel on Doctrine was set up in 1960 "to deal with doctrinal matters." It was felt at that time that when any particular matter involving doctrinal issues came before the Assembly the tendency was to appoint an *ad hoc* committee to deal with it, and that, while this had advantages, it involved a complete lack of continuity—besides which such a committee suffered the handicap of being strictly confined to its remit though often in the course of its study of a subject it became apparent that a much wider field demanded to be explored. Accordingly the Panel was set up as a continuing body and given certain responsibilities which were amended, at the request of the Panel, by the Assembly in 1976. The responsibilities of the Panel as then defined are:—

(*a*) To receive from the General Assembly remits on matters concerning doctrine and to make suitable arrangements for the fulfilling of them.

(*b*) To draw the attention of the General Assembly to any matter inside the Church of Scotland or elsewhere which might have significant doctrinal implications and which might affect members of the Church of Scotland, and to make recommendations to the General Assembly as to the action to be taken.

(*c*) To be available for consultation by Committees of the General Assembly on any matter which might be of doctrinal significance.

(*d*) To assist, on request, Committees of the General Assembly which are endeavouring to co-ordinate their work in similar doctrinal areas.

(*e*) To communicate and consult on matters involving doctrine, in association with other interested Committees of the General Assembly, with bodies outside of the Church of Scotland, such as the World Council of Churches and the World Alliance of Reformed Churches.

(*f*) To inform the General Assembly if the expense of any of these undertakings be more than £100 a year, exclusive of travelling expenses, and to await the instructions of the Assembly.

(*g*) To report each year to the General Assembly.

PANEL ON WORSHIP

The Panel on Worship exists to witness to the importance of worship as a primary function of the Church. It has a Committee on Prayer and Devotion concerned with the devotional life of the Church and it incorporates also the particular concerns of the former Holy Tryst Committee. It is responsible for the commissioning and annual publications of *Pray Today* which last year sold 15,000 copies. Each year during Assembly week the Committee organises a public meeting designed to draw attention to the priority of prayer in the Church life and to explore some particular aspects of Christian devotion. As well as which it annually arranges a Retreat with a devotional theme.

The Panel organises Festivals of Praise and prepares Supplements to the Church Hymnary, and arranges for the provision of materials helpful to the devotional life of individuals and small groups. The Panel also provides copies of service books to students of divinity, and is prepared to consider requests from necessitous congregations for grants towards the purchase of music editions of the Hymnary for the use of choirs.

The Woman's Guild

The Woman's Guild is a fellowship whose aim is to unite the women of the Church in the dedication of their lives to the Lord Jesus Christ through worship, fellowship and service. It is organised in Guild Branches and Young Woman's Groups.

Membership is open to all women who accept the basis of the fellowship set out in this Aim.

Through the Delegate system in the Woman's Guild, lines of communication are firmly established between Branch, Group and Presbyterial Council and between Presbyterial Council, Central Committee and the Women's Committees of the Department of Ministry and Mission, the Department of Social Responsibility and the Board of World Mission and Unity.

In addition to 1,593 Branches, which number includes 7 in England, there are 408 Young Woman's Groups and they too are represented on Presbyterial Councils and on Central Committee. The approximate total membership at the close of 1987 was — Branches 60,563, Groups 7,413.

Worship — In both Branches and Groups, worship is an integral part of every meeting. Help in the preparation and leading of worship is given both at Training Courses held in Presbyterial Councils and at other centres, such as Carberry Tower, as well as in the literature produced by the Guild Publicity Committee, which also prepares Bible Study material. The latter has greatly encouraged and facilitated the formation of Bible Study Groups.

Fellowship — One of the strengths in a Congregation is often the fellowship formed within the Guild and reaching out to others. Thus the Church is seen to fulfil its true purpose — witnessing to the love of Christ.

Service — Through the Guild, each member is given the opportunity and encouragement to serve her congregation, the wider work of the Church and the community, using her talents to the full in so doing.

Literature — The Woman's Guild Publicity Committee is responsible for producing resource literature for use in Branches and Groups.

The Annual Theme Booklet contains suggestions for programmes and worship appropriate to the Theme which in 1989-90 is 'New Life in Christ'.

A range of leaflets specifically for Office-bearers is available, augmenting information in the Handbook.

A Topic for the Year on a subject of current interest is chosen for discussion in Branches, Groups and Councils.

The Handbook (new edition 1987) contains the Guild constitution as approved by the General Assembly and the rules for the management of Branches, Groups, Presbyterial Councils, and the Central Committee.

Spotlight, a biannual magazine for all women of the Church, is published jointly by the Guild and the Women's Councils and Committees.

Stewardship and Finance

The Board of Stewardship and Finance was established by the General Assembly in 1983. The Board consists of a Convener, Vice-Convener and twenty-four members all appointed by the General Assembly, of whom eight are ministers and sixteen are lay members of the Church. Presbytery representatives—one from each of the Presbyteries in Scotland and from the Presbytery of England—attend two meetings of the Board at which they have the full rights of members of the Board.

The Board of Stewardship and Finance has the following functions:

1. *Promoting Christian Stewardship*

The Board promotes teaching and understanding of Christian Stewardship throughout the Church.

The Board provides programmes to assist congregations in visiting members, making known the work of the Church and promoting Christian giving.

The Board also provides help to congregations through the service of its Field Staff in running conferences, meeting with officebearers and training visitors.

2. *Preparing a Co-ordinated Budget*

The Board is responsible for preparing a Co-ordinated Budget for the costs of the Ministry both active and retired, and the Mission and Aid Fund, and for finally determining the budget in July each year.

3. *Allocating the Co-ordinated Budget*

The Board is responsible, with the Board of Ministry and Mission and with Presbyteries, for allocating among congregations the Co-ordinated Budget approved by the General Assembly, and for seeking to ensure that congregations meet their obligations thereto by transmitting regularly throughout the year to the General Treasurer of the Church contributions towards their allocations.

4. *Administering the Financial Services of the Church*

The Board provides financial, administrative and accounting services for the General Assembly, the Boards and Committees of the Church.

The Board has a duty to report annually to the General Assembly on the general financial position of the Church and powers to examine the financial and statistical information of such Boards and Committees of the General Assembly as the Board shall consider appropriate.

The Board exercises control of the General Treasurer's Department, including:

(*a*) The preparation and issue of a Schedule for congregational financial returns;

(*b*) The preparation and submission of the Accounts of the Church to the General Assembly;

(*c*) The consideration of Reports received from the Auditor of the Church;

(*d*) The operation of a central banking system among the various Boards and Committees of the General Assembly;

(*e*) The custody of funds and the provision of bank arrangements;

(*f*) Taxation matters affecting both the Boards and Committees of the General Assembly and the congregations of the Church;

(*g*) The distribution of unallocated legacies.

The Board is responsible for the care, maintenance and amenity of the Church Offices, including the provision of services thereto and the allocation of accommodation among the various Boards and Committees of the Church.

The Board maintains a close liaison with the Personnel Committee for the Staff in the Church Offices and with the Church of Scotland Trust, both of which are serviced by officials of the Board.

Income of the Church for 1987

A. **Total Income**		1987	*1986*
1. *Congregational Income*			
(*a*) General Purposes—			
Offerings		£33,598,723	*£31,276,310*
Other Income		4,192,257	*3,997,376*
Extra-ordinary Income		1,487,556	*1,380,565*
		£39,278,536	*£36,654,251*
(*b*) Special Purposes		7,395,228	*6,209,764*
		£46,673,764	*£42,864,015*
2. *Miscellaneous Income*			
(*a*) Donations, Grants, Income from Trusts, Sales of Property etc.	£1,996,234		*£2,486,867*
(*b*) Bequests	1,751,931		*2,708,405*
(*c*) Income from Investments	6,739,810		*6,224,274*
(*d*) Stipend Endowments and Glebe Rents collected by General Trustees	1,451,724		*1,399,591*
	£11,939,699		*£12,819,137*
Total Income of Church	£58,613,463		*£55,683,152*

B. Analysis of Congregational Income

Year	Membership	Number of Deeds of Covenant	Total Congregational Income	Income per Capita (All Members) 1982 Actual	Income per Capita (All Members) 1982 Terms	Income per Capita (Once per annum communicants) 1982 Actual	Income per Capita (Once per annum communicants) 1982 Terms
1982	922,642	126,680	31,118,913	33·73	53·73	55·99	55·99
1983	906,444	132,200	33,781,134	37·27	35·65	61·98	59·28
1984	890,745	137,887	37,083,147	41·63	37·90	70·17	63·88
1985	874,123	141,103	40,045,430	45·81	44·15	75·86	65·11
1986	858,080	143,519	42,864,015	49·95	39·32	85·00	70·57
1987	842,417	139,487	46,673,764	55·40	41·47	96·55	76·94

C. Disposition of Congregational Income

	1984	1985	1986	1987
Local Congregational Expenditure	53.1	53.4	53.4	55.2
Local Ministry	31.0	30.7	30.8	30.2
Central Funds:				
Aid to Maintenance of the Ministry	5.2	5.2	5.0	4.1
Mission and Service and General Purposes	10.7	10.7	10.8	10.5
	15.9	15.9	15.8	14.6
	100.0%	100.0%	100.0%	100.0%

Co-ordinated Budget for 1989

The Budget for the work of the Church in 1989 is as follows:

Requirements of Central Funds

	1988	1989
Local Ministry	£	£
Stipend	10,815,000	11,540,000
National Insurance	1,360,000	1,460,000
Aged and Infirm Ministers' Fund	2,840,000	3,014,000
Housing and Loan Fund	285,000	302,000
	15,300,000	16,316,000
Mission and Aid Fund		
Aid to Maintenance of the Ministry	1,550,000	1,700,000
Home Mission	838,900	872,000
National Church Extension	537,500	560,000
Education	474,200	487,000
Education for the Ministry	528,900	572,500
Social Responsibility	383,200	400,000
World Mission and Unity and Christian Aid	1,797,000	1,790,000
	—	89,000
Communication	340,200	357,000
Central Fabric Fund	255,100	238,300
Diaconate Committee	17,500	18,500
Panel on Worship	8,000	11,000
Chaplains to H.M. Forces	4,500	4,700
General Purposes Fund	475,000	500,000
	7,210,000	7,600,000
Requirements for Local Congregational Expenditure (excluding Ministry Costs)	22,510,000	23,916,000

Deeds of Covenant

A Deed of Covenant is an obligation to pay a specified sum for a period of more than three years. Normally, the obligation is terminable on the death of the grantor. The grantor must have income taxed at the basic rate at least equivalent to the gross amount of the annual contribution.

A Certificate of Deduction of Tax (Income Tax Form R.185 A.P.) falls to be granted by the donor in respect of each first payment made under the Deed and for every payment where the net amount of the Deed is over £175. By arrangement with the Inland Revenue, second and subsequent claims for net payments of £175 or less may be made under a dispensation on claim form R248A/Ed. Such a dispensation has been granted in respect of claims on "T" Deeds. Congregational Treasurers should make application to the Inland Revenue Claims Branch when a dispensation is sought in respect of claims on "C" Deeds.

Deeds of Covenant may be made payable to the Church of Scotland ("T" Deeds) or to the local Church Treasurer ("C" Deeds).

Deeds are usually granted as "Net Deeds". This means that the actual amount paid by the grantor is fixed and does not vary with changes in the rate of tax. The following illustration is based on Income Tax at 25%.

The grantor provides by the Deed for an annual contribution of such a sum as after deduction of tax will amount to, say £156. This means that a cash payment of £156 is made by the grantor £156.00

Tax would be recoverable by the Church at 25 per cent on the gross amount of the contribution.. 52.00

Gross Contribution £208.00

From the foregoing it will be realised that by contributing in this way considerable benefit is conferred to Funds of the Church. It will be noted that with Income Tax at the present basic rate of 25% an additional 34p (approximately) is recovered for every £1 paid in cash by the grantor.

"Higher-rate" taxpayers (those paying tax in excess of 25% on parts of their income) can deduct up to the gross amount of the annual payment from their income in respect of Deeds of Covenant granted in favour of the Church. Relief is therefore obtained by such taxpayers at the highest rate at which they are liable to tax although the Church is still able to recover tax only at the basic rate of 25%.

The "higher-rate" taxpayer can, however, at no extra cost to the grantor, increase the payments under the deed so as to pass this tax advantage on to the Church. This is indeed the intention of the Government. For example, in the case of a person liable to tax on part of his income at 40% and who has granted a Deed of Covenant for £300 (net) per annum such a grantor could grant a new Deed for £375 (net) per annum at no extra cost, thus benefitting the Church by 23%.

Contributions need not necessarily be paid in one annual instalment; they may be made under the Weekly Freewill Offering System or otherwise, by arrangement.

Forms of Deeds of Covenant, and any further information on the subject, may be obtained on application to the General Treasurer, Church of Scotland, 121 George Street, Edinburgh EH2 4YN.

THE CHURCH OF SCOTLAND TRUST

The Church of Scotland Trust, established in 1932 by Act of Parliament, offers to Congregations of the Church a simple and economical medium for the investment of their funds. Congregations are at liberty to invest in The Church of Scotland Trust to an unlimited extent and it is felt that the facilities afforded thereby are preferable to the powers of investment offered by the Trustee Investments Act 1961, with all the attendant restrictions and conditions. The Church of Scotland Trust provides three Funds for Church investors:—

(a) *The Deposit Fund* is intended for short-term money and deposits are repayable on demand. Interest is calculated quarterly but paid gross half-yearly on 15th May and 15th November. The Fund is invested in short-term loans to Local Authorities, Banks and Licensed Deposit-Taking Institutions. There is no capital appreciation in the Deposit Fund and hence there is no protection for capital against inflation.

(b) *The General Investment Fund* is an equity-based Fund intended for long-term investment. The Fund, which is operated on a unit trust basis, is designed to provide steady growth in income and some protection for capital against inflation. Units can be purchased or sold monthly. Income is distributed gross half-yearly on 15th May and 15th November.

(c) *The Income Fund* is intended for long-term capital on which it is essential to obtain an immediate and consistent high yield. The Fund is invested principally in fixed interest securities. It offers little protection against inflation for income or capital. The Income Fund is operated on a unit trust basis and units can be purchased or sold monthly. Income is distributed gross half-yearly on 15th March and 15th September.

Application Forms for investment and further information may be had from the Secretary of The Church of Scotland Trust, 121 George Street, Edinburgh EH2 4YN.

PERSONNEL COMMITTEE

The Personnel Committee for Staff in the Church Offices has the function of determining the salaries, length and conditions of service of Assembly-appointed Secretaries, the General Treasurer, the Solicitor of the Church, Ministerial Committee-appointed Secretaries and all other office staff. The Committee is required to take steps to consult fully about pay and conditions with those who work in the Church Offices.

Ministry and Mission

This is a comparatively new Department which encompasses the two wide areas of work formerly covered by the Departments of Church and Ministry and of Home Mission. It is engaged in focusing the work of evangelism in all its aspects throughout Scotland.

The work of the Department functions within three "groupings". These include within them autonomous committees but indicate the main thrusts of the work:- (1) Personnel and Finance, which deals with ministers' salaries in post and in retirement and with the admission and transference of ministers; (2) Forward Planning, which includes the two autonomous committees on Church Extension and on Unions and Readjustments—the aim being to look at the need for buildings in the context of mission; and (3) The Mission Committee, which seeks to encourage and resource missionary thought and enterprise in all the parishes of Scotland and to supplement these with evangelistic endeavours that are best organised centrally and carried through on a national basis.

Such bodies as the Committees on Artistic Matters, Chaplains to her Majesty's Forces, the Diaconate, Prison Chaplains and the Iona Community Board are formally included within the structure of the Department, though they are responsible directly to the General Assembly.

MAINTENANCE OF THE MINISTRY COMMITTEE

The Ministry

The Church of Scotland is a National Church, and has the responsibility of providing the ministry of Word and Sacraments to all the people of Scotland on a territorial basis. This is achieved through the parish ministry, which is supported by the Fund for the Maintenance of the Ministry.

The Fund which is administered by the Committee on the Maintenance of the Ministry, consists of the income from all the endowments (with a few local exceptions) held by the Church for stipend purposes, all sums received from congregations for stipend, income from legacies, trusts, etc., and donations from private individuals and other sources. Another, and very important, source of income comes in the form of Aid to the Fund—namely, the contributions made by self-supporting congregations based on the principle of "the strong helping the weak".

Consolidated Stipend Endowment Fund

The General Assembly of 1981 approved the creation of the Consolidated Stipend Endowment Fund, and the creation of this Fund, which meets all the requirements of the Church of Scotland (Property and Endowments) Act, 1925, has greatly facilitated the administration of stipend endowments. The Fund is administered by the Church of Scotland General Trustees and is invested through the medium of the Church of Scotland Trust.

Each congregation which has endowment income for stipend purposes in 1981 was given a proportionate share in the Fund; and while income from Glebe Rents does not form part of the Consolidated Stipend Endowment Fund, the net sale proceeds of Glebe land constitute new capital for the Fund and are used to purchase shares in the Fund.

Endowment Grants

The Committee on the Maintenance of the Ministry makes provision for a stipend endowment when a Church Extension Charge attains full status. The Committee also makes grants to enable congregations to improve their endowment income for stipend purposes through the Further Endowment Scheme. Information about the availability of Endowment Grants and the terms and conditions on which they are made can be obtained from Mr. A. F. Gemmill, B Acc, CA., at the Church Offices.

Stipend and Aid

The Committee on the Maintenance of the Ministry has the responsibility of exercising the delegated authority of the General Assembly in the matter of the declaration of the Minimum Stipend. The actual level of the Minimum Stipend from year to year depends on various factors, but the most important factor is the continuing response of members and adherents through their offerings. Stipends above the level of the Minimum Stipend are determined by the Presbyteries and the Committee acting together.

Until 1986 each self-supporting congregation was required to contribute Aid to the Fund, the actual amount having been calculated in relation to the resources of the congregation and in accordance with a formula based on the appropriate stipend. The General Assembly of 1986 approved the terms of Joint Report submitted by the Board of Stewardship and Finance and the Committee on the Maintenance of the Ministry, and authorised the establishment of a new Fund called "The Mission and Aid Fund" for which allocations shall be made to congregations by the Board of Stewardship and Finance with the co-operation of Presbyteries and from which requirements for Aid to the Fund, together with the requirements for the Mission and Service Fund and the General Purposes Fund, shall be met. The Committee on the Maintenance of the Ministry remains responsible for preparing the budget for purposes of Aid to the Fund, taking full account of the many and varied aspects of its work, but the Committee is no longer responsible for allocation.

Congregations without sufficient resources to meet the full stipend have the balance of stipend met from the Fund, the actual level of Aid to be received having been determined in advance by the Committee and the Presbytery acting together. The amount of stipend provision to Aid-receiving congregations forms the major requirement on the Fund. The cost of supporting Community and Associate Ministers, whose appointments have been authorised by the Committee on Unions and Readjustments through its Sub-Committee on New Forms of Parish Ministry, is also met from the Fund.

Miscellaneous Provisions from the Fund

Driving Grants.—The Committee has been reviewing its policy with regard to Driving Grants and is seeking to phase out the payment of Driving Grants in cases where the congregation or linked congregations are self-supporting. Where a Driving Grant is authorised, the Committee meets the cost of Travelling Expenses either in part or in full at the approved rates, the current mileage rates being—up to 4,500 miles at the rate of 25p per mile; from 4,500 miles to 7,500 miles at the rate of 18p per mile; and mileage in excess of 7,500 miles at 12p per mile.

Death-in-Service Grants—The cost of Death-in-Service benefits at the level of three times the Minimum Stipend is a charge on the Fund, as is the cost of *ex gratia* payments to the spouses of ministers who die in service on or after attaining Normal Retirement Date or in retirement.

Pre-Retirement Course—The General Assembly of 1986 authorised the Committee to arrange Pre-Retirement Courses for Ministers and Spouses. The Courses, which will be residential and which will include sessions on such topics as Finance in Retirement, Health in Retirement, and Leisure in Retirement, will be a charge on the Fund.

The foregoing examples show some of the ways in which the Committee on the Maintenance of the Ministry applies the income accruing to the fund, and any balance in the Fund at the end of the year is available to secure and improve the level of the Minimum Stipend in the years ahead.

UNIONS AND READJUSTMENTS COMMITTEE

The General Assembly of 1984 decided to "encourage the Committee and Presbyteries to plan readjustment in the various Presbyteries, with a view to ensuring that the available resources of ministerial manpower are deployed to the best advantage, but instruct the Unions and Readjustments Committee to regard as the decisive factor determining its policies not the estimated number of ordained ministers but the widest possible provision of congregational worship and witness throughout Scotland". In carrying out this instruction, the Committee is aware that the Church of Scotland, as the National Church, has an obligation to provide the ordinances of religion throughout the whole country, and it is, therefore, necessary to match up with some skill and vision the available resources to the needs of the church in the widest sense.

In order to achieve this there are certain factors to be considered:

1. The number of ministers continues to decline, and there is every indication that the forecast of 1200 ministers available by the end of the century is an accurate one.

2. There are growth areas which require not fewer but more ministers.

3. There are situations, particularly in rural areas, where the size of the population would indicate that fewer ministers ought to be able to cope, but on the other hand geographical factors and the number of places of worship can already present great problems to a minister.

The Committee relies heavily on the breadth of experience of ministers and elders who have a wide knowledge of the many and diverse parishes in Scotland.

The Committee has two Sub-Committees—that on Policy having the remit of constantly re-examining the essentially evangelical task of readjustment in a changing society and promoting a greater degree of liaison with kindred Committees both within and without the Department of Ministry and Mission; while the Sub-Committee on New Forms of Parish Ministry has established Community and Associate Ministries in areas where more ministers, though not necessarily more buildings, are urgently required. An inhibiting factor is the number of ministers willing to undertake such duties.

NATIONAL CHURCH EXTENSION COMMITTEE

The obvious affinity between Church Extension and Unions and Readjustments has been recognised by the formation of the Forward Planning Group within the Department of Ministry and Mission.

Although the rate of new building in the public sector has declined in recent years, and the church is no longer faced with the necessity of providing buildings within vast new housing areas and new towns, there are still considerable demands made upon the resources of the Committee, mainly in three areas. There are frequent requests for new churches in growth areas, a demand which is mainly satisfied by the employment of system building. Recurring requests come from existing congregations who require additional accommodation when they have been overtaken by a sudden increase in the parish population.The Committee also seeks to assist in the repair, maintenance and development of Church Extension Churches, and of those which still have a repayment liability, particularly when local resources are quite insufficient to meet their needs. These requirements can often be met through grants and loans, the relative amounts being determined by the capacity of the congregation to repay, and, of course, the resources available to the Committee. The evangelical importance of this work can be seen in the large contribution made by many lively and considerable new congregations to the mission of the Church in Scotland, both in terms of spiritual witness and finance.

Ministers in Church Extension Parishes—The Committee is responsible for making appointments of ministers to parishes in new housing areas which have not yet been given full status by the General Assembly. Such ministers receive a special increment on their stipend of £500. The Committee is empowered to receive details of the financial position of all congregations having a repayment liability.

THE RETIREMENT SCHEME COMMITTEE

The Committee is responsible for the operation of the Church of Scotland Retirement and Death Benefits Scheme for Ministers which includes the Main Pension Fund (formerly known as the Aged and Infirm Ministers' Fund), the Insured Pension Fund and the Contributors' Pension Fund (now a Closed Fund). The Scheme is administered in terms of Regulations which have been approved by the General Assembly and which have the approval of the Superannuation Funds Office and conform to the requirements of the Commissioners of Inland Revenue.

In general, a minister who retires from a qualifying charge or appointment can apply for an annuity. The annuity will be calculated with reference to the period of pensionable service given and can be adjusted if the minister is entitled to the State Earnings Related Pension. A minister retiring on 1st July 1987 on his 65th birthday, with forty years of pensionable service completed was likely to have been granted a pension from the date of retiral of £3,017.88 per annum. Such a pension should increase from year to year, hopefully in line with at least the increase in the cost of living.

When a minister is advised to retire on grounds of ill-health, a Confidential Medical Report must be completed by the minister's own doctor and approved by the Committee's Medical Adviser before the annuity application is submitted to and considered by the Presbytery. In general, a minister retiring on grounds of ill-health will qualify to receive an annuity based on the years of potential service at Normal Retirement Date.

The Main Pension Fund also makes provision for annuities to be paid to dependants.

The Retirement Scheme Committee is indebted to the Committee on the Maintenance of the Ministry for accepting financial responsibility for payment of Death-in-Service Benefits. When a minister dies in service before attaining normal retirement date (either age 70 or age 65), there is payable to the legal personal representative a lump sum equal to three times the level of the Minimum Stipend as declared for the year in which death occurred. When a minister dies in service on or after attaining normal retirement date (either age 70 or age 65) or dies in retirement, an *ex gratia* payment of £1,000 is made to the spouse.

It must be emphasised that the foregoing is but a brief summary of the Regulations as they have been amended from time to time and that the information is offered for purposes of illustration only. Ministers who are contemplating retirement and any others who may have enquiries about retirement and death benefits should write to the Secretary of the Retirement Scheme Committee.

Housing and Loan Fund

The Church of Scotland Housing and Loan Fund for Retired Ministers and Widows of Ministers is able presently to give a certain number of loans up to a maximum loan of £20,000 at very favourable rates of interest in the case of retired ministers or of ministers who have intimated the date of their retirement to the Presbytery, and in the case of widows of ministers. In addition and as a result of the levy imposed on all congregations by the General Assembly of 1978 the Trustees purchase houses for leasing to retired ministers and widows of ministers. Further information may be had from the Rev. Duncan C. M'Phee, MA, BD at the Church Offices.

PROBATIONERS AND TRANSFERENCE AND ADMISSION OF MINISTERS COMMITTEE

The Committee on Probationers and Transference and Admission of Ministers is entrusted with the allocation of Probationers as candidates in vacancies, and it administers a scheme for the transference of Ministers under regulations approved by the General Assembly. This Committee is also responsible for processing applications for the admission of ministers and licentiates of other Churches. Copies of the regulations may be had from the Secretaries. The Committee fully realises how cumbersome its name is (in spite of its accuracy) and hopes it may be generally known as the "PTA Committee". With effect from the General Assembly of 1984 the Committee has been implementing the terms of Act V 1984, anent Settlement of Ministers. This Act was amended in 1988.

Pulpit Supply

Pulpit supply is under the control of the Committee on Probationers and Transference and Admission of Ministers.

Entitlement to Supply—A minister is entitled to six Sundays' Pulpit Supply in respect of holidays, and, in addition, to one Sunday's Pulpit Supply when he is a Commissioner to the General Assembly.

Agents—The following are the Pulpit Supply Agents to whom application should be made by ministers and congregations wishing supply and by preachers wishing engagements:—

Edinburgh—Rev. J. Clarence Finlayson, MA,
  52 Falcon Avenue, Edinburgh EH10 4AW *031–447 6550.*

Glasgow—Mrs. Margaret B. Brydone,
  9 Novar Drive, Glasgow G12 9PX *041–339 0192.*

Aberdeen—Rev. Samuel Ballantyne, MA, BD.
  26 Cairncry Road, Aberdeen AB2 5DP [*0224*] *Aberdeen 483049.*

Dundee—Rev. James A. Bremner, MA,
  122 Glamis Road, Dundee DD2 2ET [*0382*] *Dundee 69473.*

Office Fee—The General Assembly of 1978 decided to discontinue the practice of charging an office fee, so that neither the minister giving nor the congregation receiving the supply has now to pay for the service.

Supply Fee and Expenses—The General Assembly of 1982 approved new regulations governing the amount of Supply Fees and expenses, to become operative as from 1st July 1982. These are as follows:—

(i) The Pulpit Supply Fee shall be at the rate of 3p for every £10 of Stipend (·3 per cent of Stipend). In the case of Minimum Stipend Charges, some of which have supplements of one kind or another, Unions, Linkings, Islands, Shetland etc. the fee shall be calculated on the basis of the basic Minimum Stipend (i.e. £27.90 in 1988).

(ii) The Fee thus calculated shall be payable in the case of those authorised to conduct Public Worship in terms of Act II 1986, Sec. 3. In the case of all others conducting Public Worship in terms of the said Act, Sec. 5 a reduced fee of 50% of the Supply Fee shall be payable.

(iii) A minister in a Charge who supplies a vacant pulpit without requiring to provide Pulpit Supply in his own Charge shall not receive a fee, but may receive an honorarium not exceeding £10 each Sunday.

(iv) The same fee shall be payable, irrespective of the number of Services conducted, but, if the preacher is not prepared to conduct all the Services for which he or she has been engaged, so that it is necessary to engage one or more other preachers, the Fee shall be shared equally between them or among them.

(v) In all of the above cases, necessary Travelling Expenses shall be paid (bus fare, railway standard class, steamer cabin fare). Where there is no convenient public conveyance the use of a private car shall be paid for at the lowest current rate for Travelling Expenses (for 1989, 12p per mile). In exceptional circumstances, to be approved in advance, the cost of hiring may be met.

(vi) Weekend Board and Lodging may be claimed at a maximum rate of £20 for the weekend (receipts should be exhibited), but it is expected that, where possible, Weekend Board and Lodging will be provided voluntarily or at a reduced cost by members or adherents.

The fee and expenses should be paid to the person giving the supply before he leaves on the Sunday. Alternatively, he may be handed a voucher to forward for payment to the Secretaries of the Ministry and Mission Department.

MISSION COMMITTEE

(a) Presbytery Development Process

The General Assemblies of 1985 to 1988 gave strong approval to a strategy for mission which seeks development at both Presbytery and Parish level to encourage the growth of missionary parishes, i.e. congregations renewed in their own life and concerned in every way appropriate to their setting to share the Good News of Jesus Christ.

The Committee is endeavouring to develop resources centrally in both personnel and material to encourage this process. In particular the Rev. Peter Neilson has been appointed National Organiser for Evangelism to guide and co-ordinate this work, and four other appointments have been made to regional areas.

(b) Evangelism

As the name indicates, this Committee is concerned with the spread of the Gospel and that through channels other than the traditional parish ministry. In particular the Committee is responsible for the following—

(a) *St. Ninian's, Crieff*—This Centre, which is concerned with the training of Church members for the work of evangelism both in special non-parochial projects and in the setting of the parish, was established in 1958. The Warden is the Rev. Peter T. Bisset. Conferences and courses of training on evangelism are organised at St. Ninian's for varied groups, and accommodation is provided for up to 80 residents. *[0764] Crieff 3766.*

(b) *Summer Mission*—In 1988 about 800 volunteers in 40 teams took part in Summer Mission at 30 different centres—these included seaside and holiday resorts, and some urban areas. Rev. Bill Hunter is Summer Mission Organiser. *[0764] Crieff 3766.*

(c) *Carberry Tower*—This centre for training in ministry and mission is a residential centre with, at the moment, 87 beds. It is presently being extended and refurbished. A very varied programme is offered. Information may be had from the Joint Wardens, The Revs Jock and Margaret Stein. *031–665 3135.*

(d) *Glasgow Lodging House Mission*—This work is centred in the Institute in East Campbell Street, Glasgow, and its object is to care for the thousands of homeless in Scotland's industrial capital. Oversight of the work is given by a Management Committee appointed by the Presbytery of Glasgow. The Chaplain to the Mission is a Lay Missionary, Mr. James M'Pherson, and his wife is the Lady Superintendent. *041–552 0285.*

(e) *Bridgeton St. Francis-in-the-East Church House*—For more than thirty years the Committee has provided financial support for the activities of this Centre in Bridgeton, Glasgow, which provides club facilities for young and old who have little or no Church background. A Club Leader and a Girls' Leader are in charge of the work under a Committee of Management whose Chairman is the Minister of the Parish. *041–774 8788.*

(*f*) *The Netherbow*—This centre for the Arts was opened in 1972 in the High Street of Edinburgh next to John Knox's House. As well as mounting an Arts Programme of its own, the Netherbow is a resource-centre for congregations seeking to enrich their worship, and a meeting place for all interested in drama, music, painting, literature and crafts. The facilities include a theatre, two galleries, a craft and book shop, and a restaurant. *031–556 9579.*

(*g*) *Badenoch Christian Centre* at Kincraig, opened in 1976, is designed to combine Christian mission with the enjoyment of the many outdoor pursuits available in the surrounding countryside. The Centre is residential and mainly self-catering, and is available to individuals, families, and groups. The Parish Minister of Alvie and Insh is Warden (Rev. John R. Lyall *[054 04] Kincraig 373*), and the Home Mission's *Evangelist* in Speyside.

(*h*) *The Compass Ski Club* is an independent association which exists to promote the Christian faith among those who find recreation in the mountains. It is centred at Glenshee Lodge. The Committee assists by maintaining one of its missionaries, Mr. Sandy Falconer, as Warden *[025 085] Glenshee 209.*

(*i*) *International Student and Community Work*—The Committee gives grant support to the Edinburgh Christian Council for Overseas Students which employs an International Secretary. In 1963 the Committee called the Rev. Emmanuel Johnson from Pakistan to minister to the communities of Pakistanis and Indians settled in the Glasgow area. An Asian bookshop now operates at 117 Allison Street, Crosshill *041–423 9440.* Grants are also given in support of the International Community work carried on under the auspices of the YWCA in Edinburgh (*031–556 1168*), in Dundee (*0382 41058*), and in Glasgow (*041–339 6118*) where a member of the Committee's staff is based at the International Flat.

(*j*) *The Church and Pre-School Groups*—The Committee encourages congregations to sponsor Playgroups and Mother and Toddler Groups in Church Halls.

(c) Parish Assistance

(*a*) *Lay Field-Workers*—The Committee in 1988 had in its employ 80 lay field staff of whom the majority are commissioned deaconesses, deacons and missionaries engaged in missionary and pastoral enterprise of the Church. Such missionaries and deaconesses undergo a prescribed period of training, usually extending over at least two years, and one year's probationary service in a parish, before being commissioned to their task by the Presbytery under whose jurisdiction they are serving—in the case of missionaries, by instruction of the General Assembly, and in the case of deaconess candidates by commendation of the Diaconate Board.

By far the larger group is associated with the work of parishes, 4 in Gaelic-speaking crofting communities, 2 in the Shetland Islands, and most of the others in the large and turbulent new housing areas of our towns and cities where the number of ordained ministers is distressingly low in relation to the size of population.

Field staff serve under the direction of the Committee and were paid at a rate of £7,374 for 1988, with certain seniority increments. Housing, or a housing allowance, is provided. There is a contributory pension scheme, though a number who were too old to enter the scheme receive at retiral an *ex gratia* annual payment from the Committee.

(*b*) *Student Summer Assistance*—The Committee promotes a scheme whereby certain parishes in the Highland area which have a large influx of visitors during the summer months are given the assistance of students from the Divinity Halls for periods of two or four months. This scheme both helps the parishes and gives valuable experience to students. Application should be made to the Secretary in January each year.

(*c*) *Craigengower*—At this holiday home in Tighnabruaich, congregational parties of men and women can spend a week away from their city parishes.

(*d*) *Mission Priority Parishes*—The Committee endeavours to take special interest in the work of such areas, designated by Presbyteries, mainly by the channelling of available resources.

(d) Chaplaincies

This Committee is concerned in the important field of chaplaincy work—in industry, university, and hospital.

(*a*) *Church and Industry*—The aim of the Committee's Industrial Mission is three-fold (*a*) to provide pastoral care and a witness to the Gospel for men and women in all branches of industry in their place of work; (*b*) to assess in the interest of the Gospel the nature of the influence which industry exerts both on individuals and on society; (*c*) to promote the desire for just relationships and understanding at all levels of our industrial society. The work, which is fully ecumenical in character, is now organised in ten of the major industrial areas of the country. There are over 100 part-time Industrial Chaplains and 9 full-time Industrial Chaplains The organiser of the Committee's Industrial Mission is Rev. Donald M. Ross, MA. A list of the full-time Industrial Chaplains will be found at page 39.

(*b*) *Hospital Chaplaincies*—The Committee administers the scheme by which, under the 1947 Health Act, ministers are appointed as Chaplains to all hospitals in Scotland. There are fourteen full-time and over three hundred part-time chaplains. Appointments of chaplains are made by the Secretary of the Committee as "the appointing authority" on the nomination of the Presbytery of the bounds. Presbyteries are responsible for the oversight of chaplains' work. The Committee employs six full-time chaplains' assistants. A list of full-time Hospital Chaplains is to be found on page 37.

(*c*) *Universities and Colleges*—In six of the eight Universities of Scotland, Chaplains are appointed and maintained by the University authorities. In the Universities of Strathclyde and Stirling the Committee has had to undertake the responsibility of financing the appointment of Chaplains whose job it is to commend the Gospel and exercise pastoral care of students. The Committee gives financial support to maintain a part-time chaplaincy at Napier College, Edinburgh. A list of University Chaplains will be found on page 39.

(e) Society, Religion and Technology Project

This project, initiated in 1970, studies the impact of new technologies on society, and helps the Church to form its response in ways which are practical and prophetic. The Director of the Project is Dr. David J. Pullinger.

(f) Women's Council

This, which meets twice a year, consists of delegates from Presbyterial Councils of the Woman's Guild. Its function is to stimulate among women members of the Church a deeper interest in the whole work of the Department. An Executive Committee is appointed by the Department, and this plans the meetings of the Council and the Annual Rally held in the Assembly Hall, Edinburgh, at the end of April.

Full-time Chaplains to Hospitals

EDINBURGH

ROYAL INFIRMARY *(031–229 2477)*—
Rev. T. Stewart M'Gregor, MA, BD, 19 Lonsdale Terrace, Edinburgh EH3 9HL. *031–229 5332. Chaplain's Assistant*—Miss Anne Mulligan, DCS, c/o Chaplains' Office.

NORTHERN *(031–332 1241)*; EASTERN *(031–554 2266)*; WESTERN *(031–332 2525 Ext. 4112)*; LEITH *(031–554 3211)* HOSPITALS—
Rev. Melville F. Schofield, MA, 25 Rowantree Grove, Currie, EH14 5AT *031–449 4745. Chaplain's Assistant*—Rev. Alison M. Barclay (Mrs.) MA, BD, DipEd, 20 Coates Gardens, Edinburgh EH2 5LE.

ROYAL EDINBURGH HOSPITAL *(031–447 2011)*—
Rev. Roy L. Manson, MA, 4 Murieston Drive, Livingston EH54 9AU *[0506] Livingston 34746. Chaplain's Assistant*—Mrs Alison C. W. Wagstaff, BA, 27 Cambridge Gardens, Edinburgh EH6 5DH *031–554 6702.*

DUMFRIES

CRICHTON ROYAL *(0387 55301 Ext. 256)* and NITHBANK *(0387 53151)* HOSPI-TALS—Rev. John Johnston, MA, BD

GLASGOW

ROYAL INFIRMARY, G4 0SF *(041–552 3535)*—
Rev. Kenneth J. Pattison, MA, BD, STM, 46 Berridale Avenue, Glasgow G44 3AE. *041–637 2697.*

GARTNAVEL ROYAL HOSPITAL *(041–334 6241)*—
Rev. Derek Haley, BD, DPS, 9 Kinnaird Crescent, Bearsden, Glasgow G61 2BN. *041–942 9281.*

DUNDEE

DUNDEE ACUTE HOSPITALS *([0382] Dundee 60111—Ext. 2755)*—
Rev. Robert Rae, LTh, 47 Mains Loan, Dundee DD4 7AJ. *[0382] Dundee 450158.*

ABERDEEN

ROYAL INFIRMARY *([0224] Aberdeen 681818)*—
Rev. Alan C. Swinton, MA, 38 Harcourt Road, Aberdeen AB2 4NZ. *[0224] Aberdeen 319340. Chaplain's Assistant*—Mrs. Mary A. Edward, Mackie Hall, Craibstone, Bucksburn.

ROYAL CORNHILL HOSPITAL *([0224] Aberdeen 681818)*—
Rev. W. M. M. Campbell, BD, CPS, 43 Murray Terrace, Aberdeen AB1 2SA. *[0224] 591174. Chaplain's Assistant*—Miss Christina A. MacDonald, MA, DPS.

ABERDEEN CITY GROUP HOSPITALS *([0224] Aberdeen 68188—Ext. 284)*—
Rev. A. Scott Hutchison, MA, BD, DD, Linsue, Drumoak, Banchory AB3 3AA *[033 08] Drumoak 3705. Chaplain's Assistant*—Rev. Alison M. Hogg, BD, 9 Craigton Avenue, Aberdeen AB1 7RP *[0224] Aberdeen 312270.*

INVERNESS

INVERNESS HOSPITALS *([0463] Inverness 234151)*—
Rev. C. Arthur Fraser, BA, 11b Island Bank Road, Inverness IV2 4QN. *[0463] Inverness 232897.*

AYR

AILSA HOSPITAL *[0292] Ayr 265136*—Rev. John Banks, BD.

KILMARNOCK

CROSSHOUSE HOSPITAL (*[0563] Kilmarnock 21133*)—
Rev. Alastair R. Moodie, MA, BD, JP, 18 Forest Grove, Kilmarnock KA3 1UP *[0563] Kilmarnock 33772.*

MELROSE

BORDERS GENERAL HOSPITAL (*[0896] Galashiels 4333*)—
Rev. Gillian M. Morton (Mrs.) MA, BD, PGCE, 8 Ormiston Grove, Melrose TD6 9SR *[089 682] Melrose 2033.*

In addition to the above there are over three hundred part-time chaplains serving almost all the hospitals in Scotland. Communications concerning patients may be addressed to "The Church of Scotland Chaplain" at the hospital concerned.

Organisers for Evangelism

National Organiser
Rev. Peter Neilson, MA, BD, 37 Strathalmond Park, Edinburgh EH4 8AH *031–339 5835*

Organiser for Edinburgh and South East
Rev. Mary B. Morrison, MA, BD, 2 St. Bernard's Crescent, Edinburgh EH4 1NP *031–332 6117*

Organiser for Glasgow and South West
Rev. John Campbell, BA, LTh, 3 Herries Road, Glasgow G41 *041–423 3760*

Organiser for Central Area
Rev. Michael W. Frew, BSc, BD, 52 Rose Crescent, Perth PH1 1NT *[0738] Perth 27722*

Organiser for Highland Area
Rev. Alasdair MacLennan, BD, Adjola, 14 Urquhart Road, Dingwall IV15 9PE *[0349] Dingwall 63970.*

University Chaplaincies

Aberdeen	Alan A. S. Reid, MA, BD, STM *0224 40241*
Dundee	Robert Gillies *0382 2381 Ext. 332*
Edinburgh	Helen H. R. Alexander, BD *031–667 1011*
Glasgow	David A. R. Millar, MA *041–334 8769* Georgina M. Baxendale, BD (Mrs.) *041–334 8769*
Heriot Watt	W. Crawford Anderson, L Th *031–343 1277*
St. Andrews	Douglas Galbraith, BD, B Mus
Stirling	Graham K. Blount, MA, BD *0786 63760*
Strathclyde	Andrew T. MacLean, BA, BD *041–552 4400 Ext. 2442*

Full-time Industrial Chaplains

Rev. Hugh Ormiston *0324–473 067*	Forth Valley	Coal and Electricity
Rev. Norman B. Orr *041–332 4458*	Glasgow	Shipbuilding and Engineering
Rev. John B. Potter *069 84 28345*	North Lanarkshire	Steel and Electronics
Rev. Donald M. Ross *031–225 5722*	Edinburgh	Industrial Mission Organiser
Rev. John Walker (Episcopal appointment) *0382 825165*	Dundee	Textiles, Unemployment, Micro-electronics and YTS
Rev. William Rayne (Methodist appointment) *041–959 1548*	Glasgow	Engineering and Transport
Rev. W. Andrew Wylie *0224 573181*	North East	Oil
Rev. Alister J. Goss	Inverclyde	Marine Construction, Electronics and Engineering

In addition to the full-time chaplains there are over 100 parish ministers and the ministers of other denominations regularly visiting the industrial locations in their area.

Prison Chaplains

Establishment	Chaplain	Church
Aberdeen (Craiginches)	Michael V. A. Mair, MA, BD	Holburn West
Castle Huntly Institution	*Vacant*	
Cornton Vale Institution	A. Sheila Blount (Mrs.), BA, BD	—
	Norma A. Ronald, DCS	
Dumfries Institution	William M'Kenzie, DA	Laurieknowe Troqueer
Dungavel	Alistair L. Jessamine, MA, BD	Strathaven Rankin
Edinburgh (Saughton)	John Murrie, BD	Kirkliston
	Ewen Maclean, MA, BD	Edinburgh
	Charlotte L. Henderson (Mrs.)	Limekilns
Glasgow (Barlinnie)	Edward V. Simpson BSc, BD	Giffnock South
	Alexander Tait	St. Enoch's Hogganfield
	Stuart D. Rogerson, BSc, BD	Baillieston, Mure Memorial
Low Moss, Bishopbriggs	*Vacant*	
	George Cranston	Rutherglen Wardlawhill
Glenochil Young Offenders	Norman Swinburne, BA	Sauchie
	George T. Sherry, LTh	Menstrie
	T. R. Taylor, BD	Clackmannan
Greenock	Alexander Chestnut, BA	Greenock
	William Shackleton	Greenock Wellpark West
Inverness	Alastair S. Younger, BSc, ASSc	St. Columba's High
Longriggend Remand Institution	Robert C. Nelson BA, BD	Caldercruix
Noranside Institution	A. W. Mackinnon	Brechin
Penninghame	David W. M'Creadie	Kirkmabreck
Perth	J. Bruce Thomson, BD	Scone Old
	Hector Houston	Rhynd
Perth—Friarton Senior Detention Centre	Duncan M. Bruce, MA	Perth
Peterhead	William N. T. Hodge	Longside
	G. M. Allan Fawkes, BA, BSc	Lonmay
Polmont Institution	Hugh Talman, MA	Polmont
Shotts	Robert A. Anderson, MA, BD, DPhil	Overtown
	Andrew Campbell, BD	Motherwell St. Margaret's

ASSOCIATED COMMITTEES

CHAPLAINS TO HM FORCES

Parish Ministers and Leaders of Youth should encourage their men and women who go on Service to make themselves known to the Chaplain wherever they go. Letters and commendations sent to Chaplains are also welcomed and these if need be can be channelled through the Honorary Secretary.

Vacancies for Chaplains, whether Regular, Reserve or Auxiliary, occur periodically. Full information may be obtained from the Honorary Secretary, Mr. Thomas M. Hunter, WS, 42 Melville Street, Edinburgh EH2 7HA *(031–225 6502)*.

Forces Registers.—The General Assembly of 1970 approved legislation whereby the Committee is required to maintain a Register of all persons admitted to full communion during their period of service in the Forces. The Committee is further required to issue to such persons on request on their returning to civilian life a certificate testifying that they had been admitted to full communion.

The Committee also maintains a Record of all who have received Baptism during their period of service. For a certificate to this effect, application giving relevant particulars should be made to the Secretary of the Committee.

The co-operation of parish ministers is sought to ensure that these services are taken advantage of, so that when a retired service man or woman attaches to a congregation the minister concerned should get in touch with the Secretary of the Committee with a view to securing a Certificate of Admission to Communion (the equivalent of "lines") or a Certificate of Baptism as the case may be.

At the present time Registers are being meticulously prepared and maintained and little use is being made of them.

A List of Chaplains, together with their units and addresses, is given in List A on page 252.

ADVISORY COMMITTEE ON ARTISTIC MATTERS

The Committee was set up in 1934 to advise congregations and Presbyteries on the most appropriate way of carrying out renovations, alterations and re-ordering of interiors, having regard to the architectural quality of Church buildings. It also advises on the installation of stained glass, tapestries, memorials, furniture and furnishings.

Congregations contemplating alterations to their buildings or the introduction of new furnishings, etc., are urged to consult the Committee at an early stage. In the case of Churches built before 1840, congregations are obliged to seek the advice of the Committee.

Members of the Committee and of its local area panels are prepared, where necessary, to visit Churches and meet office-bearers. The Committee's services are given free.

In recent years the General Assembly has conferred these additional duties on the Committee—(1) preparation of reports on the architectural, historic and aesthetic, merit of the buildings of congregations involved in questions of readjustment, (2) verification of the propriety of repair and renovation work forming the basis of grant applications to the Historic Buildings Council for Scotland, (3) establishment of an Organ Sub-Committee to offer advice on the maintenance and installation of pipe organs, (4) setting up of a Depository for surplus Church furniture and furnishings, and (5) compilation of a Register of Churches.

DIACONATE COMMITTEE

Deacons and deaconesses are engaged in the service of the Church of Scotland in work of pastoral, evangelistic, educational or social nature and have, under a call from God, pledged themselves to the service of Jesus Christ and His Church and have been trained and commissioned thereto in conformity with the Church's doctrine and discipline. The Committee, formerly the Diaconate Board, is responsible for many matters concerning commissioning and administration and acts as an executive of the Diaconate Council. The majority of Deacons and Deaconesses are appointed by the Department of Ministry and Mission to serve in parishes, but some serve with other Committees of the Church, and some with other organisations in appointments approved by the Committee. Fuller particulars may be obtained by writing to the Secretary, The Diaconate Committee, 121 George Street, Edinburgh EH2 4YN. A List of the Diaconate will be found on page 284 (List H).

IONA COMMUNITY BOARD

Though essentially independent from the Church, for purposes of reporting at the General Assembly the Board is regarded as falling within this Department.

PRISON CHAPLAINCIES BOARD

The General Assembly of 1964 set up a Prison Chaplaincies Board which is responsible for advising the Scottish Home and Health Department regarding the appointment and terms of service of all ministers acting as Chaplains in Prisons, Borstals and other types of detention centre. Annual Conferences for Prison Chaplains are organised by the Board. A list of Prison Chaplains is given on page 40.

World Mission and Unity

Since 1984 this Department has been responsible to the General Assembly for the following remit:

(1) To play its full part in proclaiming Jesus Christ.

(2) To promote and support relations between the Church of Scotland and other Churches.

(3) To develop partnership in mission.

(4) To engage in dialogue with people of other faiths.

(5) To appoint and receive representatives to and from other Churches, in accordance with the regulations of the General Assembly.

(6) To present for approval by the General Assembly nominations to ecumenical councils, and contributions directly payable to them by virtue of membership.

(7) To promote education for world development, universal mission and unity.

(8) To participate in and encourage ecumenical initiatives at home and abroad.

The Board, with 90 members, 43 nominated by Assembly and 47 appointed by Presbyteries, is now divided into ten committees, responsible for the areas of work listed below:

Global.—Relations with the World Council of Churches and the World Alliance of Reformed Churches, co-ordination of specialist groups including Christian-Jewish consultations, Working Party on Racism, Community of Women and Men, Faith and Order, Dialogue with Other Faiths, Theological Education and Ministry Training, Health and Healing.

Local Involvement.—Organising communications with Presbytery WMU committees, Presbyterial Councils and Kirk Session or Congregational Representatives, Faithshare and Ecumenical exchanges, Publications and Publicity, Overseas Bursars, liaison with Christian Aid in Scotland.

Personnel.—Recruitment, Selection and Training of Youth Share volunteers and Overseas Missionaries, Staff Support and Resettlement.

Africa (sub-Saharan) Latin-America and the Caribbean.—Relations with partner churches, their institutions and councils of churches in Kenya, Tanzania, Malawi, Zambia, Zimbabwe, South Africa, Ghana, Nigeria; and in Jamaica and Grand Cayman, Belize, Bermuda, Trinidad, Argentina, Brazil and Chile.

Middle East and North Africa.—The work of the Israel Council of the Church of Scotland and the Presbytery of Jerusalem (49); St. Andrew's Scots Memorial Church and Hospice, Jerusalem, the Sea of Galilee Centre and Church, Tiberias, and Tabeetha School, Jaffa; Middle East Council of Churches; links with the Coptic Orthodox and Evangelical Churches in Egypt and the Episcopal Church of Sudan.

Asia.—Relations with partner churches, their institutions and councils of churches in India, Pakistan, Bangladesh, United Mission to Nepal, Sri Lanka, China Christian Council and the Amity Foundation, Hong Kong, Taiwan and Korea.

Europe.—The Presbytery of Europe (48), Scottish Mission, Budapest, the Conference of European Churches and other European Church organisations.

United Kingdom and Eire.—Inter-Church Process, British Council of Churches, Scottish Churches Council and joint study groups with Anglicans, Baptists, Orthodox, Reformed Churches in Scotland and Roman Catholics, International Centres in Scotland.

The **Finance** Committee co-ordinates the budgets; the **Executive** Committee is responsible for the overall functioning of the other committees; while the **Women's Business** Committee exists to guide the work of the 65 Women's Presbyterial Councils of the Woman's Guild.

A *World Mission and Unity Year Book* is available with more details of our partner churches and of people currently serving abroad.

MAIN CONCERNS IN 1989

Partnership in Mission with a Worldwide Church.—Four major issues are likely to assume importance as the Church of Scotland deepens its participation in Mission in six continents. Deliverance 5 of last year's Assembly Report reads, "Reaffirm the Church's undiminished commitment to sharing of its resources of people and money for mission in six continents as contemporary evidence of its 'labouring for the advancement of the Kingdom of God throughout the world.' (First Article Declaratory.),, These are—

(1) The nature of the Gospel Mission, which will be looked at by many churches and councils of churches under the theme "Mission in Christ's Way";

(2) The inter-related questions of Justice, Peace and the Integrity of Creation;

(3) The question of how best to share the churches' human, financial and other resources worldwide, in an age of grave inequalities;

(4) The Inter-Church Process of prayer, reflection and debate by the British Churches together, on the nature and purpose of the Church in the light of its mission.

Vacancies Overseas.—The Board welcomes enquiries from men and women interested in serving in the Church overseas. This is usually with indigenous denominations with which we are in partnership and with related organisations, in the countries listed above, or in Church of Scotland overseas congregations in Europe, the Caribbean, Latin-America, and Sri Lanka, or our work in Israel. Apart from specific vacancies which are regularly circularised, there is scope for people with a wide variety of skills willing to be trained for work overseas wherever needs arise. Those interested in more information should write to the Personnel Secretary Mrs Sue Pattison in the first instance.

Resource Sharing.—Most of our overseas work is in the so-called "Third World" or "South" in nations on the other side of the widening gap between rich and poor. These churches are desperately short of financial and technical resources which we can to some extent meet with personnel and grants. However, they are more than willing to share their resources with us, including things which the Church in the West often lacks: enthusiasm in worship, hospitality and evangelism, and a readiness to suffer and struggle for righteousness, and in many areas a readinesss to sink denominational differences. Mutual sharing in the World Church expresses its international nature, and has much to offer a divided world.

Christian Aid.—Christian Aid is the official relief and development agency of those churches in Britain and Ireland, including the Church of Scotland, which are members of the British Council of Churches. Christian Aid's mandate is to challenge and enable us to fulfil our responsibilities to the poor of the world. Half a million volunteers and collectors, some fifty Board and Committee members, and nearly 200 paid staff make this possible, mainly with money given by millions of supporters. The Church of Scotland marks its commitment as a church to this vital part of its mission through an annual grant, amounting to £85,000 in 1987, from the Mission and Aid Fund, transmitted through World Mission and Unity, which keeps in close touch with Christian Aid in its work. Up-to-date information about projects and current emergency relief work can be obtained from the Scottish National Secretary, Ernest Cairnduff, Christian Aid, 41 George IV Bridge, Edinburgh EH1 1EL, *031–220 1254,* the three regional secretaries, Tony Ashcroft, 33 Melville Street, Glasgow G41 2JL, *041–423 9435;* Isabel Carr, 11 Headsmuir Avenue, Carluke ML8 5UQ, *0555 50475;* John Wylie, 15 Darnhall Drive, Perth PH2 0HA, *0738 32570;* or the Director, Michael Taylor, Christian Aid Office, P.O. Box 100, London SE1 7RT, *01–620 4444.*

Accommodation in Israel.—The Church of Scotland has two Christian Guest Houses in Israel which provide comfortable accommodation for pilgrims and visitors to the Holy Land. Further information is available from the Joint Directors, St. Andrew's Hospice, P.O. Box 14216, Jerusalem, and the Administrator, Sea of Galilee Centre, P.O. Box 104, Tiberias.

**FULL LIST OF OVERSEAS APPOINTMENTS
IN LIST E, PAGE 267**

**FULL LIST OF RETIRED MISSIONARIES
IN LIST K PAGE 299**

INTERCHURCH ORGANISATIONS

World Council of Churches

"The World Council of Churches is a fellowship of Churches which confess the Lord Jesus Christ as God and Saviour according to the Scriptures, and therefore seek to fulfil together their common calling to the Glory of the one God, Father, Son and Holy Spirit". Over 300 Churches in all parts of the world constitute the Council's membership. The Council works through various Commissions and Programme Units, and through Working Parties based locally. In 1989, from May 22 to June 1, it is holding a World Conference on Mission and Evangelism, in San Antonio, Texas, USA on the theme "Your Will Be Done: Mission in Christ's Way". In the summer of 1990 it will bring the worldwide Christian process on "Justice, Peace, and the Integrity of Creation" to a climax in a global convocation in Seoul, South Korea. In February 1991 it will hold its Seventh Annual Assembly in Canberra, Australia. Meanwhile it has launched the Ecumenical Decade "Churches in Solidarity with Women" which runs from 1988 to 1998. It produces a regular Ecumenical Press Service, and it produces a monthly journal, *One World*. It operates from the Ecumenical Centre in Geneva, 150 route de Ferney, 1211 Geneva 20, Switzerland.

The General Secretary is The Rev. Dr. Emilio Castro.

World Alliance of Reformed Churches
(Presbyterian and Congregational)

The World Alliance of Reformed Churches dates from 1875 when twenty-one Reformed and Presbyterian Churches sent delegates to London where they formed "The Alliance of the Reformed Churches Throughout the World Holding the Presbyterian System". It now includes Churches of the Congregational tradition.

The President of the Alliance, appointed in 1982, is Rev. Dr. Allan Boesak, Minister in the Dutch Reformed Mission Church, South Africa.

The present membership of the Alliance stands at around 150 Churches in 76 different countries. The total number of people belonging to this worldwide family is estimated to be over 70 million.

Its next General Council will be held August 15-27, 1989 in Seoul, Republic of Korea.

The WARC publishes a quarterly magazine in English, *Reformed World,* a publication which has appeared—under a variety of names—since 1879. WARC headquarters are in the Ecumenical Centre at 150 route de Ferney, 1211 Geneva 20, Switzerland. Tele. 010 41 22 916227. General Secretary of the Alliance is the Rev. Edmond Perret. In addition there are two departments: 1. Theology and 2. Co-operation and Witness.

Conference of European Churches

The Church of Scotland is a member of the Conference of European Churches on which over 100 Churches from every European nation are represented, and which thus crosses the divisions between the East and West of the continent. Its current work includes a programme on "The Church's Mission in a Secularised Europe", defence of human rights, and a mutual aid fund to help poorer Churches. The major event of 1989 is the European Ecumenical Assembly on "Peace with Justice" in Basel, Switzerland on May 14-21. A unique feature of this Assembly is that it is jointly sponsored by the European Council of Churches and of Catholic Bishops' Conferences in Europe. The General Secretary is Mr. Jean Vischer. The Scottish representative on the Advisory Committee is Mrs. Nansie Blackie. The office is in the Ecumenical Centre at 150 Route de Ferney, 1211 Geneva 20, Switzerland, tele. 010 41 22 916111.

British Council of Churches

In 1942 the action of 16 Churches, of which the Church of Scotland was one, in conjunction with several interdenominational organisations, constituted the British Council of Churches. Composed of representatives appointed by the Churches in agreed proportions, and meeting twice a year in Assembly, the Council is the official instrument of the Churches for facilitating common action: for promoting the study of matters of common Christian interest: and for furthering the cause of Christian unity. The Council operates through various Divisions—on Ecumenical Affairs, International Affairs, Community Affairs, World Mission, and Christian Aid. The Council is consultative, not legislative; but its statements and plans receive widespread endorsement by its component Churches whose thought and action are increasingly guided by them.

At the present time there are over 30 British Churches representing most denominations in the membership of the Council, as well as several associate members and four interdenominational bodies. The oriental Orthodox Churches recently came into membership. The Roman Catholic Church in England and Wales and the Roman Catholic Church in Scotland are represented by consultant observers.

Communications should be addressed to The Rev. Dr. Philip Morgan, General Secretary, British Council of Churches, Inter-Church House, 35–41 Lower Marsh, London SW1 7RL. *01–620 4444, FAX 620 0719.*

Scottish Churches Council

The Scottish Churches Council, re-constituted in 1964, comprises representatives of all the Churches and religious organisations in Scotland which are members of the British Council of Churches. The Roman Catholic Church participates in its work with an "observer" status.

The purpose of the Council is four-fold—(*a*) to initiate and promote in Scotland inter-church co-operation in prayer, study, service and mission at every level of Church life; (*b*) to interpret and make relevant to the Scottish situation the thought, life and witnesss of Churches and Christian bodies outwith Scotland; (*c*) to commend consideration in Scotland of the studies, policies and activities of the British Council of Churches, the World Council of Churches, and the Conference of European Churches, and to take action as seems appropriate; (*d*) to provide facility for the Churches in Scotland to give united expression of opinion on matters which they deem important, and, on occasion, to present a Christian viewpoint on matters of public interest.

The offices of the Council are situated at Scottish Churches House, Dunblane. The House, as an instrument of the Council, seeks to promote retreats, ecumenical encounters and "frontier" consultations. It is also available for groups with their own residential programme. Applications should be made to the Warden, Scottish Churches House, Dunblane FK15 0AJ. *[0786] Dunblane 823588.*

The present Chairman of the Council is the Very Rev. W. B. Johnston, MA, BD, DD., Colinton. Communications should be addressed to Rev. Canon Kenyon Wright, General Secretary, Scottish Churches Council, Scottish Church's House, Dunblane FK15 0AJ.

Inter-Church Process

In 1989 churches throughout Britain and Ireland are invited to commit themselves to closer relationships with one another and to new and more adequate structures of relationship, to supersede the British Council of Churches and the Scottish Churches Council in 1990.

In writing to advertisers please mention the "Year-Book"

Social Responsibility

The Department of Social Responsibility came into being on 1st January, 1976 to unify the work of three Committees—Social Service, Moral Welfare, and Women's Committee on Social and Moral Welfare. It consists of 44 Assembly-appointed members together with a representative from each Presbytery, and it meets three times a year. The Women's Council which meets three times annually consists of women members of the Board of Social Responsibility, Presbyterial Council representatives and eight representatives of the Young Woman's Group.

The purpose of the Board of Social Responsibility could be broadly defined as—

(a) to secure in the Church informed opinion on contemporary social and ethical issues;

(b) to encourage balanced judgments on these issues in the light of Christian faith and practice, and to press these judgments at all levels of influence; and

(c) to offer compassionate service through the varied establishments it operates, and to encourage and enable increasing caring work at parish level.

The work of the Board is operated in two sections as follows, each involving both thought and practice.

COMMUNITY CARE

List D Schools

Ballikinrain School for Junior Boys, near Balfron. [0360] Balfron 40244.

Geilsland School for Senior Boys, Beith. [050 55] Beith 2556.

Epilepsy

Westhaven, 2 Upper Bourtree Drive, High Burnside, Rutherglen. *041–634 4563.*

Drug Addiction Centres

Rainbow House, 1 Belhaven Terrace, Glasgow G12 0TF. *041–339 2691.*
Spectrum, Tynepark, Haddington, East Lothian [062 082] *Haddington 2444.*
Simpson House, 52 Queen Street, Edinburgh EH2 3NS. *031–225 6028.*

Mentally Handicapped

Sutherland Hostel, (for Adults), 44 Sutherland Avenue, Pollokshields, Glasgow, G41 4ES *041–427 1989.*

Wolfson House, (for Adults), 45 Milton Road East, Edinburgh EH15 2NL. *031–669 1216.*

Florentine House, 33 Queen Mary Avenue, Glasgow G42 8DS. *041–423 4130.*

Keith Lodge, (for Children), Cameron Street, Stonehaven. [0569] *Stonehaven 62213.*

Kensaleyre, Isle of Skye. [047 032] *Skeabost Bridge 350.*

Ryehill House (for Adults), 16-18 Cobden Street, Dundee. [0382] *Dundee 69991.*

Rehabilitation Centres and Hostels

The Tom Allan Centre, 23 Elmbank Street, Glasgow G2 4PD. *041–221 1535.*

Westercraigs Alcohol Problems Resource Centre, 21 Westlands Drive, Glasgow G14 9NY. *041–959 1679.*

Kirkhaven, 176 Duke Street, Glasgow G31 1JH. *041–551 9187.*

Simpson House, 52 Queen Street, Edinburgh EH2 3NS. *031–225 6028.*

Malta House, 1 Malta Terrace, Edinburgh EH4 1HR. *031–332 3217.*

The People's Palace, 190 High Street, Edinburgh EH1 1RW. *031–225 4795.*

Ronachan House, Argyll. Christian Renewal Centre. *[088 04] Clachan 252.*

Deeford Hostel, 59 Riverside Drive, Aberdeen AB1 7LE. *[0224] Aberdeen 585453.*

AGE CARE

With 44 Homes for the elderly throughout Scotland, the Church has made a substantial contribution to the work of caring for aged people. The wide geographical distribution of these Eventide Homes provides a Church Home within or adjacent to the boundaries of most presbyteries.

The List of Homes is as follows:—

Aberdeen—

Balmedie House—Balmedie, Aberdeenshire AB4 0XU. *[035 84] Balmedie 2244.*

Cliff House—Cults, Aberdeen AB1 9PS. *[0224] Aberdeen 867620.*

Ashley Lodge—253 Great Western Road, Aberdeen AB1 6PP. *[0224] Aberdeen 585558.*

Rubislaw Park—Rubislaw Park Road, Aberdeen AB1 8DA. *[0224] Aberdeen 30641.*

Alloa—

Inglewood—Tullibody Road, Alloa FK10 2HU. *[0259] Alloa 722424.*

Alness—

Dalmore House—Alness, Ross-shire IV17 0UZ. *[0349] Alness 882270.*

Ardrossan—

South Beach House—7 South Crescent Road, Ardrossan KA22 8DU. *[0294] Ardrossan 68234.*

Ayr—

Cumnor Hall—18 Racecourse View, Ayr KA7 2TY. *[0292] Ayr 266450.*

Flatlets—7 Broomfield Road, Ayr KA7 2SP. *[0292] Ayr 262742.*

Banchory—

Bellfield—Banchory, Kincardineshire AB3 3XS. *[033 02] Banchory 2692.*

Broughty Ferry—

Duneaves—7 Claypots Road, Broughty Ferry, Dundee DD5 1BX. *[0382] Dundee 738559.*

Callander—

Blair House—Trossachs, Callander FK17 8HX. *[0877] Trossachs 6230.*

Campbeltown—

Auchinlee—Campbeltown, Argyll PA28 6EN. *[0586] Campbeltown 52568.*

Collessie—

Kinloch House—Ladybank, Cupar, Fife KY7 7UT. *[0337] Ladybank 30463.*

Dornoch—

Oversteps—Dornoch, Sutherland IV26. *[086 281] Dornoch 393.*

Dumfries—

Devorgilla House—33 George Street, Dumfries DG1 1EH. *[0387] Dumfries 54007.*

Dunbar—

St. Andrew's—34 High Street, Dunbar. *[0368] Dunbar 62474.*

Edinburgh—

The Elms—18 Whitehouse Loan, Edinburgh EH9 2EZ. *031–447 4924.*

Queen's Bay Lodge—29 Milton Road East, Edinburgh EH15 2NN. *031–669 2828.*

Varrich House—7 Church Hill, Edinburgh EH10 4BG. *031–447 4913.*

Morlich House—11 Church Hill, Edinburgh EH10 4BG. *031–447 3239.*

Fenwick—

Dunselma—Main Road Fenwick, Kilmarnock, Ayrshire KA3 6DT. *[056 06] Fenwick 218.*

Galashiels—

Netherby—60 Abbotsford Road, Galashiels TD1 3HP. *[0896] Galashiels 2666.*

Gargunnock—

Watson House—Gargunnock, Stirling FK8 3BN. *[078 686] Gargunnock 255.*

Glasgow—

Queen Mary House—52 Queen Mary Avenue, Glasgow G42 8DT. *041–423 2736.*

Eastwoodhill—238 Fenwick Road, Giffnock, Glasgow G46 6UU. *041–638 5127.*

Baxter House—10 Lowther Terrace, Glasgow G12 0RN. *041–334 1231.*

Williamwood House—Strathtay Avenue, Netherlee, Glasgow. *041–637 1168.*

Hamilton—

Well Hall—60 Wellhall Road, Hamilton ML3 9DL. *[0698] Hamilton 286151.*

Helensburgh—

Clyde View—12 East Montrose Street, Helensburgh G84 7HP. *[0436] Helensburgh 4529.*

Inverness—

Cameron House—Culduthel, Inverness. *[0463] Inverness 243241.*

Langholm—

Greenbank—Langholm, Dumfriesshire DG13. *[0541] Langholm 80229.*

Leslie—

Leslie House—Leslie, Fife KY6 3EP. [*0592*] *Glenrothes 741228.*

Loanhead—

Mayburn House—2 Hawthorn Gardens, Loanhead, Midlothian EH20 9EE. *031–440 0299.*

Meigle—

Belmont Castle—Meigle, Perthshire PH12 8TH. [*082 84*] *Meigle 244.*

Nairn—

Whinnieknowe—Mill Road, Nairn IV12 5EN. [*0667*] *Nairn 52387.*

Polmont—

St. Margaret's—St. Margaret's Crescent, Polmont, Falkirk. [*0324*] *Polmont 716149.*

Pitlochry—

Chequers—12 Atholl Road, Pitlochry, Perthshire PH16 5DH. [*0796*] *Pitlochry 2521.*

Reay—

Achvarasdal—Reay, Thurso, Caithness KW14 7RR. [*084 781*] *Reay 226.*

Sandbank—

Invereck—Sandbank, Dunoon, Argyll PA23 8QS. [*0369*] *Sandbank 6231.*

Shetland—

The Walter and Joan Gray Eventide Home—Scalloway, Shetland ZE1 0XJ. [*059 588*] *Scalloway 691.*

Skye—

Budhmor—Portree, Isle of Skye IV51 9ER. [*0478*] *Portree 2012.*

Stonehaven—

Clashfarquhar House—Robert Street, Stonehaven AB3 2DJ. [*0569*] *Stonehaven 62438.*

Troon—

Crosbie Tower (Holiday House)—South Beach Road, Troon. [*0292*] *Troon 313696.*

Cottages for the Disabled

Cottages for the disabled have been built in the grounds of Queen's Bay Lodge, Edinburgh, and also, through the Woman's Guild Project for 1974, at Eastwoodhill, Giffnock.

Kirk Care Housing Association Ltd.

Kirk Care, although a separate entity from the Board of Social Responsibility, provides housing for elderly people and is a companion organisation. The largest area of Kirk Care's work is in the erection of sheltered housing.

The Association is located at 3 Forres Street, Edinburgh EH3 6BT. *031–225 7246.*

SOCIAL INTERESTS

Secretary—Miss K. J. Gibb

The remit of the Board of Social Responsibility instructs it "to study and present essential Christian judgments on social and moral issues arising within the area of its concern". The range of its concern includes family-related matters, childlessness, abortion, divorce, sexuality, obscenity and community standards, alcohol and drug addiction, health and healing.

PUBLICITY

Publicity Officer—Mr. John R. H. Thompson

The Board welcomes every opportunity to publicise the caring work of the Church, and a range of slides, films, and videos is available from the Audio-Visual Centre. A calendar is produced each year, and is sold and distributed through the channel of the Women's Council and Social Responsibility delegates of the Woman's Guild; a newspaper is published three times a year giving news and information on the work of the Department. Leaflets and brochures highlighting areas of the Board's work are also available.

Deputation Work—Members of staff and others will gladly visit congregations and Church organisations to speak on the work as a whole or on specific aspects of it. For further particulars write to the Secretary at 121 George Street, Edinburgh EH2 4YN.

WOMEN'S COUNCIL

Convener—Mrs. Helen MacLeod

The Council comprises one representative from each Presbyterial Council of the Woman's Guild and all women members of the Board of Social Responsibility, with the Convener and Vice-Conveners of the Committee ex officio, and eight representatives from the Young Woman's Group, the last named by rotation.

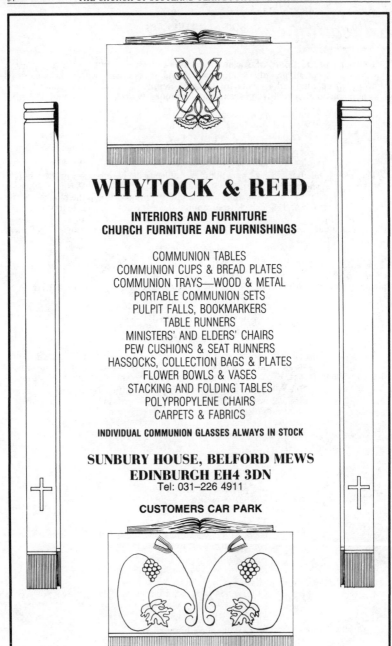

Education

The Department of Education fulfils its remit through a **Board of Education** which is responsible to the General Assembly for the whole work of the Department and operates through five Constituent Committees, three Servicing Committees and a Public Relations Group. All of these report to the Board.

The **Board of Education** has 41 members plus the Convener and Vice-Convener, 18 appointed by the General Assembly direct, 22 by the Constituent Committees, and one by the Woman's Guild.

The members of the **Constituent Committees** are appointed by the General Assembly. The Committee on Education for the Ministry includes also a representative of each of the Faculties of Divinity. The Committees are as follows—Education Committee (22), Education for the Ministry Committee (40), Board of Nomination to Church Chairs (27), Adult Education Committee (34), and Youth Education Committee (34).

The **Servicing Committees** which consist of representatives of the Board and of the Constituent Committees deal with finance, property, and staffing.

The **Public Relations Group** (also representative of the Board and of the Constituent Committees), seeks to publicise and to promote the work of the Department.

EDUCATION COMMITTEE

This committee acts for the General Assembly on all matters of education in schools, colleges or universities. It participates in the work of the Scottish Joint Committee and together with the Committee endeavours to foster co-operation between Church and school. Towards this end it seeks to support those involved in religious education in school, especially school chaplains. It is the Education Committee which is usually approached by HM Government for submission of evidence by the General Assembly in educational matters and is represented by one member on the General Teaching Council.

On behalf of the General Assembly the committee appoints to the governing bodies of the Colleges of Education and to Regional/Island Education Committees persons interested in the promotion of Religious Education in terms of Section 124 (3)(a)(1) of the Local Government Act (Scotland) 1973. The persons presently serving as Church representatives on the Regional and Islands Education Committees are as follows:—

Representatives on Regional and Islands
Education Committees

Highland	Mr. J. M'Lellan, BSc, DipEd, Drumornie, Brora, Sutherland KW9 6LS
Grampian	Rev. David S. Ross, MSc, PhD, BD 49 King Street, Peterhead AB4 6TA
Tayside	Rev. W. U. Macdonald, MA, JP 30 Muircroft Terrace West, Perth PH1 1DY
Fife	Rev. Norman R. Macaskill, MA Macainsh Manse, Lochgelly KY5 9AA
Lothian	Miss E. N. Chalmers, 24 Greenbank Road, Edinburgh EH10 5RY.
Borders	Rev. D. J. Kellas, MA, BD Mossilee Road, Galashiels TD1 1NF
Central	Rev. William Sutherland 10 Dundas Street, Bo'ness EH51 0DG
Strathclyde	Rev. Allan F. Webster, MA, BD 9 Rowallan Gardens, Glasgow G11 7LH

Dumfries and Galloway	Rev. Gilbert L. Thomson
	Leswalt High Road, Stranraer DG9 0AA
Orkney	Rev. R. Fraser Penny, BA, BD
	The Manse, Quoyloo, Stromness, Orkney KW16 3LX
Shetland	Rev. Magnus Cheyne
	30 Commercial Road, Lerwick ZE1 0AB
Western Isles	Rev. Donald Macaulay, OBE
	Lemreway, Isle of Lewis PA86 9RD

EDUCATION FOR THE MINISTRY COMMITTEE

The Committee on Education for the Ministry is charged with the recruitment, selection and education of candidates for the Ministry. It provides bursaries for candidates who are not eligible for SED awards and arranges and supervises the probationary period which students serve after their academic course has been completed. It provides In-Service Training Courses for ministers.

Intending candidates for the Ministry are required to fill up a Schedule which may be obtained from the Department of Education, 121 George Street, Edinburgh EH2 4YN. Men and women who are interested in studying for the ministry may obtain a copy of the relevant regulations along with further information by writing to the Department.

A new Act anent Selection and Training for the Full-Time Ministry (Act V) was passed by the General Assembly of 1985 and this now supersedes all earlier legislation on these matters. It is printed in full in earlier Year Books or copy may be had from the offices.

The Auxiliary Ministry

"An auxiliary minister is a person who has been ordained for life to a Ministry of Word and Sacrament exercisable under supervision on a part-time and non-stipendiary basis. . . . An applicant seeking recognition as a candidate for the Auxiliary Ministry must be a communicant member of the Church of Scotland, promoted by his Presbytery, accepted as a prospective candidate by the Committee on Education for the Ministry, and nominated as a candidate by his Presbytery."

The recruitment of candidates is declared to be a function of Presbyteries. A prospective candidate should therefore in the first instance make approach to the Clerk of his or her own Presbytery from whom particulars may be obtained. Selection and training are in the hands of the Education for the Ministry Committee.

The matter is governed by the terms of Act III, 1987.

YOUTH EDUCATION COMMITTEE

The Committee is responsible for the Christian nurture and education of the Church's young people up to the age of 16, when compulsory schooling ends. It prepares curricular and resource materials for use with Beginners/Nursery children, Sunday Schools, Bible Classes, and young teenage groups. It provides aid and training for teachers and leaders, and material to help parents with the Christian nurture of their own children. This work is promoted and developed through its full-time and part-time staff and resource centres, information about which may be obtained from the Department's office. A major concern is for those with special educational needs, including the mentally handicapped.

ADULT EDUCATION COMMITTEE

The Committee is concerned with the education and training of the Church's members and all associated with the Church above the age of 16. It provides materials, resources and ideas to promote education within the Church, especially in regard to the training of elders, the preparation of new communicants and the promotion of Church House Groups. It also provides training in the area of Group Relations and supervises both the initial training and in-service training of Readers. The Committee is responsible for developing the Department's policy of Christian education and training by extension, and St. Colm's Education Centre and College, which is the base for this, falls within the Committee's remit.

The Office of Reader

"Members of the Church of Scotland may apply for training as Readers. Applications shall be submitted in writing to the Clerk of Presbytery within whose bounds the applicant resides, or that of the congregation of which he or she is a member. The application shall be supported by a letter as to character and previous experience of Church work from the applicant's minister and by extract minute of Kirk Session."

The matter is governed by the terms of Act XXVIII, 1974 as amended by Act XXIV, 1978.

For further particulars application should be made to the Secretary of the Department or to the enquirer's own Presbytery Clerk.

FIELD STAFF

Full-Time Staff

Curriculum Officer—Rev. David G. Hamilton, MA, BD

Curriculum Assistant—Miss Ionwer Roberts

*Research and Development Officer
in Special Educational Needs*—Rev. Stewart M. M'Pherson, BD, DipMin
121 George Street, Edinburgh EH2 4YN   *031–225 5722*

Glasgow Presbytery Youth Adviser—Mr. Graham D. Aitken, MA
260 Bath Street, Glasgow G2 4JP   *041–333 9374*

Warden of Stroove—Mrs. Davina M'Clure
Stroove, 16 Montgomerie Terrace, Skelmorlie PA17 5DT
[0475] Skelmorlie 520275

CENTRE

St. Colm's Education Centre and College

20 Inverleith Terrace, Edinburgh EH3 5NX   *031–332 2230*

St. Colm's is concerned with training men and women for the home and overseas mission of the Church. The Board of Education is using it increasingly as the base for its scheme of Christian education and training by extension—the provision of facilities for the continuing education of the Church's people through the use of local leadership with the help and support of central staff and resources. The General Assembly has designated St. Colm's as the Church's Education Centre and College.

Residential Training

A pioneer establishment in the field of missionary training, St. Colm's today provides courses for students entering the service of the Church of Scotland Department of World Mission and Unity (overseas staff) and the Board of Ministry and Mission (Deaconesses, Lay Agents and specialist workers). It also serves the Presbyterian Church in Ireland in the training of Deaconesses. Various overseas Churches send students to train at St. Colm's.

The College community is international and ecumenical in character. Men and women train together, and the conviction that mission is one, whether exercised at home or abroad, is emphasised in the common core course which all students undertake and which is basic to their training.

This course, leading to the Certificate of Studies in Church and Community, is also open to men and women who may not necessarily be contemplating remunerated Church service, yet wish to equip themselves more adequately for work within their own local congregation or community.

Biblical Studies, Theology, Church History, and Social, Devotional, and Mission Studies are part of this course in which an integrated method of learning is used. Along with the courses of study go the corporate life, daily worship, and spiritual discipline of the residential community, and so the purpose of the College might be summed up as vocational formation training.

A second-year course, normally taken by candidates for the Diaconate, is more pastorally oriented and includes further biblical, theological and devotional studies, as well as a larger element of supervised practical work.

While Local Authority grants are generally available for those undertaking a full session, there are available grant resources to help in other cases. Those unable to undertake full-time residential training are offered sections of the main course in units as short as one week according to personal needs.

Entrance requirements vary according to the age and experience of applicants. Students are expected to have such educational qualifications, or such experience, and personal qualities as will enable them to benefit from the course.

The Centre offers a Training in Leadership and Service—a course which combines distance learning with face-to-face learning in local groups and at residential week-ends. Those who participate in the training will normally be involved in leadership and service in their own congregation or community and have a local support-group from their congregation.

Entrance in September is advisable. Enquiries should be addressed to the Principal, St. Colm's Educational Centre and College, 20 Inverleith Terrace, Edinburgh EH3 5NS, who will be glad to give details regarding fees for board and tuition. The College session runs from the end of September till the end of June, with Christmas and Easter vacations.

Distance Learning Courses

The Centre offers training in Leadership and Service—a course which combines distance learning with face-to-face learning in local groups and at residential weekends. Those who participate in the training will normally be involved in leadership and service in their own congregation or community and have a local support group from their congregation.

A number of courses are promoted by the Group Relations Unit in, for example, Transactional Analysis, Bereavement Care, Spirituality, etc.

The unit concerned with education in the congregation promotes elders' training at the national, presbytery and congregational levels.

National Young Adult and Youth Advisers promote work among young people from St. Colm's.

Staff

The Staff consists of:

Principal—Rev. R. Graeme Brown, BA, BD

Senior Tutor—Miss Moyra McCallum, MA, BD, DCS

Tutors—Rev. Ian Walker, BD, DipMS, Dr. Elizabeth Miller, MA, PhD, DipEd

National Adult Advisers—Mr. David R. Goodbourn, BA, MEd, DipAdEd Rev. Kenneth C. Lawson, MA, BD, Rev. Stewart G. Matthew, MA, BD

National Young Adult Adviser—Rev. Peter J. Macdonald, BD, DipMin.

National Youth Adviser—Rev. Fiona Buchan, BEd, BD

CHURCHES ADVISORY COMMITTEE FOR LOCAL BROADCASTING

The Churches Advisory Committee for Local Broadcasting (CACLB) was formed in 1967 to provide an advisory body to the Churches and to the broadcasters. Membership of the Committee is drawn from members of the British Council of Churches, the Roman Catholic Church, and the Evangelical Alliance, with representatives of the BBC and ILR, together with two members co-opted from ACLB.

Present Officers—President, Mr. Chris Wright, CBT, PO Box 38, Newmarket, Suffolk CB8 7EG *0638 730696*; Chairman, Mr. Ian Gall; Membership Secretary, Mr. Colin Dawson, 35 Surrey Grove, Sutton, Surrey SM1 3PL *01–644 2239*.

ACLB—The Association of Christians in Local Broadcasting was formed at a CACLB Conference in 1980 to assist the evident need for an association to provide "mutual society, help and comfort" for Christians involved in local radio, in whatever role. Membership is also open to those who, though not directly involved in local radio, appreciate its importance and wish to keep in touch with its problems and development. For further information about membership (£5 pa) consult Canon Paul Chalmers, 13 Berwynfa, Glyn Ceiriog, Llangollen, Clwyd LL20 7HP (*069 172 649*).

LONDON ADVISORY SERVICE

The Church of Scotland in London provides an advisory service for young single Scots who come to London to live and work. Information about suitable accommodation is available as is advice on some of the problems which the newcomer may encounter. Introduction to the Scottish community in London can be arranged.

Contact:
The Church of Scotland
London Advisory Service
Beacon House, 41 Castle Lane,
London SW1E 6DW
Telephone: 01-828 8502
(24 hour answerphone)

Communication

The Board and Department of Communication was set up in June 1983 with a remit which included the responsibility "to keep before the Church the need for effective communication both within the Church and to the world and . . . to provide for the Church of Scotland a professional service of publicity, publishing, bookselling and production of the monthly magazine *Life and Work*.

The work of the Board is controlled by Sectional Committees, namely *Life and Work,* Bookshops, St. Andrew Press, Publicity Services, Media, and Audio-Visual Production.

The Board consists of a Convener, Vice-Convener and 40 persons appointed by the General Assembly through the Nomination Committee.

While the work is now co-ordinated, the funding of the various units remains divided between the "trading" sections of *Life and Work*, Bookshops and The Saint Andrew Press, all of which are self-supporting on the basis of their commercial viability, and the other sections which rely on funding from the Mission and Aid Fund.

BOARD OF COMMUNICATION

Secretary & Director—Mr. D. Bruce Cannon

Deputy Secretary & Director—Mr. W. A. Morrison

The work of the Board is divided as follows—

Press Office

Senior Press Officer—Mrs Ann Davies *031–225 5722* and *031–226 3405*

The Press Office provides a news and information service to Press, Radio and Television. It produces newspapers for Boards of the Church and a monthly bulletin of Church news for use in church magazines. The Press Office welcomes the opportunity to assist members and ministers seeking to spread the Good News through the media.

Publicity Services

Director of Publicity—Mr. W. A. Morrison *031–225 5722* and *031–226 3614*

This part of the Board's work is concerned with the production of publicity literature, display material and exhibitions. Members of the staff will be pleased to advise local congregations and presbyteries on the best use of such materials.

An Audio-Visual Centre is in the Church Offices at 121 George Street, Edinburgh *031–225 5722*. A wide range of tape-slide sets, filmstrips and 16mm films can be hired from the A.V. Centre for use in various Church organisations and groups. Details of material available may be had on application.

N.B.—Video programmes are supplied through Church of Scotland Bookshops.

Audio-Visual Production Unit

Director—Rev. Ralph C. P. Smith, MA, STM. *031–447 3531*

From its premises at 22 Colinton Road, Edinburgh, the A.V. Unit produces and markets audio-visual aids—videos, tape-slide sets, and audio cassettes. The Church's photographer is based with the Unit. Short training courses in television, radio and video are also held here. The Church of Scotland has pioneered church production and use of video as a means of Christian communication and can now offer sixty titles for hire from any Church of Scotland bookshop, or by post from the Church of Scotland Bookshop at 119 George Street, Edinburgh EH2 4YN. It is also engaged in production of programmes for broadcast and television.

"Life and Work"

Editor—Mr. R. D. Kernohan, MA

Assistant Editor—Miss Alison Buckley, MA

Life and Work is a monthly magazine covering the work of the Church at home and abroad. It tries to maintain an informed Christian conscience within the Church and to provide a news service. It is both a news magazine and a powerful voice of opinion.

Life and Work remains remarkable value for money at 25p a copy. The price remains low in comparison with other magazines—and very low indeed for what is now recognised as a quality product. Its circulation of over 100,000 makes it an important medium for advertisers anxious to reach a large, significant, and thoughtful part of the Scottish public. The magazine's role is to circulate news of the Church and to provide a forum for views in the Church.

The Saint Andrew Press

Publishing Manager—Miss Lesley A. Taylor, MA

Since its creation in 1954 The Saint Andrew Press has been responsible for a great number of publications, many of which have made a major contribution to Christian literature. The world-renowned series of New Testament commentaries by the late Dr. William Barclay, *The Daily Study Bible,* continues to provide a large share of the sales of the Press. A sister series of commentaries on the Old Testament, by various authors, is now being published. The publishing policy of The Saint Andrew Press has recently undergone a major review which has resulted in a greater concentration on the publication of works specifically designed for the "enquiring layman". Any manuscripts should be sent addressed to the Publishing Manager.

In addition to its own publishing programme, the Press has a responsibility to provide publishing facilities for other departments of the Church and, at times, other denominations. The staff are always willing to offer professional help and advice.

The Bookshops of the Church

Bookshops General Manager—Mr. Iain G. Cameron

Assistant General Manager—Miss Elizabeth Landsman

The Church of Scotland operates attractive, well stocked Bookshops at each of the undernoted addresses and these are commended to the active support of Ministers and all Church members. The Bookshops endeavour to offer customers modern facilities and a pleasant environment in which to shop. This necessitates constant review and update of existing facilities.

An extensive range of Bibles, Hymnaries, Psalters and materials for youth work is carried, as are books on every aspect of Christian work and witness. The Edinburgh shop now houses the former Audio-Visual Centre through which videos, tape-slide sets, film strips, and 16 mm. films may be hired for use by Church organisations and groups. Details of material available may be had on application. Videos may also be hired or purchased through any of the other Bookshops.

For the convenience of Ministers and Office-Bearers, a complete range of Church Stationery is stocked. Woman's Guild Materials and most publications by Committees of the Church are also available.   Customers unable to visit the Bookshops personally can rely on prompt, careful attention from the Mail Order Service. A Church Bookstall service is also provided, and advice in this field is available from the staff.

A Second Hand Theological Book Department operates from Glasgow, buying and selling books; current lists are available on request. The Bookshops are also involved, with Meadowside St. Paul's, in the running of the Cornerstone Coffee House in Dundee.

EDINBURGH—117–119 George Street, EH2 4JN   *031–225 2229*
   Mr. David Hamilton—*Manager*   *031–225 8167*

GLASGOW—160 Buchanan Street, G1 2LL   *041–332 9431*
   Mr. Norman McCullough
   Second Hand Department—Mr. Stanley Berry

ABERDEEN—160 Union Street, AB1 1QT   *[0224] Aberdeen 644464*
   Mrs. Sheelagh Cuthbert

DUNDEE—112 Nethergate, DD1 4ED   *[0382] Dundee 20075*
   Mr. Ronald Robertson
   Cornerstone Cafe—118 Nethergate—
   Mrs. Alison Blake

AYR—57–59 Kyle Street, KA7 1RS   *[0292] Ayr 264548*
   Mr. Andrew Graham

DUMFRIES—26 Great King Street, DG1 1BD   *[0387] Dumfries 55882*
   Mr. Raymond Witty

INVERNESS—16 Fraser Street, IV1 1DW   *[0463] Inverness 226152*
   Miss M. Anne Hughes

STIRLING—70 Murray Place, FK8 2BX   *[0786] Stirling 79610*
   Mr. Michael Coleman

THE MINISTER AND MARRIAGE

Prior to 1939 every marriage in Scotland fell into one or other of two classes—regular or irregular. The former was marriage by a minister of religion after due notice of intention had been given; the latter could be effected in one of three ways—(*a*) declaration *de presenti*, i.e., acceptance of one another by the parties in presence of witnesses (often wrongly referred to as "marriage by the sheriff"); (*b*) by promise *subsequente copula*; or (*c*) by habit and repute.

The Marriage (Scotland) Act of 1939 put an end to (*a*) and (*b*) and provided for a new classification of marriage as either religious or civil—the former, conducted by a minister of religion, might be contracted in any place (Church, hotel, dwelling-house) on any day at any time, after proclamation or publication or on licence; the latter, entered into in presence of one of the registrars specially appointed by the Registrar-General for the purpose, might be contracted only in the office of the said registrar and would normally be arranged only within regular office hours and had to be preceded by publication or licence.

The law of marriage as it was thus established in 1939 had two important limitations to the celebration of marriage—first that certain "preliminaries" had to have been observed (i.e., proclamation of banns, publication of notice, or sheriff's licence); and secondly, that in respect of religious marriage the service had to be conducted according to the forms of either the Christian or the Jewish faith.

Marriage (Scotland) Act, 1977

It was these two conditions that were radically altered by the 1977 Marriage (Scotland) Act.

Since 1st January 1978, in conformity with the demands of a multi-racial society, the benefits of religious marriage have been extended to adherents of other faiths, the only requirements being the observance of monogamy and the satisfaction of the authorities with the forms of the vows imposed.

Also since 1st January 1978, in recognition of drastically changed social patterns, the calling of banns has ceased in our Churches and no longer need notices of marriage appear on the Registrar's board. All that is now necessary is that the couple should present themselves at the Office of the Registrar within whose area the wedding is to take place (irrespective of where they live), not less than fourteen clear days (i.e. fifteen days) and certainly not more than three months, before the date of the wedding, taking with them their birth certificates. The Registrar will arrange to issue a Marriage Schedule and this must be handed over to the Minister before the Service begins.

Ministers should particularly note that it is now a criminal offence to conduct a marriage service in the absence of such a Schedule. No consideration—weeping bride nor bridegroom swearing it's at home forty miles away, hysterical bride's mother nor threatening groom's father—must be allowed to interfere with the strictest adherence to this regulation.

Ministers should also note the recommendation of the General Assembly of 1962 (given on the advice of the then Procurator) that they should not officiate at any marriage until at least one day after the sixteenth birthday of the younger party.

Proclamation of Banns

Since 1978 proclamation of banns as a preliminary to marriage in Scotland has been obsolete (Act III 1978). In the Church of England, however, marriage is governed by the provisions of the Marriage Act 1949 which requires that the parties shall have been proclaimed and which provides that in the case of a party residing in Scotland a Certificate of Proclamation given according to the law or custom prevailing in Scotland shall be sufficient for the purpose. Should a minister be requested to call banns for a person resident within the Registration District wherein his Church is situated he should accede, making the proclamation on only one Sunday if the parties are known to him and he has reason to believe there is no impediment to the marriage, otherwise on two Sundays.

Proclamation should be made at the principal service of worship in the form— "There is a purpose of marriage between AB, Bachelor/Widower/Divorced, residing at

.... in this Registration District, and CD, Spinster/Widow/Divorced, residing at .... in the Registration District of ...., of which proclamation is hereby made for the first and only (second and last) time." Immediately after the second reading, or not less than 48 hours after the first and only reading, a Certificate of Proclamation signed by either the Minister or the Session Clerk should be issued in the following terms—"At ...., the .... day of .... 19...... It is hereby certified that AB, residing at ...., and CD, residing at ...., have been duly proclaimed in order to marriage in the Church of .... according to the custom of the Church of Scotland and that no objections have been offered.

(Signed) .... Minister
(or) .... Session Clerk

Marriage of Foreigners, etc.

Marriages in Scotland of foreigners, or of foreigners with British subjects, are, if they satisfy the requirements of Scots Law, valid throughout Her Majesty's dominions; but they will not necessarily be valid in the country to which the foreigner belongs. This will be so only if the requirements of the law of his or her country have also been complied with. It is therefore most important that, before the marriage, steps should be taken to obtain from the Consul or other diplomatic representative of the country concerned a satisfactory assurance that the marriage will be accepted as valid in the country concerned.

Remarriage of Divorced Persons

By virtue of Act xxvi of the General Assembly of 1959, a Minister of the Church of Scotland may lawfully solemnise the marriage of a person whose former marriage has been dissolved on divorce and whose former spouse is still alive. The Minister, however, must carefully adhere to the requirements of the Act, which, as slightly altered in 1985, are briefly as follows:—

1. The Minister should not accede as a matter of routine to a request to solemnise such a marriage. To enable him to make his decision he should take all reasonable steps to obtain relevant information, which should normally include the following:

   (*a*) Adequate information concerning the life and character of the parties. (The Act enjoins the greatest caution in cases where no pastoral relationship exists between the Minister and either or both of the parties concerned.)

   (*b*) The grounds and circumstances of the divorce case.

   (*c*) Facts bearing upon the future well-being of any children concerned.

   (*d*) Whether any other Minister of religion has declined to solemnise the proposed marriage.

   (*e*) The denomination to which the parties belong. (The Act enjoins that special care be taken in cases where one or both parties belong to a denomination whose discipline in this matter may differ from that of the Church of Scotland.)

2. The Minister should consider whether there is danger of scandal arising if he should solemnise the re-marriage, at the same time taking into careful consideration before refusing to do so the moral and spiritual effect of his refusal on the parties concerned.

3. As a determinative factor the Minister should do all he can to assure himself that there has been sincere repentance where guilt has existed on the part of any divorced person seeking re-marriage. He should also give instruction where needed in the nature and requirements of a Christian marriage.

4. A minister is not required to solemnise a re-marriage against his conscience. Every Presbytery is required to appoint certain individuals with one of whom Ministers in doubt as to the correct course of action may consult if they so desire. The final decision, however, rests with the Minister who has been asked to officiate.

THE MINISTER AND WILLS

It is not uncommon for a minister to be asked to assist in the preparation of a Will for one of his members. In this connection one or two fundamental principles should be borne in mind. In order to be valid according to the law of Scotland a testamentary writing must fulfil one of two conditions—(*a*) it must be a holograph document or (*b*) it must be duly witnessed.

(*a*) To qualify as a holograph writing the Will must be throughout in the handwriting of the testator, or, if typewritten or written by someone else, it must bear, *in the handwriting of the testator,* the words "adopted as holograph". In every case it must be signed *at the very end* by the testator. If it is handwritten there is an advantage in its claiming to be "written in my own hand", though the absence of such a phrase is not fatal—the handwriting can be proved.

(*b*) The requirement is that the testator signs the Will *on every page* (not just on every sheet) and the last page bears also the signatures of two witnesses, who should each add his or her designation and address as well as the word "witness".

Every Will should be dated, as otherwise it may not be possible to prove that it supersedes a Will of an earlier date.

Precautions.—Guard against the use of printed forms of Will which often do not conform to the requirements of Scots law. Remember there are restrictions upon how a spouse or a parent may dispose of moveable property. Above all, ministers should realise how dangerous can be the well-intentioned amateur and should seek professional advice—usually easily obtainable—in any matter affecting testamentary disposition.

Form of Bequest

Should a person wish to make a bequest for the work of the Church the following is a suitable form of words:—

I hereby leave and bequeath to the Church of Scotland for behoof of (here specify the particular Committee, Fund or Object), the sum of .... Sterling (the amount to be stated in words, and not in figures), which legacy shall be payable upon the receipt of the General Treasurer of the said Church for the time, whose receipt shall be a valid and sufficient discharge.

Minister as Notary

It should be particularly noted that while a Minister of the Church of Scotland has a power of notarial execution, this applies only to wills and other testamentary writings. He has *no authority* to attest any document which requires to be sworn "in presence of a JP or Notary Public," and it will only cause needless trouble to all concerned if he purports to do so.

Under Section 13 of the Church of Scotland (Property and Endowments) Amendment Act 1933, it is provided that a Minister of the Church of Scotland who has been appointed to a charge without limit of time or for a period of years to officiate as minister shall, in any parish in which such charge or any part thereof is situated, have the like power as regards the notarial execution of wills or other testamentary writings as is conferred by Section 18(1) of the Conveyancing (Scotland) Act 1924, on a parish minister acting in his own parish. The expression "minister" includes an assistant and successor or a colleague and successor of such minister.

The "power of notarial execution" is a power to write out a will for a person who is blind or illiterate or too ill to be able to write. For the will to be valid the utmost care must be taken to ensure that it conforms to the conditions undernoted.

The following is the form of docquet prescribed by the Conveyancing (Scotland) Act 1924 in the case when the grantor of the deed is blind or cannot write:—

Read over to, and signed by me for, and by authority of, the above-named A. B. (*without designation*), who declares that he is blind (*or* is unable to write), all in his presence, and in the presence of the witnesses hereto subscribing.

Signed by me at .... this .... day of ....

Nineteen hundred and ....

(*Signature*) .... Witness   ....
                                          (*Minister's signature*)

(*Address*) ....

(*Designation*) ....

(*Signature*) .... Witness   *Minister of the*

(*Address*) ....   *Parish of* ....

(*Designation*) ....

Note.—The above docquet should be written by the minister in his own handwriting on the last page of the will or testamentary writing, and signed by him as indicated above. The minister will not require also to sign *above* the docquet at the end of such will or writing. The prior pages (if any) should be authenticated by the minister adhibiting his own signature at the foot of each page. The two witnesses should subscribe their signatures as indicated above, should add the word "Witness" and then their addresses and designations.

The following conditions must be observed:—(1) The notarial power applies in the case of a minister acting within the bounds of any parish (i.e. civil parish) in which his charge (i.e. territorial area) or part thereof is situated (or his colleague or assistant and successor so acting), if from any cause permanent or temporary the grantor of the deed is blind or unable to write. (2) The document is first to be read over by the minister to the grantor before two witnesses who shall also hear or see authority given by the grantor to the minister to sign on his behalf. (3) The minister shall then in the presence of the grantor and of the two witnesses, add his own signature (*a*) to each page, and (*b*) to the docquet which must also be written by him. It is *essential* that the whole docquet be in the minister's own handwriting. (4) The minister may not be an executor, a trustee or a beneficiary, or have any other interest under the will or testamentary writing.

When a minister has been called upon to act as notary without previous experience he would be well advised to arrange for the will or testamentary writing to be scrutinised as soon as possible by a solicitor in order to verify that it has been validly executed.

SOCIETIES FOR CHILDREN OF THE CLERGY

The Society for the Benefit of Sons and Daughters of the Clergy
of the Church of Scotland

Chairman—Rev. Roderick Smith, DD, 13 Saxe Coburg Place, Edinburgh EH3 5BR. *031–332 2262*

Secretary and Treasurer—E. R. L. Walker, CA, 17 Melville Street, Edinburgh EH3 7PE. *031–225 6281*

Annual grants are made to sons and daughters of ministers of the Church of Scotland to enable them to prosecute their education or to undergo business training or to obtain advancement in life. The Society also gives grants to aged and infirm daughters of ministers for alimentary assistance from the Robertson Chaplin Fund, and to ministers' unmarried daughters and unmarried sisters in necessitous circumstances from the John Fund. Schedules of Application may be obtained from the Secretary.

The Glasgow Society of Sons of the Clergy

President—Rev. R. M. Tuton, MA, 2 Aileen Drive, North Mount Vernon, Glasgow G32 0RS. 041-778 1488.

Hon. Secretary and Treasurer—G. D. M. Reid, BL, 48 St. Vincent Street, Glasgow G2 5HS *041–221 8012.*

Hon. Secretary and Treasurer of "Daughters Auxiliary Fund"—G. D. M. Reid, BL (as above).

The purpose of the Society is to aid children of ministers of the Church of Scotland whose fathers have died without being able to leave adequate means for their support. Applications must be lodged with the Secretary before 1st January in each year, but emergency applications can be dealt with at any time when need arises.

Society of Sons of Ministers of the United Presbyterian Church

This Society was dissolved in 1971 and the funds transferred to the Church of Scotland to be administered according to the aims of the former society. Annual grants are made to widows and children of deceased ministers of the United Presbyterian Church.

Applications should be lodged by 31st March in each year and forms can be obtained from the Secretaries of the Church and Ministry Department, 121 George Street, Edinburgh EH2 4YN.

The Society at Aberdeen for the Children of the Clergy

President—Rev. James F. Scott, 144 Victoria Street, Dyce AB2 0BE.

Hon. Secretary and Treasurer—Mr. Angus B. Ross, 38 Westholme Avenue, Aberdeen.

Clerk—I. M. S. Park, Advocate, 6 Union Row, Aberdeen AB9 8DQ. *0224 26262.*

Annual grants are made to children of deceased ministers of the Church of Scotland. Applications to be lodged by 1st February in each year.

THE CHURCHES AND UNIVERSITIES (Scotland)
WIDOWS' AND ORPHANS' FUND

Clerk and Treasurer—Mr. Eric Hubbard, IPFA, FCCA, 121 George Street, Edinburgh EH2 4YN. *031–225 5722.*

Law Agent—A. I. Arnot, WS, 12 Bruntsfield Crescent, Edinburgh EH10 4HA.

Information about this Fund can be had from the Clerk and Treasurer.

HOLIDAYS FOR MINISTERS

The undernoted hotels provide special terms for ministers and their families. Only very general information is given below and application should be made to the person indicated for full particulars of terms, bookings, etc.

CRIEFF–Hydro—The William Meikle Fund and Paton Fund make provision whereby active ministers and their wives, deaconesses and other full-time Church workers may enjoy the amenities of the Hydro in the off-peak periods at greatly reduced rates. Chalets also available for families. Enquiries to the Resident Manager. *[0764] Crieff 2401.*

BLAIR ATHOLL—Tirinie House—The D.A. and Lady Helen Todd Endowment Trust has made it possible for Ministers and their families and others engaged in full-time Church work to enjoy holidays at reduced terms in this fine mansion-house in Glen Fender above Blair Atholl, renowned for its hospitality and home-cooking. Open April to October. Terms and other information from Lindsays, WS, 11 Atholl Crescent, Edinburgh EH3 8HE. 031-229 8851.

THE CINTRA BEQUEST

The trustees of the above have a most unusual complaint — that they are not receiving enough applications for help. Should you be a possible beneficiary please apply; if you know of anyone who could be, please pass on the information. For further particulars see the following page.

THE LYALL BEQUEST

A payment towards cost of holiday accommodation at any hotel or boarding-house in St. Andrews at rate of £25 per week each for Minister and wife up to two weeks in any year on production of receipts. Only to Ministers on Minimum Stipend.

A proportion of travelling expenses of Ministers of charges over a hundred miles from St. Andrews and wives attending Summer School of Theology. Grants towards cost of sickness and convalescence so far as not covered by National Health Scheme.

In each case application to be made to A. A. R. Carleton Esq. WS, Pagan, Osborne and Grace WS, 83 Market Street, St. Andrews KY16 9NX.

SUMMER SCHOOL AT ST. ANDREWS

A School of Theology for Ministers, organised by the Staff of St. Mary's College, St. Andrews, is held each year at St. Andrews, generally in the third week of June. Full information may be obtained from the Principal, St. Mary's College, St. Andrews.

TRUSTS AND FUNDS

The undernoted represents a list of the more important trusts available for ministers, students, congregations. A brief indication is given of the trust purposes, but application should be made in each case to the person named for full particulars and forms of application.

Dr. William K. Anderson's Trust.—Assists the widows of ministers living in the Church's Eventide Homes to secure single room accommodation. Apply Rev. F. S. Gibson, BL, BD, STM, 121 George Street, Edinburgh EH2 4YN.

The Baird Trust.—Assists in the building and repair of Churches and Halls, endows Parishes, and generally assists the work of the Church of Scotland. Apply Angus F. Sutherland, Esq., 182 Bath Street, Glasgow G2 4HG.

The Rev. Alexander Barclay Bequest.—Assists mother, daughter, sister or niece of deceased Minister of the Church of Scotland who at the time of his death was acting as his housekeeper and who is in needy circumstances. Apply W. N. Pomphrey, DL, JP, LLB, 2 Belhaven Terrace, Wishaw.

Barclay Bequest Fund.—Provides small grants for Ministers, Sons of Ministers and of Deceased Ministers of the Free and United Free Churches and of the Church of Scotland. Apply A. F. Gemmill, CA, B Ac, Factor to the Trustees, 121 George Street, Edinburgh EH2 4YN.

Bellahouston Bequest Fund.—Gives grants to Protestant evangelical denominations in the City of Glasgow and certain areas within five miles of city boundary for building and repairing Churches and Halls and the promotion of religion. Apply Mitchells, Johnston, Hill & Hoggan, 160 West George Street, Glasgow G2 2JB.

Bequest Fund for Ministers.—Assists Ministers in outlying parts. Apply D. Wilson, CA, 40 Wellington Street, Glasgow G2 6RL.

Mrs. Butler's Trust.—Makes annual grants to widows or dependent relatives of Ministers of the Church. Apply Rev. A. Gordon McGillivray, MA, BD, STM, 10 Palmerston Place, Edinburgh EH12 5AA.

Carnegie Trust.—In cases of hardship the Carnegie Trust is prepared to consider applications by students of Scottish birth, extraction, or schooling for financial assistance with the payment of their fees at the Scottish Universities. If the applicant is in receipt of a Student's Allowance or a Local Education Authority award which includes payment of fees in full, he will not be eligible for assistance from the Trust for this purpose. For further details students should apply to The Secretary, Carnegie Trust, The Merchants' Hall, 22 Hanover Street, Edinburgh EH2 2EN.

Centesima Fund.—Provides grants for relief of widows and orphans of Ministers in the Diocese of Edinburgh. Apply J. and F. Anderson, WS, 48 Castle Street, Edinburgh EH2 3LX.

Church Hymnary Trust.—Manages the business side of the Church Hymnary, including the issue of particular editions, the ingathering of royalties and their distribution among the participating Churches, and the making of all business arrangements with publishers and others.

Church of Scotland Insurance Trust Ltd.—Undertakes Insurance of Church property and pays surplus profits to Church schemes. Secretaries and Managers, Scott Oswald & Co., CA, 1 Royal Terrace, Edinburgh EH7 5AD.

Church of Scotland Ministers' Orphan and War Memorial Funds.—Affords supplementary financial assistance for orphaned children of the manse. Apply Eric Hubbard, Esq., 137A George Street, Edinburgh EH2 4YJ.

Cintra Bequest.—Assists in providing accommodation in Scotland for Missionaries on leave, or for Ministers on temporary holiday or on rest. Apply R. A. Paterson, Solicitor, 121 George Street, Edinburgh EH2 4YN.

The Rev. John Clark Fund.—Provides annuities (1) for blind persons and (2) for orphan or fatherless children of ministers and missionaries of Church of Scotland. Apply Fyfe, Ireland & Co., WS, 27 Melville Street, Edinburgh EH3 7PE.

Crombie Scholarship.—Provides grants of £100 after competitive examination at St. Mary's College, St. Andrews, to MA Students of Divinity. Apply J. & F. Anderson, WS, 48 Castle Street, Edinburgh EH2 3LX.

Mrs. Dobie's Trust.—Makes annual grants to widows or orphans of Ministers of the Church. Apply Rev. A. Gordon McGillivray, MA, BD, STM, 10 Palmerston Place, Edinburgh EH12 5AA.

The Drummond Trust.—Is prepared to assist new publications which are in keeping with its Trust Deed (i.e. of Reformed and reforming evangelical quality). Enquiries to the Honorary Secretary at c/o Hill and Robb, 3 Pitt Terrace, Stirling FK8 2EY

The Duncan Trust.—Makes grants annually to students for the Ministry in the Faculties of Arts and Divinity. Preference is given to those born or educated within the bounds of the former Presbytery of Arbroath. Applications, not later than 31st October, to G. J. M. Dunlop, Brothockbank House, Arbroath DD11 1NJ or Rev. Gavin D. Brownlie, Dishlandtown Street, Arbroath DD11 1QU.

Esdaile Trust.—Assists education and advancement of daughters of Ministers, Missionaries, and Widowed Deaconesses of Church of Scotland between 12 and 25 years of age. Applications to E. R. L. Walker, CA, Clerk and Treasurer to the Governors, 17 Melville Street, Edinburgh EH3 7PH.

Ferguson Bequest Fund.—For the maintenance and promotion of religious ordinances and education and missionary operations in the first instance in the Counties of Ayr, Kirkcudbright, Wigtown, Lanark, Renfrew and Dunbarton. Apply Angus F. Sutherland, Esq., 182 Bath Street, Glasgow G2 4HG.

Geikie Bequest.—Makes small grants to students for the Ministry, including students studying for entry to the University, preference being given to those not eligible for SED awards. Apply to the Secretary, Department of Education, 121 George Street, Edinburgh EH2 4YN.

James Gillan's Bursary Fund.—Bursaries are available for students for the ministry who were born or whose parents or parent have resided and had their home for not less than three years continually in the old counties (not Districts) of Moray or Nairn. Apply R. and R. Urquhart, 121 High Street, Forres IV36 0AB.

Haldane Trust Fund.—Provides grants to Ministers of the Church of Scotland on their first induction, towards the purchase of theological books. Apply A. C. Bennett and Fairweather WS, 54 Queen Street, Edinburgh EH2 3NX.

James Hamilton's Trust.—Grants bursaries to students at New College and makes grants to Ministers or sons of Ministers training for the Ministry, as are considered most in need of assistance. Apply Messrs. Lindsays, WS, 32 Charlotte Square, Edinburgh EH2 4ET.

The Hogarth Fund.—Provides annuities to orphan or fatherless children of Ministers and Missionaries of the Church of Scotland. Apply Fyfe, Ireland & Co., WS, 27 Melville Street, Edinburgh EH3 7PE.

The Hope Trust.—Mr. J. K. Burleigh, WS, 31 Moray Place, Edinburgh EH3 6BX.

Iona Trust.—Objects are the preservation of the Abbey buildings and others at Iona and the making of these available for public worship. Secretaries, Messrs. J. and F. Anderson, WS, 48 Castle Street, Edinburgh EH2 3LX.

The Lyall Bequest.—See page 71.

The Misses Ann and Margaret M'Millan's Bequest.—Makes grants to Ministers of the Free and United Free Churches, and of the Church of Scotland, in charges within the Synod of Argyll, with income not exceeding the Minimum Stipend of the Church of Scotland. Apply by 30th June each year to Mr. R. Mitchell, Royal Bank, 37 Victoria Street, Rothesay, Isle of Bute PA20 0AP.

The Manse Auxiliary.—Collects and distributes slightly used clothing, soft furnishings, household linen, etc., to Manses on small stipends, Missionaries, Ministers' Widows, and others, especially those in remote areas.—Enquiries to Mrs. Helen F. Louden, 88 Cockburn Crescent, Balerno, Edinburgh EH14 7HU *031–449 4467*, or to Mrs. R. A. Baigrie, 32 Inchcolm Terrace, South Queensferry EH30 9NA *031–331 4311*.

Martin Harcus Bequest.—Makes grants to poor youths resident within the City of Edinburgh desirous of entering the Ministry of the Church. Apply W. G. P. Colledge, Esq., CA, 121 George Street, Edinburgh EH2 4YN.

Morgan Bursary Fund.—Makes grants to students for the Ministry in Arts and Divinity at the University of Glasgow. Apply Rev. Alexander Cunningham, MA, BD, 260 Bath Street, Glasgow G2 4JP.

Mylne Bursary.—Theological endowment of £90 per annum to students for the Ministry. Apply J. and F. Anderson, WS, 48 Castle Street, Edinburgh EH2 3LX.

Novum Trust.—Provides small short-term grants to initiate projects in Christian research and action which cannot readily be financed from other sources. Special consideration is given to proposals aimed at the welfare of young people, the training of lay people, and new ways of communicating the faith. Applications to Secretary, Rev. Peter Neilson, MA, BD, 121 George Street, Edinburgh EH2 4YN.

Paton Trust.—Assists Ministers in ill health to have recuperative holiday outwith, and free from the cares of their parishes. Apply Hew C. Davidson, Esq., CA, Alexander Sloan & Co., 142 St. Vincent Street, Glasgow G2 5LB.

John Pringle of Elgin, Robina Pringle of Elgin and Edith Evelyn Cressy Pringle Annuitant Funds.—Makes grants respectively to retired Ministers or Ministers Emeriti, to the widows of such and to the orphan daughters of such, in each case in poor circumstances. Apply W. G. P. Colledge, Esq., CA, 121 George Street, Edinburgh EH2 4YN.

Smieton Fund.—Enables a few Ministers to have a holiday at Crieff. Benefits go to a different Synod annually. Applications to Secretary, Department of Ministry and Mission, 121 George Street, Edinburgh EH2 4YN.

Mary Davidson Smith Clerical and Educational Fund for Aberdeenshire.—Assists Ministers in Aberdeenshire and the North to purchase books, or to travel for educational purposes, and assist their families with scholarships for further education or vocational training. Apply Alan J. Innes, Esq., LLB, Burgh House, 7-9 King Street, Aberdeen AB2 3AA.

General Starke Mortification.—Payment to Moderator of General Assembly to assist in meeting expenses. Secretaries, Messrs. J. and F. Anderson, WS, 48 Castle Street, Edinburgh EH2 3LX.

Lord Mount Stephen Trusts.—Assists with stipends of Ministers of certain parishes in former Presbyteries of Strathbogie and Fordyce, Abernethy and Elgin. Factor, Secretary of the Department of Ministry and Mission, 121 George Street, Edinburgh EH2 4YN.

Young Ministers' Furnishing Loan Fund—Makes loans (of £500) to young Ministers in first charge where stipend minimum to assist with furnishing manse. Apply The Secretary, Church and Ministry Department, 121 George Street, Edinburgh EH2 4YN.

SOCIETIES AND ASSOCIATIONS

The undernoted list shows the name of the Association, along with the name and address of the Secretary.

Inter-Church Associations

World Alliance of Reformed Churches.—Rev. Edmond Perret, 150 route de Ferney 1211, Geneva 20, Switzerland. *See also p. 45.*

Scottish Churches' Council.—Scottish Churches' House, Dunblane FK15 0AJ. *[078 682] Dunblane 3588. See also p. 46.*

Scottish Temperance Alliance.—Mr. John Livingstone, The Gean House, Alloa FK10 2EL. *[0592] Alloa 2443.*

Scottish National Council of Young Men's Christian Associations.—G. C. Smith, 10 Palmerston Place, Edinburgh EH12 5AD. *031–225 5022.*

Scottish Sunday School Union for Christian Education.—General Secretary, Miss Alison W. Cunningham, DSC, 23 Strathblane Road, Milngavie G62 8AL. *041–956 3131*

Scripture Union.—Rev. Colin A. M. Sinclair, BA, BD, 280 St. Vincent Street, Glasgow G2 5RT. *041–221 0051.*

Scottish Joint Committee on Religious Education.—Rev. Alasdair J. Morton, MA, BD, DipEd, FEIS, and Mr. Frederick L. Forrester, MA, DipED, MBIM, FEIS, 46 Moray Place, Edinburgh EH3 6BH. *031–225 6244.*

The Fellowship of St. Andrew.—Rev. Donald Reid, St. John's Rectory, 21 Swinton Road, Glasgow G69 6DS.

The Fellowship of St. Thomas.—Promotes informed interest in Churches of Indian sub-continent—Miss Katherine Ramsay, MA, 32 Incholm Terrace, South Queensferry EH30 9NA. *031–331 4311.*

Scottish Christian Youth Assembly.—Chairperson, Mr. Eric Whitten, 41 Kingston Avenue, Glasgow G14 0EB.

Student Christian Movement.—Ms. Susie Harvey, 1 Bristo Square, Edinburgh EH8. *031–667 4321.*

Church of Scotland Societies

Association of General Assembly, Synod and Presbytery Clerks.—Rev. R. A. Baigrie, MA, 32 Inchcolm Terrace, South Queensferry EH30 9NA. *031–331 4311*

Association of Returned Overseas Staff—Rev. C. Forrester-Paton, Acharn, Glen Road, Peebles, EH45 9AY. *0721 20136* or Dr. T. B. M. Sloan, 10 Cowden Road, Comrie, Crieff PH6 2HN.

Central Council of Elders' and Office-Bearers' Unions of the Church of Scotland.—Rev. P. T. Bisset, BD, St. Ninian's, Crieff. *[0764] Crieff 3766*

Church of Scotland Manse Fellowship.—Mrs. L. E. Ford McLeod, 41 St. Alban's Road, Edinburgh EH9 2LT. *031–667 4176*

Church of Scotland Retired Ministers' Association.—Acting Secretary, Rev. G. Rendle Leathem, MA, BD, Mayburn House, 2 Hawthorn Gardens, Loanhead EH20 9EE. *031–440 0299*

Church of Scotland Total Abstainers Association.—Secretary, Miss Mary W. Millar, MA, 25 Sundale Avenue, Glasgow G76 7TB.

Church Service Society.—Rev. Colin R. Williamson, LLB, BD, Manse of Aberdalgie, Perth PH2 0QD. *[0738] Perth 25854*

Scottish Church Society.—Secretary, Rev. Alan D. Birss, MA, BD, 15 Main Road, Castlehead, Paisley PA2 6AJ. *041-889 3587.*

Scottish Church Theology Society.—Rev. William D. Brown, MA, West Thornlie Street, Wishaw ML2 7AR

Society of Friends of St. Andrew's Jerusalem.—Secretary, Miss Margery Turnbull, 25/7 Mortonhall Road, Edinburgh EH9 2HS.

The Church of Scotland Chaplains' Association.—Rev. W. Scott Reid, MA, DipPS, BD, PhD, 26 Inchview Terrace, Edinburgh EH7 6TQ. *031–669 5311*

The **National Church Association.**—John M. Dale, LLB, Thomas Matthew & Co., Solicitors, Galston, Ayrshire

The **National Council of Youth Fellowship.**—*General Secretary,* c/o Education Department, 121 George Street, Edinburgh EH2 4YN.

Bible Societies

National Bible Society of Scotland.—Rev. Fergus Macdonald, MA, BD, 7 Hampton Terrace, Edinburgh EH12 5XU. *031–337 9701*

West of Scotland Bible Society.—Rev. Alexander Macdonald, MA, BD, Manse of Neilston, Glasgow G78 3NP. *041–881 1958*

Scottish Colportage Society.—*President* Rev. Alexander M. Roger, BD, 11 Newton Place, Glasgow G3 7PR. *041–333 0546*

General

The **Boys' Brigade.**—*Scottish Headquarters,* Carronvale House, Carronvale Road, Larbert FK5 3LH. *[0324] Larbert 562008.*

The **Girls' Brigade.**—*Scotish Headquarters, Boys' Brigade House, 168 Bath Street, Glasgow G2 4TQ. 041–332 1765.*

The **Scout Association.**—*Scottish Headquarters,* Fordell Firs, Hillend, Dunfermline KY11 5HQ. *[0383] Dunfermline 419073*

The **Girl Guides.**—*Scottish Headquarters,* 16 Coates Crescent, Edinburgh EH3 7AH. *031–226 4511. Glasgow Headquarters,* 15 Elmbank Street, Glasgow G2

Boys' Clubs of Scotland.—53 George Street, Edinburgh EH2 2HT. *031–226 7255*

Scottish Association of Youth Clubs.—13 Eglinton Crescent, Edinburgh EH12 5DE. *031–337 1242*

Scottish Church History Society.—Rev. Colin G. F. Brockie, BSc (Eng), BD, 51 Portland Road, Kilmarnock KA1 2EQ. *[0563] Kilmarnock 25311*

Scottish Evangelical Theology Society.—*Secretary,* Rev. Robert D. Higham, BD, The Manse, Greenlaw TD10 6XF *[036 16] Greenlaw 218.*

Scottish Marriage Guidance Council.—Rev. John G. M. Watt, MA, 58 Palmerston Place, Edinburgh EH12 5AZ. *031–225 5006*

Scottish National Christian Endeavour Union.—Secretary, Headquarters, 134 Wellington Street, Glasgow G2 2XL. *041–332 1105*

Ladies' Gaelic Schools and Highland Bursary Association.—Rev. John Campbell, MA, 15 Foulden Place, Dunfermline KY12. *[0383] Dunfermline 738055*

The **Monthly Visitor Tract Society.**—122 Thirlestane Road, Edinburgh EH9 1AN.

The **Lord's Day Observance Society.**—John M'Bride, 9 Kingsburgh Road, Edinburgh EH12 6DZ. *031–337 6007*

The **Society in Scotland for Propagating Christian Knowledge.**—A. G. Cairns and Simpson, WS, 11 Alva Street, Edinburgh EH2 4PH. *031–225 6797*

The **Scottish Reformation Society.**—The Society, 17 George IV Bridge, Edinburgh EH1 1EE. *031–225 1836*

The **Leprosy Mission.**—11 Coates Crescent, Edinburgh EH3 7AL. *031–226 6338. Area Organisers*—Rev. J. G. M'Connell, 24 Craigmount Avenue North, Edinburgh EH12 8DF and Rev. A. H. Swanson, 72 Mulben Crescent, Glasgow G53 7EH.

United Society for Christian Literature.—*Scottish Secretary,* Mrs. Florence E. Christie, 41 George IV Bridge, Edinburgh EH1 1EL. *031–226 5254*

The **Africa Evangelical Fellowship.**—Mrs. R. Mackay, 280 St. Vincent Street, Glasgow G2 5RT. *041–248 5630*

The **Waldensian Missions Aid Society for Work in Italy.**—David A. Lamb, Esq., LLB, 24 York Place, Edinburgh EH1 3HL. *031–557 4452*

Young Women's Christian Association of Great Britain, Scottish Council.—Miss S. A. Moyes, DCS, 7 Randolph Crescent, Edinburgh EH3 7TH. *031–225 7592*

Tear Fund.—Bridgemon Road, Teddington, Middlesex TW11 9AJ. *Scottish Secretary,* Peter Chirnside, 342 Argyle Street, Glasgow G2 8LY. *041–221 5476*

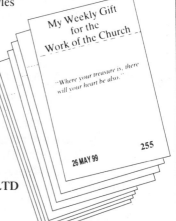

PRESBYTERY LISTS

EXPLANATION OF STATISTICS AND CONTRACTIONS

Synods and Presbyteries

The *Correspondents* of a Synod are those neighbouring Synods with which it exchanges Corresponding Members.

In every case a Presbytery is required to appoint a *Correspondent for the Transference of Communicants.* Unless otherwise stated the Presbytery Clerk acts in this capacity.

Parishes

In each Presbytery Parishes are arranged in alphabetical order, except that those in towns are arranged alphabetically under the name of the town.

A name in *italics* denotes a Mission under the care of the Parish below which it is listed.

In most cases of Linked Charges the names of both are set out together and their particulars given at the point where the first of them in alphabetical order would normally be found. Both Parishes are of equal status and each name appears in its proper place in the alphabetical list.

Ministers

The years given after a Minister's name are the year in which he was ordained and that when he was inducted or introduced to the charge shown. Where only the ordination year is given this is also the year of induction. Where a union or linking has taken place under a "sitting" minister the year shown for induction refers to induction to the original charge.

An *Associate* Minister is shown immediately beneath the Minister of the charge and his address and particulars are given at that point and not at the end of the Presbytery List as in the case with an *Assistant* Minister and an *Auxiliary* Minister.

The names of retired Ministers and of Ministers who qualify for a seat in Presbytery though they are employed otherwise than in parishes are shown in alphabetical order at the end of each Presbytery list. The former parish or appointment of a retired Minister is printed in parentheses. In these cases the year of ordination is given and also the year of appointment or retirement as the case may be. In the case where a Minister retires from a terminable appointment the name of the charge and the date of his retirement may be either that of his regular charge or his terminable appointment though almost without exception it is the latter.

Assistants, etc.

The names of Ordained Assistants, Lay Missionaries and Deaconesses employed in parishes are shown under these parishes. The Ordained Assistants, being members of Presbytery, appear again in the list at the end of the Presbytery. Deacons and Deaconesses are now Corresponding Members of Presbytery. Further particulars of their addresses etc. are to be found in List H. For convenience their telephone numbers are shown in the Presbytery Lists.

Telephone Numbers

Both the name of the exchange and its STD figure-equivalent are given. It may be in some cases that neither of these is appropriate, but even in such cases the name will enable a caller to find the code which applies. Until the whole country has gone over to STD it is not possible to operate one single simple system.

Addresses

Every effort has been made to secure the correct postal address for all manses. In most cases, and certainly where there is more than one congregation in a town, the words "Manse of . . ." should precede the name of the parish and be followed by the name of the town. In the case of larger towns wherever the information was available a street name and number have been given. Postal codes are also shown and should invariably be used. Normally the address shown for a minister not in a parish is his home address. For business purposes he should be contacted at the address shown in List C or other appropriate List.

Statistics

The statistics are those for 1987. They are all taken from returns made respectively to the General Interests Department, the General Treasurer, the Education Department, the Maintenance of the Ministry Committee and the Woman's Guild.

Com.   Number of Communicants on Roll at end of 1987.

Eld.   Number of Elders.

W.G.   Membership of Woman's Guild—including Young Woman's Groups.

S.S.   Number in Sunday Schools.

B.C.   Number in Bible Classes, including Junior, Senior and Boy's Brigade Classes.

C.L.   Christian Liberality is the total amount contributed for all purposes by the congregation and its agencies.

As'd   Amount allocated to congregation for Mission and Service Fund for 1987.

Gi'n   Total amount contributed to Mission and Service Fund in 1987, making no allowance for late contributions but including late returns (if any) for 1986.

Stp.   Stipend paid in 1987. Unless an asterisk appears beside the figure it is to be presumed that a Manse is provided, the amount paid by way of Manse Allowance being included.

*   Parish in which worship must be conducted in Gaelic.

†   Parish in which it is desirable that the Minister should speak Gaelic.

¶   Minister has been inducted to the Parish on the basis of Terminable Tenure.

v   No stipend figure is given since the charge was vacant (or united or linked) during part of the year.

[E]   Church Extension charge.

SUPPLEMENTARY LISTS

List A—Chaplains to H. M. Forces.—Includes only Chaplains who are Church of Scotland Ministers.

List B—Professors and Lecturers.—Contains the names of all Ministers of the Church who are engaged in full-time service as Professors or Lecturers in the Faculty of Divinity in a Scottish University.

List C—Non-Parochial Appointments.—All are Ministers of the Church of Scotland and most are members of Presbyteries as indicated.

List D—Missionaries.—Contains the names of all Missionaries of the Church who have the full status of Ministers of the Church of Scotland and that in spite of the fact that they are also in most cases members of courts of the indigenous Churches.

"STOP PRESS"

The following alterations and corrections were received too late to be incorporated in their proper place in the text of the book.

97 Dalkeith St John's and King's Park — Alistair K Ridland *Read* 13 Weir Crescent, Dalkeith EH22

99 Prestonpans—Moira Herkes (Mrs) *Read* East Loan, Prestonpans EH32 9ED

100 Sawers, E A H TD *Read* 18 Lydgait Gardens, Haddington EH41

106 Lusk, John C BA BD *Read* 20 Ochlochy Park, Dunblane FK15 0DU

119 Annbank *Read* Kenneth L Johnston BA LTh 1969 1989

122 Prestwick South *Read* Vacant

123 *Add* Girdwood Thomas B 1949 1988 (Prestwick South)

133 Caldwell *Read* John P Cubie MA BD 1961 1989

140 Kirkintilloch St David's Memorial *Read* John Hay Paterson BD 1977 1989

142 Blairbeth Rodger Memorial *Read* Vacant

142 Cambuslang Trinity St Paul's *Read* Vacant

151 Martin James *Read* (0698) Cambusnethan 385825

155 Airdrie Flowerhill *Read* Vacant

166 Mitchell Andrew S *Read* BA BD DipREd AdvDipEd

169 Communion — Kilarrow *Read* 1 Mr Je Sp De

185 Lochgelly St Andrew's *Read* Vacant

186 Buckhaven *Add* Kenneth G Russell BD CCE Assoc 1986 1988 3 Carlisle Crescent, Buckhaven KY8 1DW [0592] Kirkcaldy 712323

187 Leven St Andrew's—Alexander R Forsyth *Read* 1973 1985 5 Forman Road, Leven KY8 4HH

194 Bendochy with Kinclaven *Read* Vacant

196 Cargill Burrelton with Collace *Read* Richard Frazer 1988 ..

198 Perth St Andrew's *Read* Vacant

200 *Add* M'Cormick Alastair F 1960 1989 Bahamas St Andrew's Manse, PO Box N 1099, Nassau

201 Abernyte *Delete* Robert Daly MA JP : *Read* Vacant

205 *Delete* MacDonald John A (Dundee Balgay)

211 Mannofield—John F Anderson *Read* MA BD FSAScot

214 *Add* Scouller Michael D BSc BD 1988 1988 .. Chaplain Army Oakington Barracks, Cambridge CB4 5EJ

241 Portree—John Ferguson *Read* LTh BD

264 *Delete* Stalker D M G BD

266 *Add* M'Cormick Alastair F 1960 1989 America Bahamas 28

271 Bahamas *Read* Rev Alastair F M'Cormick and Mrs M'Cormick, St Andrew's Manse, PO Box N 1099, Nassau

276 *Add* Portchmouth Roland J NDD ATD (Bendochy with Kinclaven 1988) 1984

276 Robertson Alan O *Add* Merchiston Castle School, Colinton, Edinburgh EH3 0PU

280 *Delete* Stalker D M G BD

282 *Delete* Scouler Michael D

291 Presbytery of Annandale and Eskdale *Read* Brown S Jeffrey BA 11 Well Road, Moffat DG10 9AR [0683] Moffat 20475

Page
296   *Add* Presbytery of Kirkcaldy— Paterson, Mrs Maureen 91 Dalmahoy Crescent, Kirkcaldy [0592] Kirkcaldy 262300

296   Presbytery of Perth—Blair Anne *Read* Blair Anne B 11 Moredun Terrace, Perth PH2 0DA

List E—Overseas Stations.—Shows the staffing position of Overseas Stations under the direction of the Overseas Council.

List F—Unattached Ministers.—These are Ministers who have retired from the charges noted in brackets during the year indicated, who have retained their status as Ministers of the Church of Scotland, but who have not retained their seats in Presbytery and Synod. Only those whose names carry an asterisk hold current "practising certificates" under the Act of 1987 and are entitled to perform the functions of the ministry.

List FF—Act VIII 1980 has made it easy for a retired minister who wishes to do so to resign his seat in Presbytery and provides that he shall remain under the supervision and jurisdiction of the Presbytery which accepted his resignation. So far almost all such resignations appear to have been in the Presbytery of Edinburgh. They may be regarded as "Unattached Ministers" but in a slightly different way from those hitherto appearing in List F.

List G—Roll of Probationers.—This List is divided into two parts according to whether the persons concerned are probationers or licentiates in terms of Act VII of 1985. It does not contain the names of probationers who have been ordained as assistants since they have become Ministers without Charge and appear either under a Presbytery or in List F.

List H—Roll of Diaconate.—Shows the names and sphere of service along with the addresses of all active Deacons and Deaconesses and of Lay Missionaries and Agents under the care of the Church. It also shows a list of all Retired Deacons, Deaconesses and Lay Missionaries.

List J—Roll of Readers.—Shows the names and addresses of all Readers and is arranged according to Presbyteries.

List K—Retired Missionaries.

PRESBYTERY NUMBERS

Aberdeen	31	Falkirk	22	Melrose	4
Abernethy	36	Glasgow	16	Moray	35
Angus	30	Gordon	33	Mull	21
Annandale	7	Greenock	15	Orkney	45
Ardrossan	12	Hamilton	17	Paisley	14
Ayr	10	Inverness	37	Peebles	4
Buchan	34	Irvine	11	Perth	28
Caithness	41	Jedburgh	6	Ross	39
Deeside	32	Kilmarnock	11	St. Andrews	26
Dumbarton	18	Kincardine	32	Shetland	46
Dumfries	8	Kirkcaldy	25	Skye	42
Dundee	29	Kirkcudbright	8	South Argyll	19
Dunfermline	24	Lanark	13	Stirling	23
Dunkeld	27	Lewis	44	Stranraer	9
Dunoon	20	Lochaber	38	Sutherland	40
Duns	5	Lochcarron	42	Uist	43
Edinburgh	1	Lorn	21	West Lothian	2
England	47	Lothian	3	Wigtown	9
Eskdale	7	Meigle	27		

LIST OF SYNODS, PRESBYTERIES AND PARISHES

For Meaning of Contractions, Symbols, etc., see pages 79 and 80

SYNOD 1 — LOTHIAN

Meets at Palmerston Place Church, Edinburgh, on the second Wednesday of April
Correspondents: The Borders; Forth; Fife; Clydesdale
Clerk: Rev. ALAN B. FORREST, MA., 8 M'Lardy Court, Uphall EH52 5SL [0506] *Broxburn 852788*

1. EDINBURGH

Meets at Palmerston Place Church, Edinburgh, on the first Tuesday of October, November, December, February, April and May, and on the second Tuesday in September and on the last Tuesday of June. When the first Tuesday of April falls in Holy Week the meeting is on the second Tuesday.

Clerk: Rev. A. GORDON M'GILLIVRAY, MA, BD, STM, 10 Palmerston Place, Edinburgh EH12 5AA 031-225 9137

Charge	Minister	Ord.	Ind.	Address and Tel. No.	Com.	Eld.	W.G.	S.S.	B.C.	C.L. £	As'd £	Gi'n £	Stp. £
Abercorn *linked with* Dalmeny	Ivor Gibson, MA	1957	1980	Dalmeny, South Queensferry, EH30 9TT 031-331 1869	151 237	11 12	13 15	10 11	2 2	5784 7330	....	195 253	8648
EDINBURGH— Albany Deaf Church of Edinburgh	Malcolm M. Rew, BD	1974	1988	49 Albany Street, EH1 3QY 031-556 3128	175	19	.....	.....	.....	1337	363	363	9000
Balerno	Henry A. Shepherd, MA, BD	1962	1980	3 Johnsburn Rd., Balerno, Midlothian EH14 7DN 031-449 3830	1070	59	108	204	60	56595	6443	6994	.....
Barclay	D. Graham Leitch, MA, BD	1974	1980	38 Cluny Gardens, EH10 6BN 031-447 8702	646	59	60	33	9	66765	16566	16566	10497
Blackhall St. Columba	Ernest G. Sangster, BD, TH M Sarah E. C. Nicol (Mrs.), BSC, BD *Associate*	1958 1985	1976 1987	5 Blinkbonny Crescent, EH4 3NB 031-332 3070 6E Fair-o-Far, EH4 6QE	1439	92	84	124	64	87456	22630	24812	11130
Braid	Angus W. Morrison, MA, BD	1959	1977	2 Cluny Avenue, EH10 4RN 031-447 1871	566	43	53	12	3	38641	8391	8391	9363

Congregation	Minister			Address									
Bristo Memorial Craigmillar	Eric W. S. Jeffrey, JP, MA	1954	1978	3 Spence Street, EH16 5AG 031-668 2722	298	6	32	8	7	12534	.....	130	8646
	Agnes M. Rennie, DCS	.....	.....	Deaconess—see List H 031-661 8475									
Broughton McDonald	I. Alasdair Elders, MA, BD	1964	1973	103 East Claremont Street, EH7 4JA 031-556 7313	436	31	.....	21	15	28384	6986	1665	9363
Burdiehouse	Iain A. Macdonald, LTH	1986	1988	76 Lasswade Road, EH16 6SF 031-664 2287	388	14	.....	15	3	11910	.....	50	v
Canongate	Charles Robertson, MA	1965	1978	Manse of the Canongate, EH8 8BN 031-556 3515	432	31	24	.....	.....	30436	6874	6874	8446
Carrick Knowe	William W. Clinkenbeard, BSC, BD, STM	1966	1971	40A Harlaw Road, Balerno, Midlothian, EH14 7AX 031-449 6984	1092	56	155	144	18	48310	6855	6855	*11622
Cluny	George A. M. Munro	1968	1973	20 Braidburn Crescent, EH10 6EN 031-447 1617	988	76	63	60	19	92141	23431	23489	11691
Colinton	William B. Johnston, MA, BD, DD	1945	1964	The Manse, Colinton, EH13 0JR 031-441 2315	1532	89	84	146	24	110162	18583	19894	10119
	Marion E. Dodd, BD	1988	.....	Assistant—see List on page 89									
Colinton Mains	John H. C. Fenemore	1980	.....	173 Colinton Road, EH14 1BZ 031-443 1966	530	65	53	53	34	20623	2385	771	8646
Corstorphine— Craigsbank	George D. W. Grubb, BA, BD	1962	1971	22 Belgrave Road, EH12 6NF 031-334 3557	1290	74	66	110	47	63118	15577	15577	10200
	Ann Inglis (Mrs.), LL.B, BD Associate	1986	.....	4 Sycamore Gardens, EH12 7JJ 031-334 8882									
Old	Ian D. Brady, BSC, ARCST, BD	1967	1976	23 Manse Road, EH12 7SW 031-334 5425	1024	62	108	82	25	74883	12886	12886	9615
St. Anne's	J. William Hill, BA, BD	1967	1976	23 Belgrave Road, EH12 6NG 031-334 3188	690	59	61	87	13	47272	13451	14251	9615
St. Ninian's	Colin R. Martin, MA, BD	1956	1966	17 Templeland Road, EH12 8RZ 031-334 2978	1663	94	70	195	90	86239	24554	24817	11376
Craigentinny St. Christopher's	Duncan Shaw, PH.D, TH.D.R, JP	1951	1959	4 Sydney Terrace, EH7 6SL 031-669 1089	317	13	.....	19	0	22982	.....	.....	8697
Craiglockhart	Andrew F. Headden, BA, BD	1981	1985	202 Colinton Road, EH14 1BP 031-443 2020	834	65	57	106	27	107573	13378	13508	9672
Craigmillar Park	William Paterson, BD	1977	1984	14 Hallhead Road, EH16 5OJ 031-667 1623	455	38	36	39	9	52416	13952	14727	10497
Cramond	C. M. Maclean, MA	1949	1957	Manse of Cramond, EH4 6NS 031-336 2036	1687	102	49	93	61	91190	29750	29750	11691

Charge	Minister	Ord.	Ind.	Address and Tel. No.	Com.	Eld.	W.G.	S.S.	B.C.	C.L. £	As'd £	Gi'n £	Stp. £
Currie	Gordon M'Lean, LTH	1972	1982	1 Kirkgate, Currie, Midlothian, EH14 6AL 031-449 4719	1738	82	97	249	74	61574	11909	7909	9993
	S. Ann Campbell Associate	1988	....	34 Mansfield Road, Balerno, EH14 7LF 031-449 3704									
Davidson's Mains	J. R. H. Middleton, LL.B, BD	1981	1988	Quality Street, EH4 5BB 031-336 3078	1126	73	97	114	46	57682	13829	13829	9993
Dean	J. Gordon Grant, MA, BD	1957	1987	1 Ravelston Terrace, EH4 3EF 031-332 5736	350	26	53	6	....	20591	3067	3232	v
Drylaw [E]	Ian Y. Gilmour, BD	1985	....	23 Hillview, EH4 2AF 031-343 1643	363	13	26	70	21	16507	....	....	9147
	Morag Crawford, DCS	....	....	Deaconess—see List H 031-332 2253									
Duddingston	William H. W. Ramsay	1966	1972	Manse of Duddingston, EH15 3PX 031-661 4240	916	48	79	56	17	35439	8143	8143	9363
Fairmilehead	Murray Chalmers, MA	1965	1974	40 Frogston Road West, EH10 7AJ 031-445 1789	1325	86	64	240	65	119028	27500	27500	11130
Gilmerton	D. M. Skinner, MBE, JP, MIES	1962	....	43 Ravenscroft Street, EH17 8QJ 031-664 2147	336	10	15	30	....	15285	....	....	8646
Gorgie	David J. B. Anderson, MA, BD	1974	1986	90 Myreside Road, EH10 5BZ 031-337 2284	848	45	52	45	6	41516	11527	12123	9615
	Matilda Wilson, DCS	....	....	Deaconess—see List I 031-228 1475									
Granton	Elizabeth M. Henderson, MA, BD	1985	1986	8 Wardie Crescent, EH5 1AG 031-551 2159	601	39	65	83	34	22135	3170	1303	8646
Greenbank	Ian G. Scott, BSC, BD, STM	1965	1983	112 Greenbank Crescent, EH10 5SZ 031-447 4032	1183	99	95	161	65	101895	33189	33239	12249
Greenside	Andrew F. Anderson, MA, BD	1981	....	80 Pilrig Street, EH6 5AS 031-554 3277	582	30	30	12	7	41176	7388	7388	9363
Greyfriars Tolbooth and Highland Kirk	David M. Beckett, BA, BD	1964	1983	12 Tantallon Place, EH9 1NZ 031-667 8671	558	51	....	11	....	50920	12485	12735	9615
High (St. Giles')	Gilleasbuig I. Macmillan, MA, BD	1969	1973	St. Giles' Cathedral, EH1 1RE 031-225 4363	880	58	....	29	....	102350	21941	21941	12642
Holyrood Abbey	James Philip, MA	1948	1958	100 Willowbrae Avenue, EH8 7HU 031-661 2841	473	41	35	33	14	94853	28445	28445	11736
Holy Trinity	Stanley A. Brock, BD	1977	1983	16 Thorburn Road, EH13 0BQ 031-441 5218	383	16	20	46	11	28032	3064	3064	v
	John K. Collard, Associate MA, BD	1986	....	12 Sighthill Crescent, EH11 4QE 031-453 6279									
	Mary Deacons	....	....	Agent—see List H									

Congregation	Minister		Address									
Inverleith	D. Hugh Davidson, MA	1965	43 Inverleith Gardens, EH3 5PR 031-552 3874	714	49	52	36	20	47245	12909	12909	9363
Juniper Green	G. G. Cameron, MA, BD, STM	1957	476 Lanark Road, Juniper Green, EH14 5BQ 031-453 3494	786	46	88	85	50	58687	14180	15500	9993
Kirkliston	John Murrie, BD	1953	The Manse, Kirkliston, EH29 9DJ 031-333 3298	605	34	34	106	10	58210	4938	4938	8883
Kirk o' Field	Farquhar M. M'Arthur, BD, LTH	1974	31 Hatton Place, EH9 1UA 031-667 7954	549	46	39	30	15	22271	5364	7148	7329
Leith—												
North	Alistair G. C. M'Gregor, QC, BD	1987	22 Primrose Bank Road, EH5 3JE 031-551 2802	589	48	52	37	19	39288	7165	7165	v
	Jean M. Potts, DCS	....	Deaconess—see List H 031-557 2144									
St. Andrew's	John Cook, MA, BD	1966	13 Claremont Park, EH6 7PJ 031-554 7695	589	39	30	64	16	27919	4641	4641	9000
St. Paul's	John M. Tait, BSC, BD	1985	52 Pilrig Street, EH6 5AS 031-554 1842	447	30	32	81	32	29982	3418	3418	9000
St. Serf's	S. W. Peat, BSC, PHD, BD ¶	1977	1 Denham Green Terrace, EH5 3PG 031-552 4059	475	36	40	40	8	32634	2783	2783	9000
St. Thomas' Junction Road	D. Campbell Stewart, MA	1957	28 Summerside Street, EH6 4NU 031-554 5039	664	41	45	14	24	28290	6310	6681	9363
South	John M. Kellet, MA	1962	7 East Hermitage Place, EH6 8AA 031-554 3062	1698	98	60	32	47	77356	10377	10412	10497
	Angus R. Mathieson, BD	1988	Assistant—see List on page 90									
Wardie	Thomas Thomson, MA	1954	35 Lomond Road, EH5 3JN 031-552 3328	855	72	101	107	47	126383	12255	12255	9363
Liberton	John W. M. Cameron, MA, BD	1957	7 Kirk Park, EH16 6HZ 031-664 3067	1397	76	115	134	15	93057	18038	18293	10686
Liberton Northfield	William H. Thomson	1964	9 Claverhouse Drive, EH16 6BR 031-658 1754	476	17	50	27	....	21187	....	....	v
Lochend linked with Restalrig	John W. Dickson, MA, BD	1986	43 Moira Terrace, EH7 6TD 031-669 7329	321	16	28	24	4	17770	....	....	*10146
				482	10	52	19	4	13629	1900	251	8646
London Road	W. Scott Reid, RD, MA, DIPPS, PHD	1950	26 Inchview Terrace, EH7 6TQ 031-669 5311	910	45	66	38	6	38811	10110	10110	9363
Marchmont St. Giles'	Donald M. Stephen, TD, MA, BD, THM	1962	19 Hope Terrace, EH9 2AP 031-447 2834	490	47	61	13	15	50142	12781	12784	9615
Mayfield	William J. G. M'Donald, MA, BD, DD	1953	26 Seton Place, EH9 2JT 031-667 1286	1141	80	104	185	44	101112	30913	36123	11691

Charge	Minister	Ord.	Ind.	Address and Tel. No.	Com.	Eld.	W.G.	S.S.	B.C.	C.L. £	As'd £	Gi'n £	Stp. £
Morningside	John F. Kirk, MA, BD, PH D	1955	1970	5 Cluny Avenue, EH10 4RN 031-447 4647	436	25	32	11	2	26109	1515	679	8883
Morningside United	J. Stewart Miller, MA, BD, STM	1954	1975	1 Midmar Avenue, EH10 6BS 031-447 8724	385	43	22	21	7	49404	7352	7352	9993
Muirhouse [E]	Frederick D. F. Shewan, MA, BD	1970	1980	35 Silverknowes Road, EH4 5LL 031-336 4546	259	13	19	14	...	12596	...	...	9147
Murrayfield	Clarence W. Musgrave, BA, BD, TH M	1966	1980	45 Murrayfield Gardens, EH12 6DH 031-337 5431	859	82	46	140	21	102721	22755	22755	11130
Newcraighall and Richmond Craigmillar	Mary O. M'Kenzie	1976	1987	29 Brunstane Road South, EH15 2NG 031-669 1133	306	14	20	12	13	10506	...	...	v
	Agent—see List H Margaret R. Allan, MA, BD												
Newhaven	Alexander R. Aitken, MA	1965	1975	11 Laverockbank Terrace, EH5 3BL 031-552 8906	487	21	61	55	32	34731	6310	6310	9114
New Restalrig	Vacant			19 Abercorn Road, EH8 7DP 031-661 4045	759	32	61	97	8	48995	8793	8793	9114
Old Kirk	Ian A. Moir, MA, BD	1962	1983	24 Pennywell Road, EH4 4HD 031-332 4354	403	26	38	60	38	12779	...	507	8847
	Maureen Hutchison (Mrs.), DCS			Deaconess—see List H 031-332 8020									
Palmerston Place	John P. Chalmers, BD	1979	1986	37 Caiyside, Huntington View, EH10 7HW 031-445 5197	1043	97	62	58	18	98753	25953	7420	11691
Pilrig and Dalmeny Street	Neil G. Campbell, BA, BD	1988	...	Assistant—see List on page 88	775	34	45	64	46	26851	3057	3057	v
	W. Iain C. Dunn, DA, L TH	1983	1988	78 Pilrig Street, EH6 5AS 031-554 3509									
Polwarth	Douglas M. Murray, MA, BD, PH D	1976	1980	9 Merchiston Bank Gardens, EH10 5EB 031-447 2741	707	48	51	38	8	53105	10698	11698	9615
Portobello—Old and Windsor Place	Ian G. Wotherspoon, LTH	1967	1982	6 Hamilton Terrace, EH15 1NB 031-669 5312	873	60	74	44	16	42671	8361	8361	9528
St. James'	Malcolm M. Macdougall, BD	1981	...	63 Durham Terrace, EH15 1QG 031-669 1767	487	33	31	40	...	27876	3241	3241	8264
St. Philip's Joppa	John Weir Cook, MA, BD	1962	1988	6 St. Mary's Place, EH15 2QF 031-669 2410	1004	68	128	124	39	59218	16368	5508	v
Priestfield	Alistair Skinner, BD	1964	1975	13 Lady Road, EH16 5PA 031-668 1620	370	41	34	34	...	26990	4398	4498	8772

Congregation	Minister			Address									
Queensferry	John G. Carrie, BSc, BD	1971	......	South Queensferry, EH30 9HY 031-331 1100	994	43	128	178	55	36070	5791	6101	9000
Ratho	Michael R. R. Shewan, MA, BD	1985	......	Ratho, Newbridge, Midlothian, EH28 8NP 031-333 1346	490	22	43	47	......	67529	......	......	8646
Reid Memorial	Brian M. Embleton, BD	1976	1985	20 Wilton Road, EH16 5NX 031-667 3981	589	30	45	31	11	86557	10220	10790	9615
Restalrig	*see Lochend*												
St. Aidan's *linked with*	S. Edwin P. Beveridge, BA	1959	1983	65 Balgreen Road, EH12 5UA 031-337 7711	439	20	32	35	6	13898	1461	957	8646
Stenhouse Saughton				*Assistant—see* List on page 88	244	15	44	22	......	9732	982	544	
St. Andrew's and St. George's	{ Andrew R. C. McLellan, TD, MA, BD, STM Richard F. Baxter, OBE, MA, BD	1970 1954	1986 1983	25 Comely Bank, EH4 1AL 031-332 1372	543	43	43	23	7	95605	14650	14650	9993
St. Andrew's Clermiston	*Vacant*	......	......	19 Clermiston Road North, EH4 7BL 031-336 3933	560	27	25	24	4	22390	......	265	v
St. Bernard's Stockbridge	John R. Munro, BD	1976	1983	38 India Street, EH3 6HB 031-226 3131	537	40	55	34	1	34280	4295	3579	9000
St. Catherine's Argyle	Victor W. N. Laidlaw, BD	1975	......	5 Palmerston Road, EH9 1TL 031-667 2814	498	41	79	70	43	54700	13425	15226	9672
St. Colm's	Ian P. Renton	1958	1966	1 Merchiston Gardens, EH10 5DD 031-337 1107	502	34	37	11	......	28500	3926	3926	8736
St. Cuthbert's	{ T. C. Cuthell, MA, BD Peter M. Gardner, BD	1965 1988	1976	22 Learmonth Terrace, EH4 1PG 031-332 6138 *Assistant—see* List on page 89	1059	75	......	24	12	67650	21713	21713	11376
St. David's Broomhouse	C. Peter White, BVMS, BD, MRCVS	1974	......	33 Traquair Park West, EH12 7AN 031-334 1730	305	16	44	23	14	44406	4233	4233	9000
St. George's West	{ Robert L. Glover, BMUS, BD, ARCO Anne T. Logan (Mrs.), MA, BD	1971 1981	1985 1987	10 Craigleith Gardens, EH4 3JW 031-332 6421 *Assistant—see* List on page 89	756	89	44	14	8	82353	17398	17596	11691
St. John's Oxgangs	J. Ronald Dick, BD	1973	1988	2 Caiystane Terrace, EH10 6SR 031-445 1688	542	30	32	54	11	17506	......	236	v
St. Martin's	Wendy F. Drake (Mrs.), BD	1978	......	5 Duddingston Crescent, EH15 3AS 031-669 3427	373	17	37	44	15	14331	......	341	8646
St. Mary's *linked with*	Robert Johnston, MTHEOL	1973	1988	19 Eildon Street, EH3 5JU 031-557 6052	248	24	37	13	......	23977	1719	1779	v
St. Stephen's					520	24	30	13	......	15984	3181	3181	

Charge	Minister	Ord.	Ind.	Address and Tel. No.	Com.	Eld.	W.G.	S.S.	B.C.	C.L. £	As'd £	Gi'n £	Stp. £
St. Michael's	Margaret R. Forrester (Mrs.), MA, BD	1974	1980	25 Kingsburgh Road, EH12 6DZ 031-337 5646	839	42	49	78	38	42261	5688	5688	*10383
St. Nicholas' Sighthill	Kenneth J. Mackay, MA, BD	1971	1976	122 Sighthill Loan, EH11 4NT 031-453 6921	1010	41	58	117	32	38990	4992	4992	9000
St. Stephen's	see St. Mary's												
St. Stephen's Comely Bank	John W. Craig, MA, BD	1951	1963	8 Blinkbonny Crescent, EH4 3NB 031-332 3364	871	47	31	80	34	52870	9805	5427	9363
Salisbury	Brian C. Casebow, MA, BD	1959	1967	25 Fountainhall Road, EH9 2LN 031-667 1780	354	26	51	12	2	31048	4718	4718	9000
Slateford Longstone	William R. Taylor, MA, BD	1983	1986	50 Kingsknowe Road South, EH14 2JW 031-443 2960	587	34	65	52	24	22486	3300	1123	8646
Stenhouse Saughton	See St. Aidan's												
Tron Kirk Moredun	Ronald M. Maxton, MA	1955	1968	4 West Savile Road, EH16 5NG 031-667 4364	357	18	15	20	11	8210	.....	.....	8646
Viewforth	Tom Gordon, MA, BD	1974	1982	12 West Castle Road, EH10 5AU 031-229 7045	643	57	49	62	6	57337	10265	10354	9114

Minister	Ord.	Ret.	App.	Charge	Address and Tel. No.
Alexander, Helen J. R., MA, BD	1981	.....	1986	Associate Chaplain University of Edinburgh	Chaplaincy Centre, Bristo Street, EH8 9AL 031-667 1011
Anderson, Hugh, MA, BD, PHD, DD	1951	1985		(University of Edinburgh)	5 Comiston Springs Avenue, EH10 6NT 031-447 1401
Anderson, W. Crawford, LTH	1972		1980	Chaplain, Heriot Watt University	51 Queen's Avenue, EH4 2DG 031-343 1277
Auld, A. Graeme, MA, BD, PHD	1973		1973	University of Edinburgh	3 Denham Green Terrace, EH5 3PG 031-552 2910
Baigrie, R. A., MA	1945	1985		(Kirkurd with Newlands)	32 Incholm Terrace, South Queensferry, EH30 9NA 031-331 4311
Balfour, Thomas, MA, BD	1945	1985		(Ministry and Mission Department)	12 Crosswood Crescent, Balerno, Midlothian, EH14 7HS 031-449 3941
Barr, Gavin	1945	1971		(New Restalrig)	50 Craiglockhart Drive South, EH14 1JB 031-443 2549
Baxter, Richard F., OBE, MA, BD	1954		1983	Assistant at St. Andrew's & St. George's	52 Morningside Drive, EH10 5ND 031-447 7735
Bernard, Neil C., MA	1939	1976		(Overseas Council)	12 Lockerby Cottages, EH16 6OU 031-664 6310
Bigwood, William C., MA, BD, DD, FEIS	1929	1971		(St. Andrew's and St. George's)	5/2 Clark Place, EH5 3BQ 031-551 2218
Blakey, Ronald S. MA, BD, MTH	1962		1988	Assembly Council	Flat 3, 21 Stuart Crescent, EH12 8XR 031-339 3979
Brown, R. Graeme, MA, BD	1961		1981	Education Department St. Colm's	23 Inverleith Terrace, EH3 5NX 031-332 1156
Buchan, Fiona M.	1988		1988	National Youth Adviser	4 Comiston Place, EH10 6AF 031-447 9175
Burnside, William, MA	1942	1982		(West Kilbride Overton)	48/10 North Gyle Grove, EH12 8LF 031-339 1167
Campbell, Alastair V., BD, THD	1966		1969	University of Edinburgh	34 Lockharton Avenue, EH14 1AZ 031-443 3250
Carmichael, William, BSC, FLS	1972	1987		(Restalrig)	60 Kirk Brae, EH16 6HU 031-664 2779
Cheyne, Alexander C., MA, BD, BLITT, DLITT	1958	1986		(University of Edinburgh)	12 Crossland Crescent, Peebles, EH45 8LF [0721] Peebles 22288

Name			Charge / Appointment	Address
Conacher, Philip, MA	1933	1968	(John Ker Memorial)	35 Craiglockhart Drive South, EH14 1JA 031–443 0082
Cumming, David P. L., MA	1957	1985	Ministry and Mission Department	5 Strathalmond Green, EH4 8AG 031–339 6462
Cunningham, Richard, MA	1938	1978	(Garvald and Morham)	7 Lockerby Cottages, EH16 6QU 031–664 3797
Dempster, William M., OBE, MA, STM	1935	1975	(Paris)	4 Lockerby Cottages, EH16 6QU 031–666 2125
Dodd, Marion E., BD	1988	1988	*Assistant at Colinton*	64 Redford Loan, EH13 0AT 031–441 3917
Doyle, Ian B., MA, BD, PHD	1946	1977	Ministry and Mission Department	21 Lygon Road, EH16 5QD 031–667 2697
Dunlop, A. Ian, TD, MA, BD	1939		(St. Stephen's)	59 Meggetland Terrace, EH14 1AR 031–443 1087
Easton, David R., MA	1937	1977	(Greenock St. Paul's)	68 Spottiswoode Street, EH9 1DH 031–447 3217
Elliot, George, MA, BD, STM	1958	1973	Board of Stewardship and Finance	99 Greenbank Crescent, EH10 5TB 031–447 4017
Ferguson, David A. S., MA, BD, D PHIL	1984	1986	University of Edinburgh	3 Caerlaverock Court, EH2 8UE 031–339 1726
Finlayson, J. Clarence, MA	1930	1972	(Grange)	52 Falcon Avenue, EH10 4AW 031–447 6550
Forrester, Duncan B., MA, BD, D PHIL	1962	1978	University of Edinburgh	25 Kingsburgh Road, EH12 6DZ 031–337 5646
Fuller, James W., FIAC	1973	1978	(Rome)	21 St. Bernard's Crescent, EH4 1NR 031–332 5233
Gardner, Peter M., BD	1988	1988	*Assistant at St. Cuthbert's*	1 Rossie Place, EH7 5SF 031–661 0866
Gibbons, Harry V.	1927	1965	(Monifieth Panmure)	6 Brunstane Road, EH15 2EY 031–669 3157
Gibson, Frank S., BL, BD, STM, DSWA	1963	1972	Social Responsibility Department	Cairnbank, Morton Street South, EH15 2NB 031–669 3635
Gibson, John C. L., MA, BD, D PHIL	1959	1962	University of Edinburgh	15D Cramond Green, Cramond Road North, EH4 6NH 031–336 2251
Gillon, J. Blair, MA	1935	1980	(Borthwick *with* Heriot)	Baile-an-or, Mill Road, Worton, Devizes, Wilts 0380 5229
Grant, C. A., MA	1958	1978	(John Ker Memorial)	113/2 West Savile Terrace, EH9 3DX 031–667 3948
Gray, John, MA, BD, DD	1939	1978	(University of Edinburgh)	14 Elliot Place, EH14 1DR 031–441 3449
Hardy, Basil G., MA, BD	1946	1984	(Dundee Meadowside St. Paul's)	296 Gilmerton Road, EH17 7PR 031–664 3314
Heatlie, A. J., MA, BD	1943	1981	(Candlish)	7a Savile Terrace, EH9 3AD 031–667 9045
Heavenor, E. S. P., MA, BD, PHD	1943	1986	Crieff St. Michael's)	38 Craiglockhart Loan, EH14 1JS 031–444 1322
Hutchison, Alex S., MA, BD, DD	1940	1977	(Bowden)	47 Murrayfield Gardens, EH12 6DH 031–337 5182
Kiltie, Thomas W., MA, BD	1958	1988	(Department of World Mission and Unity)	36 St. Clair Terrace, EH10 5PS 031–447 4665
Lamont, Allan D., BSC, BD	1941	1975	(Nakuru)	Mayburn House, 2 Hawthorn Gardens, Loanhead, EH20 9EE 031–440 0299
Lawson, Kenneth C., MA, BD	1963	1984	*Adviser in Adult Education*	—
Leathem, G. Rendle, MA, BD	1932	1975	(Springfield)	56 Easter Drylaw View, EH4 2QP 031–332 4265
Levison, Frederick, MA	1937	1977	(Eccles *with* Greenlaw)	2 Gillsland Road, EH10 5BW 031–228 3118
Levison, Mary I. (Mrs.), BA, BD	1978	1983	(*Assistant at St. Andrew's & St. George's*)	2 Gillsland Road, EH10 5BW 031–228 3118
Logan, Anne T. (Mrs.), MA, BD	1981	1987	*Assistant at St. George's West*	63 St. Alban's Road, EH9 2LS 031–667 3881
Louden, R. Stuart, TD, DD, DLITT	1938	1978	(Greyfriars)	88 Cockburn Crescent, Balerno, Midlothian, EH14 7HU 031–449 4467
Lyon, D. H. S., MA, BD, STM	1952	1986	(Board of World Mission and Unity)	30 Mansfield Road, Balerno, EH14 7JZ 031–449 5031
M'Caskill, G. I. L., MA, BD	1953	1980	(Monimail *with* Springfield)	—
Macdonald, Donald I. M., MA, BD	1940	1985	(Kippen)	37 Barony Terrace, EH12 8RF 031–334 4773
M'Donald, James I. H., MA, BD, MTH, PHD	1958	1980	University of Edinburgh	1 Cargil Court, Cargil Terrace, EH5 3NE 031–552 4046
MacDonald, Peter J., BD, DIPMIN	1986	1986		23 Ravelston House Road, EH4 3LP 031–332 2172
M'Donald, Sandy, BA, CMIW SC	1957		*Youth Adviser, Department of Education*	18/7 Muirhouse Drive, EH4 4TN 031–336 2868
Macfarlane, Alwyn J. C., MA	1951	1973	(Glasgow Newlands South)	4/9 Belhaven Place, EH10 5JN 031–447 9564
M'Gillivray, A. Gordon, MA, BD, STM	1957	1970	Presbytery Clerk	7 Greenfield Crescent, Balerno, Midlothian, EH14 7HD 031–449 4747
M'Gregor, T. Stewart, MA, BD	1943		*Chaplain, Edinburgh Royal Infirmary*	69 Lonsdale Terrace, EH3 9HL 031–229 5332
M'Intosh, Hamish, MC, MA, BD		1983	(Auchterarder St. Andrew's and West)	19 Falcon Gardens, EH10 4AP 031–447 3516
M'Intyre, Ailsa G., BD, DIPCE	1979	1988	*Chaplain, George Heriot's*	23 Inverleith Terrace, Edinburgh, EH3 5NX 031–332 2230
M'Intyre, John, CVO, DLITT, DD, D UNIV, FRSE	1941	1986	(University of Edinburgh)	22/4 Minto Street, EH9 1RQ 031–667 1203

Minister	Ord.	App.	Ret.	Charge	Address and Tel. No.
Mackay, Donald G. M., MA, BD, STM	1938		1982	(Greenbank)	36 Buckstone Dell, EH10 6PG 031-445 1041
M'Kean, David, MA, STM	1942		1982	(Paris)	79 Baberton Mains Drive, EH14 3DA 031-442 2128
MacKenzie, J. Angus	1951		1969	(Bargeddie)	11 Western Place, EH12 5QA 031-337 2040
MacLean, Ewen A., MA, BD, HCF	1945		1982	(Greyfriars, Tolbooth and Highland)	4 Mansionhouse Road, EH9 1TZ 031-667 0720
MacLeod, George F., MC, DD (Lord MacLeod of Fuinary)	1924		1938	(Govan Old)	23 Learmonth Terrace, EH4 1PG 031-332 3262
Macmillan, James, MA	1935		1975	(Corstorphine St. Anne's)	2 East Savile Road, EH16 5ND 031-667 1475
M'Phee, Duncan C., MA, BD	1953	1978		Ministry and Mission Department	94 Balgreen Road, EH12 5UB 031-337 5230
Mactaggart, Ian, MA, BD	1941		1983	(Craigmillar Park)	15 West Mains Road, EH9 3BG 031-667 3091
Malcolm, John W., MA, BD, PH D	1939	1986	1981	(Uddingston Park)	38 Corstorphine Hill Crescent, EH12 6LL 031-334 0838
Manson, Robert L., MA	1956	1986		Chaplain, Royal Edinburgh Hospital	4 Murieston Drive, Livingston, EH54 9AW [0506] Livingston 34746
Marshall, A. Scott	1984	1984		Community Minister at Drylaw, Muirhouse and Old Kirk	30 West Pilton Gardens, EH4 6AF 031-332 0413
Marshall, James S., MA, PH D	1939		1979	(Associate South Leith)	4 Claremont Park, EH6 7PH 031-554 5518
Mathers, Robert C. M., DD	1936		1974	(St. Matthew's)	40 Canaan Lane, EH10 4SU 031-447 3009
Mathieson, Angus R., BD	1988	1988		Assistant at South Leith	4 Hermitage Park, EH6 8HB 031-554 6335
Matthew, Stewart G., MA, BD	1969	1979		Education Department	10 Silverknowes Midway, EH4 5PP 031-336 5990
Maxwell, William	1958		1983	(Stenhouse Saughton)	15/4 Meadowhouse Road, EH12 7HW 031-334 5923
May, John R., MA	1948		1978	(Rothesay West)	The Elms, 18 Whitehouse Loan, EH9 9EZ 031-447 4924
Middleton, J. Clyne, MA	1947		1987	(Lockhart Memorial)	72 Pilrig Street, EH6 5AJ 031-554 7596
Morris, Gordon C., MA, BD	1941		1984	(Buenos Aires)	42 Regent Street, EH15 2AX 031-669 4570
Morrison, Mary B. (Mrs.), MA, BD	1978	1986		Evangelism Area Organiser	2 St. Bernard's Crescent, EH4 1NP 031-332 6117
Morton, Andrew R., MA, BD	1956	1982		Board of World Mission and Unity	11 Oxford Terrace, EH4 1PX 031-332 6592
Murison, William G.	1951	1971		Department of World Mission and Unity	11 Hailes Gardens, EH13 0JL 031-441 2460
Neilson, Peter, MA, BD	1975	1986		National Organiser for Evangelism	37 Strathalmond Park, EH4 8AH 031-339 5835
Nisbet, John A.	1942		1977	(Kinghorn)	51 Spottiswoode Road, EH9 1DA 031-447 2577
O'Neill, John C., MA, BD, PH D	1960	1985		University of Edinburgh	9 Lonsdale Terrace, EH3 9HN 031-229 6070
Orr, John F., MA	1949		1987	(St. John's Oxgangs)	2/34 Pentland Drive, EH10 6PX 031-445 2876
Orr, J. M'Michael, MA, BD, PH D	1949		1986	(Aberfoyle with Port of Menteith)	13 Ladysmith Road, EH9 3EX 031-667 5577
Page, Ruth, MA, BD, D PHIL	1976	1979		University of Edinburgh	7 Seton Place, EH9 2JT 031-662 4564
Paterson, Ian M., MA	1947		1985	(Eccles with Greenlaw)	21 Springvalley Gardens, EH10 4QE 031-447 7864
Paterson, J. M. K., MA, ACH, BD, DD	1964		1987	(Milngavie St. Paul's)	58 Orchard Drive, EH4 2DZ 031-332 5876
Paterson, John M.	1976		1987	(Blackbraes and Shieldhill)	9 Saughtonhall Circus, EH12 5RG 031-337 0095
Porteous, Norman W., DD	1929		1968	(University of Edinburgh)	3 Hermitage Gardens, EH10 6DL 031-447 4632
Re'emi, S. Paul, DLITT	1962		1977	(Tiberias)	1c Coillesdene Loan, EH15 2LG 031-669 5496
Reid, George T. H., MC, MA, BD, DD	1935		1975	(Aberdeen Langstane)	33 Westgarth Avenue, EH13 0BB 031-441 1299
Reid, Ian J. M., OBE, BA	1944		1986	(Kilwinning Abbey)	68 Thirlestane Road, EH9 1AR 031-447 4980
Reid, J. K. S., CBE, TD, MA, DD	1939		1976	(University of Aberdeen)	8 Abbotsford Court, 18 Colinton Road, EH10 5EH 031-447 6855
Ritchie, Joseph S., MBE, MA	1936		1980	(Haddington West)	77 West Savile Terrace, EH9 3DP 031-667 4381
Robinson, Keith S. P., JP, MA	1950		1986	(North Merchiston)	52 Inverleith Row, EH3 5PX
Rose, John M., MA	1930		1985	(West St. Giles')	39 Mansionhouse Road, EH9 2JD 031-667 1676
Ross, Andrew C., MA, BD, STM, PH D	1958	1966	1972	University of Edinburgh	27 Colinton Road, EH10 5DR 031-447 5987

Ross, Donald M., MA — Industrial Chaplaincy Organiser — 1953 1980 — 21 Ormidale Terrace, EH12 6DY 031–337 5622

Ross, Robin A., MA, BD — Department of World Mission and Unity — 1977 1988

Sangster, George B. C., DSC, MA, BD — (Associate St. Andrew's Nairobi) — 1948 1983 — 126 Caroline Terrace, EH12 8QS 031–339 8255

Schofield, Melville F., MA — Chaplain, Northern Hospitals — 1960 1988 — 25 Rowantree Grove, Currie, EH14 5AT 031–449 4547

Scollay, John, BSC — (Douglas New St. Bride's) — 1955 — 22 Grange Terrace, EH9 2LE 031–667 3793

Serle, William, OBE, MB, CHB — (Drumoak) — 1959 — 8 Hallcroft Gardens, Ratho, Newbridge, EH28 8SG 031–333 4325

Shields, Matthew — (Newington St. Leonard's) — 1934 — 39/2 Sciennes Road, EH9 1NS 031–667 3557

Sim, John G., MA — (Kirkcaldy Old) — 1946 — 7 Grosvenor Crescent, EH12 5EP 031–226 3390

Small, R. Leonard, CBE, DD — (St. Cuthbert's) — 1931 — 5 Craighill Gardens, EH10 5PY 031–447 4243

Smith, Angus, MA, LTH — Chaplain, Army — 1965 1972 — Senior Chaplain, Army HQ (Scotland), EH1 2YX 031–336 1761

Smith, Ralph C. P., MA, STM — Director Audio-Visual Production — 1960 1984 — 2 Blackford Hill View, EH9 3HD 031–667 7258

Smith, Roderick, DD — (Braid) — 1933 — 13 Saxe Coburg Place, EH3 5BR 031–332 2262

Steel, David, MA, BD, DD, LLD — (Linlithgow St. Michael's) — 1936 — 39 Newbattle Terrace, EH10 4SF 031–447 2180

Stewart, James S., DD — (University of Edinburgh) — 1924 — St. Rafael's, 6 Blackford Avenue, EH9 2LA 031–667 3601

Thomson, J. G. S. S., MA, BD, BA, PHD — (Wigtown) — 1951 — 4 Drum Brae South, EH12 5SJ 031–334 6035

Torrance, Thomas F., MBE, D.LITT, DD, DSC, DR THEOL, D THEOL, DR TEOL, FBA, FRSE — (University of Edinburgh) — 1940 — 37 Braid Farm Road, EH10 6LE

Walker, Grahame R., FCII — (Torphins) — 1959 1987 — 40/2 West Craigs Crescent, EH12 8NA 031–339 7372

Walker, Horace, OBE, MA, BD, DD — (Home Board) — 1935 1977 — 4/3 Belhaven Place, EH10 5JN 031–447 9666

Walker, Ian, BD, DIPMS — Tutor at St. Colm's — 1973 1984 — 21 Inverleith Terrace, EH3 5NX 031–343 2038

Watt, Adrian, G., MA — (St. Michael's) — 1939 — The Elms, 18 Whitehouse Loan, EH9 2EZ 031–447 4924

Weatherhead, J. L., MA, LLB — Board of Practice and Procedure — 1960 1985 — 28 Castle Terrace, EH1 2EL 031–228 6460

Webster, W. Thoms, MA — (Dean) — 1944 — 3 Columba Road, EH4 3QU 031–343 2071

Weller, T. H. B. — (Grangemouth West) — 1965 — 88 Ferry Road, EH6 4AH 031–554 4578

Whitton, John P., MA, BD — Chaplain, Army — 1977 1976 — HQ Land Forces, Cyprus, BFPO 53

Wigglesworth, J. Christopher, MBE, BSC, PHD, BD — Department of World Mission and Unity — 1967 1987 — 12 Leven Terrace, EH3 9LW 031–228 6335

Wilkie, George D., OBE, BL — (Kirkcaldy Viewforth) — 1948 1986 — 5 Arden Street, EH9 1BR 031–229 6638

Wilkie, James L., MA, BD — Department of World Mission and Unity — 1959 1984 — 7 Comely Bank Avenue, EH4 1EW 031–343 1552

Wilkinson, John, MB, MD, FRCP, DTMANDH — (Kikuyu) — 1946 1975 — 70 Craigleith Hill Gardens, EH4 2JH 031–332 2994

Wright, R. V. Selby, CVO, TD, DD, FRSE, JP — (Canongate) — 1937 1977 — 36 Moray Place, EH3 6BX 031–226 5566

Wright, W. G. A., MBE, BD — (Chaplain, Army) — 1940 1974 — 20 Lennox Street Lane, EH4 1PZ 031–332 8663

Young, George A., MA — (St. Bernard's Stockbridge) — 1942 1983 — 14 Ainslie Place (1st Flat), EH3 6AS 031–225 4854

ADDRESSES OF EDINBURGH CHURCHES

Albany — Albany Street

Balerno — Johnsburn Road, Balerno

Barclay — Barclay Place 031–229 6810

Blackhall St. Columba — Queensferry Road 031–332 4431

Braid — Nile Grove

Bristo Memorial — Peffermill Road, Craigmillar

Broughton M'Donald — Broughton Place 031–556 4252

Burdiehouse — Gracemount Drive

Canongate — Canongate

Carrick Knowe — North Saughton Road 031–334 1505

Cluny — Cluny Gardens

Colinton — Dell Road

Colinton Mains — Oxgangs Road North

Corstorphine—
Craigsbank — Craig's Crescent
Old — Kirk Loan
St. Anne's — Kaimes Road
St. Ninian's — St. John's Road

Craigentinny — Craigentinny Road 031–447 6745

St. Christopher's

Addresses of Edinburgh Churches—*continued*

Craiglockhart	Craiglockhart Avenue
Craigmillar Park	Craigmillar Park 031-667 5862
Cramond	Cramond
Currie	Kirkgate, Currie 031-449 3260
Davidson's Mains	Quality Street
Dean	Dean Path
Drylaw	Groathill Road North
Duddingston	Duddingston
Fairmilehead	Fairmilehead
Gilmerton	Ravenscroft Street
Gorgie	Gorgie Road 031-337 7936
Granton	Boswall Parkway 031-552 3033
Greenbank	Braidburn Terrace 031-447 9969
Greenside	Royal Terrace 031-556 5588
Greyfriars	Greyfriars Place 031-225 1900
Tolbooth Highland Kirk High (St. Giles')	High Street 031-225 4363
Holyrood Abbey	Dalziel Place x London Road
Holy Trinity	Hailesland Place, Wester Hailes 031-442 3304
Inverleith	Inverleith Gardens
Juniper Green	Lanark Road, Juniper Green
Kirkliston	The Square, Kirkliston
Kirk o' Field	Pleasance
Leith—	
North	Madeira Street off Ferry Road
St. Andrew's	Easter Road
St. Paul's	Lorne Street
St. Serf's	Ferry Road
St. Thomas' Junction Road	Great Junction Street
South	Kirkgate 031-554 2578
Wardie	Primrosebank Road

Liberton	Gilmerton Road, Liberton
Northfield	Restalrig Rd. Sth. 031-554 7400
Lochend	London Road 031-661 1149
London Road	Kilgraston Road 031-447 4359
Marchmont St. Giles	Mayfield Road x W. Mayfield 031-667 1522
Mayfield	Morningside Road x Newbattle Terrace 031-447 5061
Morningside	Brunsfield Place x Chamberlain Road 031-447 3152
Morningside United	Pennywell Gardens
Muirhouse	Abinger Gardens 031-337 1091
Murrayfield	Newcraighall
Newcraighall and Richmond Craigmillar	Niddrie Mains Road
Newhaven	Craighall Road
New Restalrig	Willowbrae Road 031-661 5676
Old Kirk	Pennywell Road
Palmerston Place	Palmerston Place 031-220 1690
Pilrig and Dalmeny St.	Pilrig Street
Polwarth	Polwarth Terrace x Harrison Road
Portobello—	
Old and Windsor Place	Bellfield Street
St. James'	
St. Philip's, Joppa	Rosefield Place
Priestfield	Abercorn Terrace 031-669 3641 Dalkeith Road x Marchhall Place 031-667 2105

Queensferry	The Loan, South Queensferry
Ratho	Baird Road, Ratho
Reid Memorial	West Savile Terrace 031-451 5141
Restalrig	Restalrig Road South Stenhouse Drive
St. Aidan's	George Street 031-225 3847
St. Andrew's and St. George's	Clermiston View
St. Andrew's Clermiston	Saxe Coburg Street 031-332 0122
St. Bernard's-Stockbridge	Grange Road x Chalmers Crescent
St. Catherine's-Argyle	Dalry Road x Cathcart Place
St. Colm's	Lothian Road 031-229 1142
St. Cuthbert's	Broomhouse Crescent 031-443 9851
St. David's Broomhouse	Shandwick Place 031-225 7001
St. George's West	Oxgangs
St. John's Oxgangs	East Fettes Avenue
St. Luke's	Magdalene Drive
St. Martin's	Bellevue Crescent 031-556 4786
St. Mary's	Slateford Road
St. Michael's	Calder Road
St. Nicholas' Sighthill	St. Vincent Street
St. Stephen's	Comely Bank
St. Stephen's Comely Bank	Causewayside
Salisbury	Kingsknowe Road North
Slateford-Longstone	Chesser Avenue
Stenhouse Saughton	Moredun
Tron Moredun	Gilmore Place
Viewforth	

2. WEST LOTHIAN

Meets in St. John's Church Hall, Bathgate, on the second Tuesday of January and September, on the fourth Tuesday of June, and on the first Tuesday of every other month except July and August when there is no meeting.

Clerk: Rev. DUNCAN SHAW, BD, MTH, St. John's Manse, Mid Street, Bathgate EH48 1QD.   [0506] Bathgate 53146

Charge	Minister	Ord.	Ind.	Address and Tel. No.	Com.	Eld.	W.G.	S.S.	B.C.	C.L. £	As'd £	Gi'n £	Stp. £
Addiewell	Ronald Gall, BSC, BD	1985		Stoneyburn, Bathgate, EH47 8AU [0501] Stoneyburn 62303	139	8	27	15	1	5464	580	580	
linked with Longridge and Breich					177	7	15	28	2	7787	1100	1100	8742
linked with Stoneyburn					180	8	17	23	4	7701	735	735	
Armadale	Emmanuel Robertson, THM	1953	......	70 Mount Pleasant, Armadale, West Lothian, EH48 3HB [0501] Armadale 30358	848	52	32	107	51	29188	4852	4852	9099
Avonbridge	Thomas Crichton, MA	1965		Torphichen, Bathgate, EH48 4LT [0506] Bathgate 52794	95	6	18	24	5	6954	904	931	
linked with Torphichen					340	26	16	60	7	15408	1967	2044	9051
Bathgate— Boghall	John MacLean, MA, BD	1967	1970	1 Manse Place, Ashgrove, Bathgate, EH48 1LS [0506] Bathgate 52940	632	30	25	48	23	28861	5366	5366	8997
High	John W. Bird	1965	1974	Balbardie Road, Bathgate, EH48 1AP [0506] Bathgate 52654	1135	47	100	63	5	44148	13679	13891	10251
St. David's	Elliott G. S. Wardlaw, BA, BD, DIPMIN	1984	......	Marjoribanks Street, Bathgate, EH48 1AH [0506] Bathgate 53177	507	26	18	49	11	28868	6409	6409	9099
St. John's	Duncan Shaw, BD, MTH	1975	1978	Mid Street, Bathgate, EH48 1QD [0506] Bathgate 53146	468	31	57	50	15	34205	5466	5466	9099
Blackburn	J. A. Fletcher, BA	1951	1964	Blackburn, Bathgate, EH47 4QR [0506] Bathgate 52825	788	50	26	30	12	23184	4152	4710	9030
Blackridge	H. Warner Hardie, BD	1979	......	Harthill, Shotts, Lanarkshire, ML7 5QW [0501] Harthill 51239	260	13	22	28	14	11518	1432	1432	9921
linked with Harthill St. Andrew's					476	27	66	53	20	23439	5313	5313	
Broxburn	Andrew Moyes	1959	1976	2 Church Street, Broxburn [0506] Broxburn 852825	699	29	47	70	15	33551	4655	4655	9066

Charge	Minister	Ord.	Ind.	Address and Tel. No.	Com.	Eld.	W.G.	S.S.	B.C.	C.I. £	As'd £	Gi'n £	Stp. £
Fauldhouse St. Andrew's	Samuel Hosain, BD	1979	1985	48 Main Street, Fauldhouse, Bathgate, EH47 9BQ [0501] Fauldhouse 71190	538	21	45	52	5	23513	2699	2699	8742
Harthill	see Blackridge												9114
Kirknewton and East Calder	Allan Brown, BD	1984	......	Manse Court, East Calder, Midlothian, EH53 0EN [0506] Mid Calder 880802	792	42	59	124	31	35487	3183	3183	
Kirk of Calder	John M. Povey, MA, BD	1981	......	19 Maryfield Park, Mid Calder, Livingston, EH53 0SB [0506] Mid Calder 882495	865	31	63	89	4	28449	2840	2840	8742
Linlithgow—				Linlithgow, West Lothian, EH49									
St. Michael's	John L. Paterson, MA, BD, STM	1964	1977	[0506] Linlithgow 842195	1614	103	70	243	92	112279	20573	20573	10485
	W. Anthony McLean-Foreman, MA, BD Associate	1987	......	Cross House, Linlithgow, EH49 [0506] Linlithgow 842188									
St. Ninian's Craigmailen	Samuel M. Harris, BA, BD	1974	1980	29 Philip Avenue, Linlithgow, EH49 7BH [0506] Linlithgow 845535	819	63	88	102	20	41601	9741	9741	9432
Livingston— Dedridge	Colin R. Douglas, MA, BD, STM	1969	1987	1202 Norman Rise, Dedridge, Livingston EH54 [0506] Livingston 410668	247	17	......	117	27	......	......	43	......
Old	W. Ewing Smith, BSC,	1962	1978	1 Main Street, Livingston Village, Livingston, EH54 7AF [0506] Livingston 411360	677	31	......	80	4	36092	6340	6497	9312
St. Columba's Craigshill	Isobel J. M. Kelly, MA, BD, DIPED	1974	1985	53 Garry Walk, Craigshill, Livingston, EH54 [0506] Livingston 34536	410	21	28	19	......	12841	......	69	9147
St. Paul's	Vacant	......	......	————	395	19	......	37	59	10729	......	69	v
Longridge and Breich	see Addiewell												
Pardovan and Kingscavil linked with Winchburgh	Alan M. Gruber, BD, DIPMIN	1987	......	32 Oakbank Place, Winchburgh, West Lothian, EH52 [0506] Winchburgh 890919	106 236	9 13	35 17	16 40	 22	6321 16836	355 810	355 805	v
Polbeth Harwood	David K. Robertson	1958	1959	150 Chapelton Drive, Polbeth, West Calder, EH55 8SG [0506] West Calder 871247	397	23	......	69	5	27184	1861	2261	8742
Stoneyburn	see Addiewell												
Strathbrock	David W. Black, BSC, BD	1968	1984	Manse Park, Uphall, Broxburn, EH52 6JR [0506] Broxburn 852550	750	49	61	132	50	38704	9407	9569	9831

Torphichen	see Avonbridge											
Uphall South	Alan B. Forrest, MA	1956	1961	8 M'Lardy Court, Uphall, Broxburn, EH52 5SL [0506] Broxburn 852788	267	17	19	26	.....	12257	.....	8646
West Kirk of Calder	Thomas B. S. Dundas, LTH	1969	.....	Learmonth Crescent, West Calder, EH55 8DF [0506] West Calder 871589	421	29	30	88	10	22100	4594	9945
Whitburn—												
Brucefield	Robin Brough, BA	1968	1977	Whitburn, Bathgate, EH47 8NU [0501] Whitburn 40263	728	37	45	72	32	38002	6751	9078
South	Gordon A. M'Cracken, BD	1988	.....	5 Mansewood Crescent, Whitburn, Bathgate, EH47 8HA [0501] Whitburn 40333	440	24	47	45	5	22524	2520	v
Winchburgh	see Pardovan											

Livingston—As well as the Church of Scotland ministers noted above, the following ecumenical team is working within the New Town:—

Scottish Episcopal Church	Rev. Paul Burgess	124 Mowbray Rise, Dedridge, Livingston, EH54 [0506] Livingston 417158
	Rev. James Mein	27 Heatherbank, Livingston, EH54 6EE [0506] Livingston 32326
Congregational Union	Rev. J. Ross M'Laren	14 Torridon Walk, Livingston, EH54 5AT [0506] Livingston 32835
The Methodist Church	Temporarily vacant	

Minister	Ord.	App.	Ret.	Charge	Address and Tel. No.
Cameron, Ian, MA, BD	1953	.....	1981	(Kilbrandon and Kilchattan)	37 Burghmuir Court, Linlithgow, EH49 7LJ [0506] Linlithgow 847987
Edmond, George W. B., MA, BD	1940	.....	1975	(Ecclesmachan)	22 Deanburn Road, Linlithgow, EH49 6EY [0506] Linlithgow 843776
Hume, William	1949	.....	1983	(Whitburn South)	118 Seafield, by Bathgate [0506] Bathgate 634124
Lee, Geoffrey, CE DIP	1975	.....	1984	(Dumbarton Knoxland)	23 Kirkfield View, Livingston Village, EH54 [0506] Livingston 415861
M'Geachie, Samuel	1950	.....	1981	(Lochgoilhead and Kilmorich)	2 Pilgrim's Hill, Linlithgow, EH49 [0506] Linlithgow 847359
M'Kinnon, Dugald, MA	1941	.....	1982	(Ardoch)	22 Clarendon Crescent, Linlithgow, EH49 [0506] Linlithgow 842605
Maitland, James, MA, DD	1940	.....	1983	(Livingston St. Columba's Craigshill)	70 Cameron Way, Livingston, EH54 8HN [0506] Livingston 32413
Moore, J. W., MA	1950	.....	1983	(Daviot with Rayne)	31 Lennox Gardens, Linlithgow, EH49 [0506] Linlithgow 842534
Murray, Ronald N. G., MA	1946	.....	1986	(Pardovan and Kingscavil with Winchburgh)	42 Lennox Gardens, Linlithgow, EH49 [0506] Linlithgow 845680
Napier, James K., MA	1939	.....	1978	(Balmaghie)	217 Clement Rise, Livingston, EH54 6LR [0506] Livingston 414284

3. LOTHIAN

Meets at Musselburgh on the last Thursday of January and June and the first Thursday of other months except February, July and August when there is no meeting

Clerk: Rev. ARTHUR T. HILL, 25 Dundas Avenue, North Berwick, EH39 4PS [0620] North Berwick 3141

Charge	Minister	Ord.	Ind.	Address and Tel. No.	Com.	Eld.	W.G.	S.S.	B.C.	C.L. £	As'd £	Gi'n £	Stp. £
Aberlady	Norman L. Faulds, MA, BD	1968	1986	Gullane, East Lothian, EH31 2BG [0620] Gullane 843192	506	29	29	24	....	17940	2407	2407	10035
linked with Gullane					726	46	70	76	....	19850	5037	10987	
Athelstaneford	Kenneth D. F. Walker, MA, BD	1976	......	Athelstaneford, North Berwick, EH39 5BE [062 088] Athelstaneford 378	251	11	20	35	4	3900	768	....	8742
linked with Whitekirk and Tyninghame					176	16	16	....	....	11130	728	728	
Belhaven	Laurence H. Twaddle, MA, BD	1977	1978	Dunbar, EH42 1NH [0368] Dunbar 63098	841	28	76	80	3	22285	2307	2307	8742
linked with Spott					101	6	10	14	....	3610	371	371	
Bolton and Saltoun					250	16	22	19	....	12308	899	637	
linked with Humbie	John M. Wilson, MA, BD	1965	1985	Tweeddale Avenue, Gifford, Haddington, EH41 4QN [062 081] Gifford 515	113	7	25	11	....	7374	660	660	9261
linked with Yester					387	23	45	20	5	10263	1634	1634	
Bonnyrigg	[W. L. Armitage, BSc, BD	1976	......	9 Viewbank View, Bonnyrigg, EH19 2HU 031-663 8287	1268	57	81	210	52	47425	10208	11687	9036
	[M. Isobel M'Cully, DCS			*Deaconess—see List H* 031-663 4673									
Borthwick	John L. M'Pake, BA, BD	1987		Newtongrange, Dalkeith, EH22 4RS 031-663 2140	157	8	29	15	7	9935	645	645	v
linked with Newtongrange					460	17	69	25	....	16310	2507	2507	
Cockburnspath					260	7	16	33	....	8697	487	632	
linked with Innerwick	Paraic Reamonn, BA, BD	1982	......	Thurston, Dunbar, EH42 1SA [036 84] Innerwick 229	141	9	10	6	....	6667	177	177	8646
linked with Oldhamstocks					50	3	....	5	....	2960	421	421	
Cockenzie and Port Seton—Chalmers Mem'l	Geoffrey H. Underwood, BD, FPHS	1964	......	Braemar Villa, Port Seton, Prestonpans, EH32 0HA [087 54] Port Seton 812 481	521	24	65	77	41	29270	5352	5352	8781

Charge	Minister	Year	Address									
Old	James S. A. Cowan, BD, DIP MIN ¶	1986	Port Seton, Prestonpans, EH32 0HA [087 54] Port Seton 812 310	513	11	62	46	13	16707	1533	766	8646
Cockpen and Carrington *linked with* Lasswade	James Brown, BD	1973 1980	11 Pendreich Terrace, Bonnyrigg, EH19 2DT 031-663 6884	429	18	36	32	......	11055	1342	1342	8892
				547	31	44	31	16	41738	1462	1462	
Cranstoun, Crichton and Ford *linked with* Fala and Soutra	*Vacant*	......	Cranstoun Cottage, Ford, Pathhead, EH37 5RE [0875] Ford 320314	496	27	51	31	12	17645	3003	3003	9216
				109	6	......	10	......	5796	461	461	v
Dalkeith— St. John's and King's Park	Alistair K. Ridland, MA, BD	1982	Rosetta, Waverley Road, Dalkeith, EH22 031-660 5007	725	45	30	88	25	55687	7435	7435	10086
St. Nicholas' Buccleuch	William Brown, BD	1972	Old Edinburgh Road, Dalkeith, EH22 1JD 031-663 3036	1410	52	60	52	14	33189	9949	6155	8646
Dirleton	Ian W. Fraser, MA	1953 1968	Dirleton, North Berwick, EH39 5EL [062 085] Dirleton 333	367	23	......	8	......	16660	......	400	10254
Dunbar	William R. Chalmers, MA, BD, STM	1953 1966	Dunbar, EH42 1JY [0368] Dunbar 63749	1416	42	74	49	......	42442	100	100	
Fala and Soutra *see Cranstoun*												
Garvald & Morham *linked with* Haddington West	[Alastair H. Gray, MA, BD [James Williamson	1978 1986	15 West Road, Haddington, East Lothian, EH41 3RD [062 082] Haddington 2213 *Auxiliary*	142	7	......	22	3	4955	568	579	9018
				695	32	71	130	23	22700	3942	2956	
Gladsmuir *linked with* Longniddry	A. Graham Black, MA	1964 1973	1 Elcho Road, Longniddry, EH32 0LB [0875] Longniddry 53195	339	16	20	8	......	9452	1321	1321	9588
				718	41	94	125	60	35528	6349	9149	
Glencorse *linked with* Roslin	James A. Manson, LTH	1981	Roslin, Midlothian, EH25 9LH 031-440 2012	400	15	18	72	7	14113	2573	2573	8841
				509	23	47	87	30	15307	2486	2486	
Bilston	——	......	——	214	......	30	31	4	7237	581	647	......
Gorebridge	Stuart H. Robertson, MENG, BD	1981	100 Hunterfield Road, Gorebridge, EH23 4TT [0875] Gorebridge 20387	631	25	50	67	10	22663	3755	1482	8880
Gullane *see Aberlady*												
Haddington— St. Mary's	Alasdair W. Macdonell, MA, BD	1955 1979	Haddington, East Lothian, EH41 4BZ [062 082] Haddington 3109	1210	68	47	58	18	56546	11562	11562	10224
West *see Garvald*												

Charge	Minister	Ord.	Ind.	Address and Tel. No.	Com.	Eld.	W.G.	S.S.	B.C.	C.L. £	As'd £	Gi'n £	Stp. £
Howgate *linked with* Penicuik South	Frank Ribbons, MA, BD	1985	.....	18 Broomhill Avenue, Penicuik, Midlothian, EH26 9BG [0968] *Penicuik 74692*	71	6	14	.....	.....	9070	1869	1869	9450
Humbie	*see Bolton and Saltoun*												
Innerwick	*see Cockburnspath*												
Lasswade	*see Cockpen*												
Loanhead	Robert W. Thompson, BD	1974	1985	The Manse, Loanhead, EH20 031-440 0470	935	30	74	87	18	28065	.....	1100	8646
Longniddry	*see Gladsmuir*												
Musselburgh— Inveresk St. Michael's	Alexander E. Strachan, MA, BD	1974	1987	8 Hope Place, EH21 7QE 031-665 0545	968	67	104	68	27	24946	5049	5049	v
Whitecraig		.....	.....		.....	.....	.....	.....	.....	.....	.....	.....	.....
Northesk	Ronald H. Brown	1974	1981	16 New Street, EH21 6JP 031-665 2128	643	47	54	48	46	33092	4195	4195	8811
St. Andrew's High	Sheilagh M. Kesting, BA, BD	1980	1986	17 Edinburgh Road, EH21 6EA 031-665 2761	786	48	65	45	11	40809	4337	4337	9393
St.Clement's and St. Ninian's	Alexander F. Bonar, LTH, LRIC	1988	.....	95 New Street, EH21 031-653 6588	509	36	.....	33	2	12521	.....	500	v
Newbattle	[Vacant] Graham Austin, DCS	.....	.....	Bogwood Road, Mayfield, Dalkeith, EH22 5DY 031-663 3245 *Deacon—see List H*	713	15	46	48	30	20221	4819	.....	8742
Newton	James Robertson, LTH	1970	1976	Newton, Dalkeith, EH22 1SR 031-663 3845	257	8	30	30	12	13373	.....	76	8646
Newtongrange	*see Borthwick*												
North Berwick— Abbey	P. Hamilton Cashman, BSC	1985	.....	20 Westgate, North Berwick, EH39 4AF [0620] *North Berwick 2410*	557	22	65	87	37	26104	4810	4810	.....
Blackadder	D. J. B. M'Alister, MA, BD, PHD	1951	1960	7 Marine Parade, North Berwick, EH39 4LD [0620] *North Berwick 2132*	417	31	55	50	25	31087	5458	5498	8781
St. Andrew's	Vacant	.....	.....	50 St. Baldred's Road, North Berwick, EH39 4PL [0620] *North Berwick 2803*	697	23	38	46	9	20140	2751	2751	8781
Oldhamstocks	*see Cockburnspath*												
Ormiston *linked with* Pencaitland	Colin V. Donaldson	1982	.....	Pencaitland, East Lothian, EH34 5DL [0875] *Pencaitland 340208*	226	12	32	40	.....	9855	1027	200	.....
					294	22	.....	64	8	10650	620	620	8646

Charge	Minister	Ord.	App.	Address and Tel. No.									
Penicuik—													
North	John W. Fraser, MA, BD	1974	1982	Penicuik, Midlothian, EH26 8AG [0968] Penicuik 72213	865	63	....	122	51	26350	4832	4832	8928
St. Mungo's	William D. Irving, LTH	1985	....	31A Kirkhill Road, Penicuik, Midlothian, EH26 8HS [0968] Penicuik 72916	841	46	60	119	57	37002	6126	6126	9255
South	*see Howgate*												
Prestonkirk					617	28	48	56	....	17957	4817	4817	4817
linked with													
Stenton	James B. Lawson, MA, BD	1961	1986	Preston Road, East Linton, EH40 3DS [0620] East Linton 860227	105	6	....	18	....	3663	1022	1022	10527
linked with													
Whittinghame					53	4	8	....	....	2128	615	615	615
Prestonpans				—									
Prestongrange	Moira Herkes (Mrs.), BD	1985	1988	Prestonpans, EH2 9ED [0875] Prestonpans 810 308	927	45	23	85	17	24406	4500	4500	9318
Rosewell	*Continued Vacancy*	....	....		303	13	....	15	....	7379	....	....	v
Roslin	*see Glencorse*												
Spott	*see Belhaven*												
Stenton	*see Prestonkirk*												
Tranent	Thomas M. Hogg, BA	1986	....	244 Church Street, Tranent, EH33 1BW [0875] Tranent 610 210	139	36	67	58	....	21395	4091	4184	10002
Whitekirk and Tyninghame	*see Athelstaneford*												
Whittinghame	*see Prestonkirk*												
Yester	*see Bolton and Saltoun*												

Minister	Ord.	App.	Ret.	Charge	Address and Tel. No.
Adamson, Sidney, MA, BD	1937	....	1985	(Musselburgh Inveresk St. Michael's)	48 Hailes Gardens, Edinburgh. EH13 0JH *031—441 2471*
Bell, R. Nichol, MA, BD	1934	....	1974	(North Berwick Abbey)	Bankhead, East Linton. EH40 3DX *[062 087] Whitekirk 234*
Blades, Daniel, MA	1922	....	1980	(Fala and Soutra)	Windyknowe, 5 Fala Village, Pathhead. EH37 5SY *[087 553] Humbie 248*
Day, Colin T., MA	1947	....	1984	(Warden, Carberry Tower)	20 Hadfast Road, Cousland, Dalkeith. EH22 *031—660 5777*
Dick, David F. S., TD, MC, MA, BD	1940	....	1976	(Cockburnspath with Oldhamstocks)	9 St. Baldred's Crescent, North Berwick. EH39 4PZ *[0620] North Berwick 3256*
DuPuy, E. John, BD	1971	....	1979	(Creich with Rosehall)	27 Kippielaw Drive, Dalkeith. EH22 4HT *031—663 0273*
Eggo, Harold C. M., TD, MA	1950	....	1977	(Church and Ministry Department)	Millholme, East Linton, East Lothian. EH40 3DS *[062 086] East Linton 493*

Minister	Ord.	App.	Ret.	Charge	Address and Tel. No.
Ferrier, Walter M.	1946	……	1988	(North Berwick St. Andrew's)	3 Melbourne Road, North Berwick, EH39
Fraser, Hugh Erskine, MA	1925	……	1968	(Roslin)	46A St. Thomas' Road, Brentwood, Essex, CM14 4DF 0277 230 363
Fraser, John W., BEM, MA, BD, PHD, JP	1950	……	1983	(Farnell)	12 Quarryfoot Green, Bonnyrigg, EH19 2EJ 031-663 8037
Hill, Arthur T.	1940	……	1981	(Ormiston with Prestonpans Grange)	25 Dundas Avenue, North Berwick, EH39 4PS [0620] NB 3141
Johnston, George B., MA	1943	……	1980	(Dulnain Bridge with Grantown on Spey)	Inverallan, Queen's Road, Dunbar, EH42 1LJ [0368] Dunbar 63779
Knox, S. James, BA, MA, BD, BLITT, PHD, LICL	1944	……	1985	(Cockenzie and Port Seton Old)	76 Edenhall Crescent, Musselburgh, EH21 7JG 031-665 8057
Laird, William D., MA	1939	……	1985	(Musselburgh St. Andrew's)	37 Cairds Row, Musselburgh, EH21 031-665 6257
Lennie, Robert C., MA, BD	1942	……	1985	(Aberlady)	7 Craigielaw Cottages, Aberlady, Longniddry, EH32
					[087 57] Longniddry 473
Levack, John G., MA, BD	1934	……	1974	(Prestonkirk)	12 Highfield Road, North Berwick, EH39 4BW [0620] N. Berwick 2788
Levison, L. David, MA, BD	1943	……	1982	(Ormiston with Pencaitland)	47 Dunbar Road, Haddington, EH41 [062 082] Haddington 3291
Lund, T. Waterton, MA, BD	1940	……	1982	(Buittle with Kelton)	60 Stockerston Road, Uppingham, Rutland, Leicestershire
M'Cabe, George E., JP, BA	1967	……	1987	(Dalkeith St. John's King's Park)	34 Howe Park, Edinburgh, EH10 7HF 031-445 4144
M'Farlane, W. A., MA	1938	……	1978	(Glasgow St. Cuthbert's Queen's Cross)	Mayburn House, Loanhead, Midlothian
MacKenzie, A. Taylor, MA, BD	1937	……	1963	(Auchterless)	Flat 7, Springfield Gardens, Cromwell Road, North Berwick, EH39
					[0620] N. Berwick 2438
M'Martin, J. S., MC, MA	1947	……	1977	(Belhaven)	26 Southfield Court, Dunbar, EH42 1NL [0368] Dunbar 63248
Macrae, Norman C., MA, DIPED	1942	……	1985	(Loanhead)	6 Lonsdale Terrace, Edinburgh, EH3 9HN 031-228 6283
Maule-Brown, R., MA	1949	……	1985	(Strathy and Halladale)	5 Acredales Walk, Haddington, EH41 [062 082] Haddington 4959
Nelson, John, MA, BD	1941	……	1980	(Crawford with Wanlockhead and Leadhills)	7 Manse Road, Roslin, Midlothian, EH25 9LF 031-440 3321
Paterson, A. E. L., MA	1941	……	1985	(Musselburgh High)	14/5 Figate Court, Figate Street, Portobello, Edinburgh, EH15 031-669 1533
Robertson, Crichton, MA	1938	……	1978	(Cockpen & Carrington with Lasswade)	Robin Hill, Ludlow Road, Church Stretton, Salop
Sanderson, W. Roy, DD	1933	……	1973	(Stenton with Whittinghame)	1A York Road, North Berwick, EH39 4LS [0620] N. Berwick 2780
Sawers, E. A. H., YRD	1950	……	1989	(Cranstoun Crichton and Ford with Fala and Soutra)	1 Kirk Ports, North Berwick EH39
Sewell, Ronald N.	1957	……	1985	(Howgate with Penicuik South)	20 Marchburn Drive, Penicuik, EH26 9HE [0968] Penicuik 73177
Shirlaw, Robert, MA	1948	……	1984	(Gladsmuir)	39 Strathalmond Road, Barnton, Edinburgh, EH4 8HP 031-339 7775
Stein, John, MA, BD	1973	1986	……	Joint Warden	Carberry Tower, Musselburgh, EH21 8PY 031-665 3135
Stein, Margaret E. (Mrs.), DA, BA, DIPRE	1936	1986	……	Joint Warden	Carberry Tower, Musselburgh, EH21 8PY 031-665 3135
Stewart, Finlay J., BA, BD	1936	……	1979	(Lochgelly Churchmount)	Flat 32, 2 Hawthorn Gardens, Loanhead, EH20 9EE
Thomson, A. Downie	1944	……	1974	(Athelstaneford)	Athelstane, Gifford, Haddington, EH41 4QN [062 081] Gifford 370
Turner, Duncan M., MBE, MA	1940	……	1977	(Innerwick and Spott)	Spott, Dunbar, EH42 1RS [0368] Dunbar 62668
Whiteford, David H., OBE, MA, BD, PHD	1943	……	1985	(Gullane)	3 Old Dean Road, Longniddry, EH32 0QY [0875] Longniddry 52980
Williamson, James	1986	1986	……	Auxiliary at Garvald and Haddington	9 Amisfield Place, Haddington, EH41 [0620] Haddington 824578

SYNOD II — THE BORDERS

Meets last Thursday of April and October
Correspondents: Lothian; Dumfries and Galloway; Clydesdale
Clerk: Rev. HUGH MACKAY, KCU, MA, FSASCOT, Duns, Berwickshire TD11 3DP [0361] Duns 83755

4. MELROSE AND PEEBLES

Meets at Innerleithen on the first Tuesday of February, March, May, September, October, November, December, and on the last Tuesday of June
Clerk: Rev. CHARLES A. DUNCAN, MA, The Manse, Stow, Galashiels, TD1 2RE [057 83] Stow 237

Charge	Minister	Ord.	Ind.	Address and Tel. No.	Com.	Eld.	W.G.	S.S.	B.C.	C.L. £	As'd £	Gi'n £	Stp. £
Ashkirk	Ian M. Strachan	1959	1986	10 Victoria Crescent, Selkirk, TD7 5DE [0750] Selkirk 21873	88	5	17	.....	.....	3239	301	301	
linked with													
Caddonfoot	James H. Sinclair, MA, BD Associate	1966	1987	1 Viewfield Park, Selkirk, TD7 4LH [0750] Selkirk 21289	286	9	9	17	.....	4893	237	237	10215
linked with													
Selkirk					1212	48	79	59	5	36849	2200	2200	
					224	14	28	13		16521	2916	2916	
Bowden	James Watson, LTH	1968	1988	Bowden, Melrose, TD6 0SU [0835] St. Boswells 22220	189	12	12	15	.....	7224	908	908	v
linked with													
Lilliesleaf													
Broughton, Glenholm & Kilbucho	John D Rennie, MA	1962	1980	Broughton, Biggar, Lanarkshire, ML12 [089 94] Broughton 331	206	14	35	39	10	6534	337	337	
linked with													
Skirling					95	.....	.....	5	.....	2072	178	178	
linked with													
Stobo and Drumelzier	Thomas H. Howat, MA	1984	......	Auxiliary—*see List on page 107*	111	6	.....	17	.....	7421	254	254	8646
linked with													
Tweedsmuir					45	7	.....	9	.....	4427	248	298	
Caddonfoot	*see Ashkirk*												
Carlops					91	11	6	7	7	4946	711	533	
linked with													
Kirkurd and Newlands	Thomas W. Burt, BD	1985	......	West Linton, Peeblesshire, EH46 [0968] West Linton 60221	137	9	20	21	.....	3952	703	703	9336
linked with													
West Linton St. Andrew's					424	26	50	58	.....	15397	2304	2304	

Charge	Minister	Ord.	Ind.	Address and Tel. No.	Com.	Eld.	W.G.	S.S.	B.C.	C.L. £	As'd £	Gi'n £	Stp. £
Channelkirk	Duncan J. M'Gregor, MIFM	1982	.....	Lauder, Berwickshire, TD2 6RW [057 82] Lauder 320	112	8	12	12	.....	2867	440	440	9024
linked with													
Lauder Old					453	16	31	46	.....	15470	1845	1845	
Earlston	David W. Torrance, MA, BD	1955	1977	Earlston, Berwickshire, TD4 6DE [089 684] Earlston 236	750	16	37	42	4	21321	1809	1957	8646
Eddleston	David C. MacFarlane, MA	1957	1970	Innerleithen Road, Peebles, EH45 8BD [0721] Peebles 20568	144	4	20	10	.....	4639	194	194	
linked with													
Lyne and Manor	Nancy M. Norman, BA, MDIV, MTH Associate	1988	.....		112	6	.....	.....	.....	3502	205	205	11601
linked with													
Peebles Old					1274	58	57	60	40	61451	6452	6452	
Ettrick	Bruce B. Lawrie, BD	1974	1986	Yarrow, Selkirk, TD7 5NE [0750] Yarrow 82219	138	10	15	.....	.....	4428	.....	110	
linked with													
Yarrow					150	13	14	.....	.....	4850	.....	.....	8646
Galashiels— Old and St. Paul's	Leslie M. Steele, MA, BD	1973	1988	Barr Road, Galashiels, TD1 3HX [0896] Galashiels 2320	636	29	33	43	36	32682	3687	3687	v
St. Aidan's	Jack M. Brown, BSC, BD	1977	1981	High Road, Galashiels, TD1 2BD [0896] Galashiels 2420	939	39	60	49	46	25092	3071	3142	8646
St. John's	Stephen F. Clipston, MA, BD	1982	.....	Hawthorn Road, Galashiels, TD1 2JZ [0896] Galashiels 2573	379	14	29	48	23	20085	1987	.....	8646
St. Ninian's	David J. Kellas, MA, BD	1966	1983	Mossilee Road, Galashiels, TD1 1NF [0896] Galashiels 2058	980	45	81	69	27	26613	4076	4076	9597
Heriot	Charles A. Duncan, MA	1956	1966	Stow, Galashiels, TD1 2RE [057 83] Stow 237	42	2	.....	.....	.....	1159	.....	.....	
linked with													
Stow St. Mary of Wedale					272	15	34	29	.....	12742	.....	.....	8898
Innerleithen	John Wilson, BD	1985	.....	Innerleithen, Peeblesshire, EH46 [0896] Innerleithen 830309	652	24	72	42	15	19978	1415	1480	
linked with													
Traquair					137	9	.....	10	.....	4443	539	571	9159
linked with													
Walkerburn					146	7	27	14	.....	5683	711	741	
Kirkurd and Newlands	see Carlops												
Lauder Old	see Channelkirk												
Lilliesleaf	see Bowden												
Lyne and Manor	see Eddleston												

Charge	Minister													Address and Tel. No.
Maxton														
linked with														
Newtown	Ian G. Grainger ¶	1985	⋯	40	4	14	7	⋯	⋯	2786	⋯	⋯	8646	Newtown St. Boswells, TD6 0PG [0835] St. Boswells 22106
Melrose	Alistair G. Bennett, BSC, BD	1978	1984	341	13	17	23	13	8061	⋯	10182	10497	10725	Melrose, Roxburghshire, TD6 [089 682] Melrose 2217
				1033	63	58	96	41	54834					
Mertoun														
linked with														
St. Boswells	Glyn R. Taverner, MA, BD	1957	1983	125	8	15	13	⋯	6278	775	775	⋯	9372	St. Boswells, Roxburghshire, TD6 0BB [0835] St. Boswells 22255
Newtown	*see Maxton*			369	20	53	43	21	16896	1925	1925			
Peebles—														
Old	*see Eddleston*													
St. Andrew's Leckie	James H. Wallace, MA, BD	1973	1983	820	44	76	79	16	36932	9954	10071	⋯	9825	Innerleithen Road, Peebles, EH45 8BD [0721] Peebles 21749
St. Boswells	*see Mertoun*													
Selkirk—	*see Ashkirk*													
Skirling	*see Broughton*													
Stobo and Drumelzier	*see Broughton*													
Stow: St. Mary of Wedale	*see Heriot*													
Traquair	*see Innerleithen*													
Tweedsmuir	*see Broughton*													
Walkerburn	*see Innerleithen*													
West Linton	*see Carlops*													
Yarrow	*see Ettrick*													

Minister	Ord.	App.	Ret.	Charge	Address and Tel. No.
Auld, Ian A., MA	1935	⋯	1972	(Banchory Devenick)	Whitestoneknowe, Hydro Avenue, Peebles, EH45 8LU [0721] Peebles 20709
Bowie, William K.	1953	⋯	1984	(Innerleithen *with* Walkerburn)	73 Kingsland Terrace, Peebles, EH45 8HH [0721] Peebles 21144
Clark, James S., MA	1943	⋯	1978	(Traquair)	10 Connor Ridge, Peebles, EH45 [0721] Peebles 21988
Couper, Stewart, MA, BD	1936	⋯	1971	(The Glens)	45 Edderston Road, Peebles, EH45 9DT [0721] Peebles 20887
Donald, Thomas W., LTH, CA	1977	⋯	1987	(Bowden *with* Lilliesleaf)	The Quest, Huntly Road, Melrose, TD6 9SB [089 682] Melrose 2345
Duncan, John H., MA, BD	1933	⋯	1976	(Earlston)	20 Elliot Park, Edinburgh, EH14 1DX 031—441 2911
Forrester-Paton, Colin, MA, BD	1944	⋯	1983	(Hawick Burnfoot)	Acharn, Glen Road, Peebles, EH45 9AY [0721] Peebles 20136
Greer, Robert M., MA, BD	1939	⋯	1981	(Maxton *with* Mertoun)	Mertoun, St. Boswells, TD6 [0835] St. Boswells 22234
Grubb, Anthony J., MA, BD	1937	⋯	1986	(Deer)	Lindisfarne, 35 Brownsmuir Park, Lauder, TD2 6QD [05782] Lauder 692
Howat, Thomas H., MBE, MA	1984	1984	⋯	*Auxiliary at* Upper Tweeddale	Venlaw Bank, Innerleithen Road, Peebles, EH45 8DB [0721] Peebles 21284

Minister	Ord.	App.	Ret.	Charge	Address and Tel. No.
Irving, George, MA	1943	...	1986	(Brydekirk with Hoddam)	Westcott, Cardrona, Peebles, EH45 9HX [0896] Innerleithen 830653
Jamieson, H. M., MA, BD	1938	...	1976	(Ashkirk with Lilliesleaf)	Craigvar, High Road, Galashiels, TD1 2BD [0896] Galashiels 55447
Laing, William F., DSC, VRD, MA	1952	1988	...	Valparaiso	Casilla 40, Vina del Mar, Valparaiso, Chile
Leishman, David P., MA, BD	1939	...	1973	(St. Boswells)	Dovecote Mews, Hawick, TD9 7HH [0450] Hawick 7292
MacCuish, Donald, MA	1930	...	1978	(Caddonfoot)	Caddonfoot, Galashiels, TD1 3LG [089 685] Clovenfords 240
Mackay, Edward	1951	...	1977	(Selkirk Heatherlie)	11 Halliday's Park, Selkirk, TD7 [0750] Selkirk 20964
MacKnight, A. T., MVO, MBE, MB., CH B., MRCGP	1974	...	1986	(Colombo St. Andrew's)	Hildon, Jenny Moore's Road, St. Boswells, TD6 [0835] St. Boswells 22193
Morton, Alasdair J., MA, BD, DIPED, FEIS	1960	1977		Department of Education, Secretary	8 Ormiston Grove, Melrose, TD6 9SR [089 682] Melrose 2033
Morton, Gillian M. (Mrs.), MA, BD, PGCE	1983	1988		Hospital Chaplain	8 Ormiston Grove, Melrose, TD6 9SR [089 682] Melrose 2033
Rae, Andrew W.	1951	...	1987	(Annan St. Andrew's Greenknowe Erskine)	Roseneuk, Tweedside Road, St. Boswells, TD6 0PQ [0835] St. Boswells 23783
Rogerson, A. E., MA	1937	...	1980	(Galashiels Ladhope St. Cuthbert's)	24 Congreen Road, Tweedbank, Galashiels, TD1 3SG [0896] Galashiels 4817
Slack, J. W.	1968	...	1985	(Ashkirk with Selkirk Lawson Memorial)	17 Grenville Avenue, St. Anne's-on-Sea, Fylde

5. DUNS

Meets at Duns, in the Old Parish Church Hall, on the first Tuesday of February, March, April, May, October, November, December; on the last Tuesday in June; and in places to be appointed on the first Tuesday of September

Clerk: Rev. W. PETER GRAHAM, MA, BD, Chirnside, Duns TD11 3XL [089 081] Chirnside 269

Charge	Minister	Ord.	Ind.	Address and Tel. No.	Com.	Eld.	W.G.	S.S.	B.C.	C.L. £	As'd £	Gi'n £	Stp. £
Ayton					300	13	23	24	...	5400	400	400	
linked with													
Burnmouth					69	4	...	...	...	2264	200	...	8646
linked with													
Grantshouse and Houndwood	David J. Hebenton, MA, BD	1958	1983	Grey Gables, Beanburn, Ayton, Eyemouth, TD14 5QY [089 07] Ayton 81333	136	4	16	...	...	2586	180	180	
linked with													
Reston					108	3	...	23	...	2392	140	140	
Berwick-on-Tweed St. Andrew's, Wallace Green, and Lowick	James Blaikie, BD	1972	1986	3 Wellington Ter., Berwick on Tweed, TD15 1HW [0289] Berwick 307010	531	22	40	14	...	33373	150	1550	8646
Bonkyl and Preston					89	4	9	12	...	2333	520	520	
linked with													
Chirnside	W. Peter Graham, MA, BD	1967	1968	Chirnside, Duns, TD11 3XL [089 081] Chirnside 269	445	18	24	28	...	10933	1720	1720	9540
linked with													
Edrom Allanton					99	5	...	...	...	2557	420	420	

	Minister			Address									v
Burnmouth	*see* Ayton												
Chirnside	*see* Bonkyl												
Coldingham	Daniel G. Lindsay, BD	1978	1979	Victoria Road, Eyemouth, TD14 5JD [089 07] Eyemouth 5032	118	5	24	18	.....	6254	.....	70	
linked with St. Abb's					36	3	.....	11	.....	1192	.....	150	
linked with Eyemouth					428	28	103	80	4	21782	2310	2310	9924
Coldstream	Iain D. Penman, BD	1977	1980	Duns Road, Coldstream, TD12 4DP [0890] Coldstream 2537	774	26	35	58	15	20598	3840	3840	
linked with Eccles					151	10	18	20	.....	4192	1050	1050	1050
Duns	Hugh Mackay, KCLJ, MA, FSA SCOT	1957	1967	Duns, Berwickshire, TD11 3DP [0361] Duns 83755	740	19	96	52	.....	19628	3400	3400	100
Eccles	*see* Coldstream												
Edrom Allanton	*see* Bonkyl												
Eyemouth	*see* Coldingham												
Fogo and Swinton	Alan C. D. Cartwright, BSC, BD	1976	.....	Swinton, Duns, TD11 3JJ [089 086] Swinton 228	227	15	19	17	.....	6531	1050	1050	9660
linked with Ladykirk					39	3	16	.....	.....	2216	280	280	280
linked with Leitholm					140	11	17	.....	.....	3016	1050	1050	1050
linked with Whitsome					86	4	12	.....	.....	2658	220	220	220
Foulden and Mordington	Geraldine H. Hope (Mrs.), MA, BD	1986	.....	Hutton, Berwick-on-Tweed, TD15 1TS [0289] Berwick 86396	178	8	16	.....	.....	5307	.....	.....	
linked with Hutton & Fishwick and Paxton					165	7	16	11	.....	4141	.....	.....	8646
Gordon													
St. Michael's	Robert D. Higham, BD	1985	.....	Greenlaw, Berwickshire, TD10 6XF [036 16] Greenlaw 218	155	5	15	20	.....	3578	330	330	
linked with Greenlaw					261	15	32	11	.....	9040	1170	1170	8892
linked with Legerwood					91	6	.....	.....	.....	4695	300	300	
linked with Westruther					89	6	.....	21	.....	3581	220	220	
Grantshouse and Houndwood	*see* Ayton												
Greenlaw	*see* Gordon												
Hutton & Fishwick and Paxton	*see* Foulden												

Charge	Minister	Ord.	Ind.	Address and Tel. No.	Com.	Eld.	W.G.	S.S.	B.C.	C.L. £	As'd £	Gi'n £	Stp. £
Kirk of Lammermuir	Alexander Slorach, CA, BD	1970	1983	Cranshaws, Duns, TD11 3SJ [036 17] Longformacus 289	149	9	......	26	7	5376	......	......	
linked with													
Langton and Polwarth					182	9	21	19	6	7841	......	200	8646
Ladykirk	*see* Fogo												
Langton & Polwarth	*see* Kirk of Lammermuir												
Legerwood	*see* Gordon												
Leitholm	*see* Fogo												
Longformacus	*see* Abbey St. Bathans												
Lowick	*see* Berwick												
Reston	*see* Ayton												
St. Abb's	*see* Coldingham												
Westruther	*see* Gordon												
Whitsome	*see* Fogo												

Minister	Ord.	App.	Ret.	Charge	Address and Tel. No.
Cameron, Peter S., LLB, BD, PHD, LRAM	1984	1987	......	University of Edinburgh	Schoolhouse, Gavinton, Duns
Dunnett, W. Gavin, MBE	1968	......	1985	(Foulden and Mordington *with* Hutton & Fishwick and Paxton)	Old Smiddy Cottage, Hutton, Berwick-on-Tweed, TD15 1TS [0289] Berwick 86225
Ewing, James M., MA	1932	......	1975	(Cromarty)	Tweed Cottage, Union Bridge, Berwick on Tweed, TD15 1XQ [0289] Berwick 86442
Finnie, J. I. Crawford	1941	......	1976	(Eccles *with* Leitholm)	6 Horsleys Park, St. Andrews, KY16 8RZ
Fraser, Robert M., MA	1939	......	1979	(Gordon St. Michael's *with* Westruther)	11 Upper Loan, Stow Road, Lauder, TD2 6TR [057 82] Lauder 559
Hall, James A., THB	1960	......	1983	(Langton and Polwarth)	Gavinton, Duns, TD11 3QE [0361] Duns 82284
Lusk, John C., BA, BD	1941	......	1978	(Foulden and Mordington)	Applegarth, Glen Road, Dunblane, FK15 0DT [0786] Dunblane 823416
Macleod, Allan M., MA	1945	......	1985	(Gordon St. Michael's *with* Legerwood *with* Westruther)	Silverlea, Machrihanish, Argyll
Maben, J. A. Brydon	1965	......	1987	(Coldingham *with* St. Abb's)	Rose Cottage, Whitsome, Duns, TD11 3NB
Paterson, K. N., MA, BD, DIPED	1929	......	1972	(Pluscarden)	Glasford, Marchmont Road, Greenlaw, TD10 6YQ
Strachan, James C.	1941	......	1987	(Hobkirk *with* Southdean)	Cheviot View, Belmont Farm, Kelso, TD5 7QY [075 37] Stichill 385

6. JEDBURGH

Meets at Jedburgh on the first Wednesday of February, March, May, November and December and on the last Wednesday of June.
Meets in the Moderator's Church on the first Wednesday of October

Clerk: Rev. NEIL R. COMBE, BSC, MSC, BD, Buccleuch Road, Hawick TD9 0EL [0450] Hawick 72150
Honorary Clerk: The Rev. W. M. D. THOMPSON, MA, Oxnam Manse, Jedburgh, Roxburghshire TD8 6RD [083 56] Jedburgh 2492

Charge	Minister	Ord.	Ind.	Address and Tel. No.	Com.	Eld.	W.G.	S.S.	B.C.	C.L. £	As'd £	Gi'n £	Stp. £
Ancrum	[W. Haisley Moore, BA	1966	1981	Jedburgh, Roxburghshire, TD8 6JH [083 56] Jedburgh 3417	196	9	13	...	...	5660	884	884	
linked with													
Edgerston					58	7	...	...	...	1431	501	501	10872
linked with													
Jedburgh Old	Anne Stuart, DCS	...	...	Deaconess—see List H [083 56] Jedburgh 3552	1056	46	42	...	...	28350	8289	8289	
Bedrule					85	5	11	8	...	3100	...	120	
linked with													
Denholm	Vacant	...	...	Denholm, Hawick, TD9 8NX [045 087] Denholm 268	284	20	24	19	24	8203	...	...	8646
linked with													
Minto					88	4	12	7	...	4730	...	...	
Castleton and Saughtree	Reginald F. Campbell, BD	1979	...	23 Langholm St., Newcastleton, TD9 0QX [054 121] Liddesdale 242	209	8	46	...	...	13176	...	200	8646
Cavers and Kirkton	Adam McCall Bowie	1976	1988	Hobkirk, Hawick, TD9 8JW [054 086] Bonchester Bridge 636	206	9	9	...	...	3317	245	245	v
linked with													
Hobkirk and Southdean					191	13	...	...	...	3621	...	...	
Crailing					56	4	14	...	...	2667	368	368	
linked with													
Eckford					89	6	...	...	...	2671	566	566	
linked with													
Oxnam	W. M. D. Thompson, MA	1950	...	Oxnam, Jedburgh, TD8 6RD [083 56] Jedburgh 2492	85	5	...	...	...	6058	295	307	9144
linked with													
Roxburgh					130	5	...	12	5	3394	497	497	
Denholm	*see* Bedrule												
Eckford	*see* Crailing												
Edgerston	*see* Ancrum												

Charge	Minister	Ord.	Ind.	Address and Tel. No.	Com.	Eld.	W.G.	S.S.	B.C.	C.L. £	As'd £	Gi'n £	Stp. £
Hawick—													
Burnfoot	James M. Cowie, BD	1976	1984	29 Wilton Hill, Hawick, TD9 8BA [0450] Hawick 73181	349	23	20	48	11	11888	...	...	8646
Old	Vacant	...	...	Buccleuch Road, Hawick, TD9 0EH [0450] Hawick 72954	755	29	74	...	...	25652	3888	3888	v
linked with Teviothead					82	4	12			2061	507	507	
Teviot	Neil R. Combe, BSC, MSC, BD	1984	...	Buccleuch Road, Hawick, TD9 0EL [0450] Hawick 72150	594	32	32	59	8	26369	4192	4192	v
linked with Roberton					109	4	...	...	...	2238	419	120	
St. Mary's	Vacant	...	...		599	24	20	...	...	17438	1947	1947	v
Trinity	E. P. Lindsay Thomson, MA	1964	1972	Fenwick Park, Hawick, TD9 9PA [0450] Hawick 72705	1130	46	61	...	...	36501	5426	5441	9517
Wilton	George Watson, MA, BD	1953	1960	3 Overhall Road, Wilton Dean, Hawick, TD9 7JB [0450] Hawick 72453	625	22	25	...	...	17128	1702	...	...
Hobkirk and Southdean	*see* Cavers												
Jedburgh—													
Old	*see* Ancrum												
Trinity	John A. Riddell, MA, BD	1967	...	42 High Street, Jedburgh, TD8 6DQ [083 56] Jedburgh 3223	365	11	...	...	...	20477	1761	1761	8646
Kelso—													
North & Ednam	D. R. Gaddes	1961	1970	20 Forrestfield, Kelso, TD5 7BX [0573] Kelso 24677	1750	70	123	97	15	73150	8901	9121	10575
linked with Sprouston	Una Stewart (Mrs.), DCS	...	...	*Deaconess—see* List H [0573] Kelso 25065	174	7	...	21	...	3686	183	313	
Old	Vacant	...	...	Kelso, Roxburghshire, TD5 7JE [0573] Kelso 25087	659	32	38	32	47	16158	840	840	8646
Linton					118	5	...	...	...	3520	377	377	
linked with Morebattle and Hownam	Joseph Brown, MA	1954	1967	Kirk Yetholm, Kelso, TD5 8RD [057 382] Yetholm 308	257	11	35	...	...	9692	1393	1393	9465
linked with Yetholm					262	14	27	...	...	8979	1248	1248	
Makerstoun and Smailholm	Bruce J. L. Hay	1957	1983	Smailholm, Kelso, TD5 7PH [057 36] Smailholm 268	123	5	...	...	...	3450	222	222	8646
linked with Stichill, Hume and Nenthorn					116	8	28	...	...	2456	241	241	

Minto	see Bedrule
Morebattle and Hownam	see Linton
Oxnam	see Crailing
Roberton	see Hawick Teviot
Roxburgh	see Crailing
Southdean	see Hobkirk
Sprouston	see Kelso
Stichill, Hume and Nenthorn	see Makerstoun
Teviothead	see Hawick Old
Yetholm	see Linton

Minister	Ord.	App.	Ret.	Charge	Address and Tel. No.
Falconer, James F.	1952	......	1977	(Bedrule with Denholm with Minto)	Denholm, Rothes-on-Spey, IV33
Fox, G. Dudley A.	1972	......	1988	(Kelso Old)	
Goodbrand, Stephen, MA	1952	......	1982	(Hobkirk with Southdean)	Fiaray, Minto, Hawick, TD9 8SG [045 087] Denholm 214
Hall, John A., MA	1927	......	1968	(Strathkinness)	39 Shedden Park Road, Kelso, TD5 7AL [0573] Kelso 24790
Hamilton, Robert, MA, BD	1938	......	1979	(Kelso Old)	Dalbiac Cottage, Hermitage Lane, Kelso, TD5 7AN [0573] Kelso 24622
Logan, J. Victor, MA	1937	......	1977	(Crailing with Eckford)	Addinston Lodge, Oxton, Lauder, TD2 6QZ [057 85] Oxton 293
McConnell, Robert	1959	......	1983	(Hawick St. Margaret's and Wilton South with Roberton)	Shalom, Borthwick Mains, Roberton, Hawick. TD9 7LU [045 088] Borthwick Brae 230
MacFadden, Kenneth, MA	1925	......	1966	(Hownam with Morebattle with Yetholm)	2 Buchanan Gardens, St. Andrews, Fife, KY16 8EB [033 481] St. Andrews 1095
Tosh, David A., MA, BD	1932	......	1972	(Kirkmichael and Straloch)	Ancrum Schoolhouse, Jedburgh, TD8 6SH [083 53] Ancrum 208

ADDRESSES OF HAWICK CHURCHES

Burnfoot	Fraser Avenue	St. Mary's	Kirk Wynd	Trinity	Central Square
Old	Buccleuch Road	Teviot	Off Buccleuch Road	Wilton	Princes Street

SYNOD III — DUMFRIES AND GALLOWAY

Meets at Dumfries on fourth Wednesday of April and October
Correspondents: The Borders: Ayr; Clydesdale
Clerk: Rev. ALBERT B. ELDER, MA, 52 Moffat Road, Dumfries DG1 1NY [0387] Dumfries 52021

7. ANNANDALE AND ESKDALE

Meets at Lochmaben on the first Tuesday of February, March, April, May, September, October, November and December and on the last Tuesday in June
Clerk: Rev. C. BRYAN HASTON, LTH, The Manse, Gretna Green, Carlisle, CA6 5DU [0461] Gretna 38313

Charge	Minister	Ord.	Ind.	Address and Tel. No.	Com.	Eld.	W.G.	S.S.	B.C.	C.L. £	As'd £	Gi'n £	Stp. £
Annan— Old	Andrew Frater, BA, BD	1987	......	10 Hecklegirth Road, Annan, DG12 6BH [046 12] Annan 3438	720	31	94	101	29	30687	4794	4794	v
St. Andrew's Greenknowe Erskine	Alan C. Ross, CA, BD	1988	......	1 Annerley Road, Annan, DG12 6HE [046 12] Annan 2143	1028	64	44	40	33	44263	5483	5483	9981
Applegarth and Sibbaldbie	John J. C. Owen, LTH	1967	1980	Lochmaben, Lockerbie, DG11 1QF [0387] Lochmaben 810590	224	8	24	24	......	5709	1070	1070	9657
linked with Lochmaben					735	23	51	70	11	19123	3186	3186	
Brydekirk	Alan H. S. Taylor	1957	1987	Ecclefechan, Lockerbie, DG11 3BU [057 63] Ecclefechan 357	107	5	......	3	......	4696	......	......	v
linked with Hoddam					172	11	18	10	......	7310	......	......	
Canonbie	James B. Watson, BSC, BD	1968	1986	Langholm, DG13 0BL [03 873] Langholm 80252	243	12	......	14	......	10073	1305	1305	10092
linked with Langholm, Ewes and Westerkirk					1223	50	99	104	......	27349	5996	3240	
Carlisle	William D. Brown, BD, CQSW	1987	......	197 Brampton Road, Carlisle, CA3 9PX [0228] Carlisle 401655	557	29	56	54	6	19883	3336	3336	v
linked with Longtown					72	6	25	22	......	6463	403	403	
Dalton					125	8	......	22	......	4320	425	225	
linked with Hightae	W. Logan Kirk, MA, BD, MTH	1988	......	Hightae, Lockerbie, DG11 1JL [0387] Lochmaben 811499	117	7	14	24	......	2421	254	254	v
linked with St. Mungo					139	9	......	5	......	6275	582	......	

Charge	Minister			Address									
Dornock	Ronald S. Seaman, MA	1967	......	Dornock, Annan, DG12 6NR [0461] Eastriggs 40268	385	14	24	30	......	9175	......	......	8646
Eskdalemuir *linked with*					80	7	......	......	8	4403	......	......	8898
Hutton and Corrie *linked with*	A. Cameron Gibson, MRCVS	1962	1980	Hutton Manse, Boreland, Lockerbie, DG11 2PB [057 66] Boreland 213	227	13	20	10	8	6190	......	......	
Tundergarth					85	4	12	......	......	5847	......	16	
Gretna Old, Gretna St. Andrew's and Half Morton, and Kirkpatrick Fleming	C. Bryan Haston, LTH	1975	......	Gretna Green, Carlisle, CA6 5DU [0461] Gretna 38313	641	42	31	120	17	27789	2652	......	9264
Hightae	*see* Dalton												
Hoddam	*see* Brydekirk												
Hutton and Corrie	*see* Eskdalemuir												
Johnstone *linked with*	John M. Stewart, MA, BD	1964	1986	Beattock, DG10 9RF [068 33] Beattock 349	172	......	8	13	......	7524	......	......	8646
Kirkpatrick Juxta					199	7	38	10	......	9421	......	50	
Kirtle-Eaglesfield *linked with*					158	9	34	9	......	8461	850	850	
Middlebie *linked with*	Leslie W. Thorne	1987	......	Kirtlebridge, Lockerbie, DG11 3LY [046 15] Kirtlebridge 378	110	6	14	......	......	2716	195	195	v
Waterbeck					74	5	......	17	12	38004	251	251	
Langholm, Ewes and Westerkirk	*see* Canonbie												
Lochmaben	*see* Applegarth												
Lockerbie Dryfesdale	James M. Annand, MA, BD	1955	1966	Lockerbie, Dumfriesshire, DG11 2DW [057 62] Lockerbie 2361	1464	48	96	89	9	23381	2990	2990	9741
Longtown	*see* Carlisle												
Middlebie	*see* Kirtle-Eaglesfield												
Moffat *linked with*	Gerald C. Moule, BA, BD	1974	1975	Moffat, Dumfriesshire, DG10 9EJ [0683] Moffat 20128	704	33	55	128	56	23607	4447	2300	9742
Wamphray					72	5	......	......	......	3048	468	154	
St. Mungo	*see* Dalton												

Charge	Minister	Ord.	Ind.	Address and Tel. No.	Com.	Eld.	W.G.	S.S.	B.C.	C.L. £	As'd £	Gi'n £	Stp. £
Tundergarth	see Eskdalemuir												
Wamphray	see Moffat												
Waterbeck	see Kirtle-Eaglesfield												

Minister	Ord.	App.	Ret.	Charge	Address and Tel. No.
Alexander, Dugald C., MA, BD	1945		1977	(Dunscore)	Rosewood, Stapleton Road, Annan, DG12 6NB [046 12] Annan 3858
Fisher, D. Noel, MA, BD	1939		1979	(Glasgow Sherbrooke St. Gilbert's)	Leetside, 14 Woodlands Park, Coldstream, TD12 4LL [0890] Coldstream 2228
Fletcher, John	1939		1972	(Lockerbie Trinity)	8 Gillsland Road, Edinburgh, EH10 5BW 031-229 2785
Griffith, Hugh D., BA, PH D, HCF	1939		1986	(Lockerbie St. Cuthbert's with Tundergarth)	St. Cuthbert's, Lockerbie, DG11 2DQ [057 62] Lockerbie 2337
Kydd, George F., MA	1963		1980	(Applegarth and Sibbaldbie)	Cauldwell Cottage, Beech Grove, Moffat, Dumfriesshire, DG10 9RU [0683] Moffat 20847
M'Lean, Margaret G., BD	1978	1984		Community Minister, Annandale and Eskdale	13 High Street, Longtown [0228] Longtown 792068
Rathbone, Simeon	1943			(Buenos Aires)	1/5 Croydon Street, Lakemba, N.S.W. 2195, Australia
Stewart, Charles E., MA	1926			(Dornock)	70 The Rand, Eastriggs, Annan, DG12 6NN [046 14] Eastriggs 339

8. DUMFRIES AND KIRKCUDBRIGHT

Meets at Dumfries, on the first Wednesday of February, March, April, May, October, November, December, and the second Wednesday of June and September

Clerk: Rev. GORDON M. A. SAVAGE, MA, BD, 11 Laurieknowe, Dumfries, DG2 7AH [0387] Dumfries 52929

Charge	Minister	Ord.	Ind.	Address and Tel. No.	Com.	Eld.	W.G.	S.S.	B.C.	C.L. £	As'd £	Gi'n £	Stp. £
Anwoth and Girthon	Callum T. O'Donnell, MA, BD	1984		Gatehouse of Fleet, Castle Douglas, DG7 2EF [055 74] Gatehouse 233	55	21	38	62		31368	1755	1641	8646
Auchencairn linked with	Continued Vacancy				117	11	20	27		6970			
Rerrick					80	7				2880		120	v

Congregation	Minister	Ord.	Ind.	Address									
Balmaclellan *linked with* Kells	R. Hugh Drummond ¶	1953	1988	Kells Manse, New Galloway, Castle Douglas, DG7 3SD [064 42] *New Galloway 225*	96	6	11	8	......	......	1519	......	......	v
Balmaghie *linked with* Tarff and Twynholm	Christopher Wallace, BD	1988	......	Twynholm, Kirkcudbright, DG6 4NY [055 76] *Twynholm 204*	166	11	27	11	......	5069	......	......	v
					210	10	19	16	10	6429	787	787	
					317	11	24	......	......	11499	787	787	
Borgue	*Continued Vacancy*	......	......	——	155	6	11	......	......	1410	165	60	v
Buittle and Kelton *linked with* Castle Douglas St. Andrew's	Andrew F. Swan, BD	1983	......	10 Queen Elizabeth Drive, DG7 1HH [0556] *Castle Douglas 2585*	409	27	53	26	......	16973	3000	3000	
					547	19	66	45	7	19051	3305	3305	10575
Caerlaverock *linked with* Dumfries St. Michael's & South	John Pagan, FRSA *Colleagues*	1957	1978	39 Cardoness Street, Dumfries, DG1 3AL [0378] *Dumfries 53849*	230	7	12	......	......	4643	492	492	
	Albert B. Elder, MA	1960	......	52 Moffat Road, Dumfries, DG1 1NY [0387] *Dumfries 52021*	1450	52	84	138	18	45838	4000	4010	10056
Carsphairn *linked with* Dalry	John R. Miller, MA, BD	1958	1972	Dalry, Castle Douglas, DG7 3PJ [064 43] *Dalry, Kirkcudbright 380*	108	8	15	14	13	3752	......	......	8748
					269	11	42	19	......	13867	......	67	
Castle Douglas— St. Andrew's	*see Buittle*												
Castle Douglas— St. Ringan's *linked with* Crossmichael *linked with* Parton	Robert Hamill, BA	1956	1960	1 Castle View, Castle Douglas, DG7 1BG [0556] *Castle Douglas 2171*	421	19	84	34	......	23189	3200	3200	
					165	12	42	10	......	9396	1510	1510	10272
					71	4	20	......	......	3881	591	591	
Closeburn *linked with* Durisdeer	James W. Scott, MA, CDA	1952	1953	Durisdeer, Thornhill, Dumfriesshire, DG3 5BJ [084 85] *Durisdeer 231*	263	10	15	17	8	886	1106	1106	9084
					203	8	38	13	6	13729	1823	1823	
Colvend, Southwick and Kirkbean	Ian W. Robertson, MA, BD	1956	1974	Colvend, Dalbeattie, DG5 4QN [055 663] *Rockcliffe 255*	388	22	43	40	18	25824	3092	3092	9372
Corsock *linked with* K'patrick Durham	*Vacant*	......	......	Kirkpatrick Durham, Castle Douglas, DG7 3HD [055 665] *K. Durham 266*	90	6	17	......	......	4914	100	100	
					243	14	26	27	......	9686	......	......	8646
Crossmichael	*see Castle Douglas*												
Cummertrees	*see Ruthwell*												
Dalbeattie *linked with* Urr	Norman M. Hutcheson, MA, BD	1973	1988	Borrisleigh, Haugh Road, Dalbeattie, DG5 0AR [0556] *Dalbeattie 610029*	914	49	108	76	22	19932	5064	5244	
					312	16	41	25	......	10764	1934	1934	v

Charge	Minister	Ord.	Ind.	Address and Tel. No.	Com.	Eld.	W.G.	S.S.	B.C.	C.L. £	As'd £	Gi'n £	Stp. £
Dalry	see Carsphairn												
Dumfries—													
Greyfriars	David R. Black, MA, BD¶	1986	1987	4 Georgetown Crescent, DG1 4EQ [0387] Dumfries 57045	647	39	29	34	7	30192	5481	5481	v
Laurieknowe Troqueer	William M. M'Kenzie, DA	1958	1977	Troqueer Road, DG2 7DF [0387] Dumfries 53043	619	25	50	83	12	35452	2766	3116	9144
Lincluden linked with Holywood	Mary L. Hutchison (Mrs.), BD	1982	......	96 Glasgow Road, DG2 9DE [0387] Dumfries 64298	323	17	14	36	14	10852	659	659	8646
Lochside linked with Terregles	Thomas C. Bogle, BD	1983	1986	27 St. Anne's Road, DG2 9HZ [0387] Dumfries 52912	231	14	22	30	...	8756	439	439	8646
	Ann M. Gillespie, DCS	......	......	Deaconess—see List H	589	13	26	33	...	12259	550	292	
				[0387] Dumfries 53514	146	8	15	...	...	2681	281	281	
Maxwelltown West	Gordon M. A. Savage, MA, BD	1977	1984	11 Laurieknowe, DG2 7AH [0387] Dumfries 52929	902	41	98	84	11	36921	6328	6328	10344
St. George's	Stuart F. A. Pryce,	1963	1969	9 Nunholm Park, DG1 1JP [0387] Dumfries 52965	632	38	88	59	24	33031	5615	5615	9999
St. Mary's	Graham D. S. Deans, MA, BD	1978	1987	47 Moffat Road, Dumfries, DG1 1NN [0387] Dumfries 54873	1430	67	104	139	13	35932	7209	7209	v
St. Michael's and South	see Caerlaverock												
Dunscore linked with Glencairn and Moniaive	A. David C. Greer, MA, LL B, D MIN, DIP ADULT ED	1956	1985	Wallaceton, Auldgirth, Dumfries, DG2 0TJ [038 782] Dunscore 245	287	15	12	17	9	11751	1261	1261	8748
					303	18	44	14	...	9776	857	857	
Durisdeer	see Closeburn												
Glencairn and Moniaive	see Dunscore												
Holywood	see Dumfries Lincluden												
Kells	see Balmaclellan												
Kirkconnel	Harold G. Mudaliar, GTH, BD	1983	......	Kirkconnel, Sanquhar, DG4 6NP [065 93] Kirkconnel 241	801	28	47	60	...	22075	754	754	8646
Kirkcudbright	W. Stewart Wilson, DA	1980	......	6 Bourtree Avenue, DG6 4AU [0557] Kirkcudbright 30489	1457	57	106	71	32	73459	8955	9263	10470
Kirkgunzeon	Continued Vacancy	......	......	——	94	9	12	9	...	3433	....	....	v

Parish	Minister / reference			Address									
Kirkmahoe	Myra D. W. Smith, BD, CPS	1978	1984	Nith Cottage, Auldgirth, Dumfries DG2 0XP [038 774] *Auldgirth 358*	783	20	23	50	⋯	14711	507	⋯	8646
Kirkmichael	*see Tinwald*												
Kirkpatrick Durham	*see Corsock*												
Kirkpatrick Irongray	David K. P. Bennett, BA	1974	1987	Irongray Manse, Dumfries, DG2 9TR [0387] *Newbridge 720227*	330	15	12	14	8	9482	1029	1029	v
linked with Lochrutton					148	7	20	9	⋯	6315	493	493	
Lochend	William Holland, MA	1967	1971	New Abbey, Dumfries, DG2 8BY [038 785] *New Abbey 232*	81	5	13	⋯	⋯	2323		120	
linked with New Abbey					271	12	23	27	2	10336		145	8748
Lochrutton	*see Kirkpatrick Irongray*												
Mouswald	*see Ruthwell*												
New Abbey	*see Lochend*												
Parton	*see Castle Douglas*												
Penpont, Keir and Tynron	James R. Wilkie, MA, MTH¶	1957	1988	31 West Morton Street, Thornhill, Dumfriesshire, DG3 5NF [0848] *Thornhill 30430*	409	16	20	6	22	11394	933	933	v
Rerrick	*see Auchencairn*												
Ruthwell	Robert M. Nicol	1984	⋯	Ruthwell, Dumfries, DG1 4NP [038 787] *Clarencefield 217*	183	7	30	19	⋯	12760	513	513	
linked with Cummertrees					153	5	⋯	8	⋯	5586	449	449	8817
linked with Mouswald					106	10	13	17	⋯	5388	499	499	
Sanquhar St. Bride's	Kenneth T. Thomson, JP	1957	1984	Sanquhar, Dumfriesshire, DG4 6JL [065 92] *Sanquhar 247*	748	24	79	56	10	19349	1500	1500	9084
Tarff and Twynholm	*see Balmaghie*												
Terregles	*see Dumfries Lochside*												
Thornhill	Robert C. White, MA	1957	1976	Thornhill, Dumfriesshire, DG3 5DP [0848] *Thornhill 30395*	557	16	38	54	7	19650	2882	2882	9324
Tinwald	James S. Leishman, LTH, BD	1969	1985	Tinwald, Dumfries, DG1 3PL [0387] *Amisfield 710246*	384	12	20	68	9	11452	1152	1152	
linked with Kirkmichael					147	6	32	16	⋯	8066	950	950	9750
linked with Torthorwald					149	7	19	34	⋯	6946	585	292	
Torthorwald	*see Tinwald*												
Urr	*see Dalbeattie*												

Minister	Ord.	App.	Ret.	Charge	Address and Tel. No.
Aitken, William B., MA, BL	1955		1986	(Kirkpatrick Irongray)	Bridge Park, Whinnyhill Road, New Abbey, Dumfries, DG2 8HH [083 785] New Abbey 268
Black, Sandra (Mrs.), BSc, BD	1988	1988	......	Hospital Chaplain (Part-time)	4 Georgetown Crescent, Dumfries, DG1 4EQ [0387] Dumfries 57045
Calderwood, Walter M., MA, BD	1934		1974	(Leven Forman)	1 Rossway Road, Kirkcudbright, DG6 4BS [0557] Kirkcudbright 30128
Carmichael, J. J. A., MA	1945		1983	(Anwoth and Girthon)	Gaitgil Cottage, Twynholm, Kirkcudbright, DG6 4PH [055 74] Gatehouse 774
Craig N. Douglas, MA, BD	1947		1987	(Dalbeattie Craignair with Urr)	Langdale, Lochanhead, Dumfries, DG2 8JN [038 773] Lochfoot 222
Good, John	1940		1977	(Tongland with Twynholm)	Four Gables, Silvercraigs Road, Kirkcudbright, DG6 4BT [0557] Kirkcudbright 30617
Grant, G. V. R., MA	1948		1982	(Urray and Kilchrist)	Drum Cottage, Kirkbean, Dumfries, DG2 8DL [038 788] Kirkbean 209
Grant, James, BA	1961		1987	(Penpont Keir and Tynron)	47A Drumlanrig Street, Thornhill, DG3 5LJ [0848] Thornhill 30829
Irving, R. C., MVO, QPM, JP	1968		1979	(Crossmichael with Parton)	21 Copland Street, Dalbeattie, DG5 4EX [0556] Dalbeattie 610093
James, Richard F., MA	1945		1982	(Channelkirk with Lauder Old)	The Bield, Rhonehouse, Castle Douglas, DG7 3ND [055 668] Bridge of Dee 265
Johnston, John, MA, BD	1963	1987	......	Hospital Chaplain	6 Calside Road, Dumfries, DG1 4HA [0387] Dumfries 68857
Knox, Ian S. C.	1948		1986	(Dumfries St. Mary's)	14 Albany Lane, Dumfries DG1 1JL [0387] Dumfries 53856
MacGregor, Donald J.	1952		1979	(Closeburn)	Closeburn Manse, Thornhill, DG3 5HP [084 84] Closeburn 273
Morrison, James G., MBE, MA	1942		1980	(Rotterdam)	Craig, Kirkpatrick Durham, Castle Douglas, DG7 3ND [055 665] KD 264
Mowat, John, MA	1934		1975	(Presbytery Clerk at Aberdeen)	15 Airds Drive, Dumfries, DG1 4EW [0387] Dumfries 67463
Munro, Andrew, BD, PHD	1972		1986	(Adviser in Religious Education)	Corrieknowe, Penpont, Thornhill, DG3 4BZ [0848] Thornhill 30811
Pettigrew, Roderick, MA, BD	1959		1987	(Dalbeattie Park with Kirkgunzeon)	44 Station Road, Dalbeattie, DG5 4BW [0556] Dalbeattie 610435
Prescott, John H., BD	1960		1984	(Kirkmabreck)	55 Cartha Road, Dumfries, DG1 4JB [0387] Dumfries 56959
Raffan, Stanley J., MA, BD	1951		1987	(Hospital Chaplain)	3 Noblehill Place, Dumfries, DG1 3HQ [0387] Dumfries 61952
Robertson, Thomas R., MA, BD	1934		1976	(Broughton, Glenholm and Kilbucho with Skirling)	Langton, Burnside Loaning, Kirkcudbright, DG6 4DH [0557] Kirkcudbright 30795
Smith, Richmond, OBE, MA, BD	1952		1983	(World Alliance of Reformed Churches)	Aignish, Kippford, Dalbeattie, DG5 4LL [055 662] Kippford 624
Williamson, W. E., BA	1938		1980	(Cummertrees with Ruthwell and Mount Kedar)	63 Pleasance Avenue, Dumfries, DG2 7JT [0387] Dumfries 53343

ADDRESSES OF DUMFRIES CHURCHES

Church	Address	Church	Address	Church	Address
Greyfriars	Church Crescent	Lochside	Lochside Road	St. Mary's	St. Mary's Street
Laurieknowe		Maxwelltown West	Laurieknowe	St. Michael's and South	St. Michael's Street
Troqueer	Troqueer Road	St. George's	George Street		
Lincluden	Stewartry Road				

9. WIGTOWN AND STRANRAER

Meets at Glenluce in Old Luce Parish Church Hall on the first Tuesday of each month except January, July and August, when there is no meeting, and of June when it meets on the fourth Tuesday

Clerk: Rev. G. L. THOMSON, BA, Linden House, Leswalt High Road, Stranraer, DG9 0AA   [0776] Stranraer 2524

Charge	Minister	Ord.	Ind.	Address and Tel. No.	Com.	Eld.	W.G.	S.S.	B.C.	C.L. £	As'd £	Gi'n £	Stp. £
Bargrennan *linked with* Monigaff	A. Malcolm Ramsay, BA, LLB, DIPMIN	1986		Monigaff, Newton Stewart, DG8 6SH [0671] Newton Stewart 2143	61 571	4 21	14 24	... 40	... 18	3289 16447	442 2751	442 2751	v
Ervie Kirkcolm *linked with* Leswalt	Alexander B. Cairns, MA	1957	1982	Ervie, Stranraer, DG9 0QZ [0776] Stranraer 854225	299 235	14 8	... 52	32 26	10 12	12644 7646	466 389	466 100	8646
Glasserton and Isle of Whithorn	Wm. Campbell Cowie, MA, BD	1955	....	Isle of Whithorn, Newton Stewart, DG8 8LQ [098 85] Whithorn 342	228	10	18	16	...	9974	426	204	8748
Inch *linked with* Stranraer St. Andrew's	John H. Burns, BSC, BD	1985	1988	Bay View Road, Stranraer, DG9 8BE [0776] Stranraer 2383	308 615	22 36	22 40	31 49	7 23	8954 26513	2998 5782	2998 5782	v
Kirkcowan *linked with* Wigtown	Martin Thomson, BSC, DIPED, BD	1988	....	Harbour Road, Wigtown, Newton Stewart, DG8 9AL [098 84] Wigtown 2242	257 373	13 16	19 27	8 34	... ...	7908 25624	816 1985	816 1985	v
Kirkinner *linked with* Sorbie	Jeffrey M. Mead, BD	1978	1986	Kirkinner, Newton Stewart, DG8 9AL [098 884] Kirkinner 643	243 258	7 11	... 24	37 22	... ...	7869 9968	366 982	366 982	8646
Kirkmabreck	David W. M'Creadie	1961	1985	Creetown, Newton Stewart, DG8 7DB [067 182] Creetown 254	288	11	23	36	15	14623	1432	150	8646
Kirkmaiden *linked with* Stoneykirk	Duncan MacGillivray	1977	1988	Church Road, Sandhead, Stranraer, DG9 9JJ [077 683] Sandhead 337	333 533	10 22	59 35	21 54	... ...	13593 15958	1577 1796	1577 1796	v
Leswalt	*see* Ervie Kirkcolm												
Mochrum	*Vacant*	....	....	Port William, Newton Stewart, DG8 9QP [098 87] Port William 257	436	19	40	70	...	19367	1304	1394	8646
Monigaff	*see* Bargrennan												
New Luce *linked with* Old Luce	Graham T. Dickson, MA, BD	1985	....	Glenluce, Newton Stewart, DG8 0PU [058 13] Glenluce 319	123 492	8 29	... 60	24 36	... 15	5938 22521	709 2661	709 2661	8898
Newton Stewart Penninghame St. John's	*Vacant*	....	....	Newton Stewart, DG8 6HH [0671] Newton Stewart 2259	825	52	34	36	34	26283	4476	4476	9300

Charge	Minister	Ord.	Ind.	Com.	Eld.	W.G.	S.S.	B.C.	C.L. £	As'd £	Gi'n £	Stp. £	Address and Tel. No.
Old Luce	*see* New Luce												
Portpatrick		1972	......	305	15	20	22	10	13201	......	250	v	London Road, Stranraer, DG9 9AB [0776] Stranraer 2443
linked with	Thomas W. M'Gill												
Stranraer St. Ninian's				861	36	30	33	8	23283	3439	3439	3439	
Sorbie	*see* Kirkinner												
Stoneykirk	*see* Kirkmaiden												
Stranraer— High Kirk	David W. Dutton, BA	1973	1986	847	43	32	66	13	36508	12506	12507	9471	Leswalt High Rd., Stranraer, DG9 0AA [0776] Stranraer 3268
Old	Gilbert L. Thomson, BA	1965	1985	565	31	51	34	8	32560	7470	7470	9033	Linden, Leswalt High Road, Stranraer, DG9 0AA [0776] Stranraer 2524
St. Andrew's	*see* Inch												
St. Ninian's	*see* Portpatrick												
Whithorn St. Ninian's Priory	William M. MacMillan, LTH	1980	......	397	16	63	29	......	19112	2183	750	8646	Whithorn, Newton Stewart, DG8 8PY [098 85] Whithorn 267
Wigtown	*see* Kirkcowan												

Minister	Ord.	App.	Ret.	Charge	Address and Tel. No.
Andrews, John I., MA, BD	1943	......	1983	(Kirkmaiden)	Schoolhouse, Sandhead, Stranraer, DG9 9JIG [077 683] Sandhead 350
Armstrong, W. Sinclair	1951	......	1988	(Newton Stewart Penninghame St. John's)	
Burgess, Alex, BA	1950	......	1985	(Stranraer High)	3 Falcon Gardens, Edinburgh, EH10 4AP 031-447 2243
Campbell, James A.	1958	......	1987	(Stoneykirk)	
Cordiner, John	1950	......	1986	(Portpatrick)	Tara, Fell View Road, Stranraer, DG9 8BH [0776] Stranraer 4720
Crosgrove, John P., MA	1931	......	1981	(Sorbie)	11 Whithorn Road, Sorbie, Newton Stewart, DG8 8EL [098 85] Sorbie 217
Formston, A., MA	1945	......	1976	(Inch)	8 Culhorn Road, Stranraer, DG9 8DD [0776] Stranraer 4679
Harkes, George	1962	1988	......	*Community Minister*	11 Main Street, Sorbie, Newton Stewart, DG8 8EG
Jenkins, A. G.	1963	......	1982	(Inch)	Rathaine, Stoneykirk Road, Stranraer, DG9 [077682] Lochans 260
Jesson, W. J. M.	1971	......	1984	(Mochrum)	Auchness Farmhouse, Whithorn, Newton Stewart, DG8 8DT
M'Callum, William	1951	......	1984	(Lochryan and Glenapp)	A6, 25 Dalrymple Court, Stranraer DG9 7HT [0776] Stranraer 3951
Ogilvy, Oliver M.	1959	......	1985	(Leswalt)	8 Dale Crescent, Stranraer, DG9 0HG
O'Leary, Thomas, BD	1983	1987	......	Sri Lanka	St. Andrew's Church, Colombo, Sri Lanka

SYNOD IV—AYR

Meets at Ayr, on Second Tuesday of April and October
Correspondents: Dumfries and Galloway; Clydesdale
Clerk: Rev. C. L. JOHNSTON, MA, 33 Heathpark, Ayr KA8 9EN [0292] Ayr 289220

10. AYR

Meets at Ayr, in the County Buildings, on the first Tuesday of every month from September to May, excluding January, and on the fourth Tuesday of June
Clerk: Rev. C. L. JOHNSTON, MA, 33 Heathpark, Ayr KA8 9EN [0292] Ayr 289220

Charge	Minister	Ord.	Ind.	Address and Tel. No.	Com.	Eld.	W.G.	S.S.	B.C.	C.L. £	As'd £	Gi'n £	Stp. £
Alloway	J. Walter M'Ginty, BA	1964	1978	Alloway, Ayr, KA7 [0292] Alloway 41252	1545	71	108	220	65	159805	19500	19500	11064
Annbank	*Vacant*	......	......	57 Annbank Road, Annbank, Ayr, KA6 5AG [0292] Annbank 520257	458	22	36	54	16	21917	......	......	8646
Arnsheen Barrhill *linked with* Colmonell	J. Farquhar Lyall	1950	1981	Colmonell, Girvan, KA26 0SA [046 588] Colmonell 224	233	8	19	17	......	5521	......	......	8646
					237	12	22	......	11	129	......	......	
Auchinleck	Daniel M. Robertson, MA	1960	1967	28 Mauchline Road, Auchinleck, Ayrshire, KA18 2BN [0290] Cumnock 21108	751	35	64	100	21	31589	3900	3900	9801
Ayr— Auld Kirk of Ayr (St. John the Baptist)	T. Alan W. Garrity, BSC, BD	1969	1982	58 Monument Road, Ayr, KA7 2UB [0292] Ayr 262580	1211	76	141	56	27	56115	14500	18500	12192
Castlehill	Michael M. Dickie, BSC	1955	1967	3 Hillfoot Road, KA7 3LF [0292] Ayr 267332	1211	70	89	135	37	53177	13300	17183	11121
Newton-on-Ayr	G. Stewart Birse, CA, BD	1980	1989	5 Montgomerie Terrace, KA7 1JL [0292] Ayr 264251	689	66	70	68	48	49266	12800	13400	11898
St. Andrew's	William G. Neill, MA, BD	1971	1986	31 Bellevue Crescent, KA7 2DP [0292] Ayr 262621	994	54	69	59	18	70701	13300	13360	10974
St. Columba	William J. Christman, BA, BD	1963	1981	2 Hazelwood Road, KA7 2PY [0292] Ayr 283125	1892	103	120	165	70	87875	17100	17100	11082

Charge	Minister	Ord.	Ind.	Address and Tel. No.	Com.	Eld.	W.G.	S.S.	B.C.	C.L. £	As'd £	Gi'n £	Stp. £
St. James'	James Campbell	1979	1983	1 Prestwick Road, KA8 8LD [0292] Ayr 262420	698	46	67	136	30	23300	3410	.....	8929
St. Leonard's	Campbell M. Saunders, MA, BD	1952	1962	42 Marlepark, KA7 [0292] Alloway 241673	793	48	75	63	38	51324	116600	11690	*12441
St. Quivox	David T. Ness, LTH	1972	1988	11 Springfield Avenue, Prestwick, KA9 2HA [0292] Prestwick 278306	719	41	57	75	26	26117	7000	7000	v
Wallacetown	A. M. M'Phail, BA, MTH	1968	.....	87 Forehill Road, Ayr, KA7 3JR [0292] Ayr 269161	754	31	78	73	50	36054	7010	7356	10044
Ballantrae	Isobel J. Brain, MA (Mrs.)	1987	.....	Ballantrae, Girvan, KA26 0NH [046 583] Ballantrae 252	303	71	36	30	9	13691	800	800	v
Barr	George G. Helon, BA, BD	1984	.....	Dailly, Girvan, KA26 [046 581] Dailly 238	139	6	13	14	7	10181	.....	.....	8646
linked with													
Dailly					345	19	41	.....	.....	9957	.....	.....	
Catrine	W. Clem Robb, LTH	1968	1986	Catrine, Mauchline, KA5 6NA [0290] Mauchline 51560	376	15	60	73	.....	14716	.....	.....	8646
linked with													
Sorn					220	15	29	.....	.....	10401	.....	.....	
Colmonell	see Arnsheen												
Coylton	R. H. M. M'Alpine, BA	1968	.....	4 Hamilton Place, Coylton, Ayr, KA6 [029 257] Joppa (Ayr) 272	488	20	15	30	14	19152	1590	1590	8646
Craigie	see Symington												
Crosshill	James Crichton, MA, BD, MTH	1969	.....	30 Garden Street, Dalrymple, KA6 6DG [029 256] Dalrymple 263	234	12	42	51	.....	7921	811	811	8967
linked with													
Dalrymple					461	21	21	.....	.....	11483	1120	1120	
Dailly	see Barr												
Dalmellington	Keith W. Ross, MA, BD	1984	.....	Carsphairn Road, Dalmellington, Ayr, KA6 7RE [029 255] Dalmellington 255	896	35	117	59	.....	27082	3550	3550	9150
Dalrymple	see Crosshill												
Drongan The Schaw Kirk	James S. A. Smith	1956	1980	Watson Ter., Drongan, Ayr, KA6 7AB [029 258] Trabboch 275	383	15	35	43	27	8276	.....	.....	8646
Dundonald	Robert Mayes, BD	1982	1988	Dundonald, Kilmarnock, KA2 9HG [0563] Drybridge 850 243	886	50	127	141	5	37868	7200	7708	9066
Fisherton	John Stuart, BD, DIPMIN	1986	.....	Maybole, Ayrshire, KA19 [0655] Maybole 283102	239	14	23	14	.....	9814	900	900	8979
linked with													
Maybole West					352	16	77	.....	.....	15713	1350	1550	

Charge	Minister			Address									
Girvan—North (Old and St. Andrew's)	Fraser R. Aitken, MA, BD	1978	1983	38 The Avenue, Girvan, KA26 9DS [0465] Girvan 3203	1517	78	118	176	63	48473	13100	13600	10974
South	Iain Macnee	1975	1988	30 Henrietta Street, Girvan, KA26 9AL [0465] Girvan 3370	652	31	61	25	8	34275	6500	6700	v
Kirkmichael *linked with* Straiton	W. Gerald Jones, MA, BD, MTH	1984	1985	Kirkmichael, Maybole, Ayrshire, KA19 7PJ [065 55] Kirkmichael 286	360	18	30	37	....	9145	590	541	8646
					204	10	27	21	....	6229	539	539	
St. Cuthbert's Kirkoswald	James A. Guthrie	1969	1974	Kirkoswald, Maybole, KA19 [065 56] Kirkoswald 210	471	24	34	55	8	20735	1430	1430	8646
Lugar *linked with* Old Cumnock St. Ninian's	*Vacant*	......	......	St. Ninian's, Cumnock, KA18 [0290] Cumnock 20110	159	14	24	24	...	11828	....	....	8898
					114	13	24	...	...	6349	....	150	
Mauchline	Charles S. Morrice, BD, PHD	1959	1976	97 Loudoun St., Mauchline, KA5 5BQ [0290] Mauchline 50386	1039	38	95	136	49	52911	8000	8000	10293
Maybole—Old	*Vacant*	......	......	64 Culzean Road, Maybole, Ayrshire, KA19 8AH [065 52] Maybole 82162	611	28	62	60	44	25067	2144	2144	8646
West	*see Fisherton*												
Monkton and Prestwick North	Arthur F. S. Kent	1966	1981	40 Monkton Road, Prestwick, KA9 1AB [0292] Prestwick 77499	923	41	88	111	27	41851	11007	16057	10860
Muirkirk	William Hannah, BD	1987	......	Muirkirk, Cumnock, KA18 [0290] Muirkirk 61157	377	17	48	65	45	34191	....	....	v
New Cumnock	Andrew F. M'Gurk, LRCS, BD	1983	......	New Cumnock, Cumnock, KA18 [0290] New Cumnock 38296	860	41	75	136	39	43751	7300	7562	9804
Ochiltree *linked with* Stair	Kenneth B. Yorke, BD	1982	1987	Ochiltree, Cumnock, KA18 2PZ [029 07] Ochiltree 365	319	14	21	29	37	9658	1060	1060	v
					205	13	31	...	...	9653	1140	1490	
Old Cumnock—Crichton West	Effie C. Campbell (Mrs.), BD	1981	......	Cumnock, Ayrshire, KA18 [0290] Cumnock 20119	432	19	60	63	9	24114	2382	2402	8646
Old	Martin J. M'Kean, BD, DIPMIN	1985	......	Cumnock, Ayrshire, KA18 [0290] Cumnock 20769	560	27	50	51	16	22621	2900	2900	8646
St. Ninian's	*see Lugar*												

Charge	Minister	Ord.	Ind.	Address and Tel. No.	Com.	Eld.	W.G.	S.S.	B.C.	C.L. £	As'd £	Gi'n £	Stp. £
Patna Waterside	*Vacant*	......	......	Patna, Ayr, KA6 7JH [0292] *Patna 531213*	458	24	30	32	......	10993	......	......	8646
Prestwick—													
Kingcase	Alexander B. Douglas, BD	1979	1985	15 Bellrock Avenue, KA9 1SQ [0292] *Prestwick 79571*	1367	74	124	230	83	53516	9000	9000	10449
	William Milligan Auxiliary	1984	......	8 Masonhill Road, Ayr [0292] *Ayr 265875*									
St. Nicholas'	George R. Fiddes	1979	1985	3 Bellevue Road, KA9 1NW [0292] *Prestwick 77613*	930	49	178	116	38	53244	10800	10900	10953
South	Thomas B. Girdwood	1949	1981	68 St. Quivox Road, KA9 1JF [0292] *Prestwick 78788*	692	33	72	18	19	36363	6300	6503	9348
Sorn	*see Catrine*												
Stair	*see Ochiltree*												
Straiton	*see Kirkmichael*												
Symington *linked with*	Margaret A. Whyte (Mrs.), BA, BD	1988	......	16 Kerrix Road, Symington, Kilmarnock, KA1 5QD [056 383] *Symington 205*	453	16	31	17	......	14245	1279	1364	v
Craigie					121	6	......	......	......	4371	160	160	
Tarbolton	Ian U. Macdonald	1960	1967	Tarbolton, Mauchline, KA5 [029 254] *Tarbolton 236*	939	30	40	89	......	25533	3050	3181	8970
Troon—													
Old	John G. Webster, BSC	1964	1973	85 Bentinck Drive, KA10 6HZ [0292] *Troon 313644*	1888	76	114	305	67	86306	26550	26550	12873
Portland	Edward J. Thompson, BA, BD	1982	1988	South Beach, Troon, KA10 [0292] *Troon 313285*	864	73	70	92	15	59273	14100	14100	v
St. Meddan's	David L. Harper, BSC, BD	1972	1979	27 Bentinck Drive, KA10 6HX [0292] *Troon 311784*	1252	78	194	284	126	79202	13750	15327	11076

Minister	Ord.	App.	Ret.	Charge	Address and Tel. No.
Banks, John, BD	1968	1988	......	*Hospital Chaplain, Ailsa*	6 St. Vincent Crescent, Alloway, KA7 4QW [0292] *Ayr 42243*
Blyth, James G. S., BSC, BD	1963	......	1986	(Glenmuick)	The Manse, Ballantrae, Girvan, KA26 0NH [046 583] *Ballantrae 252*
Brain, Ernest J.	1955	......	1985	(Liverpool St. Andrew's)	5 Traemore Crescent, Prestwick, KA9 1LT [0292] *Prestwick 78534*
Caskie, Donald M., MA, HCF	1932	......	1981	(Monkton and Prestwick)	3 Park Terrace, Ayr, KA7 2AN [0292] *Ayr 280253*
Glover, R. Douglas H. Y.	1971	......	1986	(Luss)	

Name				Address
Hamilton, W. Humphrey, MA	1947	(Prestwick St. Nicholas')	1984	3 Ewenfield Avenue, Ayr KA7 [0292] Ayr 266717
Hollins, Roger M., BSC, BD, DIPED	1957 1966	Lecturer in Religious Education		Smithy Cottage, Dunure, Ayr, KA7 4LH [029 250] Dunure 273
Howat, William P., MA, BD	1940	(Auld Kirk of Ayr St. John the Baptist)	1981	25 Knoll Park, Alloway, KA7 4RH [0292] Alloway 41559
Johnston, Charles L., MA	1941	(Auchinleck Peden)	1980	33 Heathpark, Ayr, KA8 9EN [0292] Ayr 289220
Johnston, R. D. M., MA	1930	(Ayr, Sandgate)	1973	14 Eden Hall Road, Ayr, KA8 9DQ [0292] Ayr 66465
Lochrie, John S., BSC, BD	1967 1987	Teacher, Religious Education		14 Southbrae Drive, Glasgow, G13
M'Pherson, W. Muir	1967	(Auchencairn with Rerrick)	1985	10 Deveron Road, Troon [0292] Troon 317551
Mauchline, W. Morton, MA, BD	1935	(Largs St. John's)	1971	Kirk Care, Mill Court, Ayr, KA7
Morton, John, MA	1950	(Dalmellington Kirk of the Covenant)	1983	17 Bunting Place, Kilmarnock, KA1 3LE [0563] Kilmarnock 42732
Offor, C. Edward	1949	(Ayr St. James')	1982	10 Leslie Crescent, Ayr, KA7 3BW [0292] Ayr 267067
Osborne, Alastair G., MA, BD	1973 1981	Community Minister St. Quivox		Northfield Avenue, Ayr
Phillips, John S., MA	1939	(Ayr Lochside)		155 Craigie Way, Ayr [0292] Ayr 260302
Purvis, Donald W.	1980	(Fisherton with Maybole West)	1985	35 Blackburn Drive, Ayr [0292] Ayr 285699
Service, James P.	1953	(Blairdaff with Chapel of Garioch)	1983	123 South Beach, Troon, KA10 6EH [0292] Troon 311781
Sutherland, Alexander S.	1952	(Symington with Craigie)	1987	25 Woodlands Road, Girvan, KA26 [0465] Girvan 2104
Telfer, James H., MA	1938	(Ayr Trinity)	1979	
Wightman, J. P. E., BA	1938	(Girvan St. Andrew's)	1973	

ADDRESSES OF TOWN CHURCHES

Ayr—

Auld Kirk	Kirkport (116 High Street)
Castlehill	Castlehill Rd. x Hillfoot Rd.
Lochside	Lochside Road x Murray St.
Newton-on-Ayr	Main Street
St. Andrew's	Park Circus
St. Columba	Midton Road x Carrick Park
St. James'	Prestwick Road x Falkland Park Road
St. Leonard's	St. Leonard's Road x Monument Road
Wallacetown	John Street x Church Street

Girvan—

North	Montgomerie Street
South	Stair Park

Maybole—

Old	Centre of Castlehill Road
West	Foot of Coral Glen

Prestwick—

Kingcase	Waterloo Road
Monkton and Prestwick North	Monkton Road
St. Nicholas	Main Street
South	Main Street

Troon—

Old	Ayr Street
Portland	St. Meddan's Street
St. Meddan's	St. Meddan's Street

11. IRVINE AND KILMARNOCK

Meets at Kilmarnock, in the Hall of Howard Church, on the first Tuesday of every month from September to May (except January) and last Tuesday of June

Clerk: Rev. T. J. LOUDON BLAIR, MA, BD, Galston, Ayrshire, KA4 [0563] Galston 820246

Charge	Minister	Ord.	Ind.	Address and Tel. No.	Com.	Eld.	W.G.	S.S.	B.C.	C.L. £	As'd £	Gi'n £	Stp. £
Crosshouse	Ian G. Grant, BD	1981	.....	Crosshouse, Kilmarnock, KA2 [0563] Kilmarnock 21035	490	31	25	66	53	21909	1719	1719	8646
Darvel—													
Central	Ian M. W. Collins, MA, BD	1937	.....	145 East Main Street, Darvel, Ayrshire, KA17 0LW [0560] Darvel 20369	477	22	45	50	11	21333	2088	2088	8646
Irvinebank and Easton Mem[1]	Elizabeth J. W. M'Intyre	1988	.....	46 West Main St., Darvel, KA17 4AQ [0560] Darvel 20484	366	.....	40	28	29	15554	1066	944	v
Dreghorn—													
Dreghorn and Pearston Old	Gary E. Horsburgh, BA	1976	1983	96A Townfoot, Dreghorn, Irvine KA11 4EZ [0294] Irvine 21770	707	48	58	92	45	30538	3588	3588	9330
Perceton and Dreghorn	*Vacant*	.....	.....	Dreghorn, Irvine, KA11 [0294] Irvine 211857	296	8	30	15	.....	17289	918	918	8646
Dunlop	John R. Page, BD, DIPMIN	1988	.....	Dunlop, Kilmarnock, KA3 [056 04] Dunlop 278	596	34	63	62	.....	24277	5057	5057	v
Fenwick	G. Fraser H. Macnaughton, MA, BD	1982	1985	Fenwick, Kilmarnock, KA3 [056 06] Fenwick 217	533	33	62	55	21	27758	2287	2287	8937
Galston	T. J. Loudon Blair, MA,BD	1965	1980	Galston, Ayrshire, KA4 [0563] Galston 820246	1272	55	120	108	64	49303	9109	9109	10068
Hurlford—													
Hurlford Kirk	James M. Brodie, BEM, MA, BD, STM	1955	1974	Hurlford, Kilmarnock, KA1 [0563] Kilmarnock 25968	673	27	64	105	63	28709	4116	4116	8742
Reid Memorial	Elizabeth W. Houston, MA, BD, DIPED ¶	1985	.....	Hurlford, Kilmarnock, KA1 [0563] Kilmarnock 25965	524	27	34	31	9	18941	1779	1779	8646
Irvine—													
Fullarton	P. G. Thomson, MA, BD	1947	1953	48 Waterside, KA12 8QJ [0294] Irvine 79909	851	41	50	94	49	42855	8236	9021	9987
Girdle Toll	Christina M. Lane, BD	1983	.....	5 Bowhouse Rise, Girdle Toll, Irvine, KA11 1NP [0294] Irvine 213565	175	11	24	81	14	8248	.....	.....	9147
Mure	Hugh M. Adamson, BD	1976	.....	West Road, KA12 8RE [0294] Irvine 79916	559	30	50	108	19	32797	4491	4491	8646

Congregation	Minister			Address									
Old	James Greig	1966		Irvine, Ayrshire, KA12 0DL [0294] Irvine 79265	1076	64	110	...	13	54379	17618	7088	10707
Relief	*Vacant*	...	...	68 Dundonald Road, Dreghorn, Irvine, KA11 4AP [0294] Irvine 216939	665	39	151	84	43	23624	3673	1398	8646
St. Andrew's	*Vacant*	...	...	206 Bank Street, KA12 0YB [0294] Irvine 211403	986	26	200	65	66	26811	7290	3162	9111
Kilmarnock—													
Grange	Colin G. F. Brockie, BSc ENG, BD	1967	1978	51 Portland Road, KA1 2EQ [0563] Kilmarnock 25311	729	44	55	52	14	30250	7549	2776	10419
Henderson	David W. Lacy, BA, BD	1976	1989	52 London Road, KA3 7AJ [0563] Kilmarnock 23113	1196	52	91	72	19	49700	13513	9796	9948
Howard St. Andrew's	Gibson K. Boath, BA	1951	1968	12 Ingram Place, KA3 1RT [0563] Kilmarnock 22278	811	64	72	62	55	43484	12160	13602	11331
Laigh	Alistair N. Shaw, MA, BD	1982	1988	1 Holmes Farm Road, KA1 1TP	1021	60	47	81	53	63066	16413	16413	10863
Old High Kirk	William M. Hall, BD	1972	1979	107 Dundonald Road, KA1 1UP [0563] Kilmarnock 25608	480	22	47	50	18	22766	1708	1708	8958
Riccarton	Thomas W. Jarvie, BD	1953	1968	2 Jasmine Road, KA1 2HD [0563] Kilmarnock 25694	704	41	61	65	9	39143	8538	6900	9987
St. Andrew's Glencairn	R. A. K. Martin, MA	1957	1970	19 Holehouse Road, KA3 7AU [0563] Kilmarnock 25023	290	33	49	17	...	14391	...	...	8646
St. John's Onthank	Robert I. Johnstone, BD	1981	1987	84 Wardneuk Drive, KA3 2EX [0563] Kilmarnock 21815	430	18	60	86	19	47794	931	931	v
St. Kentigern's	Malcolm M. W. Hare, BA, BD	1956	1979	21 Raith Road, Fenwick, KA3 6DB [056 06] Fenwick 388	376	30	...	53	34	25314	4359	4444	9114
St. Marnock's	Thomas T. Scott	1968	1976	7 Pine Road, KA1 2EZ [0563] Kilmarnock 21665	841	48	82	68	17	53345	10812	10812	9777
St. Ninian's Bellfield	Gareth W. Davies, BA, BD	1979	...	Whatriggs Road, KA1 3RB [0563] Kilmarnock 25480	561	20	30	135	197	26307	4292	1592	8838
Shortlees	Jack Holt, BSc, BD	1985	1986	10 Howard Street, KA1 2BP [0563] Kilmarnock 21491	441	18	...	59	9	21367	1539	1539	8646
West High	Robert S. Christie, MA, BD, THM	1964	1973	25 Glasgow Road, KA3 1TJ [0563] Kilmarnock 25302	729	55	42	98	79	47949	7826	7580	10644
Kilmaurs St. Maur's Glencairn	Donald Patience, MA	1954	1963	9 Standalane, Kilmaurs, KA3 2NB [0563] Kilmarnock 38289	513	28	30	72	...	15745	500	650	8646
Newmilns Loudoun	Ian Hamilton, BA, BD, MPHIL	1979	...	Newmilns, Ayrshire, KA16 9HH [0560] Darvel 20174	736	21	33	63	26	31842	6180	7980	10068

Charge	Minister	Ord.	Ind.	Address and Tel. No.	Com.	Eld.	W.G.	S.S.	B.C.	C.L. £	As'd £	Gi'n £	Stp. £
Stewarton—													
John Knox	George H. Campbell	1958	1971	27 Avenue St., Stewarton, Kilmarnock, KA3 5AP [0560] Stewarton 82418	512	34	74	126	54	30276	5568	5795	8781
St. Columba's	Vacant	...	...	1 Kirk Glebe, Stewarton, Kilmarnock, KA3 5BJ [0560] Stewarton 82453	986	50	85	102	31	36813	7817	7927	10176
Ayrshire Mission for the Deaf	Colin G. F. Brockie, *Chaplain*	...	...	51 Portland Road, Kilmarnock, KA1 2EQ [0563] Kilmarnock 25311	...	...	...	...	...	...	...	...	...

Minister	Ord.	App.	Ret.	Charge	Address and Tel. No.
Crawford, Robert, MA	1933	...	1972	(Annan Erskine)	11 Glencraig Terrace, Fenwick, KA3 6DE [056 06] Fenwick 458
Easton, Andrew J.	1937	...	1971	(Dunlop)	Low Isle Cottage, Isle of Whithorn, Newton Stewart, DG8 [098 84] Whithorn 293
Girvan, Adam	1971	...	1983	(Old Kilpatrick Bowling)	Oaklea, 15 Darvel Road, Newmilns, KA16 9BH [0560] Darvel 20981
Goudie, Stuart M., MA, BD	1951	...	1988	(Perceton and Dreghorn)	6 Charles Street, Troon, KA10
Hewitt, Edward T., MA	1938	...	1988	(Newmilns Loudon Old)	47 East Donington Street, Darvel, KA17 0JN [0560] Darvel 20046
Jamieson, Robert C., MA	1943	...	1980	(Galston Old)	20 Brewland Street, Galston, KA4 8DR [0563] Galston 820304
Macara, Alec, MA	1928	...	1978	(Irvine Old)	39 Gailes Road, Barassie, Troon, KA10 6TB [0292] Troon 312712
M'Cardel, Philip M., BA, BD	1948	...	1988	(Stewarton St. Columba's)	
MacDonald, James M.	1964	...	1987	(Kilmarnock St. John's Onthank)	29 Carmel Place, Kilmarnock, Kilmarnock, KA3 2QU [0563] Kilmaurs 25254
MacKay, Donald	1951	...	1986	(Ardrossan St. John's)	20 Barra Wynd, Broomlands, Irvine [0294] Irvine 216585
Moodie, Alastair R., MA, BD	1971	1984	...	*Hospital Chaplain* Crosshouse	18 Forest Grove, Kilmarnock, KA3 1UP [0563] Kilmarnock 33772
Robertson, Ian H. M., MA, BD, FSA SCOT	1948	...	1983	(Wormit)	21 Lochcraig Court, Irvine, KA11 1JY
Roy, James, BA	1967	...	1982	(Irvine Girdle Toll)	10A Graham Terrace, Stewarton, KA3 5BB [056 03] Stewarton 2641

ADDRESSES OF KILMARNOCK CHURCHES

Ayrshire Mission for the Deaf	10 Clark Street
Grange	Woodstock Street
Henderson	London Road
Howard	5 Portland Road
Laigh	John Dickie Street
Old High	Church Street x Soulis Street
Riccarton	Old Street
St. Andrew's	St. Andrew's Street
Glencairn	
St. John's Onthank	84 Wardneuk Street
St. Marnock's	St. Marnock's Street
St. Ninian's Bellfield	Whatriggs Road
Shortlees	Central Avenue
West High	Portland Street

12. ARDROSSAN

Meets at Saltcoats in Landsborough Trinity Church, on the first Tuesday of February, March, April, May, October, November and December, and on the second Tuesday of January, June and September.

Clerk: Rev. E. GEORGE BALLS, MA, BD, STM, DD, 67 High Road, Stevenston KA20 3DZ [0294] Stevenston 63512

Charge	Minister	Ord.	Ind.	Address and Tel. No.	Com.	Eld.	W.G.	S.S.	B.C.	C.L. £	As'd £	Gi'n £	Stp. £
Ardrossan—													
Barony St. Johns	Alexander W. Young, BD, DIPMIN	1988	......	10 Seafield Drive, Ardrossan, KA22 8NU [0294] Ardrossan 63868	497	35	57	27	6	16503	......	......	v
Park	Alexander S. Downie	1978	1985	61 Argyle Road, Saltcoats KA21 5HE [0294] Saltcoats 64097	685	24	85	132	34	22499	2667	4050	*10146
Beith—													
High	David J. H. Harbison, MA, BD	1958	1979	2 Glebe Court, Beith, Ayrshire, KA15 1ET [050 55] Beith 2686	1164	70	64	93	12	106863	8926	9119	9690
Trinity	W. Duncan Capewell, BD	1980	......	Beith, Ayrshire, KA15 2DX [050 55] Beith 2131	404	35	53	53	7	24265	3229	3229	8886
Brodick	Ian MacLeod, LTH, BA	1969	1974	Brodick, Isle of Arran, KA27 8DN [0770] Brodick 2334	237	11	......	27	......	21580	......	184	8946
linked with													
Corrie					62	6	......	3	......	13072	......	131	
Cumbrae	A. M'Laren Smith	1971	......	Millport, Isle of Cumbrae, KA28 0EE [047 553] Millport 416	430	18	62	34	18	19502	2067	2122	8946
Dalry—													
St. Margaret's	A. Douglas Lamb, MA	1964	1973	Dalry, Ayrshire, KA24 4DA [029 483] Dalry 2234	1259	57	65	98	40	50825	13078	13078	10281
Trinity	David I. M. Grant, MA, BD	1969	......	Dalry, Ayrshire, KA24 5DA [029 483] Dalry 2263	437	32	50	56	37	45914	10431	10431	9498
Fairlie	Robert J. Thorburn, BD	1978	1980	Fairlie, Ayrshire, KA29 0AC [047 556] Fairlie 342	459	28	50	42	14	33586	3125	3125	8646
Fergushill					75	4	......	3	6	4289	......	......	v
linked with													
K'winning Erskine	T. Malcolm F. Duff, MA, BD	1985	1987	17 Woodburn Avenue, Kilwinning, KA13 7DB [0294] Kilwinning 52188	222	14	57	55	18	16422	......	250	

Charge	Minister	Ord.	Ind.	Address and Tel. No.	Com.	Eld.	W.G.	S.S.	B.C.	C.L. £	As'd £	Gi'n £	Stp. £
Kilbirnie— Auld Kirk	Douglas R. Irving, LL.B, BD, WS	1984	......	49 Holmhead, Kilbirnie, Ayrshire, KA25 6BS [0505] Kilbirnie 682348	698	33	84	93	16	33204	4603	4603	8982
St. Columba's	David Broster, BA, DIPTH, CPS	1969	1983	Kilbirnie, Ayrshire, KA25 7JU [0505] Kilbirnie 683342	718	46	50	71	28	30208	6056	5034	8973
Kildonan linked with Whiting Bay	Elizabeth R. L. Watson, BA, BD	1981	1982	Whiting Bay, Brodick, Isle of Arran, KA27 8RE [077 07] Whiting Bay 289	39	4	...	6	...	5878	...	20	8847
					143	14	...	12	3	14725	...	...	
Kilmory linked with Lamlash	Douglas Fulton	1958	......	Lamlash, Brodick, Isle of Arran, KA27 8JY [077 06] Lamlash 305	50	3	10	20	...	2989	...	120	9096
					270	15	47	19	4	11881	...	...	
Kilwinning— Abbey	William Buchan, DIPTHEOL, BD	1987	......	54 Dalry Road, Kilwinning, Ayrshire, KA13 7HE [0294] Kilwinning 52606	1184	58	48	131	20	32395	11384	11384	v
Erskine	see Fergushill												
Mansefield	Ronald J. Maxwell Stitt, THM, BRED, DMIN	1979	......	6 Almswall Rd., Kilwinning, KA13 6BN [0294] Kilwinning 52607	399	26	33	79	30	19088	...	100	8646
Lamlash	see Kilmory												
Largs— Clark Memorial	G. Melvyn Wood, MA, BD	1982	1983	31 Douglas Street, Largs, KA30 8PT [0475] Largs 672370	1324	72	139	175	65	67417	14136	14136	10605
St. Columba's	W. Stanley Carr, MA	1951	1966	17 Beachway, Largs, Ayrshire, KA30 8QH [0475] Largs 673107	1113	54	111	52	10	61231	15449	15449	10872
St. John's	David W. Maclagan, MA, EDB, THD, FPHS	1965	1972	Flat C, Vanduara, 1 Greenock Road, Largs, KA30 8PQ [0475] Largs 673258	1010	55	69	64	60	48149	12101	12116	*11907
Lochranza and Pirnmill linked with Shiskine	Andrew Barrie, BSC, BD	1984	......	Shiskine, Brodick, Isle of Arran, KA27 [077 086] Shiskine 380	69	6	14	17	...	7105	...	...	8847
					95	7	17	30	...	9439	...	...	
Saltcoats— Erskine	Margaret Thomson (Mrs), BD	1988	......	1 Montgomerie Crescent, KA21 5BX [0294] Saltcoats 61055	428	25	39	37	13	33163	6449	7447	8985
Landsborough and Trinity	D. G. Weir	1949	1954	8 Melbourne Road, KA21 5BZ [0294] Saltcoats 64285	479	34	41	32	...	16909	...	...	8898

	Minister	Ord.	App.		Address and Tel. No.									
North	John H. Robertson, BA	1965	1970		155 High Road, KA21 6JX [0294] Saltcoats 63751	907	37	45	70	6	24942	3948	......	8985
St. Cuthbert's South Beach	Brian H. Oxburgh, BSC, BD	1980	1988		10 Kennedy Road, KA21 SSF [0294] Saltcoats 603427	605	49	41	68	12	45722	10440	10440	v
Shiskine	see Lochranza													
Stevenston—Ardeer	Vacant	......	......		40 Shore Road, Stevenston, KA20 3LA [0294] Stevenston 63814	586	29	74	97	29	26901	3450	3580	8886
High	Vacant	......	......		Stevenston, Ayrshire, KA20 3DL [0294] Stevenston 63356	485	34	101	52	35	33309	4672	2017	8982
Livingstone	Iain M. Roy, MA, BD	1960	......		32 High Road, Stevenston, KA20 3DR [0294] Stevenston 64180	544	37	64	40	31	30390	3174	3482	8886
West Kilbride—Overton	Norman Cruickshank, BA, BD	1983	......		7 Meadowfoot Road, West Kilbride, KA23 9BX [0294] West Kilbride 823186	467	38	90	44	37	29794	4352	4352	9093
St. Andrew's	Duncan R. Mitchell, BA, BD	1972	1980		7 Overton Dr., W. Kilbride, KA23 9LQ [0294] West Kilbride 823142	1089	67	110	95	92	41102	10632	7323	10233
Whiting Bay	see Kildonan													

Minister	Ord.	App.	Ret.	Charge	Address and Tel. No.
Balls, E. George, MA, BD, STM, DD	1939		1980	(Saltcoats St. Cuthbert's South Beach)	67 High Road, Stevenston, KA20 3DZ [0294] Stevenston 63512
Dailly, J. R., BD, DIPPS	1979	1979	......	Chaplain, Army	c/o Mrs. J. Stewart, 7 Dykes Place, Saltcoats, KA21 6BD [0294] Saltcoats 61708
Drummond, Gilbert, LTH	1963	......	1988	(Renfrew Trinity)	12 Railles Road, Largs, KA30 8GZ [0475] Largs 686534
Ewing, James, MA, BD	1948	......	1987	(Ardrossan Barony)	3 Corse Terrace, West Kilbride, KA23 9ER [0294] West Kilbride 82323
Goudie, John W., MA, MTH	1936	......	1974	(West Kilbride Barony)	3 Avondale Road, West Kilbride, KA23 [0294] West Kilbride 822271
Kirkwood, Hugh, BA, BD	1942	......	1981	(Saltcoats Erskine)	2 Alton Way, West Kilbride, KA23 9JI [0294] West Kilbride 823932
M'Ilroy, Alexander M., LTH	1972	......	1987	(Darvel Irvinebank and Easton Memorial)	25 Hillcrest Drive, Stevenston, KA20 3AP [0294] Stevenston 601609
MacKinnon, John M., MA	1930	......	1973	(Dollar West)	142 Glencairn Street, Stevenston, KA20 3BU [0294] Stevenston 61455
MacLeod, Donald, MA	1938	......	1979	(Fairlie)	26 Kelburn Avenue, Fairlie, KA29 0AG [047 556] Fairlie 624
Macpherson, Fergus, MA, PHD	1946	1984		British Council of Churches	
Revel, William Thomson, MA	1939	......	1981	(Glasgow St. James' Pollok)	6 Stairlie Gardens, West Kilbride, KA23 [0294] West Kilbride 823929
Weir, William M., THD, THM	1951	......	1983	(Limekilns)	28 Bruntsfield Avenue, Kilwinning, KA13 [0294] Kilwinning 58406
Wills, Wm. Fraser, MA	1935	......	1974	(Kilsyth Burns)	26 York Road, Redcar, Cleveland, TS10 5AH [0642] Redcar 473171

SYNOD V — CLYDESDALE

Meets at Renfield St. Stephen's Church Centre, 260 Bath Street, Glasgow, on second Thursday of April and October
Correspondents: Argyll; Forth; Lothian; Borders; Dumfries and Galloway; Ayr
Clerk: Rev. WILLIAM W. M. BELL, MA, BD, 178 Titwood Road, Glasgow, G41 4DD *041–423 2158*

13. LANARK

Meets at Lanark on the first Tuesday of February, March, April, May, October, November and December and on the second Tuesday of June and September.
Clerk: Rev. JOSEPH HARDIE, MA, Monreith, 2 Springdale Drive, Biggar, ML12 6AZ   *[0899] Biggar 20536*

Charge	Minister	Ord.	Ind.	Address and Tel. No.	Com.	Eld.	W.G.	S.S.	B.C.	C.L. £	As'd £	Gi'n £	Stp. £
Biggar	A. Cameron Mackenzie, MA	1955	1977	61 High Street, Biggar, ML12 6DA [0899] Biggar 20227	971	48	80	111	8	44123	7953	7953	10125
Black Mount	Ian S. Sandilands	1986	....	Dunsyre, Carnwath, Lanark, ML11 8NQ [089 981] Dunsyre 321	174	9	24	20	25	7011	.....	18	8646
Carluke—Kirkton	Iain D. Cunningham, MA, BD	1980	1987	Station Road, Carluke, ML8 5AD [0555] Carluke 71262	858	42	52	206	125	34547	9118	9198	v
St. Andrew's	Vacant	....	....	120 Clyde Street, Carluke, ML8 [0555] Carluke 71218	626	36	45	79	10	24958	3837	3837	9096
St. John's	William F. Storrar, MA, BD	1984	1985	31 Lanark Road, Carluke, ML8 4HE [0555] Carluke 72259	1211	55	89	206	23	35512	5337	5337	10002
Carmichael *linked with*					164	8	19	28	.....	6127	412	412	
Covington and Thankerton *linked with*	Andrew E. Lambie, BD	1957	1985	Thankerton, Biggar, ML12 6PA [089 93] Tinto 333	181	8	15	32	.....	7725	392	453	8646
Pettinain					104	9	7	25	.....	4127	209	209	
Carnwath	Beverly G. D. D. Gauld, MA, BD	1972	1978	Carnwath, Lanark, ML11 8JY [0555] Carnwath 840259	798	36	54	70	47	23704	1957	1957	8646
Auchengray, Tarbrax and Woolfords													

Congregation	Minister			Address									
Carstairs	Melville D. Crosthwaite, BD, DIPED, DIPMIN	1984	......	80 Lanark Road, Carstairs, Lanark, ML11 8QH [0555] Carstairs 870250	331	15	58	37	10	11942	579	579	8748
linked with Carstairs Junction					213	9	38	35	6	8111	453	453	8646
Coalburn	Brian F. Cross, MA	1961	......	Coalburn, Lanark, ML11 [055 582] Coalburn 641	214	7	24	27	......	6415	......	......	
Covington and Thankerton	*see Carmichael*												
Crawford	David R. Baillie	1979	1981	Crawford, Biggar, ML12 [0322] Crawford 625	137	6	......	......	......	19058	......	......	8646
linked with Lowther					54	3	......	5	......	5120	......	......	
Crossford	Robert J. McMahon, BD	1959	1976	Crossford, Carluke, ML8 [055 586] Crossford 415	272	13	......	19	6	14501	1390	1390	8748
linked with Kirkfieldbank					194	6	24	20	16	8121	514	514	
Culter	Susan G. Cowell, BA, BD	1986	1987	Lindsaylands Cottage, Biggar, ML12 6NR [0899] Biggar 20471	130	9	25	12	......	8475	1006	1006	
linked with Libberton and Quothquan					90	6	19	11	......	4296	422	422	
linked with Symington					265	11	24	46	......	10197	1354	1554	v
Douglas St. Bride's	[*Vacant*]	......	......	Douglas, Lanark, ML11 0PZ [0555] Douglas (Lanark) 851213	448	29	60	53	......	15279	1706	1706	
linked with Douglas Water and Rigside	Agnes A. Reid, RGN, SCM, OND *Associate*	1985	......	Rigside, Lanark [055 588] Douglas Water 230	176	11	23	29	......	11323	......	......	8853
Duneaton	Moses Donaldson	1972	1978	Wiston, Biggar, ML12 6HT [089 95] Lamington 641	366	17	20	26	6	14697	1501	1501	8646
Forth St. Paul's	David D. Scott, BSC, BD	1981	......	Forth, Lanark, ML11 8AJ [0555] Forth 811748	666	31	120	105	68	24431	2518	2518	8853
Kirkfieldbank	*see Crossford*												
Kirkmuirhill	David A. Young	1972	1974	Kirkmuirhill, Lanark, ML11 [0555] Lesmahagow 892409	113	22	73	137	103	43909	11909	9249	9531
Lanark— Cairns	William M. Longmuir, LTH	1984	......	Friarsdene, Lanark, ML11 9EJ [0555] Lanark 3363	587	39	74	77	17	26328	2685	2685	8853
St. Kentigern's	James P. Wilson, MA	1959	1966	24 Cleghorn Road, Lanark, ML11 7QR [0555] Lanark 2331	535	29	37	32	......	22905	3647	3647	8853
St. Nicholas'	John M. A. Thomson, BD, THM	1978	1988	32 Braxfield Road, Lanark, ML11 9BS [0555] Lanark 2600	1207	50	55	108	13	51395	10223	10223	10572

Charge	Minister	Ord.	Ind.	Address and Tel. No.	Com.	Eld.	W.G.	S.S.	B.C.	C.L. £	As'd £	Gi'n £	Stp. £
Law	William A. F. Izett	1968	......	Law, Carluke, Lanarkshire, ML8 5LW [0698] Wishaw 373180	255	13	22	73	22	17492	......	317	8646
Lesmahagow—Abbeygreen	David S. Carmichael	1982	......	Lesmahagow, Lanark. ML11 [0555] Lesmahagow 893384	497	25	44	47	31	30921	2679	2679	8853
Old	William Niven, LTCL	1955	1968	Calsay Cottage, New Trows Road, Lesmahagow, ML11 [0555] Lesmahagow 892425	768	30	56	49	12	29499	3234	2600	8853
Libberton and Quothquan	see Culter												
Lowther	see Crawford												
Pettinain	see Carmichael												
Symington	see Culter												

Minister	Ord.	App.	Ret.	Charge	Address and Tel. No.
Ballantyne, James A.	1961	......	1985	(Black Mount)	Weston Cottages, Dunsyre, Lanark. ML11 [089 981] Dunsyre 261
Cumming, William M., MA	1937	......	1972	(Carmichael with Pettinain)	Abbeyfield, 1 Bonnington Avenue, Lanark, ML11 [0555] Lanark 3830
Hardie, Joseph, MA	1948	......	1988	(Douglas St. Bride's with Douglas Water and Rigside)	Monreith, 2 Springdale Drive, Biggar, ML12 6AZ [0899] Biggar 20536
Jones, Philip H.	1968	......	1987	(Bishopbriggs Kenmure)	81 Vere Road, Kirkmuirhill, Lanark, ML11 [0555] Lesmahagow 894326
Kennedy, David A., LTCL	1959	......	1983	(Lanark Cairns)	67 Hall Road, Nemphlar, Lanark, ML11 [0555] Lanark 4484
M'Cormick, W. Cadzow, MA, BD	1943	......	1983	(Glasgow Maryhill Old)	82 Main Street, Symington, Biggar, ML12 [089 93] Tinto 221
M'Donald, Peter D., LTH	1972	......	1984	(Edinburgh Ratho)	Roberton Cottage, Dolphinton, West Linton, EH46 [0968] Dolphinton 82330
MacEwan, Peter J., MA	1948	......	1986	(Culter with Libberton and Quothquan with Symington)	66 Shieldhill Road, Quothquan, Biggar, ML12 [089 93] Tinto 337
M'Lauchlan, L. S., MA	1940	......	1974	(Haywood, Wilsontown and Braehead)	57 Sandend Road, Glasgow G53 7DH 041-882 4046
Phillips, T. M., MA, BD	1939	......	1984	(Carlops with West Linton St. Andrew's)	20 Station Road, Biggar, ML12 6JN [0899] Biggar 20197
Thomson, John S., MA	1934	......	1972	(Covington and Thankerton with Libberton and Quothquan)	20 Whitehouse Loan, Edinburgh, EH9 2EZ 031-447 9455
Walker, R. W., MB, CHB	1941	......	1981	(Lesmahagow Abbeygreen)	16 Cumin Place, Edinburgh EH9 2JX 031-667 0578
Williamson, James A., CBE, MA, DD	1929	......	1970	(Kirkurd with Newlands)	The Old Rectory, Chapel Brae, West Linton, EH46 7HE [0968] West Linton 60288

14. PAISLEY

Meets at Paisley, in St. James's Church Hall, on the second Tuesday of each month, except January, July and August

Clerk: Rev. JAMES A. RULE, 6 St. Andrew's Road, Renfrew, PA4 0SN   041-886 2896

Charge	Minister	Ord.	Ind.	Address and Tel. No.	Com.	Eld.	W.G.	S.S.	B.C.	C.L. £	As'd £	G'n £	Stp. £
Barrhead—Arthurlie	Quintin A. Blane, BSC, BD	1979	1980	10 Arthurlie Ave., Barrhead, Glasgow, G78 2BU 041-881 3457	689	38	24	37	29	38136	6184	6184	9396
Bourock	*Vacant*	......	......	14 Maxton Avenue, Barrhead, Glasgow, G78 2BX 041-881 1462	733	50	73	110	96	44481	8268	10103	9396
South and Levern	R. M. Hetherington, MA, BD	1965	1977	3 Colinbar Circle, Barrhead, Glasgow, G78 2BE 041-880 6654	680	43	49	67	12	40548	7227	7227	9396
Bishopton Erskine	Douglas N. Alexander, MA, BD	1961	1971	Newton Road, Bishopton, PA7 5JP 0505-86 2161	1008	61	62	254	81	45318	11057	11057	10032
Bridge of Weir—Freeland	Kenneth N. Gray, BA, BD	1988	......	14 Barrcraig Road, PA11 [0505] Bridge of Weir 690918	608	41	54	124	41	42278	7968	8102	v
St. Machar's Ranfurly	Thomas C. Pitkeathly, MA, CA, BD	1984	......	Hazelwood Road, PA11 3DB [0505] Bridge of Weir 612085	880	42	68	118	70	55247	11325	11325	9780
Caldwell	*Vacant*	......	......	Uplawmoor, Glasgow, G78 4AF [050 585] Uplawmoor 215	316	16	29	32	......	25648	1962	2062	8844
Elderslie Kirk	William C. Hewitt, BD, DIPS	1978	......	282 Main Road, Elderslie, PA5 9EF [0505] Johnstone 21767	1085	60	93	145	64	65149	15821	16047	10195
Houston and Killellan	*Vacant*	......	......	Houston, Johnstone, PA6 7EL [0505] Bridge of Weir 612569	699	41	90	311	102	44760	6479	6479	9396
Howwood	Phyllis M. Wilson (Mrs.), DIPCOM, DIPRE ¶	1985	......	Howwood, Renfrewshire, PA9 1AS [050 57] Kilbarchan 2805	306	17	34	54	34	19774	1456	1456	8646
Inchinnan	J. Alan C. Mathers	1950	1970	Inchinnan, Renfrew, PA4 9PH 041-812 1688	691	36	20	86	54	34566	4721	5216	9150
Johnstone—High	Albert E. Smith, BD	1983	......	76 North Road, Johnstone, PA5 8NF [0505] Johnstone 20006	814	51	124	44	22	42365	10942	10942	10110
St. Andrew's Trinity	J. C. MacColl, BSC, BD	1966	1974	The Grange, Park Road, Johnstone, PA5 8LS [0505] Johnstone 20142	479	37	51	121	25	26753	3456	3456	9528
St. Paul's	Ian Purves, LTH — Jean B. K. Steele, DCS	1979	1984	61 Auchenlodment Road, Elderslie, PA5 9PA [0505] Johnstone 20060 041-889 9512 — *Deaconess—see List H*	1219	73	122	164	50	52492	6501	6501	9906

Charge	Minister	Ord.	Ind.	Address and Tel. No.	Com.	Eld.	W.G.	S.S.	B.C.	C.L. £	As'd £	Gi'n £	Stp. £
Kilbarchan— East	Stanley W. Palmer, BD	1980	......	Church Street, Kilbarchan, Renfrewshire, PA10 2JQ [050 57] Kilbarchan 2621	528	37	128	124	33	35817	5498	5498	9906
West	Andrew Kerr, MA, B LITT	1948	1955	Kilbarchan, Renfrewshire, PA10 2JR [050 57] Kilbarchan 2669	606	32	47	44	12	30472	8893	2721	10158
Linwood	T. Edward Marshall, BD	1987	......	Linwood, Paisley, PA3 3DL [0505] Johnstone 25131	729	39	60	97	44	30913	5284	5284	v
Lochwinnoch	Roderick M'Leod, MA, BD	1951	1962	East End, Lochwinnoch, PA12 4EP [050 584] Lochwinnoch 2075	94	9	......	......	......	8578	......	......	8646
Neilston	Alexander Macdonald, MA, BD	1967	1984	Neilston, Glasgow, G78 3NP 041–881 1958	927	49	78	190	37	56315	12866	13141	9906
New Erskine	W. J. M'Millan, BD, CA Morag Erskine, DCS	1969	1979	7 Leven Place, Linburn, Erskine, PA8 6BE 041–812 2439 / 041–812 6096 Deaconess—see List H	939	38	99	187	41	32221	......	......	8847
Paisley— Abbey	Alan D. Birss, MA, BD	1979	1988	15 Main Road, Castlehead, PA2 6AJ 041–889 3587	1003	68	30	50	9	105066	14199	14199	v
Castlehead	John Young, MTH, DIP MIN	1963	1976	17 Greenlaw Drive, PA1 3RX 041–889 3386	457	36	39	42	15	25201	3771	3771	8646
Glenburn	Francis D. Dixon, TH B, BD Margaret Cameron, DCS	1985	......	10 Hawick Avenue, PA2 9LD 041–884 4903 Deaconess—see List H 041–840 2479	780	35	55	107	51	35389	2145	2145	9150
Greenlaw	John P. Renton, LTH	1976	......	5 Leabank Avenue, Paisley, PA2 8BQ 041–884 3674	531	38	30	34	25	38691	1799	1800	8796
High	Christopher L. Levison, MA, BD	1972	1983	178 Glasgow Road, PA1 3LT 041–889 3316	629	56	35	28	23	39964	10818	10818	10284
Laigh	Thomas M. Cant, MA, BD	1964	1972	18 Oldhall Road, PA1 3HL 041–882 2277	1115	111	100	35	25	47812	11324	11324	10500
Lylesland	Thomas M. M'William, MA, BD	1964	1980	28 Southfield Avenue, PA2 8BY 041–884 2882	922	78	114	43	25	76227	6895	6895	10533
Martyrs'	George Prentice, BA, BTH	1964	1969	12 Low Road, Castlehead, PA2 6AG 041–889 2182	1001	67	60	71	62	40860	10550	10550	11289
Orr Square	Robert Morrison	1941	1948	57 Oakshaw Street, PA1 2DR 041–889 3922	448	35	30	22	8	25261	2738	2000	8646
St. Columba Foxbar	Anthony J. R. Fowler, BSC, BD Mary Johnston, DCS	1982	1985	13 Corsebar Drive, PA2 9QD 041–889 9988 Deaconess—see List H	611	50	73	65	39	26619	2342	2343	9150

Congregation	Minister	Ord.	App.	Address and Tel. No.									
St. James's	Thomas R. Campbell, MA, BD	1986	……	38 Woodland Avenue, PA2 8BH 041-884 3246	514	40	25	21	9	42948	7213	7213	9780
St. John's	Ian S. Currie, BD	1975	1980	9 Hawkhead Road, PA1 3ND 041-887 0884	600	76	50	46	56	48375	9715	8500	10032
St. Luke's	Henry B. Mealyea	1984	……	31 Southfield Avenue, PA2 8BX 041-884 6215	416	29	40	39	27	……	2222	2222	8685
St. Mark's Oldhall	Vacant	……	……	36 Newtyle Road, PA1 3JX 041-889 4279	1194	82	166	222	124	82644	19642	19642	11463
St. Ninian's Ferguslie [E]	Christopher D. Park, BSC, BD; Ian D. Maxwell, MA, BD Associate	1977 / 1977	1981 / 1982	10 Stanely Drive, PA2 6HE 041-884 3875; 156 Greenock Road, PA3 2LQ 041-889 0627	104	8	16	23	22	9494	……	150	9147
Sandyford (Thread Street)	David Kay, BA, BD, MTH	1973	1980	6 Southfield Avenue, PA2 8BY 041-884 3600	674	50	88	89	30	43645	8556	8556	9780
Sherwood	Duncan M'Lachlan, MA, BD, THM	1955	1965	5 Greenlaw Drive, PA1 3RX 041-889 3057	1007	83	50	56	64	92278	19067	19167	11463
Wallneuk North	Thomas Macintyre, MA, BD	1972	1988	27 Mansionhouse Road, PA1 3RG 041-887 8575	954	65	64	51	12	46091	11171	11171	10533
Renfrew—Moorpark	James A. Rule	1952	1954	6 St. Andrew's Rd., Renfrew, PA4 0SN 041-886 2896	287	11	20	34	26	14258	……	……	*10146
North	E. Lorna Hood (Mrs), MA, BD	1978	1979	1 Alexandra Drive, Renfrew, PA4 8UB 041-886 2074	921	59	56	190	54	49040	8873	8873	10158
Old	Peter M. Houston, FPHS	1952	1963	31 Gibson Road, Renfrew, PA4 0RH 041-886 2005	1258	71	80	262	18	68511	10557	10557	10158
Trinity	Andrew Thomson, BA	1976	1988	25 Paisley Road, Renfrew, PA4 8JH 041-886 2131	771	41	55	88	6	35572	9752	9752	10158

Minister	Ord.	App.	Ret.	Charge	Address and Tel. No.
Baxendale, Georgina M. (Mrs.) BD	1981	1986	……	Associate Chaplain, University of Glasgow	48 Sandholes Road, Brookfield, Johnstone, PA5 8UU [0505] Johnstone 21809
Bell, William W. M., MA, BD	1943	……	1983	(Presbytery Clerk)	178 Titwood Road, Glasgow, G41 4DD 041-423 2158
Craig, Gordon T., BD	1988	1988	……	Chaplain, RAF	158 Gayton Avenue, RAF Markham, King's Lynn, PE33 9HP
Daly, S. Scarlett, MA	1942	……	1984	(Paisley St. James's)	39 Fintry Avenue, PA2 8DA 041-884 3751
Lowe, Edwin, MA, BD	1950	……	1988	(Caldwell)	12 Douglas Road, Renfrew, PA4 8BB 041-887 1112
M'Arthur, John, MA	1951	……	1985	(Howwood)	29 Castlepark Gardens, Fairlie, KA29 [047 556] Fairlie 679
M'Kay, Johnston R., BA, BD	1968	1987	……	BBC	Firwood, Uplawmoor, Glasgow, G78 [050 585] Uplawmoor 294
Marr, E. R., MA	1933	……	1977	(Buttle)	21 Paton's Lane, Montrose, DD10 8JA [0674] Montrose 77289
Moffett, James R., BA	1942	……	1979	(Paisley St. Matthew's)	2 South Park Drive, Paisley, PA2 6JQ 041-840 1414
Ralston, Alex., MA	1939	……	1977	(Elderslie East)	43 Buchlyvie Road, Paisley, PA1 3AN 041-882 2206
Robertson, William, MA, BD	1935	……	1975	(Paisley Greenlaw)	

Minister	Ord.	App.	Ret.	Charge	Address and Tel. No.
Sim, Robert L., MA, BD	1939	......	1979	(Paisley Sandyford Thread Street)	61 Wheatlands Drive, Kilbarchan, PA10 2LQ [050 57] Kilbarchan 4251
Smith, Robert, MA	1934	......	1973	(Levern and Nitshill)	Flat 26, 7 Eastwood Crescent, Thornliebank, Glasgow, G46 8NS 041-620 0858
Southwell, W. Adamson, LTH	1968	......	1979	(Durris with Rickarton)	14 Douglas Avenue, Elderslie, Johnstone, PA5 9NE [0505] Johnstone 28774
Watt, J. H. Innes, MA, BD	1960	......	1985	(College of Education)	70 Lyoncross Avenue, Barrhead, Glasgow, G78 2TG 041-881 5199

ADDRESSES OF PAISLEY CHURCHES

Abbey	Town Centre	Lylesland	Rowan Street, off Neilston Rd.	St. Mark's Oldhall	Glasgow Road, Ralston
Castlehead	Canal Street	Martyrs'	Broomlands	St. Matthew's	Gordon Street
Glenburn	Nethercraigs Drive off Glenburn Road	Orr Square	Off High Street	St. Ninian's Ferguslie	Blackstoun Road
Greenlaw	Greenlaw Drive off Glasgow Road	St. Columba Foxbar	Foxbar	Sandyford (Thread Street)	Gallowhill
High	Churchill, off High Street	St. James'	Underwood Road	Sherwood	Glasgow Road
Laigh	Causeyside	St. John's	School Wynd	Wallneuk North	Off Renfrew Road
		St. Luke's	Neilston Road		

15. GREENOCK

Meets at Greenock, in one of the Churches there, on the second Tuesday of September, December, February and May, on the fourth Tuesday of October and March, and on the third Tuesday of June

Clerk: Rev. DAVID MILL, MA, BD, 105 Newark Street, Greenock, PA16 7TW [0475] Greenock 39602

Charge	Minister	Ord.	Ind.	Address and Tel. No.	Com.	Eld.	W.G.	SS.	B.C.	C.L. £	As'd £	Gi'n £	Stp. £
Gourock—Ashton	Andrew P. Lees, BD	1984	1987	32 Barrhill Road, PA19 1LA [0475] Gourock 32176	631	45	85	34	12	39345	9150	9150	v
Old	Frank J. Gardner, MA	1966	1979	90 Albert Road, PA19 1NN [0475] Gourock 31516	1184	72	96	79	120	53651	11295	11295	9999
St. John's	Neil A. M'Naught, BD, MA	1987	......	6 Barrhill Road, PA19 1JX [0475] Gourock 32143	702	57	60	71	65	40024	9867	9867	v
Greenock—Cartsdyke	Peter Webster, BD	1977	1981	84 Forsyth Street, PA16 8OY [0475] Greenock 21439	642	40	38	39	22	33017	6777	6319	9672
Finnart St. Paul's	David Mill, MA, BD	1978	1979	105 Newark Street, PA16 7TW [0475] Greenock 39602	521	38	40	32	12	41041	9318	9318	9999
Mid Kirk	Ronald G. Lawson, MA, BD	1964	1988	101 Brisbane Street, PA16 8PA [0475] Greenock 21741	903	50	50	101	66	37923	5833	5833	v

Congregation	Minister	Year 1	Year 2	Address									
Mount Kirk	James H. Simpson, BD, LLB	1964	1965	76 Finnart Street, PA16 8HJ [0475] Greenock 22338	702	48	70	42	41	29995	5942	5942	9999
Old West Kirk	[Vacant / James T. Fields, MA, BD, STM Associate / Jean Miller	……	1988	39 Fox Street, PA16 8PD [0475] Greenock 23807 / Agent—see List H	595	43	100	49	15	45211	7486	7486	9999
St. Andrew's	Ian W. Black, MA, BD	1976	1977	74 Forsyth Street, PA16 8SX [0475] Greenock 21018	572	59	54	81	38	46685	10429	10429	9999
St. George's North	W. Douglas Hamilton, BD	1975	1986	67 Forsyth Street, PA16 8SX [0475] Greenock 24003	759	46	50	53	38	31336	10016	10016	9999
St. Luke's	G. Russell Barr, BA, BD	1979	1988	50 Ardgowan Street, PA16 8EP [0475] Greenock 21048	963	73	118	36	9	10319	10397	8054	v
St. Margaret's	[Colin M. Anderson, BA, BD, STM / James M. Blue, DCS	1968	1984	258 Inverkip Road, PA16 0XR [0475] Greenock 36212 / Deacon—see List H	502	32	43	92	23	29307	2346	2346	8892
St. Ninian's	[Allan G. M'Intyre, BD / Duncan M'Quien, DCS	1985	……	5 Auchmead Road, Greenock, PA16 0PY [0475] Gourock 31878 / Deacon—see List H	563	25	52	59	11	56346	1566	1566	8646
The Union Church	Andrew S. Taylor, THB	1959	……	72 Forsyth Street, PA16 8SX [0475] Greenock 21092	623	46	50	37	8	28527	5119	5119	9672
Wellpark West	William Shackleton, MA	1960	1983	45 Denholm Street, PA16 8RH [0475] Greenock 21974	586	38	70	18	5	28839	4313	4313	9672
Inverkip	Michael J. Erskine, MA, BD	1985	1987	Inverkip, Greenock, PA16 0AT [0475] Inverkip 521207	432	23	75	85	10	17783	2761	2855	v
Kilmacolm—Old	Bernard P. Lodge, BD	1967	1980	Kilmacolm, Renfrewshire, PA13 4NJ [050 587] Kilmacolm 3174	919	57	96	62	22	64726	17549	18155	10872
St. Columba	Douglas A. O. Nicol, MA, BD / Joyce Nicol (Mrs.), DCS	1974	1982	Churchill Road, Kilmacolm, PA13 4LH [050 587] Kilmacolm 3271 / Deaconess—see List H	828	60	100	99	70	65324	15697	16047	10872
Langbank	Eustace Annesley, BA, BSC	1951	1986	Langbank, Port Glasgow, PA14 6XB [047 554] Langbank 252	191	13	……	47	9	16575	1262	1262	8646
Port Glasgow—Hamilton Bardrainney	Thomas Preston, BD	1978	……	Bardrainney Avenue, PA14 6HD [0475] Port Glasgow 706551	1102	11	29	83	71	24341	4853	500	9522
St. Andrew's	Ernest M. Scott	1957	1973	Barr's Brae, Port Glasgow, PA14 5QA [0475] Port Glasgow 41486	1296	69	73	89	112	41348	10198	10698	10470

Charge	Minister	Ord.	Ind.	Address and Tel. No.	Com.	Eld.	W.G.	S.S.	B.C.	C.L. £	As'd £	Gi'n £	Stp. £
St. Martin's	Iain Mackenzie, MA, BD	1967	1973	Clunebraehead, PA14 5SW [0475] Port Glasgow 704115	365	11	10	31	9	17689	1405	1405	8646
Quarrier's Village Mount Zion Church	R. A. Montgomery	1955	1986	Quarrier's Village, Bridge of Weir, PA11 [0505] Bridge of Weir 690498	58	5	10	7	......	17216	130	563	10872
Skelmorlie and Wemyss Bay	W. R. Armstrong, BD	1979	......	3 Montgomerie Terrace, Skelmorlie, PA17 5AR [0475] Wemyss Bay 520703	519	28	34	63	30	44487	9685	9685	9999

Minister	Ord.	App.	Ret.	Charge	Address and Tel. No.
Bruce, A. William, MA	1942	......	1981	(Fortingall and Glenlyon)	75 Union Street, Greenock, PA16 8BG [0475] Greenock 87534
Chestnut, Alexander, BA	1948	......	1987	(St. Mark's Greenbank)	131 Finnart Street, Greenock, PA16 8HT [0475] Greenock 21116
Fraser, Ian C., BA, BD	1982	1982	......	Community Minister at Greenock Cartsdyke	42 Grosvenor Road, Greenock, PA15 2DR [0475] Greenock 87702
Goss, Alister J., BD	1975	1987	......	Industrial Chaplain	14 Divert Road, Gourock, PA19 1DS [0475] Gourock 35860
Graham, Sydney S.	1987	......	......	Auxiliary Minister	The Manse, Paget West, PO Box 88, Paget 6, Bermuda
Marshall, F. J., BA	1946	1982	......	Bermuda	Duncan Place, Main Street, Inverkip, PA16 0AT [0475] Inverkip 521707
Mitchell, David D., MA	1942	......	1981	(Strone and Ardentinny)	Strathmore, Golf Road, Millport, KA28 [0475] Millport 530460
Porteous, Alexander, MA, BD	1965	......	1987	(Greenock Mid Kirk)	39 Brisbane Street, Greenock, PA15 8NR [0475] Greenock 85959
Pyper, G. Stewart, BA	1951	......	1986	(Greenock St. George's North)	2 Margaret Street, Greenock PA16 8AS [0475] Greenock 21436
Robb, Sydney H.	1943	......	1981	(Greenock Crawfurdsburn)	10 Craighill Terrace, Edinburgh, EH6 4RF 031-552 1935
Runciman, James T., MA	1937	......	1973	(Greenock Wellpark West)	34E St. John's Road, Greenock, PA19 1PQ [0475] Gourock 31834
Stevenson, Alex	1951	......	1976	(Greenock St. Andrew's)	142 Braid Road, Edinburgh, EH10 6JB 031-447 2244
Stewart, Donald H., MA	1927	......	1967	(Greenock Finnart)	Santis, Finlaystone Road, Kilmacolm, PA13 4RE [050 587] Kilmacolm 2644
Stone, W. Vernon, MA, BD	1949	......	1985	(Langbank)	11 The Terrace, Ardbeg, Rothesay, Isle of Bute, PA20 0NP [0700] Rothesay 2138
Swan, Andrew, MA	1941	......	1983	(Greenock St. Margaret's)	
Whyte, John H., MA	1946	......	1986	(Gourock Ashton)	20 Cowal View, Gourock, PA19 1EX [0475] Gourock 36788

ADDRESSES OF TOWN CHURCHES

Gourock—
Ashton — 56 Albert Road
Old — 41 Royal Street
St. John's — Bath Street x St. John's Road

Greenock—
Cartsdyke — 14 Crescent Street
Finnart St. Paul's — Newark St. x Bentinck St.
Mid Kirk — Cathcart Square

Mount Kirk — Dempster Street at Murdieston Park
Old West Kirk — Esplanade x Campbell Street
St. Andrew's — 31 Union Street
St. George's — George Square
St. Margaret's — Finch Road x Kestrel Crescent [0475] Greenock 81953
St. Ninian's — Warwick Road, Larkfield

St. Luke's — 9 Nelson Street
The Union Church — 3 Union Street
Wellpark West — Regent Street op. Wellpark

Port Glasgow—
Hamilton-Bardrainney — Bardrainney Avenue x Auchenbothie Road
St. Andrew's — Princes Street
St. Martin's — Monteith Avenue

16. GLASGOW

Meets at New Govan Church, Govan Cross, Glasgow, on the second Tuesday of each month, except July when there is no meeting

Clerk: Rev. ALEXANDER CUNNINGHAM, MA, BD
Hon. Treasurer: G. D. R. MUNRO, Esq, CA } 260 Bath Street, Glasgow G2 4JP 041-332 6606-7

Charge	Minister	Ord.	Ind.	Address and Tel. No.	Com.	Eld.	W.G.	S.S.	B.C.	C.L. £	As'd £	Gi'n £	Stp. £
Banton	*Vacant*	...	...	Banton, Kilsyth, Glasgow, G65 0QL [0236] *Kilsyth 822943*	86	8	...	28	...	6318	...	...	8646
linked with Twechar					105	7	9	12	...	5983	...	...	v
Bishopbriggs— Kenmure	Stuart D. Crawford	1987	...	Coltpark Ave., Bishopbriggs, Glasgow, G64 2AT 041-772 1468	379	14	50	54	37	23130	2700	2700	v
Springfield Cambridge	William Ewart, BSC, BD	1972	1978	39 Springfield Road, Bishopbriggs, Glasgow, G64 1PL 041-772 1540	1365	46	88	246	98	56470	13500	13717	9918
Broom	James Whyte, BD	1981	1987	3 Laigh Road, Newton Mearns, G77 5EX 041-639 2916	1324	68	103	174	68	76052	23000	17250	v
Busby— East	A. Iain Campbell, MA, DIPED	1961	1986	17a Carmunnock Road, Busby, G76 8SZ 041-644 3670	288	19	49	39	...	19373	3400	3400	9941
linked with West					321	21	56	42	13	20143	3300	3300	
Cadder	W. Jack Beaumont, MA, BD	1960	1974	6 Balmuildy Road, Bishopbriggs, Glasgow, G64 3BS 041-772 1363	1394	89	64	130	75	77959	17500	17839	11145
Campsie	John M. Robertson, BSC, BD	1975	1980	Lennoxtown, Glasgow, G65 [0360] *Lennoxtown 312372*	531	29	27	82	34	22513	1200	1200	8799
Chryston	Martin A. W. Allen, MA, BD, THM	1977	...	Main Street, Chryston, Glasgow, G69 041-779 1436	1261	45	62	220	135	69741	11200	11210	10188
Eaglesham Old and Carswell	W. Douglas Lindsay, BD, CPS	1978	1988	East Kilbride Road, Eaglesham, Glasgow, G76 0NS [035 53] *Eaglesham 3495*	1129	55	113	154	174	60703	14000	14000	10188
Gartcosh	Alexander M. Fraser, BD, DIPMIN	1985	...	66 Coatbridge Road, Glenboig, ML5 2PU [0236] *Glenboig 872274*	277	12	43	39	6	16879	400	400	8646
linked with Glenboig					261	17	21	34	8	17815	400	400	

Charge	Minister	Ord.	Ind.	Address and Tel. No.	Com.	Eld.	W.G.	S.S.	B.C.	C.L. £	As'd £	Gi'n £	Stp. £
Giffnock— Orchardhill	John M. Spiers, LTH	1972	1977	23 Huntly Avenue, Giffnock, G46 6LW 041–638 4204	753	60	96	159	35	89417	18500	18500	11145
South	Edward V. Simpson BSC, BD	1972	1983	5 Langtree Avenue, Whitecraigs, G46 7LN 041–638 8767	995	64	95	130	33	70464	21500	21500	11145
The Park	Michael Gibson, BD, STM	1974	......	41 Rouken Glen Road, Thornliebank, Glasgow, G46 7JD 041–638 3023	526	34	40	78	34	28786	4400	4400	8799
Glenboig	see Gartcosh												
Greenbank	Angus T. Stewart, MA, BD, PHD, JP	1962	1971	Clarkston, Glasgow, G76 041–644 1395	1835	101	139	328	149	139580	29000	29000	12294
Kilsyth— Anderson	James Ross, MA, BD	1968	......	Kilsyth, Glasgow, G65 [0236] Kilsyth 822345	623	20	40	90	11	23036	2300	2300	8646
Burns and Old	T. A. M'Lachlan, BSC	1972	1983	The Grange, Glasgow Road, G65 9AE [0236] Kilsyth 823116	863	52	92	75	58	38955	11000	11000	9441
Kirkintilloch— Hillhead	George A. R. Forbes, BD	1971	1977	81 Hillhead Road, Kirkintilloch, G66 2HY 041–776 1198	377	29	51	25	23	18120	......	110	8646
Park *linked with* Torrance	David Stewart, MA, DIPED, BD	1977	......	Marguerite Ave., Lenzie, Glasgow, G66 041–775 2176	300	22	33	15	25	18156	2500	2500	9216
					235	12	34	53	38	19001	780	780	
St. Columba's	William Gray, LTH	1971	1976	18 Bellevue Road, Kirkintilloch, G66 1AP 041–775 1517	1036	49	55	188	36	56659	14500	14500	10665
St. David's Memorial	*Vacant*	......	......	2 Roman Rd., Kirkintilloch, G66 1EA 041–776 1434	702	41	92	116	37	59631	14000	14000	10392
St. Mary's	Frank Haughton, MA, BD	1942	1947	Union Road, Kirkintilloch, G66 1DH 041–776 1252	953	60	55	95	45	62420	14500	14500	19665
Lenzie— Old	Donald Pirie, LTH	1975	1984	41 Kirkintilloch Road, Lenzie, Glasgow, G66 4LB 041–776 2184	620	38	......	232	61	34424	5200	5200	9240
Union	James B. Ferguson, LTH	1972	1984	Larch Avenue, Lenzie, Glasgow, G66 4LB 041–776 3831	995	76	128	214	98	75592	21000	21150	11346
Maxwell Mearns Castle	Alexander M. Roger, BD	1982	......	Waterfoot Road, Newton Mearns, G77 041–639 5169	257	24	......	71	43	75999	2200	2200	9240

Congregation	Minister	Ind.	Address / Tel.									
Mearns	Roderick D. M. Campbell, BD, FSA SCOT	1975	Newton Mearns, G77 5BU — 041-639 1410	990	57	113	80	58	64302	16000	16000	10665
	J. Owain ab Ifor Jones, *Associate*	1979	97 Maybole Crescent, G77 — 041-639 8757									
Milton of Campsie	Diane E. Stewart	1988	33 Birdstone Road, Milton of Campsie, G65 8BX — [0360] Lennoxtown 310548	473	44	91	197	8	31563	1100	1100	8646
Netherlee	A. David K. Arnott, MA, BD	1971 / 1977	532 Clarkston Rd., Glasgow, G44 3RT — 041-637 2884	1273	107	112	194	52	101396	29500	31275	12294
Newton Mearns	Graham R. G. Cartlidge, MA, BD, STM	1977	24 Cedarwood Avenue, Newton Mearns, G77 5QD — 041-639 1149	1147	80	89	241	110	83180	15500	15589	11892
Stamperland	Alastair J. Cherry, BD	1982 / 1987	109 Ormonde Avenue, Glasgow, G44 3SN — 041-637 4976	593	31	82	151	48	31628	5400	2000	v
Stepps	Fred C. Muir, MA, BD, THM, ARCM	1961 / 1972	20 Alexandra Avenue, Stepps, Glasgow, G33 6BP — 041-779 2504	622	41	25	117	46	49790	5900	5900	11646
Thornliebank	James H. Robertson, BSC, BD	1975 / 1985	73 Rouken Glen Road, Thornliebank, Glasgow, G46 7JD — 041-638 3073	477	25	84	82	18	28976	4300	2150	8979
Torrance	see Kirkintilloch Park											
Twechar	see Banton											
Williamwood	Colin Campbell, MA, BD	1940 / 1949	4 Golf Road, Clarkston, Glasgow, G76 7LZ — 041-638 1215	679	75	55	131	90	60901	12500	12500	11222
GLASGOW—												
Anderston Kelvingrove	H. Stanley C. Hood, MA, BD	1966 / 1980	16 Royal Terrace, G3 7NY — 041-332 3136	312	46	35	35	19	42203	3200	3200	8979
Baillieston—												
Mure Memorial	Stuart D. Rogerson, BSC, BD	1980 / 1986	28 Beech Ave., Baillieston, Glasgow, G69 6LF — 041-771 1217	922	46	143	106	109	79839	14000	14000	9918
St. Andrew's	Thomas C. Houston, BA	1975 / 1980	6 Muirhead Road, Baillieston, Glasgow, G69 7EY — 041-771 1791	743	38	16	90	33	42370	8300	8300	9441
Balornock North	Elizabeth W. Sutherland, BD	1972	54 Etive Crescent, Bishopbriggs, G64 1ES — 041-772 1453	230	16	36	42	31	16645	....	500	8898
linked with Barmulloch	R. M'Kenzie Smith, L.TH	1984	Auxiliary—see List on page 152	227	14	41	21	138	10316	....	....	
Balshagray	*Vacant*		20 St. Kilda Drive, G14 9JN — 041-954 9780	663	55	....	30	25	56112	9200	9200	9441
Barlanark Greyfriars	Thomas L. Pollock, BA, FSA SCOT, JP	1982	17 Kirkinner Road, Mount Vernon, Glasgow, G32 9PE — 041-778 6089	310	25	57	80	22	22072	1100	....	8646
Barmulloch	see Balornock											
Battlefield East	Alan C. Raeburn, MA, BD	1971 / 1977	110 Mount Annan Drive, G44 4RZ — 041-632 1514	934	35	40	19	39	38083	7700	5200	9711

Charge	Minister	Ord.	Ind.	Address and Tel. No.	Com.	Eld.	W.G.	S.S.	B.C.	C.L. £	As'd £	Gi'n £	Stp. £
Belhaven Westbourne	*Vacant*	...	...	140 Hyndland Road, G12 9BN 041–339 5896	171	18	...	...	...	20443	2700	3200	v
Blairbeth Rodger Memorial	Kenneth L. Johnston, BA, LTH	1969	...	4 Milrig Road, Rutherglen, Glasgow, G73 2NH 041–647 6762	240	20	...	45	8	17404	...	...	8646
Blawarthill	Neil Galbraith, BD, CERT MIN	1987	...	46 Earlbank Avenue, G14 9HL 041–954 0328	369	27	73	90	34	17434	1300	1300	v
Bridgeton St. Francis in the East	Howard R. Hudson, MA, BD	1982	1984	10 Albany Drive, Rutherglen, Glasgow, G73 3QN 041–647 9973	258	23	18	34	38	15857	400	400	8898
	Alex Mair, DCS	...	...	*Deacon—see* List H 041–774 8788									
	Margaret S. Beaton	...	...	*Agent—see* List H									
Broomhill	William B. Ferguson, BA, BD	1971	1987	27 St. Kilda Drive, G14 9LN 041–959 3204	946	68	148	90	24	67042	21000	21000	v
Burnside	David J. C. Easton, MA, BD	1965	1977	59 Blairbeth Road, Burnside, Glasgow, G73 4JD 041–634 1233	966	57	142	183	53	89166	23000	23138	11820
	Moira Gentles	...	...	*Deaconess—see* List H 041–634 3849									
Calton New *linked with* St. Andrew's	Adrian J. T. Rennie, BA, BD	1987	1988	1 Chalmers Gate, G40 1JX 041–556 4299	183	24	28	11	2	14103	1200	1971	8946
					113	10	10	...	...	5930	500	500	
Calton Parkhead	S. G. Victor Crawford	1980	1987	98 Drumover Drive, G31 5RP 041–556 2520	328	22	25	73	48	14684	...	480	v
	Ella Hutchison (Mrs.)	1988	...	*Auxiliary—see* page 151									
Cambuslang— Flemington Hallside	Robert D. Currie, BSC, BD	1984	...	103 Overton Road, Cambuslang, Glasgow, G72 7XA 041–641 2097	422	21	42	78	17	26033	1900	1900	8646
Old	Alan H. Ward, MA, BD	1978	1985	74 Stewarton Drive, Cambuslang, Glasgow, G72 8DG 041–641 3261	789	61	90	148	36	48382	10400	10400	10281
St. Andrew's	Robert P. Bell, BSC	1968	1974	37 Brownside Road, Cambuslang, Glasgow, G72 8NH 041–641 3847	702	49	88	77	45	38659	7600	7600	9240
Trinity St. Paul's	John P. Cubie, MA, BD	1961	1968	4 Glasgow Road, Cambuslang, Glasgow, G72 7BW 041–641 3414	751	46	...	73	23	44908	9800	9800	v
Camphill Queen's Park	*Continued Vacancy*	...	...	—	277	27	60	8	3	19698	1400	120	v
Candlish Polmadie	A. G. Allan	1959	1968	13 Myrtle Park, G42 8UQ 041–423 8569	107	15	24	9	...	8463	...	...	8646
Cardonald	Eric M'Lachlan, BD	1978	1983	133 Newtyle Road, Paisley, PA1 3LB 041–889 9531	907	57	62	105	19	62900	10400	10400	10392

Congregation	Minister			Address								
Carmunnock	Henry Hutchison, MA, BD, PHD, BED, MLITT	1948	1977	161 Waterside Road, Carmunnock, G76 9AJ — 041-644 1578	424	24	62	46	21	39203	2400	2400	8646
Carmyle	J. M. Davies, BSC, BD	1982	.....	3 Meryon Road, Glasgow, G32 9NW — 041-778 2625	218	12	.....	32	5	13512	1000	1000	8646
linked with Kenmuir Mount Vernon					259	15	56	38	34	17148	2600	2600	
Carntyne Old	Ronald A. S. Craig, BACC, BD	1983	.....	211 Sandyhills Road, G32 9NB — 041-778 1286	261	17	40	44	7	20395	2800	2830	9651
linked with Eastbank					301	23	64	36	23	33010	3100	3100	
Carnwadric [E]	Graeme K. Bell, BA, BD	1983	.....	62 Loganswell Road, G46 8AX — 041-638 5884	217	23	53	59	6	12559	.....	100	9147
	Christine M. M'Vean, DCS	.....	.....	Deaconess—*see* List H — 041-638 9035									
Castlemilk—East	John D. Miller, BA, BD	1970	.....	103 Castlemilk Drive, G45 9TG — 041-631 1244	262	15	18	51	31	12017	.....	.....	8646
	George Pirie, DCS	.....	.....	Deacon—*see* List H — 041-649 3280									
	Ann Lyall, DCS	.....	.....	Deaconess—*see* List H — 041-631 3643									
West	Robert C. Wotherspoon, LTH	1976	1980	156 Old Castle Road, G44 5TW — 041-637 5451	395	33	60	97	13	22638	1800	600	8646
Cathcart—Old	Alexander T. Stewart, BD	1975	1980	115 Carmunnock Road, G44 5UW — 041-637 0105	836	55	51	52	43	56983	11500	11500	10053
South	George Fairlie, BD, BVMS, MRCVS	1971	1982	82 Merrylee Road, G43 2QZ — 041-637 1104	648	48	93	49	10	66505	17500	18986	11346
Cathedral (High or St. Mungo's)	William Morris, DD, PHD, LLD, JP	1951	1967	94 St. Andrew's Drive, G41 4RX — 041-427 2757	699	53	50	17	2	52093	8700	8700	10857
Colston Milton	David J. Taylor, MA	1982	1986	118 Birsay Road, G22 7QP — 041-772 1958	503	31	42	51	14	29250	4400	4400	8799
Colston Wellpark	David Mitchell, BD, DIPPTHEO	1988	.....	7 Lundie Gardens, Bishopbriggs, Glasgow, G64 — 041-772 6144	294	16	.....	28	25	17227	.....	.....	>
Cranhill	Iain M. Greenshields, BD, DIPRS	1985	.....	31 Lethamhill Crescent, G33 — 041-770 6873	150	15	16	32	22	10844	.....	.....	8646
Crofttoot	John M. Lloyd, BD, CMIN	1984	1986	20 Victoria Road, Burnside, Rutherglen, G73 3QG — 041-647 5524	727	53	129	89	73	64235	17500	18500	11346
Crosshill Queen's Park	William Marsh, BD	1972	1974	32 Queen's Drive, G42 8DD — 041-423 2533	353	30	13	8	4	33843	5800	4700	9441

Charge	Minister	Ord.	Ind.	Address and Tel. No.	Com.	Eld.	W.G.	S.S.	B.C.	C.L. £	As'd £	Gi'n £	Stp. £
Dennistoun— Blackfriars	Alexander Welsh, MA, BD	1979	1986	41 Broompark Drive, G31 2JB 041–554 8667	459	29	55	58	...	31050	3500	3790	9240
Central	John C. Beck, BD	1975	1980	45 Broompark Drive, G31 2JB 041–554 1062	485	32	62	42	18	46875	4900	4900	9441
Drumchapel— Drumry St. Mary's	Robert E. Gilbert, BA	1960	1967	8 Fruin Road, G15 6SQ 041–944 4493	214	18	43	33	33	8777	...	50	8646
Old	John S. Purves, LLB, BD	1983	1984	6 Firdon Crescent, G15 6QQ 041–944 4566	923	60	83	78	39	54585	11200	11400	10527
St. Andrew's	E. M. H. Lewis, MA	1962	1975	4 Firdon Crescent, G15 6QQ 041–944 4554	157	13	19	48	4	7844	...	32	8847
St. Mark's	Robert A. Calvert, BSC, BD	1983	...	146 Garscadden Road, G15 6PR 041–944 5440	253	14	18	52	32	11560	...	...	8646
Eastbank	see Carntyne Old												
Easterhouse St. George's and St. Peter's [E]	Malcolm Cuthbertson, BA, BD George H. Brownlie, DCS Jennifer Guthrie, DCS	1984	... ...	2 Lochdochart Road, G34 041–773 2667 Deacon—see List H 041–882 3973 Deaconess—see List H	152	14	6	40	15	10200	...	...	9147
Eastwood	Archibald Robertson, MA, BD	1957	1977	54 Mansewood Road, G43 1TL 041–632 0724	950	55	149	50	23	95142	10500	10500	10392
Elder Park Macgregor M'l	Vacant	...	...	2 Drumoyne Avenue, G51 4AP 041–445 3529	161	13	22	31	22	8904	...	250	v
Fernhill and Cathkin	Ian R. Fisher, MA Catherine B. Anderson (Mrs.), DCS	1964 ...	1972 ...	82 Blairbeth Road, Rutherglen Glasgow G73 4JA 041–634 1508 Deaconess—see List H 041–631 3686	539	39	98	139	43	28773	4000	4000	8522
Gairbraid	Ian C. MacKenzie, MA, BD	1970	1971	1515 Maryhill Road, G20 7XL 041–946 1568	432	21	43	20	10	25779	1300	1150	8646
Gardner Street	David MacInnes, MA, BD	1968	1977	148 Beechwood Drive, G11 7DX 041–339 2816	101	14	...	13	5	29139	3400	3525	8799
Garthamlock and Craigend East [E]	Ada Younger (Mrs.), BD Catherine Bell (Mrs.), DCS	1978 ...	1988 ...	2 Findochty Street, G33 5EF 041–774 5666 Deaconess—see List H 44 Riverside Road, G43 2EF 041–649 5250	201	18	...	36	...	17194	...	100	*10647
Gorbals	David N. M'Lachlan, BD Christine Ramsden, DCS	1985 ...	... ...	041–429 5484 Deaconess—see List H	166	17	50	28	7	17313	...	...	8646

Congregation	Minister			Address / Phone										
Govan Old	Vacant	......		52 Ibrox Terrace, G51 2TE / 041-427 0321	474	39	32	40	12	31304	2200	2200	2260	8799
Govanhill	Vacant	......		143 Albert Road, G42 8UE / 041-423 0765	287	29	40	51	12	25222	2700	2700	1587	8646
High Carntyne	John D. Hegarty	1988		165 Smithycroft Road, G33 2RD / 041-770 6464	878	46	105	56	14	49487	7500	7500	8446	10326
Hillington Park	Morris C Coull, BD	1974	1983	61 Ralston Avenue, G52 3NB / 041-882 7000	730	37	146	98	43	55987	8800	8800	8874	9240
Householdhill St. Christopher's	Alan K. Sorenson, BD, DIP M	1983		29 Torridon Avenue, G41 5AT / 041-427 2596	268	16	......	31	14	18383	......	......	......	8646
Hutchesontown	Denis I. Sutherland	1963	1973	15 Fleurs Avenue, G41 5AR / 041-427 5044	139	17	......	21	......	13145	......	......	......	8646
Hyndland	John A. Macnaughton, MA, BD	1949	1968	70 Crown Road North, G12 9HW / 041-334 1002	567	38	65	56	10	77161	13200	13200	13200	10188
Ibrox	C. Blair Gillon, BD	1975	1980	3 Dargarvel Avenue, G41 5LD / 041-427 1282	647	34	......	87	50	40390	11100	11100	11100	10419
John Ross Memorial (for the Deaf)	Hugh B. Haney / Elsie M. Miller, DCS	1966 /	1982 /	132 Sandy Road, Renfrew, PA4 0BX / 041-886 3115 / Deaconess—see List H [0236] Coatbridge 26337	112	14	......	......	......	9620	140	140	140	......
Jordanhill	Finlay A. J. Macdonald, MA, BD, PH D	1971	1977	96 Southbrae Drive, G13 1TZ / 041-959 1310	953	80	46	133	48	76523	19500	19500	19500	11346
Kelvin Stevenson Memorial	William M'Areavey, BA	1950	1956	94 Hyndland Road, G12 9PZ / 041-334 5352	356	38	53	26	18	28893	4000	4000	4000	9354
Kelvinside Hillhead	Valerie G. C. Watson ¶	1987		13 Queensborough Gardens, G12 9PP / 041-339 2865	332	30	......	28	10	62107	5000	5000	5000	v
Kenmuir Mount Vernon	see Carmyle													
King's Park	G. Stewart Smith, MA, BD, STM	1966	1979	1101 Aikenhead Road, G44 5SL / 041-637 2803	1410	87	225	235	182	93334	21500	21500	21500	11616
Kinning Park	Robin D. M'Haffie, BD	1979	1981	5 Torridon Avenue, G41 5LA / 041-427 2191	339	20	35	29	......	26144	3400	3400	3400	8979
Knightswood St. Margaret's	Vacant	......		26 Airthrey Avenue, G14 9LJ / 041-959 1094	1051	48	119	88	28	49151	11100	11100	11450	10254
Langside	George J. Whyte, BSC, BD	1981	1985	33 Mansionhouse Gardens, G42 / 041-649 7779	550	45	69	68	10	42846	7900	7900	6602	9714
Lansdowne	Ian F. Galloway, BA, BD / Helen M. Hughes, DCS	1976 /	1988 /	Deaconess—see List H / 041-339 9459	336	25	......	26	4	24968	2500	2500	4400	v

Charge	Minister	Ord.	Ind.	Address and Tel. No.	Com.	Eld.	W.G.	S.S.	B.C.	C.L. £	As'd £	Gi'n £	Stp. £
Linthouse St. Kenneth's	Anne J. M. Harper, BD, STM	1979	1984	51 Morriston Crescent, Deanpark, Renfrew 041-885 1557	298	24	56	31	12	20243	950	20	8646
	{ Hugh F. Watt, BD	1986	……	Liff Place, G34 0LR 041-773 2756									
Lochwood	Ann Macdonald, DCS	……	……	Deaconess—see List H	192	11	……	40	17	11655	……	……	8646
Martyrs', The	Elaine H. Lawson ¶	1985	……	7 Seton Terrace, G31 2HU 041-554 3049	341	26	39	22	……	18910	……	500	8646
Maryhill— High *linked with* Old	{ Anthony J. D. Craig	1987	……	111 Maxwell Avenue, G61 1HJ 041-942 0074	236	14	38	23	20	15334	400	250	v
	{ Margaret H. Johnston *Associate*	1988	……	171 Broughton Road, G23 5BP 041-945 0860	251	24	……	26	……	18684	400	400	v
Merrylea	Sidney H. Coleman, BA, BD, MTH	1961	1982	72 Langside Drive, G43 2ST 041-637 6700	916	67	108	94	16	69766	16500	16500	10665
Mosspark	D. Muir M'Laren, MA, BD, MTH, PH D	1971	1984	31 Springkell Drive, G41 4AB 041-427 1500	745	66	146	28	5	50988	11000	11000	9714
Mount Florida	Hugh M. Wallace, MA, BD	1981	1987	90 Mount Annan Drive, G44 4RZ 041-632 8868	671	52	142	90	60	63240	19000	19000	v
New Bridgegate	*Continued Vacancy*	……	……	—	184	17	60	21	……	10372	1300	1300	v
New Cathcart	John Murning	1988	……	69 Parklands Road, G44 3RA 041-637 1687	508	34	70	45	29	31383	7300	7300	v
New Govan	*Vacant*	……	……	3 Melfort Avenue, G41 5LQ 041-427 0700	406	24	60	34	60	31793	2400	2400	9240
Newlands South	Iain F. Paton, BD, FCIS	1980	1985	24 Monreith Road, G43 2NY 041-632 2588	1030	82	70	132	55	106808	24500	24500	12294
North Kelvinside	William G. Alston	1961	1971	41 Mitre Road, G14 9LE 041-954 8250	233	13	54	26	73	67792	4400	4400	8799
Old Partick	John Jolly, BA	1950	1966	8 Beaumont Gate, G12 9EE 041-339 2651	223	27	……	23	18	21638	750	750	8646
Partick— East and Dowanhill	Gordon J. A. Manson	1958	1964	35 Dalsholm Road, G20 0TB 041-946 2174	498	48	40	33	13	31543	5600	5600	9240
South	*Vacant*	……	……	18 Turnberry Road, G11 5AJ 041-339 3428	424	45	48	46	58	27850	2000	2500	9090
Penilee St. Andrew	Esther M. M. Leitch, BD	1984	……	80 Tweedsmuir Road, G52 2RX 041-882 3432	377	24	59	30	6	28579	2200	2300	8646

Congregation	Minister			Address										
Pollokshaws	Andrew R. Black	1987	......	33 Mannering Road, G41 3SW, 041-649 4981	372	29	59	36	16	18338	950	950	v
Pollokshields	Harry Thomson	1959	1965	35 Aytoun Road, G41 5HW, 041-423 2055	731	56	......	31	33	93929	12000	12000	11547
Possilpark	Martin R. Forrest, BA, MA, BD	1988	......	19 Colston Drive, Bishopbriggs, Glasgow, G64 2AZ, 041-772 6227	272	19	......	26	......	24141	......	......	v
	Derek H. N. Pope	1987	......	60 Muirshiel Crescent, G53									
Priesthill and Nitshill	Douglas M. Nicol *Associate*	1987	1988	38 Priesthill Road, G53 6PZ, 041-881 5627, 041-880 8339	259	20	44	49	30	14032	......	......	v
	Margaret Corrie *Agent—see List H*												
	David H. Lunan, MA, BD	1970	1987										
Renfield St. Stephen's	Angus Turner, BD *Associate*	1976	......	121 Terregles Avenue, G41 4DG, 041-423 4493 / 304 Albert Drive, G41 5RS, 041-429 0762	538	36	52	13	12	88454	7200	7200	v
Ruchazie	Gordon R. Palmer, MA, BD, STM	1986	......	312 Gartcraig Road, G33 2TD, 041-774 0395	137	15	25	52	22	11321	......	60	8646
	Janet Anderson, DCS *Deaconess—see List H*	......	......	041-774 5329									
Ruchill	Stewart Lang, CENG, MIEE, BD	1978	......	12 Kirklee Road, G12 0ST, 041-357 1375	364	23	41	46	24	56478	1800	1350	8979
Rutherglen—Old	Alexander Thomson, BSC, BD, MPHIL, PHD	1973	1985	31 Highburgh Drive, Rutherglen, Glasgow, G73 3RR, 041-647 6178	843	46	50	49	9	70927	7400	7400	9651
Stonelaw	Alastair M. Morrice, MA, BD	1968	1987	80 Blairbeth Rd., Rutherglen, Glasgow, G73 4JA, 041-634 4366	964	70	118	135	87	75338	19000	19330	v
Wardlawhill	George Cranston, BD	1976	1983	26 Parkhill Dr., Rutherglen, Glasgow, G73 2PW, 041-647 6688	730	61	60	122	......	45938	6500	7500	8979
West	John W. Drummond, MA, BD	1971	1986	12 Albert Drive, Rutherglen, Glasgow, G73 3RT, 041-643 0234	699	27	40	30	15	34149	3800	3800	9240
St. Andrew's	*see* Calton New													
St. Andrew's East	David Hogg	1949	1971	43 Broompark Drive, G31 2JB, 041-554 3620	536	38	81	72	46	29678	3200	......	8979
St. Columba	*Vacant*	......	......		227	25	16	44	36	30091	1200	1200	8646
St. David's Knightswood	Howard G. Taylor, BSC, BD	1971	1986	60 Southbrae Drive, G13 1QD, 041-959 2904	1042	45	118	56	20	57808	15500	15500	10392
St. Enoch's Hogganfield	Alexander Tait	1967	1982	43 Smithycroft Road, G33 2RH, 041-770 7593	495	28	80	31	30	43048	3900	4154	8979

Charge	Minister	Ord.	Ind.	Address and Tel. No.	Com.	Eld.	W.G.	S.S.	B.C.	C.L. £	As'd £	Gi'n £	Stp. £
St. George's Tron	Eric J. Alexander, MA, BD	1958	1977	12 Dargarvel Avenue, G41 5LD 041-427 1402	877	66	50	146	74	157931	31500	31500	12294
	David W. Ellis, Assoc GIMECHE, GIPRODE	1962	1984	29 Arisaig Drive, Bearsden G61 2PD 041-942 3682									
St. James' (Pollok)	John T. Lang, MA	1952	1986	30 Ralston Avenue, G52 3NA 041-882 1421	522	33	57	92	39	32508	4000	4000	9240
	John Cathcart			Agent—see List H									
St. John's Renfield	Vacant			26 Leicester Avenue, G12 0LU 041-339 4637	768	61	84	110	39	82720	17500	14895	11820
St. Margaret's Tollcross linked with Tollcross Park	Peter I. Barber, MA, BD	1984		46 Drumover Drive, G31 5RP 041-554 7583	258	11	53	34	20	18233	.....	.....	8646
					110	9	.....	6	.....	9373	.....	.....	
St. Nicholas' Cardonald	Alexander C. Barr, MA, BD	1950	1967	104 Lamington Road, G52 2SE 041-882 2065	740	57	102	119	50	37485	7600	7600	9240
St. Paul's Provanmill	R. Russell M'Larty, BD	1985		14 Lochview Drive, G33 1QF 041-770 9611	142	17	30	51	30	16597	.....	.....	8646
St. Rollox	E. Gwynfai Jones, BA	1964	1967	42 Melville Gardens, Bishopbriggs, Glasgow, G64 3DE 041-772 2848	426	20	.....	23	20	22088	750	750	8646
St. Thomas' Gallowgate	H. Marshall Gibson, MA, BD	1957	1982	29 Broompark Drive, G31 2JB 041-554 0997	205	10	11	.....	2	14292	.....	.....	8646
Sandyford Henderson M'l	G. M. Philip, MA	1953	1956	66 Woodend Drive, G13 1TG 041-954 9013	318	19	29	34	.....	73152	15500	15500	10665
Sandyhills	Robert Carmont	1958	1968	60 Wester Road, G32 9JJ 041-778 2174	536	36	89	75	16	47704	3800	4000	9714
Scotstoun	Vacant			15 Northland Drive, G14 9BE 041-959 4637	782	65	118	142	20	59262	8400	8400	v
Shawlands— Cross	Alastair M. Sanderson, LTH	1971	1976	29 St. Ronan's Drive, G41 3SQ 041-632 9046	700	46	67	98	33	69127	21000	21000	11346
Old	James Millar	1949	1979	47 Dinmont Road, G41 3UJ 041-632 5817	510	27	80	32	36	49447	5800	10000	9240
Sherbrooke St. Gilbert's	Donald MacLeod, BD, LRAM, DRSAM			9 Springkell Gate, G41 4BY 041-423 3912	565	43	56	68	17	53160	11800	11800	v
Shettleston Old	Robert M. Tuton, MA	1957	1973	2 Ailean Drive, North Mount Vernon, G32 0RS 041-778 1488	824	38	64	33	45	96160	5600	5600	9240

Congregation	Minister	Ord.	App.	Ret.	Charge									
South Carntyne	Alexander H. Green, MA, BD	1986	.....		47 Broompark Drive, G31 2JB 041-554 5930	196	10	19	23	5	17769	.....	195	8646
South Shawlands	Thomas G. Macfarlane, BSC, BD, PHD	1956		1968	51 Lubnaig Road, G43 2RX 041-637 2331	443	39	.....	80	25	45831	5800	6257	9441
Springburn	W. G. Ramsay	1967	1987		3 Tofthill Avenue, Bishopbriggs, Glasgow, G64 3PA 041-762 1844	788	49	42	52	29	50578	7300	7300	v
Strathbungo Queen's Park	Norma D. Stewart, MA, MED, BD	1977	1979		5 Newark Drive, G41 4QJ 041-423 4818	476	38	53	30	25	41095	8100	8100	9441
Temple Anniesland Tollcross Park	Robert W. M. Johnston, MA, BD, STM	1964	1972		76 Victoria Park Drive North, G14 9PJ 041-959 5835	789	48	75	36	14	68658	14000	14372	10527
see—St. Margaret's Tollcross														
Toryglen	Stuart D. MacQuarrie, BD, BSC	1984	.....		Flat 56, 45 Myrtle View Road, G42 0NN 041-423 0788	336	21	64	64	4	19561	.....	.....	8646
Townhead Blochairn	W. Peter Finlay, MA, BD	1969	1988		27 Broompark Drive, G31 2JB 041-554 3233	119	9	5	25	102	18553	.....	45	v
	Miss Elizabeth White, DCS	.....		.....	*Deaconess—see List H* 041-647 2683									
Trinity Possil and Henry Drummond	Andrew T. B. M'Gowan, BD, STM	1979	1988		35 Springfield Road, Bishopbriggs, Glasgow, G64 1PL 041-772 1456	248	14	23	31	16	30346	2300	2300	8898
Tron St. Mary's	*Vacant*	.....	.....		10 Brackenbrae Rd., Bishopbriggs, Glasgow, G64 2AD 041-772 4620	278	15	22	24	8	15040	.....	.....	8646
Victoria Park	Allan F. Webster, MA, BD	1978	.....		9 Rowallan Gardens, G11 7LH 041-357 1296	217	13	34	22	4	15800	900	258	8646
Victoria Tollcross	Richard Coley, LTH	1971	.....		228 Hamilton Road, G32 9QU 041-778 2413	322	20	53	47	23	25698	1100	1100	8646
Wellington	*Vacant*	.....	.....		27 Kingsborough Gardens, G12 9NH 041-339 3627	715	62	100	31	9	76955	15500	16500	11346
Whiteinch	Gavin J. M'Fadyen	1963		1972	24 Essex Drive, G14 9NA 041-959 3132	208	21	45	7	.....	14878	.....	250	.....
Yoker— Old *linked with* St. Matthew's	Erik M. Cramb, LTH	1973	1984		15 Coldingham Avenue, G14 0PX 041-952 1738	182	16	33	.....	.....	12812	.....	.....	8646
						169	10	.....	51	.....	7425	.....	.....	.....

Minister	Ord.	App.	Ret.	Charge	Address and Tel. No.
Ainslie, W. John	1986	1986	.....	*Community Minister* at Easterhouse (Broomhill)	58 Binns Road, G33 5HX 041-774 4474
Aitchison, James, MA, BD	1947	.....	1986	(Tollcross Central *with* Park)	1 Castleton Avenue, Newton Mearns, G77 041-639 2471
Aitken, Andrew J., BD, APHS, MTH	1951	.....	1981		18 Dorchester Avenue, G12 0EE 041-357 1617

Minister	Charge	Ord.	App.	Ret.	Address and Tel. No.
Aitkenhead, S. M.	(New Cathcart)	1951	....	1981	70 Cartside Road, Busby, G76 8QQ *041-644 4341*
Barr, David, MA, BD	(*Chaplain*, Royal Infirmary)	1938	....	1984	17 Victoria Park Gardens South, G11 7BX *041-339 5364*
Bell, John L., MA, BD	Iona Community	1978	1988		416 Great Western Road, G4 9HZ *041-334 0688*
Bisset, John M., MA	(Abbotsford Chalmers *with* St. Ninian's Wynd)	1938	....	1973	45 Moulin Road, G52 3PJ *041-882 5375*
Bone, Robert T.	(Malawi)	1960	....	1984	6 Burnbank Terrace, Kilsyth, G65 0AE
Bowie, Allan, MA	(Rutherglen West)	1944	....	1985	2 Broomhill Drive, Rutherglen, G73 3QH *041-647 2255*
Brice, Dennis G., BSC, BD	Taiwan	1981	1981		Third Floor, Apartment 4, Lane 17, Alley 17, Wo Lung Jei, Taipee, Taiwan 106
Bryden, William A., BD	(Yoker Old *with* St. Matthew's)	1977	....	1984	145 Bearsden Road, G13 1BS
Bussey, Oscar, MA, BD, PHD	(Tollcross Central)	1947	....	1976	6C Graham House, Berryhill Road, Seafar, Cumbernauld *[023 67] Cumbernauld 22530*
Campbell, John, BA, LTH	Organiser for Evangelism	1973	1986		3 Herries Road, G41 4DE *041-423 3760*
Cooke, John M., MA, BD	(Fowlis Wester *with* Monzie)	1950	....	1982	2 Wellfield Court, Giffnock, G46 7QJ *041-638 4749*
Cran, James	(Bishopbriggs Springfield Cambridge)	1941	....	1977	23 Cedar Road, Bishopbriggs, G64 1TA *041-762 1836*
Crombie, William D., MA, BD	(Calton New *with* St. Andrew's)	1947	....	1987	32 Westburn Drive, Bearsden, G61 4BH *041-943 0235*
Cunningham, Alexander, MA, BD	*Presbytery Clerk*	1961	1980		103 Glenmavis Road, Airdrie, ML6 0PQ *[0236] Airdrie 63012*
Currie, Robert, MA	*Community Minister*	1955	1984		61 Dowanside Road, G12 9DL *041-334 5111*
Davidson, Robert, MA, BD, DD	University of Glasgow	1956	1972		357 Albert Drive, G41 5PH *041-427 5793*
Davidson, Robert	(Ruchazie)	1945	....	1980	42 Mains River, Park Mains, Erskine, PA8 7JP *Park Mains 3143*
Duncan, George B., MA	(St. George's Tron)	1938	....	1977	Little Shepherds, Colman's Hatch, Hartfield, East Sussex, TN7 4HF
Dunlop, M. William B., LLB, BD	(Zambia)	1981	....	1987	1 Hughenden Terrace, G12 9XR *041-334 4529*
Easton, Michael S.	(New Govan)	1942	....	1988	176 Titwood Road, G41 4DD
Edwards, Michael S.	*Chaplain*, R.A.F.	1982	1982		R.A.F. Guttersloh, B.F.P.O. 47
Ellis, W. Howard, BA, BD	(Househillwood St. Christopher's)	1953	....	1981	1395 Pollokshaws Road, GH1 3RG *041-632 2345*
Fairweather, Ian C. H., MA, BD	(Jordanhill College of Education)	1945	....	1985	10 Hillside Road, Cardross, G82 5LW *[0389] Cardross 841551*
Fenton, Robert J., MA	(St. Kiaran's Dean Park)	1940	....	1976	16 St. Clair Avenue, Giffnock, G46 7QH *041-638 0288*
Ferrie, H. Russell, MA	(St. Vigean's and Auchmithie)	1936	....	1975	Craigoul, Spean Bridge, PH34 4EU
Forrest, Gavin W., MA, BD	(Whitburn South)	1984	....	1987	
Fraser, John G.	(Elder Park Macgregor Memorial)	1950	....	1986	17 Beaufort Gardens, Bishopbriggs, G64 2DJ *041-772 2987*
Galloway, Allan D., MA, BD, STM, PHD	(University of Glasgow)	1948	....	1982	5 Straid Bheag, Barremman, Clynder, Helensburgh, G84 0QX *[043 683] Clynder 432*
Gilchrist, George R., MA, BD, DD	(Dalrymple)	1940	....	1980	53 Alexander Avenue, Eaglesham, G76 0DP *[035 53] Eaglesham 2272*
Gillies, Iain L.	(Bluevale and Whitevale)	1955	....	1975	453 Drumoyne Road, G51 4DD *041-445 3303*
Gordon, A. J. O., MA	(Toryglen)	1941	....	1983	5 Bankholm Place, Clarkston, G76 8SH *041-644 1505*
Grieve, William F., BSC	(Camphill Queen's Park)	1931	....	1971	6 Crarae Avenue, Bearsden, Glasgow, G61 1HX *041-942 0954*
Grimstone, A. Frank, MA	(Calton Parkhead)	1949	....	1986	144C Howth Drive, Parkview Estate, Anniesland *041-954 1009*
Haley, Derek, BD, DPS	*Chaplain*, Gartnavel Royal	1960	1977		9 Kinnaird Crescent, Bearsden, Glasgow, G61 2BN *041-942 9281*
Hamilton, A. Russell	(Cambuslang St. Paul's)	1945	....	1987	
Hamilton, David S. M., MA, BD, STM	University of Glasgow	1958	1984		2 Roselea Drive, Milngavie, G62 8HQ *041-956 1839*
Hamilton, John H.	(Yoker Old)	1949	....	1980	12 Foxbar Drive, G13 3BZ *041-954 5551*
Hamilton, William	(Dennistoun Central)	1950	....	1976	28 Hargrave Avenue, Oxton, Birkenhead
Harvey, W. John, BA, BD	*Leader*, Iona Community	1965	1988		2/1 99 M'Culloch Street, G41 *041-429 3774*

Name			Charge	Address
Herron, Andrew, DD, LLD	1934	1981	(Presbytery Clerk)	36 Darnley Road, G41 4NE *041-423 6422*
Hislop, David T., MA	1940	1983	(Maryhill High)	92 Balcarres Avenue, G12 0QN *041-357 2866*
Hunter, George	1950	1987	(Scotstoun West)	Flat 1c, 256 Great Western Road, G4 8EG *041-332 7228*
Hutcheson, J. Murray, MA	1943	1987	(Possilpark)	201 Weymouth Drive, G12 0LX *041-339 4790*
Hutchison, Ella (Mrs.)	1988	1988	Calton Parkhead	
Inglis, C. G., MA	1944	1969	(Chaplain, Army)	416 Crow Road, G11 7EA *041-339 3078*
Irvine, Euphemia H. C. (Mrs.), BD	1972	1988	(Milton of Campsie)	32 Baird Drive, Bargarran, Erskine, PA8 6BB *041-812 2777*
Johnson, Emmanuel, BA, BD	1960	1963	Missionary to Ethnic Groups	13 Herriet Street, Glasgow, G41 2NN *041-423 3438*
Johnstone, David, MC, MA, BD	1951	1987	(Belhaven Westbourne)	140 Hyndland Road, G12 9BN *041-339 5896*
Jolly, Andrew J., BD	1983		Chaplain, Army	1 Duke of Wellington Regiment, BFPO 806
Jones, John D., BA	1935	1984	(Kirkconnel St. Mark's)	50 Melville Gardens, Bishopbriggs, G64 3DD *041-772 4776*
Keith, Donald, MA, BD	1971	1984	Chaplain, RN	6 Elderslie Gardens, Falkirk, FK2 0DN *[0324] Falkirk 711487*
Liddell, Matthew, MA, BD	1943	1972	(St. Paul's (Outer High) and St. David's (Ramshorn))	17 Traquair Drive, G52 2TB *041-810 3776*
Lindsay, James A., MC, MA	1936	1976	(Burnside)	113 Rosslyn Avenue, Rutherglen, Glasgow, G73 3EZ *041-647 5053*
Macdonald, John A., MA	1939	1978	(Thornliebank)	87 Cartside Road, Busby, Glasgow, G76 8QD *041-644 1230*
Macdonald, Murdo Ewen, DD	1939	1984	(University of Glasgow)	24 Falkland Street, G12 9PR *041-334 2087*
M'Farlan, Donald M., MA, PHD	1940	1985	(Jordanhill College of Education)	94 Southbrae Drive, G13 1TZ *041-959 4370*
M'Gregor, R. Murray, MA, BD, PHD	1950	1983	(St. Margaret's Polmadie)	Riverside Cottage, Riverside Terrace, Busby, G76 8EA *041-644 3919*
M'Intyre, J. Ainslie, MA, BD	1963	1984	(University of Glasgow)	60 Bonnaughton Road, Bearsden, G61 4DB *041-942 5143*
Mackay, A. K.	1938	1976	(Kirkintilloch Park)	11 Oak Dr., Lenzie, Kirkintilloch, Glasgow, G66 4BT *041-776 1726*
M'Kay, James, BL	1940	1986	(Blawarthill)	51 Wykeham Road, G13 *041-959 5286*
M'Kay, Johnston R., TD, MA, BD, LLD	1938	1978	(Greenock Finnart St. Paul's)	1 Mitre Court, Mitre Road, Glasgow, G11 *041-339 2457*
Mackay, W. Murray, MA, STM	1931	1976	(Newton Mearns)	123 Ayr Road, Newton Mearns, G77 6RF *041-639 6302*
MacKenzie, John, MA, BCOM	1932	1971	(Greenhead Barrowfield)	2 Peveril Court, Burnside, G73 4RE *041-634 1018*
MacLean, Andrew T., BA, BD	1980	1985	Chaplain to Strathclyde University	44 Forfar Avenue, G52 3JQ *041-883 5956*
Maclean, John, MA	1948	1977	(St. Andrew's Plantation)	18 Pelham Road, Droitwich, Worcester, WR9 8NT
MacLeod, William J., DIPTH	1963	1988	(Kirkintilloch St. David's Memorial)	42 Hawthorn Drive, Banknock, Bonnybridge FK4 1LF *[0324] 840667*
M'Murtrie, D. W., MA, ATCL, ARPS	1939	1965	(Summertown)	9 Iain Drive, Bearsden, Glasgow, G61 4PD *041-942 0293*
M'Phail, Douglas D.	1950	1982	(Carnwadric)	1 Rockmount Avenue, Thornliebank, G46 7BW *041-638 5024*
Marshall, James A., BA	1965	1987	(Camphill Queen's Park)	30 Glencairn Drive, G41 4PW *041-423 0076*
Martin, James, MA, BD, DD	1946	1987	(High Carntyne)	9 Magnolia Street, Wishaw, ML2 7EQ *[069 83] Cambusnethan 385825*
Millar, David A. R., MA	1956	1982	Chaplain to Glasgow University	11 The Square, The University, Glasgow, G12 8OG *041-334 8769*
Miller, T. Boyd	1938	1977	(Kirkintilloch Hillhead)	8 Alloway Quadrant, Harestanes, Kirkintilloch, G66 2PF *041-775 2133*
Minto, Archibald, MA, STM	1931	1983	(Crieff St. Andrew's)	1 Kirklee Place, G12 0TU *041-339 9843*
Morrison, Alex A., MA, BD, PHD	1939	1979	(Campsie)	4D Service Street, Lennoxtown, G65 7JP *[0360] Lennoxtown 311352*
Morton, Thomas, MA, BD, LGSM	1947	1986	(Rutherglen Stonelaw)	54 Greystone Avenue, Burnside, Rutherglen, G73 3SW *041-647 2682*
Myers, Frank	1952	1987	(Springburn)	28 Viewfield Road, Bishopbriggs, G46 2AF *041-772 4137*
Neil, Herbert K.	1951	1978	(Portmoak)	111 Hyndland Road, G12 9JB *041-339 7753*
Newlands, George M., MA, BD, PHD	1970	1986	University of Glasgow	82 Highburgh Road, G12 9EN *041-334 4712*
Norwood, David W., BA	1948	1980	(Lisbon)	8 Strathtay Avenue, Netherlee, G44 3YA *041-633 1823*
Orr, David C., MA	1940	1980	(Govan Old)	80 Queen's Drive, G42 8BJ *041-423 3267*
Orr, Norman B., BSC, ARCST	1958	1981	Industrial Chaplain	7 Sherbrooke Drive, G41 5EE *041-427 6342*
Orrock, David W., MA	1950	1983	(Lenzie Union)	8 Kirkton Crescent, Milton of Campsie, G65 8OP *[0360] Lennoxtown 313078*

Minister	Charge	Ord.	App.	Ret.	Address and Tel. No.
Pacitti, Stephen A., MA	Taiwan	1963	1977	......	Min Chuan, Sixth Street No. 5, Meilwun, Hualien, Taiwan 950 Republic of China
Pattison, Kenneth J., MA, BD, STM	*Chaplain*, Royal Infirmary	1967	1984		46 Berridale Avenue, G44 3AE *041–637 2697*
Peterkin, W. Neilson, MA	(Broom)	1945	......	1986	7 Craigie Drive, Newton Mearns, G77 *041–639 2329*
Philip, Robert A., BA, BD	(Stepps St. Andrew's)	1937	......	1981	14 Elmete Mount, Round Hay, Leeds, LS8 2NU
Porter, Richard, MA	(Govanhill)	1953	......	1988	58 Hillend Road, G76 7XT *041–639 4169*
Pritchard, J. Stanley, MA	(B.B.C.)	1938	......	1970	3 Queen Margaret Road, G20 6DP *041–946 4263*
Rae, D. L.	Kolhapur	1955	1955		Church of Scotland Mission, Pune, Western India
Rennie, Walter	(Maybole Cargill Kincraig)	1963	......	1978	6A Campbell House, Berryhill Road, Cumbernauld, G67 1LX *[023 67] Cumbernauld 32709*
Ritchie, L. A., MA, BD	(*Chaplain* to Glasgow University)	1943	......	1982	34 Baldric Road, G13 3QJ *041–954 9277*
Robertson, R. Campbell	*Community Minister* at Anderston	1967	1979		Flat 12b, 30 St. Vincent Terrace, G3 8UT *041–204 1541*
Ross, Robert M. F., FPHS	(Plantation)	1936	......	1971	Williamwood House, Strathtay Avenue, G44 *041–637 1168*
Salter, Frederick H., MA	(Rothiemurchus and Aviemore)	1951	......	1974	Monadhliath, PH20 1DD *[0554 03] Newtonmore 431*
Shanks, Norman J., MA, BD	University of Glasgow	1983	1989		Hillview, Holehouse Road, Eaglesham, G76 0GF *[035 53] E'ham 2314*
Shearer, Thomas, MA, BD, BLITT	(Orwell)	1939	......	1977	280 St. Vincent Street, G2 5RT *041–221 0051*
Sinclair, Colin, A. M., BA, BD	*Secretary*, The Scripture Union	1981	1988		44 Middlemuir Road, Lenzie, G66 4ND *041–776 0870*
Smith, J. Rankine, MA, BD	(Barmulloch)	1945	......	1982	23 Aberfeldy Street, G31 3NS *041–554 3189*
Smith, R. M'Kenzie	*Auxiliary Minister* at Balornock North	1984	1984		Flat F, 11 Laird Place, G40 1JP *041–556 2748*
Stevenson, G. M., MA	(Martyrs')	1941	......	1984	12 Ripon Drive, G12 0DX *041–339 2098*
Stewart, John M.	(Colston Milton)	1950	......	1980	68 Randolph Road, G11 7JL *041–339 9815*
Thomson, Harry C., MA, BD, PH D	(Anniesland Cross)	1937	......	1971	498 Clarkston Road, G44 3QE *041–637 1630*
Towart, W. J., MA, BD	(Priesthill)	1944	......	1987	2 Central Avenue, Mount Vernon, Glasgow, G32 9JP *041–778 2525*
Walker, A. Cameron	(Baillieston Old)	1943	......	1966	11 Dundas Avenue, Torrance, G64 4BD *[036 089] Torrance 2122281*
Walker, A. L.	(Trinity Possil and Henry Drummond)	1955	......	1988	4/17 Gillsland Road, Edinburgh, EH10 5BW *031–228 6965*
Weir, C. J. Mullo, MA, BD, DPHIL, DD	(University of Glasgow)	1932	......	1968	

ADDRESSES OF GLASGOW CHURCHES

Bishopbriggs—	
Kenmure	Viewfield Rd., Bishopbriggs
Springfield Cambridge	Springfield Road, Bishopbriggs
Broom	Mearns Road, Newton Mearns *041–639 3528*
Giffnock—	
Orchardhill	Church Rd. *041–638 3604*
South	Eastwood Toll *041–638 3594*
The Park	Ravenscliffe Drive
Bridgeton St. Francis in the East	Queen Mary Street x Bernard Street
Broomhill	Randolph Rd. x Marlborough Ave. *041–334 2540*
Burnside	Church Avenue, Burnside *041–634 4130*
Calton New	Well Street at Bain Square
Calton Parkhead	122 Helenvale Street
Cambuslang—	
Flemington Hallside	265 Hamilton Road
Old	Cairns Road
Eastbank	679 Old Shettleston Road
Easterhouse St. George's and St. Peter's	Boyndie Street
Eastwood	Mansewood Road
Elder Park Macgregor Memorial	Crossloan Road x Craigton Road
Fernhill and Cathkin	Neilvaig Drive
Gairbraid	1517 Maryhill Road
Gardner Street	Gardner St. x Muirpark St.
Garthamlock and Craigend East	Porchester St. x Balveny St.

Greenbank	Eaglesham Rd., Clarkston
Kilsyth—	
Anderson	Kingston Road
Burns and Old	Church Street
Lenzie Old	Kirkintilloch Rd. x Garngaber Av.
Union	Moncrieff Av. x Kirkintilloch Rd.
Maxwell Mearns Castle	Waterfoot Road
Mearns	Mearns Road, Newton Mearns
Netherlee	Ormonde Dr. x Ormonde Avenue
Newton Mearns	Ayr Road, Newton Mearns 041-639 7373
Stamperland	Stamperland Gardens, Clarkston 041-637 4999
Stepps	Whitehill Avenue
Thornliebank	Woodlands Road
Williamwood	Vardar Avenue x Seres Avenue, Clarkston
GLASGOW—	
Anderston Kelvingrove	Argyle St. x Elderslie St. 041-221 9408
Baillieston—	
Mure Memorial	Beech Avenue, Garrowhill
St. Andrew's	Church Street
Balornock North	57 Northgate Road 041-558 6186
Balshagray	Broomhill Cross
Barlanark Greyfriars	Edinburgh Rd. x Hallhill Road
Barmulloch	Ryehill Road x Quarrywood Road
Battlefield East	1216 Cathcart Road 041-632 4206
Belhaven-Westbourne	Westbourne Gardens 041-339 3194
Blairbeth Rodger Memorial	Kirkriggs Gardens
Blawarthill	Millbrix Avenue

St. Andrew's	Main Street x Clydeford Road
Trinity, St. Paul's	Main Street
Camphill-Queen's Park	20 Balvicar Drive 041-423 3731
Candlish-Polmadie	Cathcart Rd. x Calder St.
Cardonald	2141 Paisley Road West 041-882 1051
Carmyle	South Carmyle Avenue
Carntyne Old	862 Shettleston Road
Carnwadric	556 Boydstone Road, Thornliebank
Castlemilk—	
East	Barlia Terrace 041-634 5735
West	Carmunnock Road 041-634 1480
Cathcart—	
Old	119 Carmunnock Road
South	92 Clarkston Road 041-637 6658
Cathedral	Cathedral Square 041-552 0220
Colston Milton	Egilsay Crescent 041-772 1922
Colston Wellpark	1378 Springburn Road
Cranhill	Bellrock Cres. x Bellrock Street 041-774 5593
Croftfoot	Croftpark Ave. x Crofthill Rd. 041-637 3913
Crosshill Queen's Park	40 Queen's Drive
Dennistoun—	
Blackfriars	Whitehill Street
Central	Armadale Street
Drumchapel—	
Drumry St. Mary's	Drumry Road East 041-944 1998
Old	Garscadden Road 041-944 3758
St. Andrew's	Kinfauns Drive 041-944 2566
St. Mark's	Kinfauns Drive

Gorbals	Eglinton St. x Cumberland St.
Govan Old	866 Govan Road 041-445 1532
Govanhill	Daisy St. nr. Allison St.
High Carntyne	358 Carntynehall Road 041-778 4186
Hillington Park Househillwood	24 Berryknowes Road
St. Christopher's	Meikle Road
Hutchesontown	284 Old Rutherglen Road
Hyndland	Hyndland Rd. op. Novar Drive 041-339 1804
Ibrox	Carillon St. x Clifford St. 041-427 0896
John Ross Memorial	West Regent Street 041-221 0794
Jordanhill	Woodend Dr. x Munro Rd.
Kelvin Stevenson Memorial	Belmont St. at Belmont Bridge 041-339 1750
Kelvinside Hillhead	Huntly Gardens
Kenmuir Mount Vernon	London Road, Mount Vernon
King's Park	242 Castlemilk Road 041-632 1131
Kinning Park	Plantation Street
Knightswood St. Margaret's	Knightswood Cross
Langside	Ledard Road x Lochleven Road 041-632 7520
Lansdowne	Gt. Western Road at Kelvin Bridge
Linthouse St. Kenneth's	9 Skipness Drive
Lochwood	Lochend Road x Liff Pl.
Martyrs', The	St. Mungo Avenue
Maryhill—	
High	7 Sandbank Street
Old	1956 Maryhill Road 041-946 3512
Merrylea	78 Merrylee Road 041-637 2009

Addresses of Glasgow Churches—*continued*

Mosspark	149 Ashkirk Drive *041-882 2240*	
Mount Florida	1123 Cathcart Road	
New Bridgegate	69 Dixon Road	
New Cathcart	Newlands Road nr. Clarkston Road	
New Govan	Govan Cross	
Newlands South	Riverside Road x Langside Drive *041-632 3055*	
North Kelvinside	153 Queen Margaret Drive	
Old Partick	Church Street nr. Dumbarton Road	
Partick—East and Dowanhill	20 Lawrence Street	
South		
Penilee St. Andrew	Bowfield Crescent x Bowfield Avenue *041-882 2691*	
Pollokshaws	223 Shawbridge Street	
Pollokshields	Albert Drive x Shields Rd.	
Possilpark	124 Saracen Street	
Priesthill	Freeland Drive x Muirshiel Crescent	
Renfield St. Stephen's	Bath Street x Holland Street *041-332 8482*	
Ruchazie	Elibank St. x Milncroft Rd. *041-774 3838*	
Ruchill	Ruchill St. nr. Maryhill Rd. *041-946 0466*	
Rutherglen—Old	Main St. at Queen St.	
Stonelaw	Stonelaw Rd. x Dryburgh Avenue *041-647 5113*	
Wardlawhill	Hamilton Road	

West	Glasgow Road, nr. Main St.
St. Andrew's	St. Andrew's Square
St. Andrew's East	681 Alexandra Parade *041-554 1485*
St. Columba	300 St. Vincent Street *041-221 3305*
St. David's	Boreland Dr. nr. Lincoln Avenue *041-959 1024*
Knightswood	
St. Enoch's Hogganfield	860 Cumbernauld Road *041-770 5694*
St. George's Tron	163 Buchanan Street *041-221 2141*
St. James' Pollok	Lyoncross Rd. x Byrebush Road *041-882 4984*
St. John's Renfield	22 Beaconsfield Road *041-339 7021*
St. Margaret's Tollcross	179 Braidfauld Street
St. Nicholas' Cardonald	Hartlaw Cres. nr. Gladsmuir Rd.
St. Paul's Provanmill	Langdale St. x Greenrigg St.
St. Rollox	Fountainwell Road
St. Thomas Gallowgate	Gallowgate opp. Bluevale St.
Sandyford-Henderson Memorial	Kelvinhaugh Street at Argyle Street
Sandyhills	Baillieston Road nr. Sandyhills Road
Scotstoun—East	Earlbank Avenue x Ormiston Avenue
West	Queen Victoria Drive x Dumbarton Road
Shawlands—Cross	Shawlands Cross *041-649 2012*
Old	1120 Pollokshaws Road

Sherbrooke	Nithsdale Rd. x Sherbrooke Avenue *041-427 1968*
St. Gilbert's	111 Killin Street *041-778 2484*
Shettleston Old	
South Carntyne	538 Carntyne Road *041-778 1343*
South Shawlands	Regwood St. x Deanston Dr. *041-649 4656*
Springburn	Springburn Road x Atlas Street *041-557 2345*
Strathbungo Queen's Park	168 Queen's Drive *041-423 0517*
Temple Anniesland	869 Crow Road *041-959 1814*
Tollcross Central	1088 Tollcross Road
Tollcross Park	Drumover Drive nr. Tollcross Road
Toryglen	Glenmore Avenue, nr. Prospecthill Road
Townhead Blochairn	178 Roystonhill
Trinity Possil and Henry Drummond	Crowhill Street x Broadholm Street
Tron St. Mary's	128 Red Road
Victoria Park	Broomhill Drive
Victoria Tollcross	1134 Tollcross Road
Wellington	University Ave. x South-park Ave. *041-339 0454*
Yoker—Old	Dumbarton Road
St. Matthew's	Hawick Street

17. HAMILTON

Meets at Hamilton, in the Parish Halls, on the first Tuesday of February, March, May, September, October, November, December and on the third Tuesday of June

Presbytery Office: 18 Haddow Street, Hamilton, ML3 7HX [0698] *Hamilton 286837*

Clerk: Rev. JAMES H. WILSON, LTH, Bellside Road, Cleland, ML1 5NP [0698] *Cleland 860260*

Assistant Clerk: Rev. JAMES G. BLACK, BD, DPS, 16 Inglewood Crescent, East Kilbride, G75 8QD [035 52] *East Kilbride 23992*

Treasurer: Mr. DAVID FORRESTER, CA, Belmont, Lefroy Street, Coatbridge, ML5 1PN [0236] *Coatbridge 21892*

Charge	Minister	Ord.	Ind.	Address and Tel. No.	Com	Eld.	W.G.	S.S.	B.C.	C.L. £	As'd £	Gi'n £	Stp. £
Airdrie—													
Broomknoll	*Vacant*	......	....	51 Cromarty Road, Airdrie, ML6 9RL [0236] *Airdrie 51555*	697	54	92	91	71	48104	10180	9740	10272
Clarkston	Andrew Ritchie, BD, DIPMIN	1984	....	Forrest Street, ML6 7BE	709	41	48	61	21	35129	9957	7969	10572
Flowerhill	John Hay Paterson, BD	1977	....	31 Victoria Place, ML6 9BX [0236] *Airdrie 63025*	938	63	75	80	13	42435	12565	12565	10272
High	George M'Cabe, TD	1963	....	17 Etive Drive, ML6 9QL [0236] *Airdrie 62010*	524	27	64	42	26	31370	2725	2725	8646
Jackson	William Wylie	1960	....	48 Dunrobin Road, ML6 8LR [0236] *Airdrie 63154*	648	30	62	135	34	35211	9483	4333	10722
New Monkland *linked with* Greengairs	Alan A. Ford, BD, AIB SCOT	1977	....	Glenmavis, Airdrie, ML6 0NW [0236] *Airdrie 63286*	662 218	35 7	43 23	110 22	72 16	30590 7779	5454 1399	2962 700	9822
St. Columba's	Margaret F. Currie, BED, BD	1987	....	Hazelwood, Arthur Avenue, ML6 9EZ [0236] *Airdrie 62029*	398	27	37	32	38	17577	2459	2459	v
Wellwynd	Adam J. Learmonth	1966	1980	39 Woodview Drive, ML6 9HJ [0236] *Airdrie 62193*	535	37	46	25	7	31682	6839	6839	9822
West	Peter M. Gordon, MA, BD	1958	1985	Arthur Avenue, ML6 9EZ [0236] *Airdrie 63022*	645	50	70	71	19	43874	9061	9061	10869
Bargeddie	Alistair Malcolm, BD, DPS	1976	....	Bargeddie, Baillieston, Glasgow, G69 6UB 041-771 1322	350	15	15	29	13	30267	4318	4318	8646

Charge	Minister	Ord.	Ind.	Address and Tel. No.	Com.	Eld.	W.G.	S.S.	B.C.	C.L. £	As'd £	Gi'n £	Stp. £
Bellshill—													
Macdonald Memorial	William M. Glencross, LTH	1968	1973	346 Main Street, Bellshill, ML4 1BA [0698] *Bellshill 842177*	416	33	.....	37	17	34739	5587	5587	9972
Orbiston *linked with*	*Vacant*	.....	.....	65 Crossgates, Bellshill, ML4 2EE [0698] *Bellshill 748447*	391	22	23	39	17	13984	2043	2043	9753
St. Andrew's	James W. M'Leod, MA	1965	1982	16 Croftpark Street, Bellshill, ML4 1EY	382	21	45	36	31	26108	3748	3748	
West				[0698] *Bellshill 842877*	1177	66	85	62	39	51400	13306	13306	10869
Blantyre—													
Livingstone Memorial	James E. Hunter, LTH	1974	.....	286 Glasgow Road, Blantyre, G72 9DB [0698] *Blantyre 823794*	404	19	26	28	6	22092	1648	1648	8646
Old	Peter O. Price, CBE, QHC, BA, FPHS	1960	1985	High Blantyre, G72 9JA [0698] *Blantyre 823130*	550	32	20	76	27	43645	7049	7049	9822
St. Andrew's	James C. Gregory, LTH	1968	1978	9 Lochalsh Place, Blantyre, Glasgow, G72 9LU [0698] *Blantyre 827982*	256	16	.....	111	28	18381	940	940	8646
Bothwell	Robert J. Stewart, MA, BD, STM	1959	1977	Bothwell, Glasgow, G71 8PQ [0698] *Bothwell 853189*	974	59	.....	120	31	81839	13397	13397	11466
Calderbank *linked with*	James R. Nelson, BD, DIPTHEOL	1986	.....	Chapelhall, Airdrie, ML6 8SG [0236] *Airdrie 63439*	245	17	35	25	4	41071	1829	2732	9372
Chapelhall					466	23	.....	85	27	32856	2603	2603	9750
Caldercruix, Longriggend and Meadowfield	Robert C. Nelson, BA, BD	1980	.....	Main Street, Caldercruix, Airdrie, ML6 7RF [0236] *Caldercruix 842279*	341	19	16	61	24	26889	6467	6467	.....
Carfin	*see Newarthill*												
Chapelhall	*see Calderbank*												
Chapelton *linked with*	Alastair L. Jessamine, MA, BD	1979	.....	15 Lethame Road, Strathaven, ML10 6AD [0357] *Strathaven 20019*	229	11	50	40	21	91122	1925	1925	10272
Strathaven Rankin					714	50	68	160	54	40683	8236	8236	
Cleland	James H. Wilson, LTH	1970	.....	Bellside Road, Cleland, ML1 5NP [0698] *Cleland 860260*	396	22	52	52	33	32005	3667	3667	8646
Coatbridge—													
Blairhill Dundyvan	Iain A. Whyte, BA, BD, STM	1968	1987	18 Blairhill Street, ML5 1PG [0236] *Coatbridge 32304*	704	38	64	59	12	35868	6652	6720	v
Calder	Keith Saunders, BD	1983	.....	26 Bute Street, Coatbridge, ML5 4HF [0236] *Coatbridge 21516*	784	49	61	68	32	34757	4754	5204	9822

Coatdyke	Ian W. MacBain, LTH	1971	1979	Quarry Street, ML5 3PU [0236] Coatbridge 23885	311	37	35	40	49	17182	……	……	8646
Coats	T. Jardine Johnstone, MA, BD	1948	……	Jackson Street, ML5 3NL [0236] Coatbridge 21181	487	27	44	12	15	46073	1963	1963	8646
Dunbeth	James F. Dunn	1959	1977	Weir Street, ML5 3EU [0236] Coatbridge 22372	391	30	36	11	7	32546	7341	7341	10287
Gartsherrie	Continued Vacancy	……	……	77 Eglinton Street, ML5 3JF [0236] Coatbridge 22000	463	43	30	23	7	24868	3585	3585	v
Maxwell	J. T. M'Nay	1955	1976	4 Laird Street, ML5 3LJ [0236] Coatbridge 32740	601	40	40	24	16	28195	5033	5033	9822
Middle	Andrew M. M'Cance, BSC	1986	……	47 Blair Road, ML5 1JQ [0236] Coatbridge 23792	568	38	49	43	42	27028	4712	4712	9084
Old Monkland	James G. Munton, BA	1969	……	Brandon Way, ML5 5QG [0236] Coatbridge 23788	517	21	45	65	17	22969	5200	3043	10125
Townhead	Charles A. Leggat, BD	1980	……	Crinan Crescent, ML5 2LH [0236] Coatbridge 23150	517	27	57	78	38	21175	3473	3473	8646
Dalserf	D. Cameron M'Pherson, BSC, BD	1982	……	Dalserf, Larkhall, ML9 3BN Larkhall 882 195	378	25	40	59	39	26436	2292	2292	8646
East Kilbride—													
Claremont	Keith M. Steven, MA, ED B / Maureen M'Fadzean, DCS	1978 / ……	……	16 Glen Clunie, East Kilbride, G74 2IR [035 52] East Kilbride 31497 / Deaconess—see List H [035 52] East Kilbride 46027	1434	98	……	250	108	52920	13397	13397	11466
Greenhills [E]	John Brewster, MA, BD, DIPED	1988	……	21 Turnberry Place, East Kilbride, G75 8TB [035 52] East Kilbride 42564	418	17	……	105	110	11373	……	50	v
Moncreiff	Alastair S. Lusk, BD / James B. Falconer, Associate	1974 / 1982	1983 / 1984	16 Almond Drive, East Kilbride, G74 2XH [035 52] East Kilbride 38639 / 64 Glen Prosen, East Kilbride, G74 3TA [035 52] East Kilbride 22437	1589	81	114	198	27	68714	12390	12390	11670
Old	James Gilfillan, LTH	1967	1975	40 Maxwell Drive, East Kilbride, G74 4NG [035 52] East Kilbride 20732	1000	70	156	57	41	46913	11052	11100	11469
South	John C. Sharp, BSC, BD, PHD / Katrina Cameron, DCS	1980 / ……	……	7 Clamps Wood, East Kilbride, G74 2HB [035 52] East Kilbride 47993 / Deaconess—see List H	838	50	60	101	32	40649	8805	8805	10272
West	David E. P. Currie, BSC, BD	1983	……	1 Barr Terrace, East Kilbride, G74 1AP [035 52] East Kilbride 20753	659	35	……	80	9	44685	5533	5533	9084
Westwood	James G. Black, BD, DPS	1978	1986	16 Inglewood Crescent, East Kilbride, G75 8QD [035 52] East Kilbride 23992	1381	51	125	303	111	65417	14161	14161	11469

Charge	Minister	Ord.	Ind.	Address and Tel. No.	Com.	Eld.	W.G.	S.S.	B.C.	C.L. £	As'd £	Gi'n £	Stp. £
Glassford *linked with* Strathaven East	William T. Stewart, BD	1979	......	Westdene, Strathaven, ML10 6BA [0357] Strathaven 21138	205	9	......	47	21	12590	1188	1188	9672
Greengairs *see* Airdrie New Monkland													
Hamilton— Burnbank *linked with* North	Raymond D. M. M'Kenzie, BD	1978	1987	9 South Park Road, ML3 6PJ [0698] Hamilton 424609	339	21	42	26	4	16066	3064	3064	v
Cadzow	Arthur P. Barrie, LTH	1973	1979	3 Carlisle Road, ML3 7BZ [0698] Hamilton 421664	983	60	100	138	50	48357	11706	11906	10125
Gilmour and Whitehill	Robert Brown, BSC	1962	1972	86 Burnbank Centre, Burnbank, ML3 0NA [0698] Hamilton 284201	394	27	65	39	19	23300	3255	3255	8646
Hillhouse	James G. Mackenzie, BA, BD; Marion Buchanan (Mrs.), DCS	1980;	......	66 Wellhall Road, ML3 9BY [0698] Hamilton 422300; Deaconess—see List H [0698] Hamilton 824325	640	44	34	140	84	31969	6420	6420	9372
North *see* Hamilton Burnbank													
Old	Hugh R. Wyllie, MA	1962	1981	62 Union Street, ML3 6NA [0698] Hamilton 420002	1026	76	53	54	36	120552	18430	20540	12963
St. Andrew's	Norman B. M'Kee, BD	1987	......	15 Bent Road, ML3 6QB [0698] Hamilton 891361	479	34	30	45	36	32334	4748	4748	v
St. John's	Robert M. Kent, MA, BD	1973	1981	12 Castlehill Crescent, ML3 7DG [0698] Hamilton 425002	901	56	......	106	52	52309	14026	14390	11469
South *linked with* Quarter	Ben Johnstone, MA, BD	1973	1975	Quarter, Hamilton, ML3 7XA [0698] Hamilton 424511	562	26	......	70	24	28488	6305	6564	8748
Trinity	Iain G. Matheson, BMUS, BD	1985	......	69 Buchan Street, ML3 8JY [0698] Hamilton 423753	618	28	24	63	53	21218	3094	2270	8646
West	James Stanley Cook, BD, DIP PSS	1974	......	43 Bothwell Road, ML3 0BB [0698] Hamilton 458770	630	36	47	101	80	30992	7210	7210	9372
Holytown	James S. Salmond, BA, BD, M.TH, B.TH	1979	......	Holytown, Motherwell, ML1 5RU [0698] Holytown 832622	499	21	......	60	16	21580	2335	2335	8646
Kirk o' Shotts	Sheila M. Spence (Mrs.), MA, BD	1979	......	Salsburgh, Shotts, ML7 4NS [069 887] Salsburgh 208	377	13	......	18	......	14279	686	686	8646
Larkhall— Chalmers (Strutherhill)	James Whitton, MA, BD, PHD	1955	1962	Quarry Road, Larkhall, ML9 1HH Larkhall 882 238	397	22	......	33	10	18781	2153	......	8646

Congregation	Minister	Year	Year	Address									
St. Machan's	Alexander C. Wark, MA, BD, STM	1982	......	38 Machan Road, Larkhall, ML9 1HG *Larkhall 882 457*	982	43	61	178	38	62307	9754	9754	10125
Trinity	Colin D. Johnston, MA, BD	1986	......	13 Machan Ave., Larkhall, ML9 2HE *Larkhall 881 401*	473	24	43	69	44	27834	2392	2392	8646
Motherwell—													
Clason Memorial	John Handley	1954	1961	7 Orchard Street, ML1 3JE *[0698] Motherwell 62733*	286	17	44	24	......	27576	2965	3025	9372
Crosshill	W. Stuart Dunn, LTH	1970	1982	15 Orchard Street, ML1 3JE *[0698] Motherwell 63410*	645	56	110	61	52	44892	12697	12697	10172
Dalziel	William C. Bruce, MA, BD	1961	1968	8 Calderbank Terrace, ML1 1LW *[0698] Motherwell 63414*	778	66	61	47	36	60683	13693	12793	11319
Manse Road	Thomas J. G. Seath, BD	1980	1985	10 Hamilton Drive, North Lodge, ML1 2QA *[0698] Motherwell 52420*	445	33	30	53	13	20301	1447	1447	8646
North	Alison Paul, MA, BD / Andrew Flockhart, DCS	1986	......	47 Douglas Street, ML1 3JQ *[0698] Motherwell 64098* / Deacon—see List H *[0698] Motherwell 51563*	410	34	......	40	31	21450	2706	123	8646
St. Andrew's	*Vacant*	......	......		572	39	55	18	12	29258	4899	5029	9372
St. Margaret's	Andrew M. Campbell, BD	1984	......	70 Baron's Road, ML1 2NB *[0698] Motherwell 63803*	637	27	36	90	16	26580	3003	4441	8646
St. Mary's	David W. Doyle, MA, BD	1977	1987	19 Orchard Street, ML1 3JE *[0698] Motherwell 63472*	1188	82	137	167	77	60701	16737	1672	v
South Dalziel	J. B. Allan, BA	1965	1977	62 Manse Road, ML1 2PT *[0698] Motherwell 63054*	818	85	117	56	21	59851	17463	14325	11616
Newarthill *linked with* Carfin	George S. Noble, DIPTH / John McAlpine *Auxiliary*	1972	......	Church Street, Newarthill, ML1 5HS *[0698] Cleland 860316*	701	27	45	104	37	28701	5053	5053	9084
Carfin		1978	......	201 Bonkle Road, Newmains, Wishaw, ML2 *[055 23] Wishaw 374410*	71	6	......	7	3	4184	376	636	......
Newmains— Bonkle *linked with* Coltness Memorial	*Vacant*	......	......	158 Manse Road, Wishaw, ML2 9BL *[0698] Cambusnethan 383858*	260	18	24	69	......	16536	2781	2790	10125
Coltness Memorial					368	29	32	27	33	27040	6421	3000	8646
New Stevenston Wrangholm Kirk	Barbara D. Quigley, MTHEOL, TH M, DPSS	1979	......	222 Clydesdale St., New Stevenston, Motherwell, ML1 4IQ *[0698] Holytown 832533*	325	11	......	64	19	24945	3189	700	8646
Overtown	Robert A. Anderson, MA, BD, D PHIL	1980	1986	Overtown, Wishaw, ML2 0QP *[0698] Wishaw 372330*	392	23	70	70	18	26547	4130	3634	8646

Charge	Minister	Ord.	Ind.	Address and Tel. No.	Com.	Eld.	W.G.	S.S.	B.C.	C.L. £	As'd £	Gi'n £	Stp. £
Quarter	*see Hamilton South*												
Shotts—													
Calderhead	William D. Beattie	1985	.....	Kirk Road, Shotts, ML7 5ET [0501] *Shotts 20042*	676	38	16	118	88	38581	5919	7588	8940
Erskine	*Vacant*	.....	.....	Shotts, Lanarkshire, ML7 4AQ [0501] *Shotts 21400*	308	13	25	53	6	14029	.....	.....	8646
Stonehouse St. Ninian's	C. Raymond Vincent, MA, FSA (SCOT)	1952	1981	Stonehouse, Lanarkshire, ML9 3NX *Stonehouse 792364*	622	38	78	124	24	32463	6145	6145	9672
Strathaven— Avendale Old and Drumclog	R. Forbes Walker	1987	1988	Strathaven, Lanarkshire, ML10 6BA [0357] *Strathaven 20077*	821	62	72	75	37	39412	7933	7933	10422
East	*see* Glassford												
Rankin	*see* Chapelton												
Uddingston— Burnhead	{ J. M. Grady { Lorraine McKirdy, DCS	1967	1973	Laburnum Road, Uddingston, G71 5DB [0698] *Uddingston 813716* Deaconess—see List H [0698] *Uddingston 818439*	412	22	20	89	23	25674	3759	3759	8646
Old	R. J. M. Andrew, MA	1955	1983	1 Belmont Ave., Uddingston, G71 7AX [0698] *Uddingston 814757*	964	60	90	138	55	49929	11904	11904	10001
Park	Earlsley M. White, BA	.....	1988	25 Douglas Gardens, Uddingston, G71 7HB [0698] *Uddingston 817256*	358	28	35	36	11	23271	2764	2800	v
Viewpark	{ George K. Barr, ARIBA, BD { Lorraine McKirdy, DCS	1967	....	14 Holmbrae Road, Uddingston, G71 6AP [0698] *Uddingston 813113* Deaconess—see List H [0698] *Uddingston 818439*	614	35	55	167	79	38200	8065	8165	10422
Wishaw— Cambusnethan—North	*Vacant*	.....	.....	350 Kirk Road, Wishaw, ML2 8LH [0698] *Cambusnethan 381305*	691	33	24	106	49	35462	7259	7259	9822
Old and Morningside	Douglas R. Murray, MA, BD	.....	1979	22 Coronation Street, Wishaw, ML2 8LF [0698] *Cambusnethan 384235*	884	51	47	90	90	56392	14016	14016	10869
Chalmers	Ian O. Coltart	1988	.....	161 Kirk Road, Wishaw, ML2 7BZ [0698] *Wishaw 372464*	731	54	.....	60	14	44814	10760	10760	v

Congregation	Minister	Ord.	App.										Address and Tel. No.
Craigneuk and Belhaven	Iain Paul, BSC, PHD, BD, PHD	1976	......	412	39	47	18	5	26627	5593	5593	9084	100 Glen Road, Wishaw, ML2 7NP [0698] Wishaw 372495
Old	*Vacant*	......	......	635	39	40	58	54	28542	6163	6163	9372	130 Glen Road, Wishaw, ML2 7NP [0698] Wishaw 375134
St. Mark's	Henry J. W. Findlay, MA, BD	1965	1967	723	39	112	167	42	38827	6958	6958	9372	Coltness Road, Wishaw, ML2 7EX [0698] Wishaw 384596
Thornlie	William D. Brown, MA	1963	1969	538	41	39	51	12	35897	6737	6737	10125	West Thornlie St., Wishaw, ML2 7AR [0698] Wishaw 372356

Minister	Ord.	App.	Charge	Ret.	Address and Tel. No.
Baird, George W., MA	1944	......	(Crimond *with* St. Fergus)	1984	42 Neilsland Drive, Motherwell, ML1 3EB [0698] Motherwell 62088
Beattie, William G., BD, BSC	1951	......	(Hamilton St. Andrew's)	1986	33 Dungavel Gardens, Hamilton, ML3 7PE [0698] Hamilton 423804
Brown, John E., MA, BD, DD	1939	......	(Hamilton St. John's)	1980	1 Mayfield Terrace, Insch, Aberdeenshire, AB5 6XL [0464] Insch 20705
Campbell, John	1974	......	(Coatbridge Middle)	1985	18 Bellsdyke Road, Airdrie, ML6 9BU [0236] Airdrie 53607
Campbell, T. K., MA	1939	......	(Bothwell St. Bride's)	1975	16 Green Street, Bothwell, G71 8RL [0698] Bothwell 852262
Clausen, Claus W., BD	1986	1986	*Community Minister* at Hamilton Trinity	......	10 Allanton Lea, Hamilton, ML3 8ET
Cotter, James L., MA, BD	1933	......	(Dalserf)	1973	50 South Beach, Troon, Ayrshire, KA10 6EF [0292] Troon 312722
Cowper, Macknight C., MA, BD, STM	1947	......	(East Kilbride West)	1983	17 Manor Place, Edinburgh, EH3 7OH 031—225 6214
Douglas, Andrew M., MA	1937	......	(Hamilton Cadzow)	1978	21 Allanshaw Street, Hamilton, ML3 6NZ [0698] Hamilton 429176
Frame, William H., BTH	1975	......	(Newmains Coltness Memorial *with* Bonkle)	1988	24 Kent Street, Dunfermline, KY12 0DJ [0383] Dunfermline 620033
Fraser, James P.	1951	......	(Strathaven Avendale Old and Drumclog)	1988	26 Hamilton Road, Strathaven, ML10 6JA
Gallan, Alex., MA	1955	......	(Wishaw Cambusnethan North)	1988	15 Airbles Crescent, Motherwell, ML1 3AP [0698] Motherwell 64474
Gunn, Daniel E.	1943	......	(Rothes)	1980	Lethame Road, Strathaven, ML10
Heron, John	1951	......	(Ochiltree)	1979	Bennachie, 17 Stonehouse Road, Sandford, Strathaven, ML10 6PD [0357] Strathaven 22629
Hudson, Eric V., LTH	1971	1978	Religious Broadcasting STV	......	
Kerr, J. Lyon, JP	1940	......	(Overtown)	1979	46 Waverley Drive, Wishaw, ML2 7JW [0698] Wishaw 351603
King, Crawford S., MA	1958	......	(Glenboig)	1984	77 Faskine Avenue, Airdrie, ML6 9EA
M'Bride, John S., MA	1942	......	(Wishaw Cambusnethan Old)	1979	127 Wishaw Road, Wishaw, ML2 8EN [0698] Wishaw 376913
M'Crum, Robert, BD	1982	1986	*Chaplain, R.N.*	......	*HMS Raleigh*, Torpoint, Cornwall, PL11 2PD
Macdonald, D. F. M., CBE, MA, LLB	1948	......	(General Administration Committee)	1985	29 Auchingramont Road, Hamilton, ML3 6JP
M'Tavish, Alastair J., MA	1947	......	(Motherwell St. Andrew's)	1981	4 Prince's Crescent, Dollar FK14 7BN
Malloch, Robert J.	1987	1987	*Chaplain*	......	*1 A & S H*, Roman Barracks, Colchester, Essex
Martin, William, MA	1933	......	(Kenmuir Mount Vernon)	1973	18 Cairndow Court, Glasgow, G44
Melrose, J. I. H. Loudon, MA, BD, MED, FSA(SCOT)	1955	1970	College of Education	......	1 Laverock Avenue, Hamilton, ML3 7DD [0698] Hamilton 427958
Mitchell, James C., MA	1939	......	(Motherwell Dalziel North)	1969	131 St. John's Close, Knowle, Solihull, B93 0NL [0564] 772561
Sawers, Hugh, BA	1968	......	(Motherwell St. Andrew's)	1988	2 Rosemount Meadows, Castlepark, Bothwell, G71
Sim, James, W.	1950	......	(Shotts Erskine)	1988	21 Austine Drive, Low Waters, Hamilton, ML3 7YE

ADDRESSES OF TOWN CHURCHES

Airdrie—

Broomknoll	Broomknoll Street
Clarkston	Forrest Street
Flowerhill	89 Graham Street
High	North Bridge Street
Jackson	Glen Road
New Monkland	Glenmavis
St. Columba's	Thrashbush Road
Wellwynd	Wellwynd
West	Wellwynd

Coatbridge—

Blairhill Dundyvan	Blairhill Street
Calder	Calder Street
Coatdyke	East Muiryhall Street
Coats	Jackson Street
Dunbeth	Top of Weir Street
Gartsherrie	Church Street
Maxwell	Bottom of Weir Street
Middle	Bank Street
Old Monkland	Woodside Street
Townhead	Crinan Crescent

East Kilbride—

Claremont	St. Leonard's
Greenhills	Greenhills Centre
Moncreiff	Calderwood Road
Old	Montgomery Street
South	Baird Hill, Murray
West	Kittoch Street
Westwood	Belmont Drive, W'wood

Hamilton—

Burnbank	High Blantyre Road
Cadzow	Woodside Walk
Gilmour and Whitehill	Glasgow Road, Burnbank
	Abbotsford Rd., Whitehill
Hillhouse	St. Ninian's Rd. x Castlehill Terrace
North	Windmill Road
Old	Leechlee Road
St. Andrew's	Avon Street
St. John's	Duke Street
South	Strathaven Road
Trinity	Neilsland Sq. off North Rd.
West	Burnbank Road

Motherwell—

Clason Memorial	Windmillhill Street
Crosshill	Windmillhill St. x Airbles St.
Dalziel	Merry St. and Muir St.
Manse Road	Gavin Street
North	Chesters Crescent
St. Andrew's	Muir Street
St. Margaret's	Shields Road
St. Mary's	Avon Street
South Dalziel	504 Windmillhill Street

Uddingston—

Burnhead	Laburnum Road
Old	Old Glasgow Road
Park	Main Street
Viewpark	Old Edinburgh Road

Wishaw—

Cambusnethan—

North	Kirk Road
Old	Kirk Road
Chalmers	East Academy Street
Craigneuk and Belhaven	Shieldmuir Street
	Craigneuk Street
Old	Main Street
St. Mark's	Coltness Road
Thornlie	West Thornlie Street

18. DUMBARTON

Meets at Dumbarton in Riverside Church Halls, on the first Tuesday of February, March, April, May, October, November, December, and on the second Tuesday of January, June and September (and April when the first Tuesday falls in Holy Week).

Clerk: Rev. DAVID P. MUNRO, MA, BD, STM, 8 Collylinn Road, Bearsden, Glasgow, G61 4PN   041–942 0366 and 8999

Charge	Minister	Ord.	Ind.	Address and Tel. No.	Com.	Eld.	W.G.	S.S.	B.C.	C.L. £	As'd £	Gi'n £	Stp. £
Alexandria—													
North	Douglas W. Bell, MA, LLB, BD	1975	.....	Luss Road, Alexandria, G83 8QP [0389] Alexandria 58043	507	27	.....	25	5	30211	4302	2785	9114
St. Andrew's	Roy J. M. Henderson, BD, DIPMIN	.....	1988	32 Ledrich Avenue, Balloch, G83 [0389] Alexandria 51315	750	32	30	38	8	25526	4606	4606	v
Arrochar	Ewen S. Nicoll, MA, BD	1973	1986	Luss, Alexandria, G83 8NZ [043 686] Luss 240	108	5	18	26	6	5315	.....	.....	8646
linked with													
Luss					154	5	18	10	.....	12405	.....	.....	
Baldernock	Alex J. Robertson	1974	1985	Bardowie, Milngavie, G62 6ES [036 02] Balmore 471	252	19	31	25	11	22321	500	500	8646
Bearsden—													
Killermont	Robert Jack, MA, BD	1950	.....	39 Woodvale Ave., Bearsden, G61 2NY 041–942 4422	1107	74	162	225	85	63733	20305	20778	11718
New Kilpatrick	Alastair H. Symington, MA, BD	1971	1985	51 Manse Road, Bearsden, G61 3PN 041–942 0035	2346	126	157	306	62	184969	52678	53326	13992
	Ian G. Gough, MA, BD Associate	1974	1985	19 Gartconnel Road, Bearsden, G61 3BW 041–942 0725									
North	David P. Munro, MA, BD, STM	1953	1967	8 Collylinn Road, Bearsden, Glasgow, G61 4PN 041–942 0366	787	64	162	98	68	61745	14105	14867	11064
South	John W. F. Harris, MA	1967	1987	61 Drymen Road, Bearsden, Glasgow, G61 2SU 041–942 0507	1163	79	145	50	39	85528	23331	23331	v
Westerton Fairlie Memorial	Iain J. M. Telfer, BD, DPS	1978	1979	3 Canniesburn Road, Bearsden, G61 1PW 041–942 2672	749	49	211	109	78	55149	11167	14704	10146
linked with													
Dalmuir	James F. Gatherer, BD Associate	1984	.....	9B Burnside Court, Dalmuir, Clydebank, G81 4PE 041–941 3317	363	15	52	110	7	15958	.....	415	
Overtoun													
Bonhill	Ian H. Miller, BD	1975	.....	1 Glebe Gardens, Bonhill, Alexandria, G83 9HT [0389] Alexandria 53039	806	44	178	.....	42	84299	100	100	9327

Charge	Minister	Ord.	Ind.	Address and Tel. No.	Com.	Eld.	W.G.	S.S.	B.C.	C.L. £	As'd £	Gi'n £	Stp. £
Cardross	Andrew J. Scobie, MA, BD	1963	1965	Cardross, Dumbarton, G82 5LB [0389] Cardross 841289	681	44	136	50	64	55033	11067	11067	10740
Clydebank— Abbotsford	Thomas M. Logan, LTH	1971	1988	35 Montrose St., Clydebank, G81 2PA 041-952 5151	541	39	69	87	37	30923	4850	4850	>
Faifley	John Dillon, BA, BD	1985	......	Kirklea, Cochno Road, Hardgate, Clydebank, G81 6PT [0389] Duntocher 76836	451	24	78	76	45	25783	2896	273	9327
Kilbowie	Sheila Munro Vacant	......	......	Agent—see List H 5 Melfort Avenue, Clydebank, G81 2HX 041-952 1381	471	29	32	119	44	22570	3245	3245	9759
Radnor Park	Paul R. Russell, MA, BD	1984	......	Spencer Street, Clydebank, G81 3AS 041-952 1025	555	35	44	28	26	34924	6614	4515	9393
St. Andrew's	Joseph Stewart, LTH	1979	......	Parkhall Road, Dalmuir, Clydebank, G81 3RJ 041-952 2116	537	27	65	31	17	22698	3525	3525	9327
St. Cuthbert's	Christine M. Goldie, LLB, BD	1984	......	13 Manor Road, Glasgow, G15 6SJ 041-944 4435	221	21	39	23	8	13610	......	......	8646
Craigrownie linked with Rosneath St. Modan's	Malcolm Wright, LTH	1970	1984	Edenkiln, Argyll Road, Kilcreggan, G84 0JU [043 684] Kilcreggan 2274	352 279	22 14	41 30	64 48	9 21	18844 20513	3180 2644	2898 2741	9702
Dalmuir Overtoun	see Bearsden Westerton												
Dumbarton— Riverside	John B. Cairns, LTH, LLB	1974	1985	5 Kirkton Road, Dumbarton, G82 4AS [0389] Dumbarton 62512	1286	74	115	190	48	82716	24669	20933	13413
St. Andrew's	Vacant	......	......	17 Manswood Drive, Dumbarton, G82 2HB [0389] Dumbarton 62063	421	16	24	56	18	20577	1163	1163	8646
West Kirk	James M. Thomson, BA	1952	1960	Clydeview, Clydeshore Road, G82 4AG [0389] Dumbarton 62950	651	50	79	81	18	36200	6535	5570	10389
Duntocher	Robert J. M'Alpine, BDS, BD	1988	......	Roman Road, Duntocher, Clydebank, G81 6BT [0389] Duntocher 78846	654	28	51	121	37	33774	3300	3300	>
Garelochhead	Vacant	......	......	Old School Road, Garelochhead, Helensburgh, G84 [0436] Garelochhead 810022	296	14	18	70	20	16671	880	880	8646

Charge	Minister	Ord.	App.	Charge (Address)								
Helensburgh—												
Park	James H. Brown, BD	1977	.....	35 East Argyle Street, Helensburgh, G84 7EL [0436] *Helensburgh 2209*	673	41	166	66	52577	12021	12021	10527
St. Columba	Frederick M. Booth, LTH	1970	1982	46 Suffolk Street, Helensburgh, G84 9QZ [0436] *Helensburgh 2054*	706	43	99	24	40329	9178	9178	10740
The West Kirk	David W. Clark, MA, BD	1975	1986	37 Campbell Street, Helensburgh, G84 9NH [0436] *Helensburgh 4063*	1167	70	105	15	66058	17366	17366	12363
Jamestown	Donald A. MacQuarrie, BSC, BD	1979	.....	Appin House, Drymen Road, Balloch, Alexandria, G83 8HT [038 982] *Alexandria 52734*	709	33	69	22	36130	8363	8363	10308
Kilmaronock Gartocharn	Walter W. Lyall	1951	1956	Kilmaronock Manse, Alexandria, G83 8SB [036 06] *Drymen 295*	331	9	23	.....	16979	1140	2010	8646
Luss	*see Arrochar*											
Milngavie—												
Cairns	J. Roy H. Paterson, MA	1953	1964	4 Cairns Drive, Milngavie, Glasgow, G62 8AJ 041-956 1717	933	55	107	73	69089	17913	17913	11385
St. Luke's	Douglas M. Copp, BA, FPHS, DIPED	1965	1971	70 Hunter Road, Milngavie, Glasgow, G62 041-956 4740	923	44	124	70	46357	11254	11254	10596
St. Paul's	Fergus C. Buchanan, MA, BD	1982	1988	8 Buchanan Street, Milngavie, Glasgow, G62 8DD 041-956 1043	1354	75	172	72	83080	24161	24161	v
Old Kilpatrick Barclay	Colin Campbell, MA, BD, FSASCOT	1940	1944	Old Kilpatrick, Glasgow, G60 5DW [03898] *Duntocher 72995*	303	10	38	27	12095	.....	.....	8646
Old Kilpatrick Bowling	Alistair J. M'Kichan, MA, BD	1984	.....	Old Kilpatrick, Glasgow, G60 5JQ [03898] *Duntocher 73130*	597	28	70	14	26217	6500	4500	10308
Renton Trinity	Agnes A. Moore, BD	1987	.....	Main Street, Renton, Dumbarton, G82 4PU [0389] *Alexandria 52017*	461	28	46	13	18537	2337	2337	v
Rhu and Shandon	A. D. Stirling, B SC	1956	1971	Ardenconnel Way, Rhu, Helensburgh, G84 8LX [0436] *Rhu 820213*	385	32	84	17	40098	11606	11606	10197
Rosneath St. Modan's	*see Craigrownie*											

Minister	Ord.	App.	Ret.	Charge	Address and Tel. No.
Beattie, John A.	.....	1951	1984	(Dalmuir Overtoun)	30 Roman Crescent, Old Kilpatrick, G60 5JU [0389] *Duntocher 79424*
Bolton, Albert F.	.....	1944	1983	(Arrochar)	25 Braehead Avenue, Milngavie, G62 6DH 041-956 1423
Borthwick, Stewart P. W., THM, THD, FPHS	1951	.....	1987	(Clydebank Abbotsford)	125 Thistle Neuk, Old Kilpatrick, G60 5LZ [0389] *Duntocher 74560*

Minister	Ord.	App.	Ret.	Charge	Address and Tel. No.
Buchan, Isabel C. (Mrs.), BSC, BD	1975	1985	......	Teacher, Religious Education	Schoolhouse, Baldernock, Balmore, G64 4AS Balmore 20649
Buchanan, George, OBE, MA, DD	1931	......	1977	(Christ Church, Bermuda)	5788 Holland Street, Vancouver, V6N 2B1, B.C., Canada
Devlin, Samuel, MA	1943	......	1984	(Baldernock)	77 Rosslyn Avenue, Rutherglen, Glasgow, G73 3EZ 041-647 8777
Dutch, Henry D. M., FIPR, FSASCOT	1986	......	......	Auxiliary Minister	16 Blackwood Road, Milngavie 041-956 3530
Easton, I. A. G., MA	1945	1988	......	Teacher, Religious Education	6 Edgehill Road, Bearsden, G61 3AD 041-942 4212
Ferguson, Archibald M., MSC, PH.D, FRINA	1988	1988	......	Auxiliary Minister	The Whins, Barrowfield, Cardross, G82 [0389] Cardross 1517
Gray, Ian A.	1949	......	1981	Curriculum Officer Education Dept.	82 West Clyde Street, Helensburgh, G84 8BB [0436] Helensburgh 3283
Hamilton, David G.., MA, BD	1971	1980	......	(Buchanan with Drymen)	79 Finlay Rise, Dougalston Mews, Fairways, Milngavie 041-956 4202
Hamilton, J. I. Hay, MA, BD	1936	......	1978	(Colmonell)	20 Ledcameroch Road, Bearsden, Glasgow, G61 4AE 041-942 0327
Hunter, G. Lindsay, BD, PHD, APHS	1949	......	......	Teacher, Religious Education	49 Lynn Drive, Milngavie, Glasgow, G62 8HL 041-956 3040
Keddie, David A.., MA, BD	1966	1983	......	Teacher, Religious Education	52 Station Road, Bearsden, G61 4AL 041-942 1408
Lawson, Alexander H.., THM, THD, FPHS	1950	......	1988	(Clydebank Kilbowie)	1 Glebe Park, Mansewood, Dumbarton, G82 3HE [0389] Dumbarton 42030
Macfarlane, William J. E.., MA, BD	1953	......	1987	(Alexandria St. Andrew's)	3 Inchfad Road, Balloch, G83 8SY [0389] Alexandria 58185
Mackenzie, Ian M., MA	1967	1973	......	BBC	1 Glenan Gardens, Helensburgh, G84 8XT [0436] Helensburgh 3429
Meiklejohn, William, MA	1938	......	1978	(Rosneath St. Modan's)	Tulliallan,, 79 Springfield Road, Linlithgow, EH49 7JP
Mitchell, Andrew S.., BA, BD, HDIPRED	1965	1984	......	Teacher, Religious Education	105 Sinclair Street, Helensburgh, G84 9HY [0436] Helensburgh 6197
Morton, Andrew Q.., MA, BSC, BD, FRSE	1949	......	1987	(Culross and Torryburn)	4 Upper Adelaide Street, Helensburgh, G84 7HT [0436] Helensburgh 5152
Rae, Scott M.., BD, CPS	1976	1981	......	Chaplain, RN	HMS Neptune, Faslane, Helensburgh
Spence, C. K. O.., MC, TD, MA, BD	1949	......	1983	(Craigrownie)	11 Cairndhu Gardens (Flat 4), Helensburgh, G84 8PG [0436] Helensburgh 78838
Warnock, John, MA, BD	1934	......	1975	(Biggar Gillespie Moat Park with Elsrickle)	Kelvingrove, Clynder Road, Garelochhead, Helensburgh, G84 0EL [0436] Garelochhead 810250
Willox, Henry N., MBE, MA, BD	1933	......	1971	(Carnwath)	28 Waverley Court, 16 West King Street, Helensburgh, G84 8UL [0436] Helensburgh 2281
Wilson, Roy	1986	......	......	Auxiliary Minister	45 Kessington Road, Bearsden 041-942 3291

ADDRESSES OF TOWN CHURCHES

Clydebank—
Abbotsford — Town Centre
Faifley — Off Glasgow Rd., Duntocher
Kilbowie — Kilbowie Road
Radnor Park — Radnor Street
St. Andrew's — Janetta Street
St. Cuthbert's — Linnvale

Dumbarton—
Riverside — High Street
St. Andrew's — Off Bonhill Road
West Kirk — West Bridgend

Helensburgh—
Park — Charlotte Street
St. Columba — Sinclair Street
The West Kirk — Colquhoun Square

SYNOD VI — ARGYLL

Meets on second Wednesday of April at Inveraray
Correspondens: Clydesdale; Southern Highlands
Clerk: Rev. WILLIAM T. HOGG, MA, BD, The Manse, Dalmally, PA33 1AS [083 82] Dalmally 227

19. SOUTH ARGYLL

Meets at Tarbert on the last Tuesday of January, March, April, June, September, October and November
Clerk: Rev. ALISTAIR J. DUNLOP, MA, FSA SCOT, The Manse, Carradale, Campbeltown, PA28 6QG [058 33] Carradale 253

Charge	Minister	Ord.	Ind.	Address and Tel. No.	Com.	Eld.	W.G.	S.S.	B.C.	C.L. £	As'd £	Gi'n £	Stp. £
Ardrishaig *linked with* South Knapdale	J. Edward Andrews, MA, BD, DIP CG	1985	......	Ardrishaig, Argyll, PA30 8HD [0546] Lochgilphead 3269	277 35	20 4	48	29 8	16	22374 2434	1651 188	1371 188	8646
Campbeltown— Highland	Charles M. Henderson	1952	1964	Kirk Street, Campbeltown, Argyll. PA28 6BN [0586] Campbeltown 52759	696	32	39	116	27	26690	3844	3944	9399
Lorne Street	*Vacant*	......	......	Burnbank Court, Campbeltown, Argyll. PA28 6JU [0586] Campbeltown 52065	459	45	20	36	33	25766	3753	3753	v
Lowland	*Vacant*	......	......	Campbeltown, Argyll. PA28 6AN [0586] Campbeltown 52468	802	37	72	72	5	31124	5436	8606	9490
Craignish *linked with* Kilninver and Kilmelford	Robert C. M. Carmichael, MA	1948	1975	Kilmelford, Oban, PA34 4XA [085 22] Kilmelford 229	49 71	4 6	....	10 19	....	4277 5411	....	....	8748
Cumlodden and Lochfyneside	Roderick MacLeod, MA, BD, PH D, JP	1966	1985	Furnace, Inveraray, Argyll, PA32 8XU [049 95] Furnace 288	143	15	27	25	.....	11729	.....	.....	8646
Gigha and Cara †	*Vacant*	......	......	Gigha, Argyll, PA41 7AA [058 35] Gigha 245	59	4	12	8	.....	7377	.....	200	8946
Glassary and Kilmartin	Norman R. Whyte, BD, DIP MIN	1982	......	Kilmichael Glassary, Lochgilphead, PA31 8QA [054 684] Dunadd 271	152	9	17	11	.....	10116	.....	.....	8646

Charge	Minister	Ord.	Ind.	Address and Tel. No.	Com.	Eld.	W.G.	S.S.	B.C.	C.L. £	As'd £	Gi'n £	Stp. £
Glenaray and Inveraray	John E. M'Quilken, MA, BD	1969	1983	Inveraray, Argyll, PA32 8XT [0499] Inveraray 2060	173	10	23	25	8	15269	990	990	8646
Jura	Vacant	......	......	Craighouse, Isle of Jura, PA60 7XG [049 682] Jura 226	47	8	......	14	......	7408	......	12	8946
Kilarrow linked with Kilmeny	[Vacant	......	......	Bowmore, Isle of Islay, PA43 7LH [049 681] Bowmore 271	176	13	26	51	......	16740	......	......	v
	[David W. Davidson Auxiliary	1987	......	Graniel, Glenegedale, Port Ellen, Isle of Islay, PA42 [0496] Port Ellen 2194	64	9	13	33	4	5502	......	......	v
					21	4	......	......	......	2119	231	231	
Kilberry linked with Tarbert	Alexander M'Callum, BD	1987	......	Tarbert, Loch Fyne, Argyll, PA29 6TY [088 02] Tarbert 288	236	18	56	52	40	20693	2404	2404	v
					108	10	30	17	......	8536	......	......	
Kilcalmonell linked with Skipness	Archibald Lamont, MA	1952	1971	Whitehouse, Tarbert, Argyll, PA29 6XS [088 073] Whitehouse 224	33	4	......	......	......	2801	......	......	8748
					84	2	16	20	......	5456	901	1248	
Kilchoman† linked with Portnahaven†	R. B. Donaldson, B SOC SC	1953	1987	Port Charlotte, Isle of Islay, PA48 7UD [049 685] Port Charlotte 241	38	2	14	11	......	3058	524	524	v
Kildalton and Oa †	Jean E. Stewart (Mrs.)	1983	......	Port Ellen, Isle of Islay, PA42 7DB [0496] Port Ellen 2447	150	15	19	54	10	39063	......	......	8847
Killean and Kilchenzie	John H. Paton, BSC, BD	1983	1984	Muasdale, Tarbert, Argyll, PA29 6XD [058 32] Glenbarr 249	214	14	35	19	14	17354	1387	1387	8646
Kilmeny	see Kilarrow												
Kilninver and Kilmelford	see Craignish												
Lochgilphead	John R. Callen, MA, BD	1962	......	Lochgilphead, Argyll, PA31 8QZ [0546] Lochgilphead 2238	274	21	20	65	4	25752	2634	2701	9009
North Knapdale	David Montgomery	1961	1971	Tayvallich, Lochgilphead, PA31 8PN [054 67] Tayvallich 229	78	7	......	14	4	6941	......	500	8748
Portnahaven	see Kilchoman												
Saddell and Carradale	Alistair J. Dunlop, MA, FSASCOT	1965	1979	Carradale, Campbeltown, PA28 6QG [058 33] Carradale 253	290	14	40	60	5	17141	1464	1464	8646
Skipness	see Kilcalmonell												
Southend	Roderick H. M'Nidder	1987	......	Southend, Campbeltown, Argyll, PA28 6RQ [058 683] Southend 274	267	14	44	42	......	13059	956	956	v
South Knapdale	see Ardrishaig												
Tarbert	see Kilberry												

Minister	Ord.	App.	Ret.	Charge	Address and Tel. No.
Cormack, John R. H., MA, BD	1941	......	1981	(Campbeltown Lowland)	21 Dell Road, Campbeltown, PA28 [0586] *Campbeltown 4265*
Doyle, D. Brock, MA	1934	......	1974	(Bowling)	Abbeyfield House, Carradale, Campbeltown, PA28
					[058 33] Carradale 218
Fraser, Alexander, MA, BD	1938	......	1978	(Cumlodden and Lochfyneside)	6 Bridge Terrace, Furnace, Inveraray, Argyll, PA32
Gordon, David C.	1953	......	1988	(Gigha and Cara)	16 Braeside Road, Largs, KA30 8HD
Loudon, George W. H., MA, BD, STM	1938	......	1979	(Bolton and Saltoun)	Church Cottage, Dippen, Carradale, Campbeltown, PA28
					[058 33] Carradale 341
Nelson, William C., MA, BD	1949	......	1987	(Southend)	18 Kintyre Gardens, Campbeltown, PA28 [0586] *Campbeltown 54088*
Robertson, Donald	1936	......	1976	(Lochalsh and Stromeferry)	Flat 1, Weem House, Manse Brae, Lochgilphead, PA31 8QZ
					[0546] Lochgilphead 3603
Somerville, A. G., MA	1942	......	1982	(Glenaray and Inveraray)	18 Glenglip, Ardrishaig, Argyll, PA30 8HF *[0546] Lochgilphead 2831*

COMMUNION SUNDAYS

Ardrishaig	2 Ap., 1 Nv.
Campbeltown—all churches	1 My., Nv.
Craignish	1 Je., Nv.
Cumlodden and Lochfyneside	3 My., Nv.
Gigha and Cara	1 My., Nv.
Glassary and Kilmartin	*K'martin*—1 Je., Nv.
	K'michael—1 Ap., 1 Sp.
	Lochgair—1 My., Oc.
Glenaray and Inveraray	1 Ap., Jl., Oc., Dc.
Jura	2 Jl.
Kilarrow	1 My., Au., Nv.
Kilberry *with* Tarbert	1 My., 1 Oc.
Kilcalmonell	1 Jl., 3 Nv.
Kilchoman	1 Ja., 2 Dc., E.
Kildalton	1 Ja., Je., Oc., E.
Killean and Kilchenzie	1 Mr., Jl., Oc.
Kilmeny	2 My., 3 Nv.
Kilninver and Kilmelford	2 Je., Oc.
Lochgilphead	1 Ap., 1 Nv.
North Knapdale—	
Inverlussa and	
Bellanoch	2 My., Nv.
Tayvallich	2 My., Nv.
Portnahaven	3 Jl.
Saddell and Carradale	2 My., 1 Nv.
Skipness	2 My., Nv.
Southend	1 Je., 1 Dc.
South Knapdale	1 Sp.

20. DUNOON

Meets at Dunoon St. John's, on the first Tuesday of February, April, September and November and on the last Tuesday of June; and at Rothesay Trinity on the first Tuesday of March, October and December

Clerk: Rev. RONALD SAMUEL, TD, BSC, BD, STM, 12 Crichton Road, Rothesay, Isle of Bute, PA20 9JR *[0700] Rothesay 2797*

Charge	Minister	Ord.	Ind.	Address and Tel. No.	Com.	Eld.	W.G.	S.S.	B.C.	C.L. £	As'd £	Gi'n £	Stp. £
Ascog	Duncan A. Ballantyne, BD, FSA SCOT	1986	......	Craigmore, Rothesay, Isle of Bute, PA20 9LD *[0700] Rothesay 2506*	77	6	14	......	......	4800	750	750	8847
linked with													
Rothesay					171	11	16	29	6	12430	1162	1290	
Craigmore													
St. Brendan's													

Charge	Minister	Ord.	Ind.	Address and Tel. No.	Com.	Eld.	W.G.	S.S.	B.C.	C.L. £	As'd £	Gi'n £	Stp. £
Dunoon—Old and St. Cuthbert's	Ronald A. A. Gale, LTH	1982	......	1 Royal Crescent, Dunoon, PA23 7AH [0369] Dunoon 4043	606	48	83	72	14	31887	6745	6745	9507
St. John's	Vacant	......	......	7 Gordon Street, Dunoon, Argyll. PA23 7EJ [0369] Dunoon 2128	363	21	45	46	24	40621	5040	5040	v
linked with Sandbank					163	10	...	11	10	9368	368	385	v
					236	20	70	39	11	15948	2229	2229	v
Innellan	Hugh Conkey, BSC, BD	1987	......	Innellan, Argyll, PA23 7SH [036 983] Innellan 276	177	10	...	20	8	8230	1462	1462	v
linked with Inverchaolain and Toward													
Kilfinan	Iain C. Barclay, MA, BD	1976	1988	Tighnabruaich, Argyll, PA21 2DX [070 081] Tighnabruaich 349	17	3	7	...	...	1361	143	158	
linked with Kyles					233	8	30	36	...	14373	1061	1061	v
Kilmodan and Colintraive	Douglas W. Wallace, MA, BD	1981	1982	Glendaruel, Colintraive, Argyll, PA22 3AA [036 982] Glendaruel 232	143	10	18	9	14	10938	...	50	8646
Kilmun St. Munn's	James S. H. Cutler, CENG, MISTRUCTE, BD	1986	......	Laurel Grove, Blairmore, Dunoon, PA23 8TE [036 984] Kilmun 313	117	7	21	...	...	5087	...	129	8646
linked with Strone and Ardentinny					170	17	30	21	4	25619	...	50	8646
Kingarth and Kilchattan Bay	Iain A. Laing, MA, BD	1971	1983	10 Bishop Ter., Rothesay, Isle of Bute, PA20 9HF [0700] Rothesay 2407	98	5	36	13	...	6828	1188	1188	9507
linked with Rothesay The High Kirk					492	26	50	30	8	21222	2946	2946	9507
Kirn	May M. Allison (Mrs.), BD	1988	......	Stewart Street, Kirn, Dunoon, Argyll, PA23 8DS [0369] Dunoon 2220	604	35	56	93	24	42003	8225	8272	v
Kyles	see Kilfinan												
Lochgoilhead and Kilmorich	James S. Marshall, BA, BD, FFA, MDIV	1986	......	Lochgoilhead, Argyll, PA24 8AA [030 13] Lochgoilhead 369	136	11	30	12	...	10736	...	...	8646
North Bute	Quintin Finlay, BA, BD	1975	1983	32 Marine Place, Rothesay, Isle of Bute, PA20 0LF [0700] Rothesay 2873	314	24	29	24	2	14681	1276	549	8847
Rothesay—Craigmore	see Ascog												
The High Kirk	see Kingarth												
Trinity	Ronald Samuel, TD, BSC, BD, STM	1960	1970	12 Crichton Road, Rothesay, Isle of Bute, PA20 9JR [0700] Rothesay 2797	764	38	54	88	59	37104	6780	6780	9507

Sandbank	*see* Dunoon St. John's				
Strachur and Strathlachlan	Iain K. Stiven, MA, BD, MED	1960	1988	Strachur, Cairndow, PA27 8DG [036 986] Strachur 246	
Strone and Ardentinny	*see* Kilmun				

199 15 24 28 14 24665 8646

Minister	Ord.	App.	Ret.	Charge	Address and Tel. No.
Bell, J. R.	1944	.....	1973	(Rothesay St. John's)	Kyles View, Mount Stuart Road, Rothesay, PA20 9DY [0700] Rothesay 2341
Currie, Walter T., MA	1963	.....	1976	(Glasgow Pollokshaws)	Woodbank, Sandbank, Dunoon, PA23 8PD [036 985] Sandbank 6339
Fulton, Robert M., MA	1939	.....	1985	(Ascog *with* Rothesay Craigmore St. Brendan's)	Undercliffe, 20 Craigmore Road, Rothesay, PA20 9LB [0700] Rothesay 4478
Graham, John, MA	1944	.....	1987	(Dunoon St. John's *with* Sandbank)	Upper Balmoral, 187 Marine Parade, Hunter's Quay, Dunoon, PA23 8HF [0369] Dunoon 2452
Gray, John A.	1950	.....	1986	(Glasgow Baillieston Mure Memorial)	Holyns, Ardentinny, Dunoon, PA23 8TR [036 981] Ardentinny 243
Hamilton, Patrick J. R., MA	1948	.....	1979	(East Kilbride South)	La Madrugada, Tighnabruaich, PA21 2BE [070 081] Tighnabruaich 586
Makins, Gordon W. G., BA	1954	.....	1986	(Kilmun St. Munn's *with* Sandbank)	The Old Manse, Kilmun, Argyll, PA23 8SD [036 984] Kilmun 461
Miller, Harry Galbraith, MA, BD	1941	.....	1985	(Iona and Ross of Mull)	An Cala Ciatach, Bannatyne Mains Road, Port Bannatyne, Rothesay, PA20 0PH [0700] Rothesay 2920
Morton, James, MA	1930	.....	1971	(Millport West)	7 Millfat, Auchtermuchty, KY14 7BQ [0337] Auchtermuchty 28968
Munro, Iain R.	1965	.....	1985	(Barra)	The Cottages, Invereck, Dunoon, PA23 8OS [0369] Dunoon 6634
Roberts, Alexander, MA	1936	.....	1973	(Dunblane St. Blane's)	Ranikhet, Kilbride Avenue, Dunoon, PA23 7LH [0369] Dunoon 2182
Smith, W. C. B., MBE, JP	1936	.....	1974	(Glassary)	Cuilmuich, Carrick Castle, Lochgoilhead, PA24 8AF [030 13] L'goilhead 254
Sommerville, Douglas F.	1948	.....	1976	(Inverchaolain and Toward)	17 Westfield, Dunoon, PA23 8RS [036 984] Kilmun 603
Stewart, Donald, MA	1944	.....	1984	(Fenwick)	Seafield, Toward, Dunoon, PA23 7HG [036 987] Toward 206

COMMUNION SUNDAYS

Ascog	1 My., Nv.	
Craigmore	1 My., Nv.	
Dunoon—		
Old and St. Cuthbert's	1 Fb., My., Nv.	
St. John's	1 My., Nv.	
Innellan	1 Mr., Je., Sp., Dc.	
Inverchaolain and Toward	l Je., Dc.	
Kilfinan	l Ap., Oc.	
Kilmodan and Colintraive	1 My., Nv.	
Kilmun	1 My., Nv.	
Kingarth and Kilchattan Bay	3 Mr., Nv.	
Kirn	1 My., l Oc.	
Kyles	1 My., Nv.	
Lochgoilhead and Kilmorich	2 Mr., Je., Sp., Nv. / l Au., E.	
North Bute	1 My., Nv.	
Rothesay—		
The High Kirk	1 Fb., 2 My., 1 Nv.	
Trinity	1 Fb., My., Nv.	
Sandbank	1 Ja., My., Nv.	
Strachur and Strathlachlan	l Mr., 2 Je., l Oc.	
Strone and Ardentinny	l Ap., Jy., Oc.	

21. LORN AND MULL

Meets at Oban, in Kilmore and Oban Parish Church Hall, on the first Tuesday of each month, except January, August and September

Clerk: Rev. WALTER M. RITCHIE, ACIS, Appin, Argyll, PA38 4DD [063 173] Appin 206

Treasurer: JAMES A. ANDERSON, BI, Cottach, Connel, Argyll, PA37 [063 171] Connel 470

Charge	Minister	Ord.	Ind.	Address and Tel. No.	Com.	Eld.	W.G.	S.S.	B.C.	C.L. £	As'd £	Gi'n £	Stp. £
Appin†	Walter M. Ritchie, ACIS	1973	1981	Appin, Argyll, PA38 4DD [063 173] Appin 206	110	10	30	9	...	5316	...	...	8646
linked with Lismore					66	8	...	9	...	5561	...	...	8646
Ardchattan†	Jeffrey A. M'Cormick, BD	1984	......	Ardchattan, Connel, Argyll, PA37 1QZ [063 171] Connel 364	228	23	20	35	10	19227	...	112	8646
Coll†	George M. Donaldson, MA, BD	1984	......	Isle of Tiree, PA77 6TN [087 92] Scarinish 377	19	3	14	8	...	1777	...	...	8946
linked with Tiree†	Vacant	......	......		131	9	25	23	7	15015	...	...	8946
Colonsay and Oronsay†	Vacant	......	......	Isle of Colonsay, PA61 7YW [095 12] Colonsay 307	19	1	...	...	...	1369	...	...	8946
Connel	William A. B. Ritchie, M.THEOL	1977	1984	St. Oran's Manse, Connel, Argyll, PA37 1PQ [063 171] Connel 242	232	16	...	50	13	17578	...	7	8646
Glenorchy and Inishael†	William T. Hogg, MA, BD	1979	1981	Dalmally, Argyll, PA33 1AS [083 82] Dalmally 227	120	9	46	25	6	9014	...	30	8646
linked with Strathfillan	Herbert F. Gunneberg *Associate*	1962	1981	Tyndrum, Crianlarich, FK20 8RY [083 84] Tyndrum 244	61	6	24	19	2	6850	...	...	8646
Iona and Ross of Mull†	Vacant	......	......	Bunessan, Isle of Mull, PA72 [068 17] Fionnphort 227	37	3	...	...	...	3300	...	124	v
linked with Kilfinichen and Kilvickeon					35	4	...	...	...	3469	...	...	
Kilbrandon and Kilchattan†	Malcolm A. Ritchie	1955	1982	Easdale, Oban, PA34 4RF [085 23] Balvicar 240	108	8	27	35	16	14548	...	...	8646
Kilchrenan and Dalavich†	Vacant	......	......	Taynuilt, Argyll, PA35 1HG [086 62] Taynuilt 204	54	7	10	...	...	5485	...	...	8646
linked with Muckairn					188	15	23	33	6	24094	...	...	8646

Charge	Minister	Ord.	App.	Address and Tel. No.								
Kilfinichen and Kilvickeon†	*see* Iona											
Kilmore and Oban	Andrew B. Campbell, BD, DPS	1979		Strathearn, Breadalbane Street, Oban, PA34 5PA [0631] Oban 62322	1204	90	103	149	23	61500	8959	8959	v
	T. David Watson, B SC, BD *Associate*	1988											
Mull, Isle of—													
Kilninian and Kilmore† *linked with* Salen and Ulva	Alan T. Taylor, BD	1980		Tobermory, Isle of Mull, PA75 6PS [0688] Tobermory 2226	55	6	15	9	......	5147	......	......	v
Tobermory *linked with* Torosay and Kinlochspelvie	William Pollock, MA, BD, PHD *Associate*	1987		Salen, Aros, Isle of Mull, PA72 6JF [068 03] Aros 359	42	4	14	18	......	3851	......	......	9096
					121	15	16	22	......	13030	......	60	
					38	8	......	7	6	3554	......	90	

Lismore† — *see* Appin
Muckairn† — *see* Kilchrenan
Salen and Ulva — *see* Mull
Strathfillan† — *see* Glenorchy
Tiree — *see* Coll
Tobermory — *see* Mull
Torosay and Kinlochspelvie — *see* Mull

Minister	Ord.	App.	Ret.	Charge	Address and Tel. No.
Crawford, Ron L.,	1961	......	1988	(Colonsay and Oronsay)	——
Forsyth, James	1970	......	1988	(Kilchrenan and Dalavich *with* Muckairn)	——
Galbraith, David O., MA, BD	1940	......	1980	(Muckairn)	Achnameadhonach, Balindeor, Taynuilt, Argyll, PA35 1JS
MacCallum, Duncan A.	1934	......	1976	(Connel)	Ardlynn, Deirdre Road, Connel, PA37 1PH [063 171] Connel 443
Macdonald, John H., TH B, TH M	1950	......	1975	(Melrose High Cross)	17 Argyll Square, Oban, PA34
Macdonald, Norman	1936	......	1983	(Ardchattan)	Rhugarbh Appin [063 173] Appin 210
MacInnes, John E.	1963	......	1987	(Snizort)	26 Castle Road, Dunbeg, Oban [0631] Oban 64873
MacKechnie, J. M., MBE, MA	1938	......	1978	(Kilchrenan and Dalavich)	Eastwing, Manton Grounds, Windermere, Cumbria
Macmillan, Kenneth M.	1938	......	1980	(Appin)	20A Northumberland Street, Edinburgh, EH3 6LS
Troup, Harold J. G., MA	1951	......	1980	(Garelochhead)	Tighshee, Isle of Iona, PA76 [068 17] Fionnphort 309

SYNOD VII — FORTH

Meets at Dunblane on the fourth Thursday of April

Correspondents: Fife; Clydesdale; Lothian; Perth and Angus

Clerk: THOMAS KINLOCH, MA, Delta, 5 Rulley View, Denny, FK6 6QQ   [0324] Denny 825441

22. FALKIRK

Meets at St. Andrew's, Falkirk on the first Tuesday of September, October, November, December, February, March, April and May, and on the fourth Tuesday of June

Clerk: Rev. C. R. HERIOT, BA, The Manse, Brightons, Falkirk, FK2 0IP   [0324] Polmont 712062

Charge	Minister	Ord.	Ind.	Address and Tel. No.	Com.	Eld.	W.G.	S.S.	B.C.	C.L. £	As'd £	Gi'n £	Stp. £
Airth	Ann M. Ballentine, MA, BD ¶	1981	......	Airth, Falkirk, FK2 8IQ [032 483] Airth 474	257	15	32	51	15	20429	.....	425	8646
Blackbraes and Shieldhill	J. Andrew M'Mullin, MA	1960	1988	Shieldhill, Falkirk, FK1 2EG [0324] Falkirk 21938	460	25	20	60	.....	17478	1609	1609	8667
Bo'ness—													
Old	William Sutherland	1964	1971	10 Dundas Street, Bo'ness, EH51 0DG [0506] Bo'ness 822206	943	41	46	87	11	34050	5606	5606	9339
St. Andrew's	Albert O. Bogle, BD	1981	......	Bo'ness, EH51 9DT [0506] Bo'ness 822195	608	27	59	103	25	31948	4524	4540	9339
Bonnybridge	John Jackson, MA	1958	1973	32 Larbert Road, Bonnybridge, FK4 1EE [0324] Bonnybridge 812621	809	28	37	73	7	24155	1736	2869	8667
Bothkennar and Carronshore	William D. Whitelaw ¶	1984	......	11 Hunter's Place, Greenmount Park, Carronshore, Falkirk [0324] Larbert 570525	403	22	16	44	12	19145	.....	100	8646
Brightons	Charles R. Heriot, BA	1962	1967	Brightons, Falkirk, FK2 0IP [0324] Polmont 712062	793	44	74	178	62	41470	7995	8195	9552
Carriden	Iain M. Robertson, MA	1967	1978	Carriden, Bo'ness, EH51 [0506] Bo'ness 822141	795	42	34	41	24	34072	4776	4776	8979
Cumbernauld—													
Abronhill [E]	{Neil W. Barclay, BSC, BED, BD / Marilyn Douglas, DCS	1986 /	......	26 Ash Road, Cumbernauld, G67 3ED [0236] Cumbernauld 723833 / Deaconess—see List H [0236] Cumbernauld 732136	757	35	55	137	27	20393	.....	135	9147

Congregation	Minister		Address								
Condorrat	Bruce M'Nicol, BL, BD, JP	1967 1969	11 Rosehill Dr., Cumbern'd, G67 4FD [0236] Cumbernauld 721464	711	24	....	416	103	31410	1276	1276	8646
	Thomas Bisek, STM *Associate*	 1985	82 Cairngorm Gardens, Balloch, Cumbernauld, G67									
Kildrum	*Vacant*	....	Clouden Rd., Cumbernauld, G67 2IQ [0236] Cumbernauld 723204	745	42	....	74	20	49267	100	100	9339
Old	Graham A. Duncan, BED, BD	1977 1988	Baronhill, Cumbernauld, Glasgow, G67 2SD [0236] Cumbernauld 721912	321	14	....	53	17	15271	710	....	8646
	Douglas S. Paterson, MA, BD	1986 1984	46E Braeface Road, Cumbernauld, G67 [0236] Cumbernauld 722743									
St. Mungo's [E]	Angus M. Wells, BD DIPMIN *Associate*	1987	59C Douglas House, Allanfauld Road, Cumbernauld, G67 [0236] Cumbernauld 720735	755	44	....	107	52	32900	100	160	8979
	Norma A. Ronald, DCS	....	Deaconess—see List H [0236] Cumbernauld 721538									
Denny—												
Dunipace North *linked with* Dunipace Old	*Vacant*	....	Dunipace Manse, Denny, Stirlingshire, FK6 6QJ [0324] Denny 823640	453	15	....	31	7	18129	2229	2229	8979
				211	10	....	....	....	7864	1478	1478	
Old	Richard Smith, BD	1976 1983	31 Duke Street, Denny, FK6 6NR [0324] Denny 824508	769	38	28	80	9	25396	3292	3292	8979
Westpark	R. Douglas Cranston, MA, BD	1986	Baxter Crescent, Denny, FK6 5EZ [0324] Denny 823782	1170	44	73	80	4	41989	7592	7592	9552
Dennyloanhead *linked with* Haggs	Roger A. F. Dean	1983	Watson Place, Dennyloanhead, FK4 2BG [0324] Bonnybridge 813786	335	26	17	17	6	12448	1006	1006	8979
				378	29	35	47	39	14348	1654	1937	
Falkirk— Bainsford	F. Derek Gunn, BD	1986	Mungalhead Road, Falkirk, FK2 7LJ [0324] Falkirk 21087	580	18	41	57	43	26538	4233	4305	9339
Camelon— Irving	John M'Callum	1962	Dorrator Road, Camelon, Falkirk, FK1 4BN	484	12	25	37	17	17170	....	515	8646
St. John's	James K. Wallace, MA, BD ¶	1988	24 Rennie Street, Falkirk, FK1 5QW [0324] Falkirk 23035	674	28	35	43	18	26900	3705	2110	v
Erskine	Graeme W. M. Muckart, MTH, FSASCOT ¶	1983	Burnbrae Road, Falkirk, FK1 5SD [0324] Falkirk 23631	570	46	33	28	14	34935	5868	5868	9552
Grahamston United	Duncan E. M'Clements, MA, BD	1967 1976	30 Russel Street, Falkirk, FK2 7HS [0324] Falkirk 2446I	747	43	37	57	29	61760	7503	7503	9552

Charge	Minister	Ord.	Ind.	Address and Tel. No.	Com.	Eld.	W.G.	S.S.	B.C.	C.L. £	As'd £	Gi'n £	Stp. £
Laurieston *linked with* Redding and Westquarter	Ronald J. M'Dowall, BD	1980	……	11 Polmont Rd., Laurieston, FK2 9QQ [0324] *Falkirk 21196*	437	27	55	53	15	28682	2852	2852	8979
	Neil Martin, DCS	……	……	*Deacon—see List H*	262	15	40	51	12	15219	1630	1665	
Old and St. Modan's	M. Leith Fisher, MA, BD	1967	1979	9 Major's Loan, Falkirk, FK1 5QF [0324] *Falkirk 23063*	1394	78	86	221	88	73640	14603	14603	10725
	Ronald W. Smith, BA, BED, BD *Associate*	1978	……	19 Neilson Street, Falkirk, FK1 5AQ [0324] *Falkirk 21058*									
St. Andrew's	Robert M'Ghee, DD	1959	1972	1 Maggiewood's Loan, F'kirk, FK1 5SJ [0324] *Falkirk 23308*	877	52	40	60	31	59796	14022	14022	10725
St. James'	Alan B. Telfer, BA, BD	1983	……	25 Neilson Street, Falkirk, FK1 5AQ [0324] *Falkirk 21605*	511	22	……	62	13	23722	2002	2002	8742
West	Martin R. B. C. Reid	1960	1968	38 Camelon Road, Falkirk, FK1 5SH [0324] *Falkirk 23242*	485	16	20	16	1	79269	3186	3186	8979
Grangemouth—Charing Cross and West	Daniel L. Mathers, BD	1982	……	36 Thistle Avenue, Grangemouth, FK3 8YQ [0324] *Falkirk 474511*	433	23	29	42	27	34429	730	730	8646
Dundas	Douglas B. Blair, LTH	1969	……	5 Abbotsgrange Rd., Grangemouth, FK3 9JD [0324] *Grangemouth 482467*	438	25	24	23	7	16966	1667	1667	8742
Grange	Elaine W. M'Kinnon, MA, BA, BD ¶	1988	……	3 Ronaldshay Crescent, Grangemouth, FK3 9JH [0324] *Grangemouth 482500*	459	18	35	14	25	16119	1401	563	v
Kerse	Ean M. Simpson	1963	1973	142 Bo'ness Road, Grangemouth, FK3 9BX [0324] *Grangemouth 482109*	863	63	70	46	7	25745	6999	1500	9783
Kirk of the Holy Rood	Gordon Ferguson	1972	……	Bowhouse Road, Grangemouth, FK3 [0324] *Grangemouth 471595*	949	36	……	82	19	23900	3827	3827	8979
Old	James M. Gibson, LTH, LRAM	1976	1978	Ronaldshay Crescent, Grangemouth, FK3 9JH [0324] *Grangemouth 472868*	920	47	67	84	46	40355	10000	1166	10725
Haggs *see Dennyloanhead*													
High Bonnybridge St. Helen's	John Watson¶	1961	1972	26 Duncan Street, Bonnybridge, FK4 1DP [0324] *Bonnybridge 813450*	226	15	23	15	10	8000	……	……	*10146
Larbert—East	Eric J. Murray	1958	1964	1 Cortachy Avenue, Carron, Falkirk [0324] *Larbert 562402*	857	31	20	139	53	33833	5885	3819	9783
Old	Clifford A. J. Rennie, MA, BD	1973	1985	38 South Broomage Avenue, Larbert, FK5 3ED [0324] *Larbert 562868*	1231	65	73	138	35	65004	13983	13983	10725
West	Evelyn M. Young (Mrs.), BSC, BD	1984	……	11 Carronvale Rd., Larbert, FK5 3LZ [0324] *Larbert 562878*	710	47	……	66	78	33313	5979	6988	9339

Congregation	Minister			Address and Tel. No.								
Muiravonside	Stanley Hill, LTH	1967	1984	Maddiston, Falkirk, FK2 [0324] Polmont 712876	430	27	21	23	15	21804	400	400	8646
Polmont Old	Graham M. Thain, LL.B., BD	1988	......	Polmont, Falkirk, FK2 0QY [0324] Polmont 715166	767	37	......	73	68	34561	6796	6796	9552
Redding and Westquarter	see Falkirk Laurieston												
Slamannan	Samuel B. Ovens	1982	......	Slamannan, Falkirk, FK1 [032 485] Slamannan 307	369	15	16	63	......	21455	......	......	8646
Stenhouse and Carron	Robert K. Hardie, BD	1968	1969	Stenhousemuir, Larbert, FK5 4BU [0324] Larbert 562393	789	48	41	111	31	31670	4809	4809	8838

Minister	Ord.	App.	Ret.	Charge	Address and Tel. No.
Brown, Gavin S., MA, BD	1938	......	1979	(Falkirk Laurieston)	4 Polmont Park, Polmont, Falkirk, FK2 0XT [0324] Polmont 715244
Chaplin, David, MA, BD	1953	......	1982	(Falkirk Erskine)	13 Manse Road, Dollar, FK14 7AL [025 94] Dollar 2627
Cordiner, James, MA	1945	......	1975	(Savoch)	53 Garry Place, Hallglen, Falkirk, FK1 2QL
Fleming, A. A., BSC, JP	1938	......	1978	(Howgate)	60 Muirhead Road, Stenhousemuir, FK5 4JD [0324] Larbert 556500
Gillon, George, MA, CF, JP	1940	......	1980	(Airth)	43 Strathmore Avenue, Dunblane, FK15 9HX [0786] Dunblane 823495
Goodman, Richard A.	1976	......	1986	(Isle of Mull Associate)	15 Almond Court, Grangemouth, FK3 8PY [0324] Grangemouth 482422
Holland, John C.	1976	......	1985	(Strone and Ardentinny)	2 Breadalbane Place, Polmont, Falkirk, FK2 0RF [0324] Polmont 712716
Honeyman, John	1957	......	1974	(Clatt with Rhynie)	6 Abbot's View, Polmont, Falkirk, FK2 0QC [0324] Polmont 713251
Lawrie, Robert G., MA	1938	......	1976	(Denny Old)	Beechfield, Glasgow Road, Denny [0324] Denny 822126
Lyall, William R.	1954	......	1987	(Grangemouth Grange)	3 Kinacres Grove, Bo'ness, EH51 [0506] Bo'ness 826739
Mechie, W. M.	1946	......	1984	(Kirknewton and East Calder)	4 Haygate Avenue, Brightons, Falkirk, FK2 0TL [0324] Polmont 713490
Munro, Henry, BA, LTH, LTI	1971	......	1988	(Denny Dunipace North with Old)	Viewforth, High Road, Maddiston, Falkirk, FK2 0BL [0324] Polmont 712446
Ormiston, Hugh C., BSC, BD, MPHIL	1969	1980	......	Industrial Chaplain	26 Abbot's Road, Grangemouth, FK3 8JF [0324] G'mouth 473067
Robson, James, MA, BD	1951	......	1987	(Falkirk Camelon St. John's)	59 Anson Avenue, Falkirk, FK1 5JB [0324] Falkirk 26913
Talman, Hugh, MA	1943	......	1987	(Polmont Old)	Niagara, 70 Lawers Crescent, Polmont, FK2 0RQ [0324] Polmont 711240

ADDRESSES OF TOWN CHURCHES

Falkirk—
Bainsford — Hendry Street, Bainsford
Camelon—
Irving — Dorrator Road, Camelon
St. John's — Glasgow Road x Stirling Road
Erskine — Cockburn Street x Hodge Street
Grahamston — Church Street
Laurieston — Main Falkirk Road
Old and St. Modan's — Kirk Wynd
St. Andrew's — Newmarket Street
St. James' — Thornhill Road x Firs Street
West — West Bridge Street

Grangemouth—
Charing Cross and West — Charing Cross
Dundas — Bo'ness Road
Grange — Park Road
Kerse — Abbot's Road
Kirk of the Holy Rood — Bowhouse Road
Old — Ronaldshay Crescent

23. STIRLING

Meets at Dunblane, in the Cathedral Hall, on the second Thursday of September; and at Bridge of Allan Chalmers, on the second Thursday of every other month except January, July and August when there is no meeting.

Clerk: Rev. GEORGE A. M'CUTCHEON, MA, 13 Harviestoun Road, Dollar, FK14 7HG [025 94] Dollar 2609

Charge	Minister	Ord.	Ind.	Address and Tel. No.	Com.	Eld.	W.G.	S.S.	B.C.	C.L. £	As'd £ 1931	Gi'n £ 1931	Stp. £
Aberfoyle *linked with* Port of Menteith	David K. Speed, LTH	1969	1986	Loch Ard Road, Aberfoyle, Stirling, FK8 3SZ [087 72] Aberfoyle 391	245	12	50	31	17	16629	383	383	9159
					102	7	....	20	4	7352	383	383	
Alloa— North	David S. F. Couper, MA, BD	1988	....	30 Claremont, Alloa, FK10 2DF [0259] Alloa 216845	443	27	58	19	....	24734	5137	5137	v
St. Mungo's	Keith F. Hall, BD	1981	1987	37a Claremont, Alloa, FK10 2DG [0259] Alloa 213872	1403	74	75	59	16	136860	18272	18563	v
West	Alan M'Kenzie, BSC, BD	1988	....	29 Claremont, Alloa, FK10 2DF [0259] Alloa 214204	618	37	77	41	12	29545	5556	6000	v
Alva	G. Hutton B. Steel, MA, BD	1982	....	The Manse, Alva, FK12 5JT [0259] Alva 60262	843	43	100	116	27	33986	6795	6795	10032
Balfron	John Jamieson, LTH	1967	....	Balfron, Glasgow, G63 0SX [0360] Balfron 40285	389	20	....	63	120	24206	5579	4750	8895
Balquhidder	James W. Benson, BA, BD, TD	1975	1982	Balquhidder, Lochearnhead, FK19 8NY [087 74] Strathyre 235	133	4	20	13	....	6874	....	....	8646
Bannockburn— Allan	Robert S. Fyall, MA, BD	1986	....	Bogend Road, Bannockburn, FK7 8NP [0786] Bannockburn 814692	696	34	30	48	10	25419	5810	5810	9495
Ladywell	Charles D. M'Millan, LTH	1979	....	57 The Firs, FK7 0EG [0786] Bannockburn 812467	828	38	60	56	7	30110	5068	5138	8646
	Janette M'Naughton, DCS	....	....	*Deaconess—see* List H [0786] Bannockburn 816244									
Bridge of Allan— Chalmers	Graham K. Blount, LLB, BD ¶	1976	1983	34 Kenilworth Road, Bridge of Allan, Stirling, FK9 4EH [0786] B. of A. 832118	357	23	40	67	31	28156	6688	6688	10578
Holy Trinity	John C. Nicol, MA, BD	1965	1985	29 Keir St., Bridge of Allan, Stirling, FK9 4QJ [0786] B. of A. 832093	713	37	69	114	32	42018	6840	6840	9837

Congregation	Minister	Ord.	Ind.	Address									
Buchanan *linked with* **Drymen**	W. J. R. Hay, MA, BD	1959	1981	Buchanan, Drymen, Glasgow, G63 0JE [036 087] *Balmaha 212*	108	12	33	18	…	8295	575	575	8646
					313	17	…	33	4	15932	2457	2457	
Buchlyvie *linked with* **Gartmore**	Moira G. MacCormick, LTH	1986	……	8 Culbowie Avenue, Buchlyvie, Stirling, FK8 [036 085] *Buchlyvie 249*	245	12	40	29	7	13191	1026	1026	8646
					103	11	…	21	5	8178	457	457	
Callander	Iain M. Goring, BSC, BD	1976	1985	Aveland Park Road, Callander, FK7 8EN [0877] *Callander 30097*	875	40	58	125	26	53859	8854	8854	10617
Cambusbarron The Bruce Mem'l	William Craig, BA, LTH	1974	……	22 Douglas Ter., Stirling, FK7 9LL [0786] *Stirling 64108*	508	20	36	62	…	19266	1484	1484	8646
Clackmannan	T. Ralph Taylor, BD	1974	1984	Clackmannan, FK10 4JH [0259] *Alloa 214238*	928	30	…	95	43	30658	6634	6634	10077
Coalsnaughton	Malcolm H. MacRae, MA ¶	1986	……	Coalsnaughton, Tillicoultry, FK13 6LJ [0259] *Tillicoultry 50272*	288	9	23	26	9	11454	…	50	8646
Cowie *linked with* **Plean**	William T. Cullen, BA, LTH	1984	……	Plean, Stirling, FK7 8BX [0786] *Bannockburn 813287*	318	15	20	24	8	9309	1282	1151	8646
					345	15	…	30	42	12532	1305	1305	
Dollar *linked with* **Glendevon** *linked with* **Muckhart**	Arthur R. C. Gaston, MA, BD	1969	1975	2 Manse Road, Dollar, FK14 7AJ [025 94] *Dollar 2601*	753	46	51	52	68	48185	7278	7278	
	Vacant	……	……		60	5	…	…	…	2806	506	566	9465
				Muckhart, Dollar, FK14 7JN [025 981] *Muckhart 464*	177	11	27	27	6	12288	1660	1660	
Drymen—	*see* Buchanan												
Dunblane— Cathedral	Colin G. M'Intosh, BSC, BD	1976	1988	Dunblane, FK15 0AQ [0786] *Dunblane 822205*	1256	78	103	127	20	61187	21767	23344	v
St. Blane's	George G. Cringles, BD	1981	1988	49 Roman Way, Dunblane, FK15 9DJ [0786] *Dunblane 822268*	660	33	17	110	32	29920	5376	5540	8985
Fallin	Eleanor D. Muir, MTHEOL, DIPPTHEOL ¶	1986	……	5 King Street, Fallin, Stirling, FK7 7JX [0786] *Bannockburn*	306	17	15	40	4	20231	…	…	8646
Fintry	Arthur James Doherty, DIPTH, CASS	1957	1988	Fintry, Glasgow, G63 0YQ [036 086] *Fintry 345*	166	11	17	27	11	19905	…	…	8646
Gargunnock	Catherine A. Hepburn, BA, BD	1982	……	Gargunnock, Stirling, FK8 3BQ [078 686] *Gargunnock 678*	276	15	…	33	17	15676	1076	592	8646
Gartmore	*see* Buchlyvie												
Glendevon	*see* Dollar												

Charge	Minister	Ord.	Ind.	Address and Tel. No.	Com.	Eld.	W.G.	S.S.	B.C.	C.L. £	As'd £	Gi'n £	Stp. £
Killearn	Robert C. Symington, BA	1954	1981	Killearn, Glasgow, G63 9LF [0360] Killearn 50268	822	42	89	109	3	46265	16686	16686	11787
Killin and Ardeonaig†	David J. H. M'Naughton, BD, CA	1976	1983	Killin, Perthshire, FK21 8TN [056 72] Killin 247	260	20	41	40	21	16882	1664	1664	8646
Kilmadock	Michael S. Dawson, BTECH, BD	1979	……	Doune, Perthshire, FK16 6EL [0786] Doune 841437	457	16	……	83	6	17519	2995	2995	8646
Kincardine-in-Menteith *linked with* Norrieston	Robert W. W. Irvine	1965	1988	Thornhill, Stirling, FK8 3PW [078 685] Thornhill 604	224	14	17	21	……	6582	771	771	8646
					233	11	22	26	14	10280	1208	1208	
Kippen	J. Marshall Scoular	1954	1986	Kippen, Stirling, FK8 3DN [078 687] Kippen 229	433	24	58	64	……	26211	3141	3141	8646
Lecropt	William M. Gilmour, MA, BD	1969	1983	5 Henderson Street, Bridge of Allan, Stirling, FK9 4NA [0786] Bridge of Allan 832382	349	22	30	29	8	22277	1509	1509	8646
Logie	David M. B. A. Smith, MA, BD, DUNIV, JP	1950	1965	28 Millar Place, Stirling, FK8 1XD [0786] Stirling 75085	913	68	46	81	19	46848	16156	16019	12576
Menstrie	George T. Sherry, LTH	1977	……	Menstrie, FK11 7EA [0259] Alva 61461	554	37	43	107	26	31894	6891	6891	9456
Muckhart	*see Dollar*												
Norrieston	*see Kincardine-in-Menteith*												
Plean	*see Cowie*												
Port of Menteith	*see Aberfoyle*												
Sauchie	Norman Swinburne, BA	1960	1975	Sauchie, Alloa, FK10 3JX [0259] Alloa 212037	1024	42	39	52	15	38654	10130	10130	11073
Stirling—													
Allan Park South *linked with* Church of the Holy Rude	Ian M. P. Davidson, MA, BD	1954	1985	21 Drummond Place, Stirling, FK8 2JE [0786] Stirling 74154	420	41	51	13	12	35791	6365	6365	11667
					283	34	……	19	……	26176	6329	6631	
North	Paul M. N. Sewell, MA, BD	1970	1978	18 Shirra's Brae Road, FK7 0BA [0786] Stirling 75378	795	36	50	96	40	41973	7638	7638	9510
St. Columba's	Barry W. Dunsmore, MA, BD	1982	1988	9 South Street, FK9 5NL [0786] Stirling 74011	611	54	10	85	31	30667	7384	7364	v

Charge	Minister	Ord./App.										Address and Tel. No.
St. Mark's	Alexander B. Noble, MA, BD, TH M	1982	......	598	19	26	32	6	13520	1272	110	8646	176 Drip Road, FK8 1RR [0786] Stirling 73716
St. Ninians Old	J. Stirling, B SC, BD	1962	1969	1230	51	60	88	10	48042	14150	14150	13002	7 Randolph Road, FK8 2AJ [0786] Stirling 74421
Viewfield	Iain M. Macritchie, BSC, BD	1987	......	731	49	51	35	37	34974	7684	7684	v	7 Windsor Place, FK8 2HY [0786] Stirling 74534
Strathblane	Alex. F. Fleming, MA, BD	1966	1983	585	32	60	35	39	30439	5796	5796	9465	Strathblane, Glasgow, G63 9AQ [0360] Blanefield 70226
Tillicoultry	John Russell, MA	1959	1978	1317	59	140	97	18	38878	10367	10449	11211	Tillicoultry, FK13 6PD [0259] Tillicoultry 50340
Tullibody St. Serf's	Andrew B. Dick, BD, DIP MIN	1986	......	729	23	122	30	28	24248	3619	3257	8646	Tullibody, Alloa, FK10 2RG [0259] Alloa 213236

Minister	Ord.	App.	Ret.	Charge	Address and Tel. No.
Anderson, Robert S.	1988	1987	......	*Field Officer*	Scottish Church's House, Dunblane, FK15 0AJ [0786] Dunblane 823588
Anderson, W. Grant, MA, BD	1946	......	1985	(Stirling St. Columba's)	9 South Street, Cambuskenneth, FK9 5NL [0786] Stirling 74011
Archibald, A. S., MA	1929	......	1972	(Crawford)	3 Chisholm Avenue, Causewayhead, Stirling, FK9 5QU [0786] Stirling 61070
Arnott, Merricks, MA	1932	......	1972	(Rosneath St. Modan's)	6 Haldane Avenue, Bridge of Allan, Stirling, FK9 4TA, [0786] Bridge of Allan 833381
Begg, R. W. A.	1935	......	1974	(Kippen)	Roundelwood, Drummond Terrace, Crieff, PH7 4AE [0764] Crieff 3806
Brodie, P. P., MA, BD, LL.B, BD	1942	......	1986	(Alloa St. Mungo's)	13 Victoria Square, Stirling, FK8 [0786] Stirling 64763
Burnett, John B.	1964	......	1985	(Dollar, *Associate*)	30 Manor House Road, Dollar, FK14 [025 94] Dollar 2892
Campbell, Patrick D. G., MA	1949	......	1984	(Geneva)	30 Harviestoun Road, Dollar, FK14 7HG [025 94] Dollar 2172
Clark, John, FPHS	1949	......	1988	(Dunblane St. Blane's)	25 Beecham Drive, Dunblane, FK15 9HW [0786] Dunblane 825398
Eadie, William	1947	......	1975	(Kilberry *with* Tarbert)	Flat 6, 15 North Church Street, Callander, FK17 8EW [0877] Callander 31075
Edie, Charles B., MA	1946	......	1984	(Stirling Church of the Holy Rude)	20 Chapel Place, Dollar, FK14 7DW [025 94] Dollar 2489
Hughes, Andrew, MA	1941	......	1979	(Dollar St. Columba's)	Senior Chaplain, HQ Scotland, Edinburgh, EH1 2YX
Hynd, R. Stewart	1966	1966	......	*Chaplain, Army*	Ladysneuk Road, Cambuskenneth, Stirling, FK9 5NF [0786] Stirling 61646
Jamieson, G. T., BA	1936	......	1969	(Stirling Viewfield)	Delta, 5 Rulley View, Denny, FK6 6QQ [0324] Denny 825441
Kinloch, Thomas, MA	1938	......	1978	(Bannockburn Ladywell)	58 Carseview, Bannockburn, Stirling, FK7 8LH [0786] Bannockburn 815448
Laing, John M., MA	1948	......	1985	(Buchlyvie *with* Gartmore)	19e Cultenhove Road, Stirling, FK7 9GD [0786] Stirling 62832
Lamb, John T., BD	1978	1980	......	*Community Minister* at St. Ninians Old	Rochill, Port of Menteith, Stirling, FK8 3LF [087 75] Port of Menteith 284
Leask, Rebecca M. (Mrs.)	1977	......	1985	(Callander St. Bride's)	
Lees, J. G., MA	1944	......	1984	(North Berwick Abbey)	18c Buccleuch Court, Cathedral Square, Dunblane, FK15 0AR [0786] Dunblane 823792

Minister	Ord.	App.	Ret.	Charge	Address and Tel. No.
Liddel R., MA, BD	1939	……	1985	(Gartly with Kennethmont)	20 Victoria Square, Stirling, FK8 2QZ [0786] Stirling 65415
M'Callum, Iain D., MA	1943	……	1984	(Stirling Allan Park South)	8b Hope Street, St. Andrews, KY16 [0334] St. Andrews 77902
M'Cutcheon, George A., MA	1948	……	1984	(Clackmannan)	13 Harviestoun Road, Dollar, FK14 7HG [025 94] Dollar 2609
Macdonald, R. M., OBE, MA, DD	1929	……	1968	(Calabar)	14 North Church Street, Callander, FK17 8EG [0877] Callander 30352
M'Intosh, Hamish N. M., MA	1949	……	1987	(Fintry)	1 Forth Crescent, Stirling [0786] Stirling 70453
M'William, Stuart W., MA, STM	1941	……	1981	(Killearn)	Terreran, Main Street, Gartmore, Stirling, FK8 3RN [087 72] Aberfoyle 640
Muirhead, R. L., APHS	1950	……	1981	(Gargunnock)	6 Livingstone Avenue, Callander, FK17 8EF [0877] Callander 30610
Orrock, Archibald A., MA, BD	1938	……	1982	(Teacher, Religious Instruction)	3 Kilbryde Court, Dunblane, FK15 9AX [0786] Dunblane 822821
Rennie, Alistair M., MA, BD	1939	……	1986	(Kincardine Croick and Edderton)	13 Tullich Terrace, Tillicoultry, FK13 6RD [0259] Tillicoultry 57563
Ritchie, J. M., MA, BD	1950	……	1985	(Coalsnaughton)	Nazareth Hospital, EMMS, Box 11, 16100 Nazareth, Israel
Shields, Martin B., MA	1929	……	1973	(Luss)	29 Ochlochy Park, Dunblane, FK15 0AL [0786] Dunblane 824155
Silcox, John R., MA	1976	1984	……	School Chaplain	Queen Victoria School, Dunblane, FK15 0JA [0786] Dunblane 824944
Stewart, William, MA, BD, DD	1936	……	1978	(Lecropt)	Pilgrim House, 44 Netherby Road, Edinburgh, EH5
Thomson, George F. M., MA	1956	……	1988	(Dollar with Glendevon with Muckhart, Associate)	—
Turnbull, K. J., MA, BD	1948	……	1984	(Bridge of Allan Holy Trinity)	4 Montrose Road, Causewayhead, Stirling, FK9 5SF [0786] Stirling 62536
Turner, William, MA, BD	1934	……	1970	(Gargunnock)	Tulmore, Gargunnock, Stirling, FK8 3BQ [078 686] Gargunnock 206
Walker, David S., MA	1939	……	1978	(Makerstoun with Smailholm with Stichill, Hume and Nenthorn)	St. Helen's, Kilbryde Crescent, Dunblane, FK15 9AZ [0786] Dunblane 823846
Watt, Robert, MA, BD	1943	……	1982	(Aberdeen Woodside South)	1 Coldstream Avenue, Dunblane, FK15 9JN [0786] Dunblane 823632

ADDRESSES OF STIRLING CHURCHES

Allan Park South	Dumbarton Road	St. Columba's	Park Terrace	St. Ninians Old	Kirk Wynd, St. Ninians
Holy Rude	St. John Street	St. Mark's	Drip Road	Viewfield	Barnton Street
North	Springfield Road				

SYNOD VIII—FIFE

Meets on second Tuesday of April and, if so resolved, October at a place to be resolved

Correspondents: Lothian, Perth and Angus; Forth

Clerk: Rev. PETER McPHAIL, MA, BD, 44 Doocot Road, St. Andrews, Fife, KY16 8QP [0334] St. Andrews 73093

24. DUNFERMLINE

Meets at Dunfermline, in the Abbot House, Maygate on the first Thursday of each month except January, July and August when there is no meeting, and June when it meets on the last Thursday

Clerk: Rev. NORMAN R. MACASKILL, MA, 82 Main Street, Lochgelly, Fife, KY5 9AA [0592] Lochgelly 780435

Charge	Minister	Ord.	Ind.	Address and Tel. No.	Com.	Eld.	W.G.	S.S.	B.C.	C.L. £	As'd £	Gi'n £	Stp. £
Aberdour St. Fillan's	John Scott, LTH	1969	1975	Aberdour, Fife, KY3 0TT [0383] Aberdour 860349	521	34	42	96	10	38367	6845	8120	9960
Ballingry	Sharon E. F. Colvin, BD, LTCH (Mrs.)	1985	......	Ballingry, Lochgelly, KY5 8PA [0592] Ballingry 861663	172	12	13	13	......	8045	......	......	8646
Beath	Peter C. Rae, BSC, BD	1968	1969	Stuart Pl., Cowdenbeath, KY4 9BN [0383] Cowdenbeath 511033	104	4	......	......	......	6307	......	......	8898
linked with Cowdenbeath North					241	10	......	26	19	16962	......	365	
Blairingone	Alex. G. Downie	1953	......	Saline, Dunfermline, KY12 9PL [0383] New Oakley 852240	107	3	......	6	3	3300	180	180	8898
linked with Saline					406	16	29	86	16	13579	600	675	
Cairneyhill	R. J. Henderson, DSO, MA, BD	1953	1984	Limekilns, Dunfermline, KY11 3HT [0383] Limekilns 872341	173	15	......	80	18	6768	641	641	9432
linked with Limekilns	Charlotte M. Henderson, (Mrs.)	1986	......	Auxiliary—see List on page 185	472	31	......	58	16	23009	3487	3487	
Carnock	Vacant	......	......	Carnock, Dunfermline, KY12 9JG [0383] New Oakley 850327	529	15	38	68	29	20075	1300	678	8742
Cowdenbeath—Cairns	George I. Hastie, MA, BD	1971	1988	66 Barclay St., Cowdenbeath, KY4 9LD [0383] Cowdenbeath 515089	409	20	34	18	15	13808	......	......	>
North	see Beath												
West	Evan J. Ross, LTH	1986	......	1 Foulford Rd., Cowdenbeath, KY4 9AS [0383] Cowdenbeath 512533	212	12	19	31	5	20566	......	......	8646
linked with Mosgreen and Crossgates	William G. Tait	1986	......	Auxiliary—see List on page 185	305	13	......	41	......	10296	......	......	

Charge	Minister	Ord.	Ind.	Address and Tel. No.	Com.	Eld.	W.G.	S.S.	B.C.	C.L. £	As'd £	Gi'n £	Stp. £
Culross and Torryburn	Alison E. P. Norman, MA, BD	1987	......	Culross, Dunfermline, KY12 8JD [0383] Newmills 880231	295	22	......	......	18	14235	......	......	v
Dalgety	Peter K. Elston	1963	1971	9 St. Colme Drive, Dalgety Bay, Dunfermline, KY11 4LQ [0383] Dalgety Bay 822316	633	30	34	263	47	36031	4034	4200	9339
Dunfermline— Abbey	Stewart M. Macpherson, MA	1953	1969	116 Halbeath Road, Dunfermline, KY11 4LA [0383] Dunfermline 721022	1060	54	......	47	32	126704	4924	4924	10515
Gillespie Memorial	A. Gordon Reid, BSC, BD	1982	1988	4 Killin Court, KY12 7XF [0383] Dunfermline 723329	707	61	29	102	47	52466	11099	12455	10620
North	Vacant	......	......	51 Cameron Street, KY12 8DP [0383] Dunfermline 721061	389	19	......	23	2	26089	2513	2513	9042
St. Andrew's Erskine	James Laird, MA, BD, PH D	1967	1973	114 Grieve Street, KY12 8DW [0383] Dunfermline 726166	604	32	46	30	6	30783	2915	1200	9159
St. Leonard's	Alexander B. Mitchell, BD	1981	......	12 Torvean Place, KY11 4YY [0383] Dunfermline 721054	734	31	59	143	17	38808	3550	3604	8970
St. Margaret's	Colin C. R. Macpherson, MA, BD	1958	1966	38 Garvock Hill, KY12 7UU [0383] Dunfermline 723955	1006	50	69	89	39	38440	7517	7517	10077
St. Ninian's	Charles M. Cameron, BA, BD, PH D	1980	......	51 St. John's Drive, KY12 7TL [0383] Dunfermline 722256	605	27	61	58	14	21845	1812	172	8898
St. Paul's	Frank T. Smith, MA	1957	1964	6 Park Avenue, KY12 7HX [0383] Dunfermline 721124	388	28	......	14	3	22117	3395	3395	9741
Townhill	William E. Farquhar, BA, BD	1987	......	Dunfermline, KY12 0EZ [0383] Dunfermline 723835	557	37	32	104	39	34718	6796	6796	v
Inverkeithing— St. John's linked with North Queensferry	William G. G. Baird	1977	......	34 Hill St., Inverkeithing, KY11 1AB [0383] Inverkeithing 412422	274	17	18	49	38	15473	942	942	8748
					118	10	15	10	7	10654	324	324	
St. Peter's	George G. Nicol, BA, D PHIL	1988	......	14 Chapel Place, Inverkeithing, Fife, KY11 1NQ [0383] Inverkeithing 412626	455	22	......	43	25	24600	2872	2872	9159
Kelty	Alistair J. Drummond, BSC, BD, TH M	1986	......	13 Bath Street, Kelty, KY4 0AG [0383] Kelty 830291	515	38	45	50	7	34251	1868	1868	9144
Limekilns	see Cairneyhill												
Lochcraig	James F. Todd, BD, CPS	1984	......	Lochcraig, Lochgelly, KY5 8AQ [0592] Ballingry 860315	242	12	17	11	......	8703	......	......	8646

Congregation / Minister	Ord.	App.	Charge / Address and Tel. No.										
Lochgelly—													
Macainsh — Norman R. Macaskill, MA	1962	......	82 Main Street, Lochgelly, KY5 9AA [0592] Lochgelly 780435	563	42	60	37	2	18902	1423	1423	8898
St. Andrew's — Kenneth G. Russell, BD, CCE	1986	......	Station Road, Lochgelly, KY5 9QX [0592] Lochgelly 780319	552	34	32	28	5	23516	3047	2015	9150
Mossgreen and Crossgates — see Cowdenbeath West													
North Queensferry — see Inverkeithing													
Rosyth — Stanley Scoular	1963	1971	42 Woodside Ave., Rosyth, KY11 2LA [0383] Inverkeithing 412776	730	32	20	59	......	30626	3258	3423	9288
Rosyth — John Buchanan	......	......	Deacon—see List H [0383] Dunfermline 417825									
Saline and Kincardine — see Blairingone													
Tulliallan and Kincardine — James G. Redpath, BD, DIP PTH	1988	......	Toll Road, Kincardine, Alloa, FK10 4QZ [0259] Kincardine 30538	849	34	100	96	40	22609	4184	4184	v

Minister	Ord.	App.	Ret.	Charge	Address and Tel. No.
Aitken, E. Douglas, MA	1961	......	1987	(BBC)	73 Scotland Drive, Dunfermline, KY12 7TP [0383] Dunfermline 726590
Archibald, D. Y., BA, BD, M PHIL	1949	......	1983	(Cairneyhill with Torryburn and Newmills)	15 Barrie Street, Dunfermline, KY12 9EN [0383] Dunfermline 720410
Beck, Douglas	1935	......	1970	(Dunfermline St. Ninian's)	46 Hudson Road, Rosyth, Dunfermline, KY11 2DN [0383] Inverkeithing 416136
Campbell, John, MA	1943	......	1978	(Urquhart)	15 Foulden Place, Dunfermline, KY12 7TQ [0383] Dunfermline 738055
Cunningham, W. L., MA	1930	......	1968	(Cairneyhill)	The Gibson House, Argyle Street, St. Andrews, KY16
Fletcher, J. M., BA, BD	1939	......	1974	(Kincardine)	Kincardine, Alloa, FK10 4QD [0259] Kincardine 30331
Goring, A. C., BA, BD	1955	......	1988	(Dunfermline Gillespie Memorial)	57 Rose Street, Dunfermline, KY12 0QT [0383] Dunfermline 723971
Hall, Robert K., LTH	1968	......	1988	(Carnock)	31 Hawkcraig Road, Aberdour, KY3 0XB [0383] Aberdour 860441
Henderson, Charlotte M. (Mrs.)	1986	1986	......	Auxiliary at Cairneyhill with Limekilns	The Manse, Limekilns, Dunfermline, KY11 3HT [0383] Limekilns 872341
Jenkins, Gordon F. C., MA, BD	1968	1988	1981	Department of Education	15 Dean Bridge, Gowkhall, Dunfermline, KY12 9PE [0383] Dunfermline 851078
Johnston, John, MBE, MA, BD, JP	1932	......	......	(Inverkeithing St. Peter's)	11 Transy Place, Dunfermline, KY12 7ON [0383] Dunfermline 720527
Mackenzie, R. P., MA, BD	1936	......	1980	(Dunfermline St. Leonard's)	23 Foulis Crescent, Juniper Green, Edinburgh, EH14 5BN 031–441 4699
Meredith, Harold	1959	......	1979	(Mouswald with Torthorwald)	24 Whitelaw Place, Dunfermline, KY11 [0383] Dunfermline 739973
Neill, Bruce F., MA, BD	1966	1971	......	Chaplain, RN	46 Porterfield, Comrie, Dunfermline, KY12 9HJ [0383] Dunfermline 850797
Pogue, Victor C., BA, BD	1945	......	1980	(Baird Research Fellow)	120 Buckstone Terrace, Edinburgh, EH10 6QR 031–445 1628
Reid, Robert J., MA, BD, DIP ED	1958	......	1985	(Mossgreen and Crossgates)	10 Roseberry View, Dalgety Bay, Dunfermline, KY11 5YM [0383] Dalgety Bay 824305
Tait, William G.	1986	1987	......	Auxiliary at Cowdenbeath West with Mossgreen and Crossgates	67 Scotland Drive, Dunfermline, KY12 7TP
Whyte, J. J. Stanley, FSA SCOT	1952	......	1985	(Edinburgh Lochend)	10 Lumsdaine Drive, Dalgety Bay, Dunfermline, KY11 5YU [0383] Dalgety Bay 823253
Wood, George K., MA	1924	......	1966	(Channelkirk)	11 Venturefair Ave., Dunfermline, KY12 0PF [0383] Dunfermline 725247

25. KIRKCALDY

Meets at Kirkcaldy, in St. Brycedale Hall, on the first Tuesday of February, March, April, May, November and December, on the second Tuesday of September, and on the fourth Tuesday of June

Clerk: Rev. BRYAN L. TOMLINSON, TD, 83 Milton Road, Kirkcaldy, KY1 1TP [0592] *Kirkcaldy 260315*
Depute Clerk: Rev. A. MILLER MILLOY, DPE, LTH, 73 Loughborough Road, Kirkcaldy, KY1 3DD [0592] *Kirkcaldy 52215*

Charge	Minister	Ord.	Ind.	Address and Tel. No.	Com.	Eld.	W.G.	S.S.	B.C.	C.L. £	As'd £	Gi'n £	Stp. £
Auchterderran *linked with* Kinglassie	J. Ewan R. Campbell, MA, BD	1967	1977	7 Woodend Rd., Cardenden, KY5 0NE [0592] *Cardenden 720213*	373	19	15	34	5	19969	2005	2005	9249
					298	10	31	32	......	9613	1390	1390	
Auchtertool *linked with* Kirkcaldy Invertiel	John A. Cowie, BSC, BD	1983	......	36 Dunbar Place, Kirkcaldy, KY2 5QS [0592] *Kirkcaldy 201004*	128	3	5	......	......	3084	509	360	9096
					437	22	34	28	8	16655	1204	805	
Buckhaven	H. Dane Sherrard, BD	1971	1976	Wellesley Road, Buckhaven, Fife, KY8 1JA [0592] *Buckhaven 712870*	678	29	62	83	132	26506	6647	6647	10359
Burntisland	John C. Duncan, BD, MPHIL	1987	......	21 Ramsay Crescent, Burntisland, KY3 9JL [0592] *Burntisland 874303*	859	54	90	70	41	46518	6076	6076	v
Cardenden St. Fothad's	Maria A. G. Plate, LTH, BA ¶	1983	......	75 Carden Ave., Cardenden, KY5 0EL [0592] *Cardenden 720334*	378	21	21	19	......	23821	......	......	8646
Denbeath *linked with* Methilhill	Elizabeth F. Cranfield, MA, BD	1988	......	9 Chemiss Road, Methilhill, KY8 2BS [0592] *Buckhaven 713142*	225	10	18	11	8	8352	......	100	v
					284	13	35	19	......	8737	......	......	
Dysart	Thomas C. Geddes, MA, BD	1956	1966	109 Loughborough Road, Kirkcaldy, KY1 3DD [0592] *Kirkcaldy 51389*	738	52	50	9	......	33196	6947	6947	9909
Glenrothes— Christ's Kirk on the Green	*Vacant* / William Hanna, DCS	......	......	Greenside, Leslie, KY6 3DF [0592] *Glenrothes 745086* Deacon—see List H [0592] *Glenrothes 742292*	575	40	82	69	19	20118	1886	1886	v
St. Columba's	Alistair G. M'Leod	1988	......	36 Hayfield Road, Kirkcaldy, KY2 4DT [0592] *Kirkcaldy 203448*	933	42	39	75	16	29049	4143	4143	v
St. Margaret's	William Abernethy, LTH	1979	1988	8 Alburne Park, Glenrothes, KY6 [0592] *Glenrothes 752241*	658	40	35	68	30	32601	6424	6424	v
St. Ninian's	Violet C. C. M'Kay, BD	1988	......	1 Cawdor Dr., Glenrothes, KY6 2HN [0592] *Glenrothes 752962*	662	24	30	45	11	23208	1000	1100	v

Parish	Minister	Year	Address									
Innerleven East	James L. Templeton, BSC, BD	1975	McDonald Street, Methil, KY8 3AJ [0333] Leven 26310	473	18	35	41	.....	21109	2607	983	8646
Kennoway	David W. Denniston, BD	1981	2 Langside Cres., Kennoway, Leven, KY8 5LW [0333] K'way 352329	846	24	50	85	9	29943	1566	1566	8835
Kinghorn	C. H. M. Greig, MA, BD	1976	17 Myre Crescent, Kinghorn, Fife, KY3 9UB [0592] Kinghorn 890269	681	31	71	66	9	28651	5845	5845	9912
Kinglassie	see Auchterderran											
Kirkcaldy— Abbotshall	Bryan L. Tomlinson, TD	1969	83 Milton Road, KY1 1TP [0592] Kirkcaldy 260315	1084	71	61	88	41	49391	11929	11929	10527
Bethelfield	William M. Ashcroft, BD ¶	1985	16 Raith Crescent, KY1 [0592] Kirkcaldy 265536	378	38	40	26	15	26681	3938	3938	9024
Invertiel	see Auchtertool											
Old	John A. Ferguson, BD, DIPMIN	1988	2 Townsend Place, KY1 1HB [0592] Kirkcaldy 260448	577	48	41	61	33	54149	4500	4500	v
Pathhead	A. Miller Milloy, DPE, LTH	1979	73 Loughborough Road, KY1 3DD [0592] Kirkcaldy 52215	795	44	59	64	23	56624	7126	7126	10353
St. Andrew's	Vacant	.....	15 Harcourt Road, KY2 5HQ [0592] Kirkcaldy 260816	818	43	74	74	8	36257	6665	6665	9909
St. Brycedale	John K. Froude, MA, BD	1979	6 East Fergus Place, KY1 1XT [0592] Kirkcaldy 264480	646	28	60	76	9	47487	6565	4220	9909
St. John's	Samuel M. M'Naught, MA, BD, MTH	1968	25 Bennochy Avenue, KY2 5QE [0592] Kirkcaldy 263821	760	57	100	68	36	33788	7599	7599	9909
Templehall	Brock A. White, LTH	1971	Appin Crescent, KY2 6EJ [0592] Kirkcaldy 260156	698	25	37	35	9	29802	5508	2508	9078
	Robert A. Trimble, DCS	.....	Deacon—see List H [0592] Kirkcaldy 267924									
Torbain [E]	Denis Warnock, MA	1952	91 Sauchenbush Road, KY2 5RN [0592] Kirkcaldy 263015	377	19	43	67	23	15363	.....	149	9147
Viewforth	Angus Kerr, BD, CERTMIN, THM	1983	66 Viewforth Street, KY1 3DJ [0592] Kirkcaldy 52502	816	40	31	29	10	29323	4820	4820	v
Leslie Trinity	Gordon M. Simpson, MA, BD	1959	4 Valley View, KY6 3BQ [0592] Glenrothes 741008	559	18	49	50	25	18631	3367	3675	v
Leven— St. Andrew's	Alexander R. Forsyth, BA, MTH	.....	Forman Rd., Leven, Fife, KY8 4HH [0333] Leven 23843	1087	56	83	51	51	53395	11072	11128	10353
Scoonie Kirk	Edgar J. Ogston, BSC, BD	1976	Links Road, Leven, Fife, KY8 4HR [0333] Leven 26518	711	37	76	22	26	34294	7430	7430	v

Charge	Minister	Ord.	Ind.	Address and Tel. No.	Com.	Eld.	W.G.	S.S.	B.C.	C.L. £	As'd £	Gi'n £	Stp. £
Markinch	I. D. Gordon, LTH	1972	......	7 Guthrie Crescent, KY7 6AY [0592] Glenrothes 758264	1070	31	50	48	27	30473	7015	7015	10353
Methil	John D. Thomson, BD	1985	......	14 Methilbrae, Methil, KY8 3LW [0333] Leven 26255	635	35	75	43	9	30941	1968	3176	8646
Methilhill Thornton	see Denbeath David W. Gatt	1981	......	12 Strathore Rd., Thornton, Glenrothes, KY1 4DU [0592] Glenrothes 774328	627	17	32	70	12	18731	1441	300	8646
Wemyss	Vacant	......	......	33 Main Road, East Wemyss, Fife, KY1 4RE [0592] Buckhaven 713260	588	25	50	38	2	21385	1935	1955	8862
Windygates and Balgonie	Heather C. Olsen, BD	1978	......	Milton of Balgonie, M'inch, KY7 6QD [0592] Glenrothes 758253	465	16	39	32	7	11659	893	600	8646

Charge — Address and Tel. No.

9 Rossness Drive, Kinghorn, KY3 [0592] Kinghorn 890539
Applegarth, Sunny Park, Kinross, KY13 [057 72] Kinross 63204
28 Ferguson Place, Burntisland, KY3 [0592] Burntisland 873985

8 Bennochy Gardens, Kirkcaldy, KY2 5JG [0592] Kirkcaldy 200012
269 Michael Path, Glenrothes, KY6 [0592] Glenrothes 741192
48 Beveridge Road, Kirkcaldy, KY1 1UY [0592] Kirkcaldy 269718
324 Muirfield Drive, Glenrothes, KY6 2PZ [0592] Glenrothes 610281
76 Forth Park Gardens, Kirkcaldy, KY2 5TD
70 Napier Road, Glenrothes, KY6 1DS [0592] Glenrothes 752927
50 Kirkbank Road, Burntisland, KY3 9JA [0592] Burntisland 873710
9 Douglas Road, Leslie, KY6 [0592] Glenrothes 741009
10 Ward Street, Denbeath, Methil, Leven, KY8 3PZ [0592] Buckhaven 713422
78 Whitecraig Road, Newburgh, Fife, KY14 [033 74] Newburgh 646

Minister	Ord.	App.	Ret.	Charge
Campbell, Robert, MA	1949	......	1985	(Kirkcaldy Bethelfield)
Cooper, M. W., MA	1944	......	1979	(Kirkcaldy Abbotshall)
Crawford, Douglas F. N., MA	1950	......	1984	(Braes of Rannoch with Foss and Rannoch)
Fulton, J. Ross, MA	1941	......	1977	(Kirkcaldy Gallatown)
Mackenzie, Andrew H.	1963	......	1979	(Acharacle with Ardnamurchan)
Mackie, David, MA, BD, DIP ED	1954	......	1988	(Strachur and Strathlachlan)
MacLeod, Norman	1960	......	1988	(Orwell with Portmoak)
M'Kenzie, Donald M., TD, MA	1947	......	1986	(Auchtertool with Burntisland)
Millar, John H., MA	1946	......	1986	(Teacher, Religious Education)
Monaghan, James, TD, MBE	1950	......	1988	(Edinburgh Davidson's Mains)
Taylor, John T. H.	1947	......	1983	(Glenrothes Christ's Kirk on the Green)
Wilson, T. Watt	1955	......	1977	(Denbeath)
Young, W. Finlayson, MA	1943	......	1979	(Kinglassie)

ADDRESSES OF KIRKCALDY CHURCHES

Abbotshall	Abbotshall Road	
Bethelfield	Nicol Street x High Street	
Invertiel	Links Street	
Old	Kirk Wynd	
Pathhead	Harriet St. x Church St.	
St. Andrew's	Victoria Rd. x Victoria Gdns.	
St. Brycedale	St. Brycedale Ave. x Kirk Wynd	
St. John's	Elgin Street	
Templehall	Beauly Place	
Torbain		
Viewforth	Viewforth St. x Viewforth Terrace	

26. ST. ANDREWS

Meets alternately at Cupar, in St. John's Church Hall, and at St. Andrews, in Hope Park Church Hall, on the second Wednesday of February, March, April, May, September, October, November and December; and on the last Wednesday of June.

Clerk: Rev. JOHN W. PATTERSON, BA, BD, 49 Irvine Crescent, St. Andrews, KY16 8LG [0334] St. Andrews 72948

Charge	Minister	Ord.	Ind.	Address and Tel. No.	Com.	Eld.	W.G.	S.S.	B.C.	C.L. £	As'd £	Gi'n £	Stp. £
Abdie and Dunbog	Ian Taylor, BSC, MA, LTH, DIPED	1983	……	Cupar Road, Newburgh, Fife, KY14 6HA [0337] Newburgh 40275	200	16	26	21	……	7681	……	……	8646
linked with													
Newburgh					559	22	35	47	……	10558	……	250	
Anstruther	D. H. Alex Watson, BA, BD	1956	1982	The James Melville Manse, Anstruther, KY10 3EX [0333] Anstruther 311808	545	43	……	65	5	22746	893	893	8805
Auchtermuchty	W. James L. Galbraith, BSC, BD, MICE	1973	……	2 Burnside, Auchtermuchty, KY14 7AQ [0337] Auchtermuchty 28519	586	26	33	55	22	33335	1972	1972	8646
Balmerino	Andrew L. Stevenson, LLB, MLITT, DIPED	1984	……	5 Westwater Place, Newport-on-Tay, DD6 [0382] Newport-on-Tay 542626	303	24	33	26	……	15447	670	770	8724
linked with													
Wormit					355	21	102	69	32	15876	1435	1435	
Boarhills	Peter C. Douglas	1966	……	Dunino, St. Andrews, KY16 8LU [033 488] Boarhills 270	105	5	……	……	……	5689	……	……	8748
linked with													
Dunino					134	5	……	13	……	4786	……	100	
Cameron	see St. Andrews												
Carnbee	Charles G. Thrower, BSC	1965	1970	Pittenweem, Fife, KY10 2LR [0333] Pittenweem 311 255	144	7	30	……	……	6037	489	489	8898
linked with													
Pittenweem					426	18	68	30	3	18505	1775	1775	
Cellardyke	Vacant	……	……	Cellardyke, Anstruther, KY10 3BH [0333] Anstruther 310810	526	23	83	53	8	22012	1779	2338	8646
linked with													
Kilrenny					144	11	10	16	17	18060	……	279	
Ceres	Walter Learmonth, LTH	1968	……	Ceres, Cupar, KY15 4HQ [033 482] Ceres 233	547	21	32	54	……	18937	4945	3086	10098
linked with													
Springfield					176	7	20	……	……	5054	895	895	
Crail	William J. Macintyre, MA, BD, DD	1951	1956	Crail, Fife, KY10 3XE [033 350] Crail 358	527	32	80	36	9	26361	5018	5018	9651
linked with													
Kingsbarns					142	10	……	4	8	5322	450	450	
Creich, Flisk and Kilmany	Clifford Strong, LTH	1983	……	Brunton, Cupar, Fife, KY15 4PA [033 77] Luthrie 332	226	9	22	16	……	6538	1158	1158	8982
linked with													
Monimail					206	12	……	11	……	8522	1000	1250	

Charge	Minister	Ord.	Ind.	Address and Tel. No.	Com.	Eld.	W.G.	S.S.	B.C.	C.L. £	As'd £	Gi'n £	Stp. £
Cupar—													
Old & St. Michael of Tarvit	Derek G. Browning, BA, BD	1987	......	Eden Manse, Cupar, Fife, KY15 4HQ [0334] Cupar 53196	962	46	54	78	48	39929	12484	12484	v
St. John's	J. K. Porteous, DD	1944	1956	Cupar, Fife, KY15 [0334] Cupar 53367	922	37	80	95	20	37639	6653	6919	9465
Dairsie	Alexander Strickland, LTH	1971	1981	Dairsie, Cupar, Fife, KY15 4RS [0334] Cupar 53283	171	9	16	26	....	8791	1100	1100	9561
linked with Kemback					149	8	20	6	2	8993	1153	1153	
linked with Strathkinness					231	16	36	26	....	10053	1380	1380	
Dunino	see Boarhills												
Edenshead and Strathmiglo	Thomas G. M. Robertson, LTH	1971	1984	Strathmiglo, Fife, KY14 [033 76] Strathmiglo 256	447	23	48	70	14	17872	1441	1481	9018
Elie	Peter Meager, MA, BD	1971	1986	30 Bank Street, Elie, Leven, Fife, KY9 1BW 033 330 685	348	17	41	33	16	22028	3465	3465	9495
linked with Kilconquhar and Colinsburgh					238	15	12	18	3	11213	1733	1733	
Falkland	Iain A. M. Wright, MA, BD	1983	1984	Freuchie Road, Falkland, Fife, KY7 [0337] Falkland 57252	426	19	....	53	3	24800	1817	1817	9570
linked with Freuchie					412	16	20	36	....	15054	1760	2375	
Guardbridge	see Leuchars												
Howe of Fife	Iain M. Forbes, BSC, BD	1964	1983	Ladybank, Fife, KY7 7ND [0337] Ladybank 30513	1010	40	10	127	1	37670	2894	2894	8982
Kemback	see Dairsie												
Kilconquhar and Colinsburgh	see Elie												
Kilrenny	see Cellardyke												
Kingsbarns	see Crail												
Largo and Newburn	Rosemary Frew (Mrs.)	1988	......	Upper Largo, Fife, KY8 [033 36] Upper Largo 286	435	28	26	50	3	23770	2386	2386	v
linked with Largo St. David's					236	13	48	57	13	14198	1148	1148	
Largoward	David Reid, LTH, FSASCOT	1961	1983	St. Monans, Fife, KY10 2DD [033 37] St. Monans 258	86	3	17	10	....	3469	400	482	8646
linked with St. Monans					321	12	78	74	21	20078	1885	2185	
Leuchars													
St. Athernase	Alexander K. Cassells, MA, BD	1961	1983	Leuchars, Fife, KY16 0EN [033 483] Leuchars 226	545	19	24	66	....	15846	988	988	8646
linked with Guardbridge					126	2	13	10	2	2586	160	160	

Parish	Minister	Ord.	Ind.										Address and Tel. No.
Monimail	*see* Creich												
Newburgh	*see* Abdie												
Newport-on-Tay	W. G. Black, MA, BD	1983	1985	690	44	34	53	27	35897	6923	6923	9651	Blyth Street, Newport-on-Tay, DD6 [0382] Newport-on-Tay 543165
Pittenweem	*see* Carnbee												
St. Andrews—													
Holy Trinity	Charles Armour, MA	1939	1949	1192	27	62	43	….	33491	6135	6135	9054	17 Queen's Gardens, St. Andrews, KY16 9TA [0334] St. A. 7494
Hope Park	William Henney, MA	1957	1978	1066	80	60	137	30	62970	13322	13600	9909	20 Priory Gdns., St. Andrews, KY16 8WX [0334] St. A. 72912
Martyrs'	John W. Patterson, BA, BD	1948	1958	518	32	50	36	14	31492	3956	4140	9024	49 Irvine Crescent, St. Andrews, KY16 8LG [0334] St. A. 72948
St. Leonard's *linked with* Cameron	Lawson R. Brown, MA	1960	1980	924 / 124	63 / 10	57 / 14	67 / 14	46 / ….	50385 / 5264	14100 / 450	14261 / 459	1151	26 Hepburn Gardens, St. Andrews, KY16 9DE [0334] St. A. 72793
St. Monans	*see* Largoward												
Springfield	*see* Ceres												
Strathkinness	*see* Dairsie												
Tayport	G. L. Edington	1952	1965	496	16	55	66	….	44740	1717	1717	10416	8 Dougall Street, Tayport, DD6 9JB [082 65] Tayport 2548
Wormit	*see* Balmerino												

Minister	Ord.	App.	Ret.	Charge	Address and Tel. No.
Adam, William, MA, BD	1942	……	1982	(Leuchars St. Athernase *with* Guardbridge)	St. Michaels, Leuchars, Fife, KY16 0DU [033 483] Leuchars 8148
Alexander, Jas. S., MA, BD, BA, PHD	1966	1973	……	University of St. Andrews (Strathkinness)	5 Strathkinness High Road, St. Andrews, KY16 [0334] St. Andrews 72680
Bennett, Alestair, TD, MA	1938	……	1976	Strathkinness	7 Bonfield Park, Strathkinness, St. Andrews, KY16 9SY [033 485] Strathkinness 249
Best, Ernest, MA, BD, PHD	1949	……	1982	(University of Glasgow)	13 Newmill Gardens, St. Andrews, KY16 8RY [0334] St. Andrews 73315
Bews, James, MA	1942	……	1981	(Dundee Craigiebank)	21 Balrymont Court, St. Andrews, KY16 8XT [0334] St. Andrews 76087
Black, Matthew, MA, DD, DLITT, FBA	1939	……	1978	(University of St. Andrews)	40 Buchanan Gdns., St. Andrews, KY16 9JT [0334] St. Andrews 74686
Bogie, A. P., MA, FSA SCOT	1944	……	1979	(Forgan)	7 Gourlay Wynd, St. Andrews, KY16 8HP
Calder, Alastair S., TD, MA	1932	……	1974	(Grantully and Strathtay)	1 Cairnsden Gardens, St. Andrews, KY16 8SQ [0334] St. A. 75113
Cameron, G. Stuart, BA, BD	1942	……	1986	(Fort Augustus)	10 Kinbrae Park, Newport-on-Tay, DD6 8HE [0382] Newport-on-Tay 543093
Cameron, H. L. M.	1965	……	1980	(Edenshead)	
Cameron, James K., MA, BD, PHD	1953	1957	……	University of St. Andrews	Priorscroft, 71 Hepburn Gardens, St. Andrews, KY16 9LS [0334] St. Andrews 73996

Minister	Ord.	App.	Ret.	Charge	Address and Tel. No.
Caseby, Alexander CBE, MA, BD, STM, PHD, DLITT, LL D, DD	1947	……	1965	(Carlops)	4 Macduff Road, Glenrothes, KY7 4BT [0592] Glenrothes 755120
Craig, Robert,	1943	……	1984	(Jerusalem)	West Port, Falkland, KY7 7BL [0337] Falkland 57238
Dickie, Edgar P., MC, BA, MA, DD, LLD	1927	……	1967	(University of St. Andrews)	19 Hepburn Gardens, St. Andrews, KY16 9DG [0334] St. A. 73617
Duncan, James, SDA, NDA	1962	1972	……	Teacher, Religious Education	14 Largo Road, Lundin Links, Leven, KY8 6DG
Dyer, T. J., MA	1939	……	1979	(Largo St. David's)	2 Southfield, St. Andrews, KY16 8AF [0334] St. Andrews 73022
Fleming, John R.., MA, BD, TH D, DD	1936	……	1977	(University of St. Andrews)	41 Kilrymont Road. St. Andrews, KY16 8DE [0334] St. A. 72093
Hall, G. B., BA, BD, PHD	1964	1973	……	University of St. Andrews	2 Broomfaulds Avenue, St. Andrews, KY16 8SJ [0334] St. Andrews 75882
Henderson, George Maclean, MA	1946	……	……	(Cults with Kettle)	6 Eden Park, Cupar, KY15 4HS [0334] Cupar 53138
Honeyman, A. M., MA, BD, B LITT, PHD	1936	……	1967	(University of St. Andrews)	c/o Migdale Hospital, Bonar Bridge, IV24 3AP
Howieson, R. A.., JP, MA	1937	……	1977	(Newport-on-Tay St. Thomas's)	3 Baker Lane. St. Andrews, KY16 [0334] St. Andrews 73711
Hutchison, James N.	1945	……	1972	(Anstruther St. Adrian's)	6 West Braes Crescent, Crail, KY10 3RP [033 35] Crail 520
Inglis, John H. A., MA	1933	……	1973	(Penpont and Keir)	The Craigs, Balmullo, Fife, KY16 0BG [033 987] Balmullo 350
Kinnis, Robert L., MA, BD	1931	……	1972	(Baillieston Mure Memorial)	3 Queen's Terrace, St. Andrews, KY16 9QF [0334] St. Andrews 74589
Kitchin, John A., MA	1936	……	1977	(Perth North)	10 Radernie Place, St. Andrews, KY16 [0334] St. Andrews 76792
Law, Arthur, ACIB	1968	……	1988	(Kincardine in Menteith with Norrieston)	13 South Road, Cupar, KY15 5JF [0334] Cupar 54213
Lithgow, Thomas	1945	……	1982	(Banchory Devenick with Maryculter)	124 Balgarvie Crescent, Cupar, Fife, KY15 4EH [0334] Cupar 55537
Lyall, David, BSC, BD, STM, PHD	1965	1987	……	University of St. Andrews	1 Abbotsford Place. St. Andrews, KY16 9HQ [0334] St. Andrews 72435
Lyon, James E.	1940	……	1976	(Kilconquhar and Colinsburgh)	Croma, Shore Street, Cellardyke, Anstruther, KY10 3BD [033 33] Anstruther 10684
M'Craw, William, MA, BD	1928	……	1963	(Monimail)	17 Edenbank Road, Cupar, Fife, KY15 4HE [0334] Cupar 52521
M'Kane, William, MA, PHD, DLITT, FBA	1949	1967	……	University of St. Andrews	51 Irvine Crescent, St. Andrews, KY16 8LG [0334] St. A. 73797
Mackenzie, J. A. R., MA	1947	……	1987	(Largo St. David's)	39 Kilburn, Lundin Links, Leven, KY8
Mackie, Steven G.., MA, BD	1956	1974	……	University of St. Andrews	South View, 59 Lade Braes, St. Andrews, KY16 [0334] St. Andrews 74149
Maclauchlan, F. J. L., MC, MA	1926	……	1967	(Swinton)	Invereck, Sandbank, Dunoon, PA23 8QS
M'Leish, David N., MA	1938	……	1977	(Fisherton)	3 Morton Crescent, St. Andrews, KY16 8RA [0334] St. Andrews 74049
MacLeod, Allan, MA, BD	1936	……	1981	(Dunoon Old)	8 Spottiswoode Gardens, St. Andrews, KY16 8SB [0334] St. Andrews 73738
MacNab, Hamish, S. D., MA	1948	……	1987	(Kilrenny)	Fairhill, Northmuir, Kirriemuir, DD8 [0575] Kirriemuir 72564
M'Phail, Peter, MA, BD	1940	……	1982	(Creich, Flisk and Kilmany)	44 Doocot Road, St. Andrews, KY16 8QP [0334] St. Andrews 73093
Martin, James D.., MA, BD, PH D	1962	1969	……	University of St. Andrews	22 Kilrymont Road. St. Andrews, KY16 8DE [0334] St. Andrews 77361
Mathews, John, MA, BD	1939	……	1982	(Cellardyke)	18 Green Brig Road, Kilconquhar, Leven, Fife, KY9
Petty, Philip W. P., BA, BD	1962	……	1979	(Prestwick North)	[033 334] Colinsburgh 649 16 Priestden Park, St. Andrews, KY16 8DL [0334] St. Andrews 72859
Porter, R. H.	1939	……	1951	(Glasgow Paisley Road)	4 Viewpark Drive, Burnside, Rutherglen, Glasgow, G73 3QD
Rae, Francis William, MA, BD, STM, DD	1936	……	1976	(Dairsie with Kemback)	10 Hallowhill, St. Andrews, KY16 8SF [0334] St. Andrews 76302
Rough, J. Stewart, MA	1926	……	1971	(St. Monans)	1 Mount Prospect, Largo Road, St. Andrews, KY16 8RW
Salters, Robert B., MA, BD, PHD	1966	1971	……	University of St. Andrews	Vine Cottage, 119 South Street, St. Andrews, KY16 9UH [0334] St. Andrews 74885 [0334] St. A. 73198

Shaw, D. W. D., BA, BD, LL B, WS	1960	University of St. Andrews	40 North Street, St. Andrews, KY16 9AQ	[0334] St. Andrews 77254
Stobie, C. I. G., MA	1942	(Fyvie)	16 Market Street, St. Andrews, KY16 9NS	[0334] St. Andrews 76806
Sutherland, D. G., MA	1946	(Aberdeen Causewayend)	4 Mount Melville Crescent, Strathkinnes, KY16 9XS	[033 485] Strathkinnes 338
Taylor, Alexander T. H., MA, BD	1938	(Dunoon St. Cuthbert's)	4 The Pleasance, Strathkinnes, Fife, KY16 9SD	[033 485] Strathkinnes 585
Titterington, T. J., MA	1949	(Abdie and Dunbog)	Dunbog, Newburgh, Fife, KY14 6JF	[0337] Newburgh 40374
Turnbull, James J., MA	1940	(Arbirlot with Colliston)	Woodlands, Beech Ave., Ladybank. KY7 7NG	[0337] Ladybank 30279
Wedderburn, A. J. M., MA, BD, PHD	1975	University of St. Andrews	5 Clatto Place, St. Andrews, KY16 8SD	[0334] St. Andrews 74923
Whyte, James A., MA, LLD	1945	(University of St. Andrews)	13 Hope Street, St. Andrews, KY16 9HJ	[0334] St. Andrews 72323
Wilson, Robert M'L., MA, BD, PHD, DD	1946	(University of St. Andrews)	10 Murrayfield Rd., St. Andrews, KY16 9NB	[0334] St. A. 74331

SYNOD IX—PERTH AND ANGUS

Meets on the second Wednesday of April and (if required) on the second Wednesday of October at centres to be appointed

Correspondents: Fife: Forth; Argyll: Argyll; Grampian: Southern Highlands

Clerk: Rev. JOHN MACDONALD, AEA, MA, 12 Hyndford Street, Dundee. DD2 1HQ [0382] Dundee 68655

27. DUNKELD AND MEIGLE

Meets at Dunkeld on the first Wednesday of March, April, October, November and December, and the fourth Wednesday of June, and (if required) on the first Wednesday of May

Clerk: Rev. KENNETH MACVICAR, MBE, DFC, TD, MA, Manse of Kenmore, Aberfeldy, PH15 2HE [088 73] Kenmore 218

Charge	Minister	Ord.	Ind.	Address and Tel. No.	Com.	Eld.	W.G.	S.S.	B.C.	C.L. £	As'd £	Gi'n £	Stp. £
Aberfeldy	Alexander M. Gunn, MA, BD	1967	1986	Taybridge Terr., Aberfeldy, Perthshire, PH15 2BS [0887] Aberfeldy 20656	474	24	64	80	20	30487	5555	5555	9159
linked with Amulree and Strathbraan†					44	3	.....	11	.....	1697	300	330	
Alyth	Gordon Oliver, BD	1980	1985	Alyth, Perthshire, PH11 8AW [082 83] Alyth 2104	1106	42	95	62	13	37508	8718	8718	9765
Amulree	see Aberfeldy												
Ardler, Kettins and Meigle	Fraser, M. C. Stewart, BSC, BD	1980	1986	Meigle, Perthshire, PH12 8SB [082 84] Meigle 278	658	23	64	34	13	13861	3242	3242	9147

Charge	Minister	Ord.	Ind.	Address and Tel. No.	Com.	Eld.	W.G.	S.S.	B.C.	C.L. £	As'd £	Gi'n £	Stp. £
Bendochy	Roland J. Portchmouth, NDD, ATD	1980	1984	Meikleour, Perth, PH2 6DZ [025 083] Meikleour 229	174	7	39	4	....	10959	450	450	8646
linked with													
Kinclaven					203	12	12	11	8	7863	850	850	
Blair Atholl and Struan†	James Duncan, BTH, FSASCOT	1980	....	Blair Atholl, Perthshire, PH18 5SX [079 681] E'uir Atholl 213	258	12	20	11	....	10081	1400	400	8742
Blairgowrie—St. Andrew's	G. Stuart Young	1961	1969	Blairgowrie, Perthshire, PH10 6HB [0250] Blairgowrie 2146	788	36	41	68	20	32480	4121	4121	8931
St. Mary's South	Michael R. Philip, BD	1978	1988	Emma Terrace, Blairgowrie, Perthshire, PH10 6JA [0250] Blairgowrie 2321	674	23	46	....	....	22113	4195	4195	>
Braes of Rannoch†	Archibald F. Chisholm, MA	1957	1984	Kinloch Rannoch, Pitlochry, PH16 5QA [088 22] Kinloch Rannoch 381	29	4	....	....	....	3988	400	400	8742
linked with													
Foss & Rannoch					168	11	18	23	....	10700	800	800	>
Caputh and Clunie	Alexander C. McCartney	1973	1987	Caputh, Perth, PH1 4JH [073 871] Caputh 520	323	17	....	....	....	14225	800	800	>
Coupar Angus Abbey	James H. Drysdale, LTH	1987	....	Caddam Road, Coupar Angus, Perthshire, PH13 9EF [0828] Coupar Angus 27331	685	37	45	90	18	24396	4445	4445	>
Dull and Weem	*Vacant*	....	....	Weem, Aberfeldy, P'shire, PH15 2LD [0887] Aberfeldy 20384	140	11	16	....	....	9576	850	850	8931
linked with													
Fortingall and Glenlyont†		....	....		56	....	....	....	....	4852	790	790	
Dunkeld	Tom Dick, MA	1951	1974	Cathedral Manse, Dunkeld, PH8 [035 02] Dunkeld 249	554	34	62	29	4	53554	5144	5144	8931
Fortingall and Glenlyont†	*see Dull and Weem*												
Foss and Rannoch†	*see Braes of Rannoch*												
Grantully, Logierait and Strathtay†	Irene B. Miller (Mrs.), MA, BD	1984	....	Strathtay, Perthshire, PH9 0PG [088 74] Strathtay 251	232	18	25	14	3	16989	1038	1038	8646
Kenmore†	Kenneth MacVicar, MBE, DFC, TD, MA	1950	....	Kenmore, Aberfeldy, PH15 2HE [088 73] Kenmore 218	197	14	30	22	6	21085	1230	1230	8937
linked with													
Lawers					27	4	....	4	4	1354	250	250	
Kinclaven	*see Bendochy*												
Kirkmichael, Straloch and Glenshee	Alan T. M'Kean	1982	....	Kirkmichael, Blairgowrie, PH10 7NS [025 082] Blacklunans 255	263	14	31	6	....	6550	....	700	8646
	A. J. Falconer	....	....	*Lay Missionary—see List H* [025 085] Glenshee 209									

Charge	Minister	Ord.	App.	Address and Tel. No.									
Lawers	see Kenmore												
Moulin and Pitlochry West	W. G. Shannon, MA, BD	1955	1973	Moulin Manse, Pitlochry, PH16 [0796] Pitlochry 2774	584	27	40	34	.....	25034	3655	3655	8931
Pitlochry East	Francis Martin, BL	1958	.....	Tigh-a-Chladaich, 58 West Moulin Rd., Pitlochry, PH16 [0796] Pitlochry 2619	228	13	26	17	.....	27057	440	440	10146
Rattray	Thomas W. Tait, BD	1972	.....	Blairgowrie, Perthshire, PH10 7HF [0250] Blairgowrie 2462	708	26	51	39	11	22539	3481	3481	8931
Tenandry	Vacant	.....	.....	—	60	6	14	10	2	3424	500	572	v

Minister	Ord.	App.	Ret.	Charge	Address and Tel. No.
Aitken, W. M., BD	1949	1987	.....	Ndola	High West, Urlar Road, Aberfeldy, PH15 2ET
Barbour, R. A. S., MC, DD, BD, STM	1954	.....	1982	(University of Aberdeen)	Fincastle, Pitlochry, PH16 5RJ [0796] Pitlochry 3209
Bell, F. Routledge	1944	.....	1983	(Caputh with Murthly)	Hawthornbank House, Wolfhill, Perth [082 15] Kinrossie 421
Cameron, Donald, MA, BSC, JP	1938	.....	1979	(Blair Atholl and Struan)	Taigh Ban, Moulinearn, Pitlochry, PH9 0NB [079 682] Ballinluig 466
Doig, Andrew B., DD, BD, STM	1938	.....	1982	(Secretary, National Bible Society of Scotland)	The Eildons, Moulin, Pitlochry, PH16 [0796] Pitlochry 2892
Fulton, Frederick H., MA	1942	.....	1983	(Clunie, Lethendy and Kinloch)	16 Croft Court, Blairgowrie, PH10 6BB [0250] Blairgowrie 2192
Howieson, R. M., MA	1927	.....	1968	(Blairgowrie St. Andrew's)	Coutie Cottage, Coupar Angus, Perthshire, PH13 9HF
Macartney, William M., MA	1938	.....	1978	(Vienna)	[0828] Coupar Angus 28152
Macdonald, James F., TD	1930	.....	1984	(Bendochy with Kinclaven)	16 Condor Court, Mackenzie Street, Carnoustie, DD7 6HZ
Macpherson, Norman J.,	1954	.....	1980	(Blairgowrie St. Mary's South)	31 Glenburn Drive, Inverness, IV2 4NE [0463] Inverness 230536
Thornton, D. M. B., JP, FSASCOT	1951	.....	1965	(Bendochy)	George Hotel, Perth
Young, A. F. Taylor, MA	1939	.....	1976	(Blairgowrie The Hill)	The Knock, Newton Terrace, Blairgowrie, PH10 6HG [0250] Blairgowrie 3183

COMMUNION SUNDAYS

Aberfeldy	1 monthly, E.	Dunkeld	4 Ap., Oc.	Kenmore	3 My., Nv., E., X.
Amulree and Strathbraan	3 Je., Oc.	Fortingall	1 Je., Oc., E.	Kinloch Rannoch	3 Fb., Je., Oc.
Blair Atholl and Struan	2 Fb., My., 3 Au., Oc. / 3 My., Oc.	Foss	3 Sp., E.	Lawers	3 Je., Nv.
Braes of Rannoch	3 Ap., Oc., E.	Glen Lyon	1 Je., Oc., E.	Moulin and Pitlochry West	3 Mr., Je., Oc., X., E.
Dull and Weem	3 Ap., 2 Jl., 3 Nv. / 2 Ap., Oc.	Grantully, Logierait and Strathtay	1 My., Nv.	Pitlochry East	3 Mr., Je., Oc.
				Tenandry	Ja., My., Sp., Nv.

28. PERTH

Meets at Perth, in Kirk House, St. John Street, on the second Tuesday of every month except January, July and August

Clerk: Rev. G. G. STEWART, MA, 5 Strathearn Terrace, Perth, PH2 0LS [0738] Perth 21709

Charge	Minister	Ord.	Ind.	Address and Tel. No.	Com.	Eld.	W.G.	S.S.	B.C.	C.L. £	As'd £	Gi'n £	Stp. £
Aberdalgie and Dupplin	Colin R. Williamson, LL.B, BD	1972	1984	Aberdalgie, Perth, PH2 0QD [0738] Perth 25854	182	8	14	9	3	8236	...	...	8646
linked with Forteviot					112	9	...	10	3	4915	...	100	
Abernethy & Dron	Kenneth G. Anderson, MA, BD	1967	1988	Abernethy, Perth, PH2 9JP [073 885] Abernethy 590	444	13	34	29	...	11575	1500	1500	v
linked with Arngask					242	12	26	27	...	6018	1090	1340	
					114	7	...	31	...	3481	...	...	
Aberuthven *linked with* Dunning	John A. M'Donald, MA, BD	1978	......	Newton of Pitcairn, Dunning, Perth PH2 0SL [076 484] Dunning 223	275	16	33	22	...	10546	...	...	8646
Almondbank Tibbermore	Ian Marr, MA, BD	1985	......	Pitcairngreen, Perth, PH1 3LT [073 883] Almondbank 217	429	18	...	33	5	10695	...	150	8646
linked with Logiealmond					89	4	...	3	...	1918	...	...	
Ardoch	James L. Hepburn, MA, BD	1950	1984	Braco, Dunblane, FK15 9RE [078 688] Braco 217	246	16	32	49	9	14383	...	330	8646
linked with Blackford					185	14	21	23	...	6139	...	...	
Arngask	*see Abernethy*												
Auchterarder	Andrew W. Bradley, BD	1975	1983	Auchterarder, Perthshire, PH3 1DF [076 46] Auchterarder 2210	1029	42	...	83	8	39226	8892	8997	10755
Auchtergaven and Moneydie	William MacGregor, LTH	1987	......	Bankfoot, Perth, PH1 4BS [073 887] Bankfoot 235	607	25	50	70	15	17946	2105	2105	v
Blackford	*see Ardoch*												
Cargill Burrelton	*Vacant*	......	......	Woodside, Coupar Angus, PH13 9NQ [082 87] Burrelton 352	428	16	95	32	12	13612	1300	1300	8769
linked with Collace					187	11	18	10	...	6299	681	681	
					309	10	21	22	...	14141	1950	1950	9354
Cleish *linked with* Fossoway St. Serf's and Devonside	David T. Reid, BA, BD	1959	1985	Cleish, Kinross, KY13 7LR [057 75] Cleish Hills 231	192	10	...	38	...	13441	996	996	...
Collace	*see Cargill*												

Charge	Minister			Address / Tel.									
Comrie and Strowan	P. D. Thomson, MA, BD	1968	1978	Comrie, Perthshire, PH6 2HE [0764] Comrie 70269	679	34	79	40	20	32142	5558	5558	9120
linked with Dundurn					84	6		12		6190	1094	1094	
Crieff— St. Andrew's	Bruce Ritchie, BSC, BD	1977	1987	Strathearn Ter., Crieff, PH7 3AQ [0764] Crieff 2604	439	20	124			20608	2021	2021	v
linked with St. Michael's					771	40	35	95	26	27616	6761	6761	
South and Monzievaird	H. A. G. Tait, MA, BD	1966	......	Victoria Terrace, Crieff, PH7 4AA [0764] Crieff 2325	436	29	35	38	27	24747	4386	4386	9120
Dunbarney	Vacant	......	......	Bridge of Earn, Perth, PH2 9DY [0738] Bridge of Earn 812463	543	28	33	36	9	21180	2261	2261	8937
linked with Forgandenny					99	6	13	13		4920	636	636	
Dundurn	*see* Comrie												
Dunning	*see* Aberuthven												
Errol	Douglas M. Main, BD	1986	......	Errol, Perth, PH2 7PZ [082 12] Errol 279	488	22	38	61	14	25888	3638	3638	9144
linked with Kilspindie and Rait					77	8		8		4335	350	350	
Forteviot	*see* Aberdalgie												
Fossoway St. Serf's and Devonside	*see* Cleish												
Fowlis Wester	Joseph L. Leckie, MA, MPHIL	1954	1984	Beechview, Abercairney, Crieff, PH7 3OQ [0764] Crieff 2116	133	8	14	7		9332			8646
linked with Madderty					126	8	24	8		7834			
linked with Monzie					144	9	10	22		5803		180	
Gask	Brian Bain, LTH	1980	1985	Methven, Perth, PH1 3PH [073 884] Methven 274	90	9	13	4	6	3720			8646
linked with Methven					322	26	36	37	12	12976			
Kilspindie and Rait	*see* Errol												
Kinfauns	Michael J. Ward, BSC, BD	1983	......	Glencarse, Perth, PH2 7NF [073 886] Glencarse 387	71	7	32	2		2206			8646
linked with St. Madoes					312	17		31	9	10441			
Kinross	T. Leslie Barr, LTH	1969	1979	Station Road, Kinross, KY13 7TG [0577] Kinross 62952	801	31	27	135	25	26909	6391	6391	9414
Logiealmond	*see* Almondbank												
Madderty	*see* Fowlis Wester												
Methven	*see* Gask												

Charge	Minister	Ord.	Ind.	Address and Tel. No.	Com.	Eld.	W.G.	S.S.	B.C.	C.L. £	As'd £	Gi'n £	Stp. £
Monzie	see Fowlis Wester												
Muthill *linked with* Trinity Gask and Kinkell	Stanley G. Strachan, MA, DIPED, DIPAGECON	1984	......	Muthill, Perthshire, PH5 2AR [076 481] Muthill 205	442	30	34	29	33	19049	1598	1629	8937
					76	6	25	4	......	3822	350	370	
Orwell *linked with* Portmoak	*Vacant*	......	......	3 Perth Road, Milnathort, Kinross, KY13 7XU [0577] Kinross 63461	494	28	36	36	......	17416	1552	1552	8937
					195	13	......	31	......	9795	1323	1323	
Perth— Craigend Moncreiffe *linked with* Rhynd	Hector Houston, MBE, JP	1952	1953	Rhynd, Perth, PH2 8QG [0738] Perth 25694	549	31	22	10	......	13527	......	100	8898
					118	12	......	......	......	3669	......	......	
Craigie	John Rankin, BD	1974	1988	46 Abbot Street, PH2 0EE [0738] Perth 23748	738	44	70	66	15	27925	4205	4522	v
Kinnoull	Alasdair F. Cameron, BD, CA	1986	......	1 Mount Tabor Avenue, PH2 7BT [0738] Perth 26046	602	34	84	63	16	34101	5083	5083	9189
Letham St. Mark's	Graham R. Houston, BSC, BD, MTH	1978	1982	35 Rose Crescent, PH1 1NT [0738] Perth 24167	1147	42	57	156	27	38169	6964	6964	9633
North	Robert P. Sloan, MA, BD	1968	1978	127 Glasgow Road, PH2 0LU [0738] Perth 25728	1998	125	112	234	163	89919	18765	19331	11955
	Patricia Munro, BSC, DCS	......	......	Deaconess—see List H [0738] Perth 27549									
St. Andrew's	Alastair F. M'Cormick	1960	1977	44 Hay Street, PH1 5HS [0738] Perth 21305	839	34	46	23	13	25638	6704	4591	9453
St. John the Baptist's	David D. Ogston, MA, BD	1970	1980	15 Comely Bank, PH2 7HU [0738] Perth 21755	1146	79	20	19	36	57223	9942	11011	10854
St. Leonard's-in-the-Fields and Trinity	Gordon G. Stewart, MA	1961	1970	5 Strathearn Terrace, PH2 0LS [0738] Perth 21709	938	85	45	45	29	47195	14191	14191	11364
St. Matthew's	Ewen J. Gilchrist, BD, DIPMIN	1982	1988	23 Kincarrathie Crescent, PH2 7HH [0738] Perth 26828	1137	75	71	48	11	45642	12113	12543	v
St. Stephen's	Archibald E. Millar, DIPTH	1965	1978	10 Muirton Bank, PH1 5DN [0738] Perth 21813	409	15	24	45	8	13206	......	......	8646
Portmoak	see Orwell												

Charge	Minister	App.	Address and Tel. No.								
Redgorton *linked with* Stanley	Ronald G. Greig, MA, BD	1987	Stanley, Perth, PH1 4ND [073 882] Stanley 247	197	11	......	32	4	5067	632	206 v
Rhynd	see Perth Craigend			389	22	......	46	4	13010	1455	1455
St. Madoes	see Kinfauns										
St. Martin's *linked with* Scone New	Alexander M. Millar, MA, BD	1980 1987	24 Victoria Rd., Scone, Perth, PH2 6JW [0738] Scone 51467	254	10	......	21	......	5566	1093	1093 v
Scone Old	J. Bruce Thomson, BD	1972 1983	Burnside, Scone, Perth, PH2 6LP [0738] Scone 52030	790	38	50	44	8	23654	5200	1700
Stanley	see Redgorton			1107	48	69	145	47	26250	5628	5628 9729
Trinity Gask and Kinkell	see Muthill										

Minister	Ord.	App.	Ret.	Charge	Address and Tel. No.
Alexander, J. Neil S., MA, BD, STM	1949	......	1986	(Crieff St. Andrew's)	St. Ninian's Training Centre, Crieff, PH7 4BG [0764] Crieff 3766
Bisset, Peter T., MA, BD	1952	1974	......	*Warden, St. Ninian's*	1 Black Watch, BFPO 45
Blakey, Stephen A., BSC, BD	1977	1977	......	*Chaplain, Army*	16 Juniper Place, Perth, PH1 1EZ [0738] Perth 23803
Bonomy, William, MA, BD	1946	......	1987	(Inverkip)	Gowanbank, Isla Road, Perth, PH2 7HQ [0738] Perth 32469
Brown, R. Russell, MA	1940	......	1986	(Perth Kinoull)	Vrackie, 223 Glasgow Road, Perth, PH1 [0738] Perth 26088
Bruce, Duncan M., MA	1950	......	1984	(Muthill)	26 Dalhousie Place, Arbroath, DD11 [024?] Arbroath 70670
Caldwell, James, MA	1943	......	1984	(Abernethy and Dron *with* Arngask)	Dunmuir, Western Road, Auchterarder, PH13 1JJ
Cumming, Henry, MA	1934	......	1972	(Bridge of Weir Freeland)	[076 46] Auchterarder 2738
Donaldson, Murray, MA	1939	......	1979	(Redgorton)	196 Bute Drive, Perth, PH1 3DS [0738] Perth 24563
Frew, Michael W., BSC, BD	1978	1987	......	*Evangelism Area Organiser*	52 Rose Crescent, Perth, PH1 1NT [0738] Perth 27722
Gibb, T. F., MA, BD	1939	......	1982	(Perth Trinity)	6 Kinnaird Bank, Perth, PH2 0DH [0738] Perth 25970
Gilmour, Hadden M., MA, JP	1934	......	1976	(Glenbuchat Towie)	2 Langley Cottages, Perth, PH2 7PF [0738] Perth 51582
Greenwood, Harry	1964	......	1984	(Madderty *with* Trinity Gask and Kinkell)	7 Marlee Place, Scone, PH2 6SE [0738] Scone 51868
Grimson, John A., MA	1950	......	1986	(Glasgow Wellington *Associate*)	29 Highland Road, Turret Park, PH7 [0764] Crieff 3063
Henry, Malcolm N., MA	1951	......	1987	(Perth Craigie)	Kelton, Castle Douglas, DG7 1RU
Hill, Robert S.	1967	......	1973	(Glenshee and Glenericht)	Newstead, Ancaster Road, Crieff, PH7 4AL [0764] Crieff 2975
Houston, Alexander M.	1939	......	1977	(Tibbermore)	120 Glasgow Road, Perth, PH2 0LU [0738] Perth 28056
Hunter, William F.	1986	1986	......	*Youth Officer*	St. Ninian's Training Centre, Crieff, PH7 4BG [0764] Crieff 3766
Jack, Adam, MA, BD	1936	......	1974	(Kirkcudbright St. Cuthbert's)	Glenfender, 7 Clark Terrace, Crieff, PH7 3QE [0764] Crieff 3641
Keir, Thomas H., DD	1930	......	1972	(Melrose St. Cuthbert's)	20 Langside Drive, Comrie, PH6 2HR [0764] Comrie 70627
Kennedy, S.	1937	......	1977	(Methven)	Tara, 21 College Road, Methven, PH1 3QN [073 884] Methven 456
King, R. Maurice, MA	1953	......	1982	(Jamaica)	19 Glenshee Crescent, Perth, PH2 0AL

Minister	Ord.	App.	Ret.	Charge	Address and Tel. No.
				School Chaplain	
Longmuir, T. Graeme, MA, B ED	1976	1984	.....	(Perth St. Matthew's)	The Manse, Strathallan School, Forgandenny, Perth, PH2 9HP 0738 812110
M'Bride, George H. H., MA	1945	.....	1987	(Fossoway St. Serf's and Devonside)	Flowerdale, Balmoral Road, Blairgowrie, PH10 7AF
M'Conkey, Duncan L., MA	1941	.....	1980	(Aberdalgie and Dupplin *with* Forteviot)	The Manse, Fossoway, Kinross [057 74] Fossoway 242
Macdonald, W. U., MA, JP	1939	.....	1984	(Comrie and Strowan)	30 Muircroft Terrace West, Perth, PH1 [0738] Perth 27948
M'Ghie, John, MA, BD	1935	.....	1967	(Kinross West)	c/o Wilmar, Stoneykirk Road, Stranraer, D69
Mackenzie, D. M., MA	1933	.....	1978	(Auchterarder The Barony)	2 Dupplin Road, Perth, PH1 [0738] Perth 27254
MacKenzie, Donald W., MA	1941	.....	1983	(Perth St. Paul's)	81 Kingswell Place, Perth, PH1 2DD [0738] Perth 33716
MacLean, Nigel R., MA, BD	1940	.....	1986	(Braemar *with* Crathie *Associate*)	9 Hay Street, Perth, PH1 [0738] Perth 26728
MacPhee, Duncan P.	1951	.....	1980	(Madderty *with* Trinity Gask and Kinkell)	38 Perth Road, Stanley, PH1 [0738] Perth 82537
Miller, Ian R. N., MA	1931	.....	1977	(Almondbank St. Serf's *with* Logiealmond)	Innerwick, Ferntower Road, Crieff [0764] Crieff 2176
Morris, William S.	1950	.....	1976	(Crathie)	22 Kintillo Place, Bridge of Earn, Perth, PH2 9AW [0738] Bridge of Earn 812865
Nicol, T. J. T., LVO, MBE, MC, DD	1941	.....	1977	(Scone Old)	Beech Cottage, Barrack Road, Dalginross, Comrie [0764] Comrie 70430
Robertson, Ronald, MA, BD	1938	.....	1982	(Dunbarney)	30 The Meadows, Kintillo, Bridge of Earn, PH2 [0738] Bridge of Earn 812574
Ross, W. J., MA	1944	.....	1981	(Aberdour St. Fillan's)	7 Holyrood Street, Carnoustie, DD7 6HF [0241] Carnoustie 54732
Rutherford, David W., MC, MA, BD	1935	.....	1975	(St. Martin's *with* Scone New)	152 Glasgow Road, Perth, PH2 0LX [0738] Perth 21404
Shirra, James, MA	1945	.....	1987	(Edinburgh St. Bernard's Davidson)	17 Dunbarney Avenue, Bridge of Earn, Perth, PH2 9BP [0738] Bridge of Earn 812610
Smith, Charles P., MA	1943	.....	1976	(Glasgow Kinning Park)	1 Rosebank Gardens, Glasgow Road, Perth, PH2 [0738] Perth 25036
Stephen, Adrian Hay, BD	1940	.....	1980	(Perth St. Leonard's)	The Manse, Methven, Perth, PH1 2PH [073 884] Methven 274
Taylor, Robertson, MA, BD	1946	.....	1985	(Kilspindie and Rait *with* Kinfauns)	15 Craigieknowes Avenue, Perth
Urquhart, J. MacNeill, MA	1942	.....	1980	(Stromness North)	Kilspindie, PH2 7RX
Watt, John A. R., MA, BD	1929	.....	1970	(Abernethy and Dron)	Greystanes, Comrie, PH6 2EQ [0764] Comrie 70563
Watt, Leslie G.	1961	.....	1977	(Kingussie)	106 Main Street, Roslin, Midlothian
Wright, Ninian B., MBE, BD	1930	.....	1972		Craigbeg, Dalginross, Comrie, Crieff, PH6 2ED [0764] Comrie 70712

ADDRESSES OF PERTH CHURCHES

St. Andrew's	Atholl Street	St. Matthew's	Tay Street [0738] 27708
St. John's	St. John Street [0738] 26159	St. Stephen's	Balhousie Street (North End)
St. Leonard's-in-the-Fields and Trinity	Marshall Place [0738] 32238		

Craigend Moncrieffe	Glenbruar Crescent
Craigie	Abbot Street
Kinnoull	Dundee Road nr. Queen's Bridge
Letham St. Mark's	Rannoch Road
North	Mill St. nr. Kinnoull St. [0738] 22298

29. DUNDEE

Meets at Dundee, The Steeple Church Halls, Nethergate, on the second Wednesday of February, March, April, May, September, October, November and December; and on the fourth Wednesday of June

Clerk: Rev. JAMES A. ROY, MA, BD, 3 Coupar Angus Road, Dundee DD2 3HG [0382] Dundee 611415

Hon. Treasurer: Mr. IAN C. CATHRO, OBE, 2 West Park Gardens, Dundee, DD2 1NY [0382] Dundee 68434

Charge	Minister	Ord.	Ind.	Address and Tel. No.	Com.	Eld.	W.G.	S.S.	B.C.	C.L. £	As'd £	Gi'n £	Stp. £
Abernyte	Robert Daly, MA, JP	1949	1954	Longforgan, DD2 5EU [082 622] Longforgan 238	100	8	...	14	...	4838	900	186	
linked with Inchture and Kinnaird	I. T. Adamson, MA, BSC, MSC, PHD	1986	......	Auxiliary—see List on page 204 [0382] Dundee 42280	291	14	15	49	......	8502	1562	1000	10655
linked with Longforgan					372	19	36	22	......	13602	3161	213	
Auchterhouse					160	11	25	21	6	8030	807	857	
linked with Murroes and Tealing	Helen G. Johnstone (Mrs.) MA, BD, HDIPRE	1983	......	Balgray, Tealing, Dundee, DD4 0QZ [082 621] Tealing 224	367	17	47	31	14	16537	1030	1030	9483
DUNDEE— Albany-Butterburn linked with St. David's North	Gideon G. Scott, MA, BD, THM	1963	1973	38 Albany Terrace, DD3 6HS [0382] Dundee 21394	405	25	20	10	28	24113	1331	1331	10179
					300	19	54	9	......	18538	2236	1331	
Balgay	George K. Robson, LTH, CPS	1983	1987	150 City Road, DD2 2PW [0382] Dundee 68806	541	37	31	24	29	21954	4849	4849	v
Barnhill St. Margaret's	Gordon D. Jamieson, MA, BD	1974	1986	Invermark Ter., Barnhill, DD5 2QU [0382] Dundee 79278	1223	68	96	128	67	61271	15254	15254	11538
Broughty Ferry— East	Alan H. Mackay, BD	1974	1984	8 West Queen Street, Broughty Ferry, DD5 1AR [0382] Dundee 78972	695	40	53	61	13	58336	9059	9059	10926
St. Aidan's	Keith Campbell, BSC, BD	1963	1968	63 Collingwood Street, Barnhill, DD5 2UF [0382] Dundee 79253	896	53	180	75	66	41535	10036	10036	10926
St. James'	Thomas P. Robertson	1963	1970	95 Seafield Road, Broughty Ferry, DD5 3AP [0382] Dundee 79803	422	22	49	46	8	30126	5204	5204	9483
St. Luke's and Queen Street	S. Gillies MacNab, MA, BD	1938	1959	22 Albert Road, Broughty Ferry, DD5 1AZ [0382] Dundee 79212	667	47	32	24	30	32352	7684	5108	9825
St. Stephen's and West	John U. Cameron, BA, BSC, PHD, BD, THD	1974	......	33 Camperdown St., Broughty Ferry, DD5 3AA [0382] Dundee 77403	742	33	...	48	57	30888	7871	6000	10926

Charge	Minister	Ord.	Ind.	Address and Tel. No.	Com.	Eld.	W.G.	S.S.	B.C.	C.L. £	As'd £	Gi'n £	Stp. £	M.M. £
Camperdown	*Vacant*			Myrekirk Road, DD2 4SF [0382] *Dundee* 621383	407	20	35		40	17	24104	1600		9690
Chalmers Ardler	James E. Powrie, LTH	1969		Turnberry Avenue, DD2 3TP [0382] *Dundee* 827439	547	15	39	39	91	43	42545	8527	9127	10655
	Jane Martin, DCS			*Deaconess—see* List H [0382] *Dundee* 813786										
Clepington	John E. Hawdon, BA	1961	1970	12 Rosewood Terrace, DD2 1NS [0382] *Dundee* 646212	894	51	26		49	42	25187	6372	3250	10075
Craigiebank	David J. H. Laing, BD, DPS	1976	1982	244 Arbroath Road, DD4 7SB [0382] *Dundee* 450385	796	32		57	47	44	31586	4886	4886	9696
Douglas and Angus	James M'Naughtan, BD, DIPMIN	1983		Balbeggie Street, DD4 8RJ [0382] *Dundee* 78443	548	24		57	75	15	23436	906	212	8646
	Barbara M. Urquhart, (Mrs.) DCS			*Deaconess—see* List H [0382] *Dundee* 450502										
Downfield South	Andrew J. Wilson, BA, BD	1982	1986	15 Elgin Street, DD3 8NL [0382] *Dundee* 89498	790	34	52	52	88	53	39399	4738	4786	9825
Dundee (St. Mary's)	W. B. R. Macmillan, MA, BD	1954	1978	371 Blackness Road, DD2 1ST [0382] *Dundee* 69406	1004	76	52		15	6	56325	16097	16237	13479
Fairmuir	David C. MacLeod, BSC, MENG, BD	1969	1978	6 Carseview Gardens, DD2 1NE [0382] *Dundee* 641371	529	23	25	25	59	42	27003	4294	3313	9654
Lochee— Old and St. Luke's	Roy Mackenzie, LTH	1982	1985	16 Coupar Angus Road, DD2 3HN [0382] *Dundee* 611440	794	37	46	46	36	10	28757	5580	1882	10569
West	James A. Roy, MA, BD	1965	1973	3 Coupar Angus Road, DD2 3HG [0382] *Dundee* 611415	1066	65	36	36	82	31	27910	8690	5196	10926
Logie and St. John's Cross	D. Dominic Smart, BSC, BD	1988		7 Hyndford Street, DD2 1HQ [0382] *Dundee* 641572	605	25	23	23	29		24111	6901	10421	v
Mains	Kenneth R. Thom, BD	1985		9 Elgin Street, DD3 8NL [0382] *Dundee* 825562	518	24	42	42	35	3	23559	1750		9063
	Jean Thomson (Mrs.)			*Agent—see* List H										
Mains of Fintry	Peter M. Humphris, BSC, BD	1976	1977	4 Clive Street, DD4 7AW [0382] *Dundee* 42539	468	17	20	20	53	29	24943	3605	3053	9063
Meadowside St. Paul's	Maudeen I. MacDougall, BA, BD	1978	1984	36 Blackness Avenue, DD2 1HH [0382] *Dundee* 68828	768	73	59	59	22	4	160077	10090	10090	11538

Parish	Minister	Ordained/Inducted	Address [phone]									
Menzieshill	*Vacant*	1977	Charleston Drive, DD2 4BD [0382] Dundee 67588	866	28	......	91	59	32322	5000	3000	9690
	Jack Mitchell, MA, BD, CTH	1987	*Auxiliary—see List on page 205* [0382] Dundee 642301									
Mid Craigie	Douglas J. Page, BD, CPS ¶	1987	96 Forfar Road, DD4 7BG [0382] Dundee 42426	171	5	......	14	10	3915	......	50	v
	Fay M. Lamont, DCS		*Deaconess—see List H* [0382] Dundee 500239									
Ogilvie and Stobswell	Alan J. Roy, BSC, BD	1960 1972	23 Shamrock Street, DD4 7AH [0382] Dundee 459119	1008	54	40	86	9	98047	7150	7150	12036
Roseangle Ryehill	James M Rogers, BA, BD	1955 1965	15 West Park Road, DD2 1NX [0382] Dundee 67460	641	51	58	36	8	47248	11848	14214	11292
St. Andrew's	Ian D. Petrie, MA, BD	1970 1986	77 Blackness Avenue, DD2 1JN [0382] Dundee 641695	1390	79	56	51	13	38177	7061	7061	11820
St. Columba's	J. MacKay Nimmo, MA, BD	1944 1956	7 Inverary Terrace, DD3 6BS [0382] Dundee 24466	364	19	20	25	9	9533	......	120	8646
St. David's North	*see Albany Butterburn*											
St. Peter's M'Cheyne	J. Harrison Hudson, DIPTH, MA, BD	1961 1977	22 Hyndford Street, DD2 1HX [0382] Dundee 646586	1130	82	60	30	6	59523	12840	12840	11646
Steeple	Graham W. Foster, MA, BD, THM	1973 1986	128 Arbroath Road, DD4 7HR [0382] Dundee 455411	583	41	33	47	21	45790	7689	7689	10557
Strathmartine	Robert G. Clarkson	1950 1962	9 Park Road, DD3 8NH [0382] Dundee 825380	913	53	69	167	67	50624	7942	10582	12057
The High Kirk	Henry M. Gibson, MA, BD	1960 1979	6 Adelaide Place, DD3 6LF [0382] Dundee 22955	705	52	60	46	39	49259	7219	7219	10329
Trinity	Albert B. Reid, BD, BSC	1966 1981	75 Clepington Road, DD4 7BJ [0382] Dundee 41930	1392	64	93	89	53	49159	9162	9462	11289
	Lilian Smith, DCS		*Deaconess—see List H*									
Whitfield [E]	David Donaldson, MA, BD	1969 1983	55 Chirnside Place, DD4 0TE [0382] Dundee 739757	564	20	......	39	18	13886	......	181	9147
	Hector G. M'Millan, MA	1964 1985	Longcroft, Auchterhouse, DD3 0QX [0526] Auchterhouse 343									
	Associate											
Fowlis and Liff	Charles W. Miller, MA	1953 1980	14 Liff Park, Dundee, DD2 5PH [0382] Dundee 580033	220	14	12	10	3	9417	......	......	8646
Inchture and Kinnaird	*see Abernyte*											

Charge	Minister	Ord.	Ind.	Address and Tel. No.	Com.	Eld.	W.G.	S.S.	B.C.	C.L. £	As'd £	Gi'n £	Stp. £
Invergowrie	*Vacant*	……	……	Invergowrie, Dundee, DD2 5AA [0382] *Invergowrie 562261*	915	35	67	43	22	29483	5318	5368	10557
Longforgan	*see Abernyte*												
Lundie and Muirhead of Liff	Martin R. H. Thomas, CENG, MISTRUCTE	1987	……	149 Coupar Angus Road, Muirhead of Liff, Dundee, DD2 5NN [0382] *Muirhead 580210*	505	20	35	46	6	19266	2423	2423	v
Monifieth— Panmure	David B. Jamieson, MA, BD, STM	1974	……	8A Albert Street, Monifieth, DD5 4JS [082 63] *Monifieth 2772*	573	33	77	94	60	24487	2732	2732	9063
St. Rule's	Tom Milroy	1960	1970	Church Street, Monifieth, DD5 4JP [082 63] *Monifieth 2607*	872	34	53	41	19	31818	6572	3085	10926
South	Donald W. Fraser, MA	1958	1959	Queen Street, Monifieth, DD5 4HG [082 63] *Monifieth 2646*	564	23	53	64	55	21436	1927	1925	9087
Monikie and Newbigging	Gordon R. Mackenzie, BSC, BD	1977	1985	59B Broomwell Gardens, Monikie, DD5 3QP [038 235] *Newbigging 200*	522	23	14	51	11	9491	504	……	8646
Murroes and Tealing	*see Auchterhouse*												

Minister	Ord.	App.	Ret.	Charge	Address and Tel. No.
Adamson, I. T., MA, BSC, MSC, PHD	1986	1986		*Auxiliary at* Abernyte *with* Inchture *and* Kinnaird *with* Longforgan	3 Chalmers Street, Dundee, DD4 7EZ [0382] *Dundee 42280*
Arthur, Robert, MA	1939		1975	(Dundee Old St. Paul's and St. David's)	18 Albany Terrace, DD3 6HR [0382] *Dundee 22540*
Ayre, George S., MA	1951		1983	(Dundee St. James')	6 Lochside Gardens, Tayport, DD6 9DU [0382] *Dundee 553519*
Bremner, J. A., MA	1943		1979	(Dundee Roseangle)	122 Glamis Road, DD2 2ET [0382] *Dundee 69473*
Brown, T. E., BCOM	1968		1982	(Cluny)	Pilgrim Cottage, Loch-of-Liff Road, Liff, DD2 5NN [0382] *Dundee 580265*
Chisholm, W. Douglas, MA	1943		1983	(Monifieth North and Newbigging with Monikie)	8 Musgrave Road, Chinnor, Oxon, OX9 4TF
Craig, Iain R., MA	1948		1988	(Invergowrie)	13 Balmoral View, Rattray, Blairgowrie, PH10 7LT
Doig, David M., BA, BD	1972		1986	(Dundee Mid-Craigie)	9 Clarke Avenue, Ayr, KA7 2XE [0292] *Ayr 267510*
Gray, David G., MA, BD	1937		1972	(Dundee St. Peter's)	Cortachy Cottage, Auchterhouse, DD3 0QS [038 238] *Auchterhouse 213*
Hamilton, James, BA, BD	1939		1982	(Auchterhouse)	48 Marlee Road, Broughty Ferry, DD5 3EX [0382] *Dundee 736400*
Ingram, J. R.	1954		1978	(Chaplain, R.A.F.)	6 Kinghorne Terrace, Dundee, DD3 6HX [0382] *Dundee 24803*
Keiller, J. Dennis	1953		1978	(Dundee Bonnethill)	14 Dalhousie Road, Barnhill, DD5 2SQ [0382] *Dundee 77458*
Laidlaw, John J., BD	1964	1973	……	*Adviser in Religious Education*	

Little, James E., VRD, BD	1941	(Dundee Ogilvie)	1 Dean's Park, Dunkeld, PH8 0JH [035 02] Dunkeld 02520
Macdonald, John, AEA, MA	1949	(Lochee Old)	12 Hyndford Street, DD2 1HQ [0382] Dundee 68655
Macdonald, John A.	1939	(Dundee Balgay)	30 Seymour Street, DD2 1HD [0382] Dundee 645344
Mackenzie, George R., MA, BD	1942	(Dundee Logie and St. John's Cross)	39 Middlebank Crescent, Dundee, DD2 1HZ [0382] Dundee 68491
Mitchell, Jack	1987 1987	Auxiliary at Dundee Menzieshill	10 Invergowrie Drive, Dundee, DD2 1RF [0382] Dundee 642301
Money, W. Strang, MA, BD	1943	(Steeple)	51 Regent Place, West Ferry, DD5 1AT [0382] Dundee 736291
Mowat, Gilbert M., MA	1948	(Dundee Albany Butterburn)	7 Dunmore Gardens, DD2 1PP [0382] Dundee 66013
Nicoll, Charles, JP	1951	(Downfield South)	272 Strathmartine Road, DD3 8PN [0382] Dundee 88539
Paterson, William, BSC	1927	(Dundurn)	c/o Goudie, 2 Redcastle Crescent, Broughty Ferry, DD5 3NF [0382] Dundee 76876
Rae, Robert, LTH	1968 1983	Chaplain to Dundee Acute Hospitals	47 Mains Loan, DD4 7AF [0382] Dundee 450158
Robertson, Robert, MA	1922	(Collace)	95 Seafield Road, Broughty Ferry, DD5 3AP [0382] Dundee 79803
Scott, J. Miller, MA, BD, FSASCOT, DD	1949	(Jerusalem)	8 Wortley Place, Dundee DD4 7HD [0382] Dundee 451784
Scroggie, John C.	1951	(Mains)	4 Bell Tree Gardens, Balmossie, DD5 2LJ [0382] Dundee 739354
Wilson, James F.	1944	(Montrose Melville South)	39 Scott Street, Dundee, DD2 2AL [0382] Dundee 67217

ADDRESSES OF DUNDEE CHURCHES

Albany Butterburn	2 Hill Street
Balgay	200 Lochee Road
Barnhill St. Margaret's	10 Invermark Ter., Barnhill
Broughty Ferry—	
East	370 Queen Street
St. Aidan's	440 Brook Street
St. James'	5 Fort Street
St. Luke's and Queen Street	5 West Queen Street
St. Stephen's & West Street	96 Dundee Road
Camperdown	Brownhill Rd., Camperdown
Chalmers Ardler	Turnberry Avenue
Clepington	Isla Street x Main Street
Craigiebank	Craigie Ave. at Greendyke Road
Douglas and Angus	Balbeggie Place
Downfield South	Haldane St., off Strathmartine Road
Dundee (St. Mary's)	Nethergate
Fairmuir	329 Clepington Road
High Kirk	119A Kinghorne Road
Lochee—	
Old and St. Luke's	Bright Street, Lochee
West	191 High Street, Lochee
Logie and St. John's (Cross)	Shaftesbury Rd. x Blackness Avenue
Mains	Foot of Old Glamis Road
Mains of Fintry	Fintry Rd. x Fintry Dr.
Meadowside St. Paul's	114 Nethergate
Menzieshill	Charleston Drive, Lochee
Mid Craigie	Longtown Terrace
Ogilvie and Stobswell	Top of Albert Street
Roseangle Ryehill	130 Perth Road
St. Andrew's	2 King Street
St. Columba's	Cobden Street x Logie Street
St. David's North	273 Strathmore Avenue
St. Peter's M'Cheyne	328 Perth Road
Steeple	Nethergate
Strathmartine	513 Strathmartine Road
Trinity	73 Crescent Street
Whitfield	Haddington Crescent

30. ANGUS

Meets at Forfar in St. Margaret's Church Hall, on the first Tuesday of each month, except June when it meets on the last Tuesday, and January, July and August when there is no meeting

Clerk: Rev. M. M'G. DOWIE, LTH, Jamieson Street, Forfar, DD8 2HY [0307] Forfar 6248

Depute Clerk: Rev. A. F. M. DOWNIE, MA, BD, The Manse, Hillside, Montrose, DD10 9HT [067 483] Hillside 288

Charge	Minister	Ord.	Ind.	Address and Tel. No.	Com.	Eld.	W.G.	S.S.	B.C.	C.L. £	As'd £	Gi'n £	Stp. £
Aberlemno	Brian Ramsay, BD, DPS	1980	1984	Guthrie, Forfar, DD8 2TP [024 12] Friockheim 243	204	7	8	20	2	8572	…	…	
linked with Guthrie and Rescobie					222	7	20	20	8	7757	…	…	8646
Airlie	Gordon M. Ramsay	1960	……	Airlie, Kirriemuir, DD8 5NL [057 53] Craigton 245	134	9	…	28	…	5282	…	…	
linked with Kingoldrum					70	4	…	…	…	2511	…	100	8977
linked with Ruthven					41	2	…	…	…	1837	…	20	
Arbirlot	David S. A. Grieve, MA, BD	1954	1982	Arbirlot, Arbroath, DD11 2NX [0241] Arbroath 75118	326	16	…	9	…	11113	1770	1770	
linked with Carmyllie					181	8	14	20	…	5624	1008	350	9798
linked with Colliston					160	7	15	6	…	6632	954	954	
Arbroath— Abbey	W. G. Beattie, MA, BD	1956	1977	Cliffburn Road, DD11 5BA [0241] Arbroath 72196	1171	42	68	44	8	55254	8097	8097	9873
Knox's see St. Vigean's													
Ladyloan St. Columba's	Gavin D. Brownlie, MA	1955	1961	Dishlandtown Street, DD11 1QU [0241] Arbroath 72356	1548	81	50	61	12	49745	13027	13027	11007
Old	Malcolm MacLeod, BA, BD	1979	1984	2 Seaton Road, DD11 5DX [0241] Arbroath 70253	790	41	32	34	30	32515	7024	7024	10143
St. Andrew's	Ian MacLeod, MA, BD	1954	1959	Albert Street, DD11 1RA [0241] Arbroath 73238	973	52	30	72	59	30596	7844	8529	10143
St. Margaret's	Alasdair G. Graham, BD	1981	1986	1 Charles Avenue, DD11 2EZ [0241] Arbroath 72244	795	38	…	75	15	42948	9512	9512	11142
St. Vigean's	John P. L. Munro, MA, BD, PHD	1977	1986	St. Vigean's, Arbroath, DD11 4RD [0241] Arbroath 73206	637	36	52	29	13	26315	6905	6905	10506
linked with Knox's					514	25	54	26	6	16460	3450	3450	
Barry	Walter T. A. Stewart	1964	1969	Barry, Carnoustie, DD7 7RP [0241] Carnoustie 52371	612	16	40	34	14	18384	1302	250	8646

Congregation	Minister			Address									
Brechin— Cathedral	Robert K. Mackenzie, MA, BD, PHD	1976	1986	Bishops Close, Brechin, DD9 6HH [035 62] Brechin 2783	1293	67	41	49	…	35170	8799	8799	9912
Maison Dieu *linked with* Stracathro	*Vacant*	…	……	28 Airlie Street, Brechin, DD9 6JX [035 62] Brechin 2152	661	18	15	11	7	9531	1717	2005	v
					124	4	…	…	…	5749	311	311	
Southesk	James P. R. Drysdale	1967	1978	36 Park Road, Brechin, DD9 7AP [035 62] Brechin 2789	995	32	59	45	45	27613	5066	5066	9525
Carmyllie	*see Arbirlot*												
Carnoustie	J. Colin Caskie, BA, BD	1977	1983	44 Terrace Rd., Carnoustie, DD7 7AR [0241] Carnoustie 52289	1279	51	67	102	16	53423	9799	10049	10482
Carnoustie Panbride	*Vacant*	…	……	8 Arbroath Rd., Carnoustie, DD7 6BL [0241] Carnoustie 54478	776	26	…	191	14	132765	4314	4314	9513
Colliston	*see Arbirlot*												
Dun *linked with* Hillside	Alan F. M. Downie, MA, BD	1977	……	Hillside, Montrose, DD10 9HT [067 483] Hillside 288	147	8	…	21	…	5640	610	610	9096
					491	17	…	61	10	15962	2647	2647	
Dunnichen, Letham and Kirkden	*Vacant*	…	……	7 Brachead Road, Letham, Forfar, DD8 2PG [030 781] Letham (Angus) 430	667	22	…	49	8	16973	1983	1510	8646
Eassie and Nevay *linked with* Newtyle	A. M'A. Knox, CA	1954	1982	Newtyle, Angus, PH12 [082 85] Newtyle 461	75	4	14	9	…	3041	366	1	8814
					373	12	73	21	3	13226	1367	1367	
Edzell Lethnot *linked with* Glenesk	John W. A. Forbes, BD	1973	1982	Edzell, Brechin, Angus, DD9 7TJ [035 64] Edzell 7251	484	22	74	26	…	34105	2735	3435	9057
					80	6	…	12	…	2598	340	340	
Farnell	Joseph B. Perry ¶	1955	1984	Farnell, Brechin, Angus, DD9 6WH [067 482] Farnell 236	201	11	15	11	20	8600	…	102	8646
Fern, Careston and Menmuir *linked with* Oathlaw Tannadice	*Vacant*	…	……	Tannadice, Forfar, DD8 3SH [030 785] Finavon 238	167	8	…	…	…	4273	…	…	v
					221	5	12	…	…	6044	…	…	
Forfar— East: Old	Graham Norrie, MA, BD	1967	1978	Lour Road, Forfar, DD8 2BB [0307] Forfar 64303	2217	76	69	101	55	48292	11803	11803	10506
Lowson Memorial	Malcolm M. Dowie, LTH	1971	……	Jamieson Street, Forfar, DD8 2HY [0307] Forfar 62248	1391	39	57	78	13	29048	4995	4995	11032
St. Margaret's	John M. Birrell, MA, LLB, BD	1974	1988	1 Potter's Park Crescent, Forfar, DD8 1HH [0307] Forfar 63318	1967	50	71	146	52	49946	10700	10700	11190

Charge	Minister	Ord.	Ind.	Address and Tel. No.	Com.	Eld.	W.G.	S.S.	B.C.	C.L. £	As'd £	'Gi'n £	Stp. £
Friockheim Kinnell	Ian L. Forrester, MA	1964	1967	Inverkeilor, Arbroath, DD11 5SA [024 13] Inverkeilor 222	370	15	34	30	......	10112	1105	1105	9213
linked with													
Inverkeilor and Lunan					332	16	20	32	......	10728	1647	1647	
Glamis	John A. Sherrard	1961	1982	Glamis, Forfar, Angus, DD8 1RT [030 784] *Glamis 304*	241	13	20	20	......	9904	......	......	8646
linked with													
Inverarity and Kinnettles					180	10	15	16	......	5541	......	......	
Glenesk	*see Edzell*												
Glenisla	Robert J. Ramsay, LL.B, NP, BD	1986	......	Lintrathen, Kirriemuir, DD8 5JH [057 56] *Lintrathen 226*	70	4	......	9	......	7097	......	142	
linked with													
Kilry					84	6	......	6	......	8729	......	100	8646
linked with													
Lintrathen					121	5	......	18	......	4212	......	......	
Glens, The	Dennis Leadbeater, TD	1946	1971	Cortachy, Kirriemuir, DD8 4QF [057 54] *Cortachy 246*	321	12	18	......	......	7335	......	283	8748
Guthrie and Rescobie	*see Aberlemno*												
Hillside	*see Dun*												
Inchbrayock	Philip R. M. Malloch, LL.B, BD	1970	1981	Ferryden, Montrose, DD10 9SD [0674] *Montrose 72108*	329	12	......	75	18	18119	3631	3631	
linked with													
Montrose Melville South					839	17	25	18	1	20568	5351	5351	10866
Inverarity and Kinnettles	*see Glamis*												
Inverkeilor and Lunan	*see Friockheim*												
Kilry	*see Glenisla*												
Kingoldrum	*see Airlie*												
Kirriemuir—Old	John Stevenson, MA, BD	1963	1983	20 Strathmore Avenue, Kirriemuir, DD8 [0575] *Kirriemuir 73724*	1255	52	20	67	9	33535	6445	6445	10008
St. Andrew's	Peter Youngson	1961	1988	Glamis Road, Kirriemuir, DD8 5BU [0575] *Kirriemuir 72384*	897	29	9	44	10	18577	3180	3180	v
Lintrathen	*see Glenisla*												

Montrose—

Charge	Minister	Ord.	App.	Ret.	Address and Tel. No.								
Melville South													
Old	*see* Inchbrayock												
	Laurence A. B. Whitley, MA, BD	1975		1985	2 Rosehill Road, Montrose, DD10 8ST [0674] Montrose 72447	935	52	37	37	.....	56278	8656	8656	10506
St. Andrew's	Iain M. Douglas, MA, BD, MPHIL, DIPED	1958		1980	49 Northesk Rd., Montrose, DD10 8TQ [0674] Montrose 72060	892	37	40	44	10	20727	2633	2633	8913
Newtyle	*see* Eassie and Nevay													
Oathlaw Tannadice	*see* Fern													
Ruthven	*see* Airlie													
Stracathro	*see* Brechin Maison Dieu													

Minister	Ord.	App.	Ret.	Charge	Address and Tel. No.
Becke, John C., MA	1951	......	1970	(Genoa)	East Woodrae, Aberlemno, Forfar, DD8 3PF [030 783] Aberlemno 278
Black, P. F. C., MA	1938	......	1982	(Edzell Lethnot)	Lochodley Cottage, Edzell, Brechin, DD9 7XU [035 64] Edzell 389
Brook, Norman, MA, BD	1938	......	1953	(Montrose St. Luke's)	10 St. Anne's Bungalows, Bridlington, Yorks
Burns, William G., MBE, MA, BD, JP	1942	......	1981	(Glenesk *with* Logie Pert *with* Stracathro)	9 Latch Gardens, Brechin, Angus, DD9 6NL [035 62] Brechin 2616
Campbell, T. Gemmell, MA, FSA SCOT	1942	......	1983	(Arbroath Old)	Kinloch Terrace, 25A Keptie Road, Arbroath, DD11 3ED [024] Arbroath 73298
Davidson, Peter	1950	......	1983	(Aberdeen Ferryhill North)	5 Wellington Gardens, Montrose, DD10 8QF [0674] Montrose 76369
Duncan, D. Dewar, MA	1930	......	1977	(Forfar West)	16 Taylor Street, Forfar, DD8 3JQ [0307] Forfar 63254
Gray, Robert, MA, BD	1942	......	1982	(Stonehaven Fetteresso)	21 Restenneth Place, Lunanhead, Forfar, DD8 3NF [0307] Forfar 64288
Henderson, David C., CBE, DD	1938	......	1981	(Glamis)	Isla View, Glenisla, Alyth, PH11 8PH [047 582] Glenisla 256
Innes, Peter M., MBE, MA	1938	......	1974	(Assam)	17/14 Kirk Loan, Edinburgh, EH12 7ND
Jones, William	1952	......	1987	(Kirriemuir St. Andrew's)	14 Muir Street, Forfar, DD8 3JY [0307] Forfar 63193
Kant, Everard, W.	1953	......	1988	(Kinghorn)	The Linn, Fern, Angus, DD8 3QW [035 65] Fern 289
Kidd, James	1957	......	1983	(Murroes *with* Tealing)	3 Brackley Burn Cottages, Careston, Brechin, DD9 6SA [035 63] Careston 253
Mackinnon, A. W.	1951	......	1986	(Fern, Careston and Menmuir *with* Oathlaw Tannadice)	19 Gallowhill, Brechin, DD9 6BL [035 62] Brechin 3812
Macmillan, Kenneth	1947	......	1978	(Arbroath Ladyloan St. Columba's)	8 Dalhousie Place, Arbroath, DD11 2BT [024] Arbroath 72858
Russell, A. C., CMG, ED, MA	1959	......	1976	(Aberlemno)	Balgavies Lodge, by Forfar, DD8 2TH [031 781] Letham 571
Stevens, David, MA	1935	......	1972	(Glenesk)	2 Rowan Cottages, Tarfside, Brechin, Angus, DD9 7YU [030 783] Aberlemno 359
Taylor, J. Dempster, MA, CA	1965	......	1982	(Oathlaw and Tannadice)	Crosston Farm House, Aberlemno, Forfar, DD8 3PE
White, Alexander, JP	1950	......	1978	(Aberluthnott)	Woodside Cottage, The Whins, Fettercairn, Laurencekirk, AB3 [056 14] Fettercairn 305
Whyte, David, G. H.	1942	......	1982	(Inverarity and Kinnettles)	Melvaig, Old Halkerton Road, Forfar, DD8 1HJ [0307] Forfar 63728

ADDRESSES OF TOWN CHURCHES

Arbroath—
Abbey   West Abbey Street
Knox's   Howard Street
Ladyloan   Princes Street
St. Columba's   Hamilton Green
St. Andrew's   Keptie Street
St. Margaret's   Kirk Square
The Old

Brechin—
Cathedral   Bishops Close
Maison Dieu   Witchden
Southesk   South Esk Street
Carnoustie—   Dundee Street
Panbride   Arbroath Road
Forfar—
East: Old   East High Street
Lowson Memorial   Jamieson Street
St. Margaret's   West High Street

Kirriemuir—
Old   High Street
St. Andrew's   Glamis Road
Montrose—
Melville South   Castle Street
Old   High Street
St. Andrew's   George Street

SYNOD X—GRAMPIAN

Meets at Christ's College, Alford Place, Aberdeen, on the last Tuesday of April.

Correspondents: Perth and Angus: Southern Highlands

Clerk and Treasurer: Rev. E. C. P. HOOD, MA, The Manse, Methlick, AB4 0DS [065 14] Methlick 215

31. ABERDEEN

Meets at Christ's College, Alford Place, Aberdeen, on the first Tuesday of February, March, April, May, September, October, November and December

Clerk: Rev. ANGUS H. HADDOW, BSC, 27 Ramsay Gardens, Aberdeen AB1 7AE [0224] Aberdeen 317452

Minute Clerk: Rev. ANDREW M. DOUGLAS, MA, 25 Argyle Place, Aberdeen AB2 4HU [0224] Aberdeen 636672

Hon. Treasurer: Mr. C. BIRNIE, MBE, 13 Duthie Court, Aberdeen, AB1 6NG [0224] Aberdeen 315697

Charge	Minister	Ord.	Ind.	Address and Tel. No.	Com.	Eld.	W.G.	S.S.	B.C.	C.L. £	As'd £	Gi'n £	Stp. £
ABERDEEN— Beechgrove	T. D. Allsop, MA, BD	1959	1977	156 Hamilton Place, AB2 4BB [0224] Aberdeen 642615	946	95	84	97	47	70999	17000	17000	11517

Parish	Minister			Address									
Craigiebuckler	Ian P. Douglas, LTH	1974	1982	Springfield Road, AB1 8AA [024] Aberdeen 315125	864	45	131	151	48	44226	7520	7664	10077
Denburn	Alastair F. Lamont, MA	1956	1980	122 Desswood Place, AB2 4DQ [024] Aberdeen 642845	845	51	42	35	8	28629	7000	7040	9429
Ferryhill— North	Andrew C. Christie, LTH ¶	1975	1984	50 Sycamore Place, AB1 2SZ [024] Aberdeen 580865	598	24	56	12	......	18870	1002	1153	8646
South	John H. A. Dick, MA, MSC, BD	1982	......	54 Polmuir Road, AB1 2RT [024] Aberdeen 586933	687	56	59	59	29	47377	5860	6617	9771
Garthdee	Angus H. Haddow, BSC	1963	1981	27 Ramsay Gardens, AB1 7AE [024] Aberdeen 317452	479	12	30	42	50	14836	......	100	8646
Gilcomston South	William Still	1944	1945	18 Beaconsfield Place, AB2 4AA [024] Aberdeen 64037	353	30	......	9	......	63852	15077	15077	8991
Greyfriars	George D. Goldie, ALCM	1953	1962	41 Gray Street, AB1 6JD [024] Aberdeen 584594	910	48	55	34	11	28006	3559	3559	8892
High, Hilton	Andrew M. Douglas, MA	1957	1977	25 Argyll Place, AB2 4HU [024] Aberdeen 636672	965	54	71	59	32	29515	5220	5220	9090
Holburn— Central	Alan D. M°Donald, LL.B, BD	1979	1983	433 Great Western Road, AB1 6NJ [024] Aberdeen 317155	989	70	23	24	9	48624	10670	10670	9636
West	Michael V. A. Mair, MA, BD	1968	1980	31 Cranford Road, AB1 7NJ [024] Aberdeen 318527	998	77	91	64	56	69715	18016	17039	10362
John Knox	Laurie Y. Gordon	1960	1968	23 Beechgrove Avenue, AB2 4HE [024] Aberdeen 632660	832	34	49	29	24	37087	......	......	v
Langstane Kirk	Alexander J. Geddes, MA, BD	1960	1979	14 Norfolk Road, AB1 6JR [024] Aberdeen 319747	637	61	67	10	4	76412	13013	14713	10689
Mannofield	John F. Anderson, MA, BD	1966	1975	21 Forest Avenue, AB1 6TU [024] Aberdeen 315748	1926	98	185	101	35	79302	24485	25500	11082
Mastrick	Fred Coutts, MA, BD	1973	1984	13 Beechgrove Avenue, AB2 4EZ [024] Aberdeen 638011	939	47	36	65	35	24487	3450	3912	8892
	George Gammack Associate	1985	......	57 Cairnfield Place, AB2 4LX [024] Aberdeen 634944									
Melville Carden Place	Vacant	......	......	60 Forest Road, AB2 4BP [024] Aberdeen 317560	410	29	50	22	4	24779	4950	4950	8937
Middlefield	Alan Sharp, BSC, BD	1980	......	Manor Avenue, AB2 7UT [024] Aberdeen 682483	385	15	26	90	16	11790	......	4950	8646
	Ena B. Finlayson, DCS			Deaconess—see List H [024] A'deen 818439									

Charge	Minister	Ord.	Ind.	Address and Tel. No.	Com.	Eld.	W.G.	S.S.	B.C.	C.L. £	As'd £	Gi'n £	Stp. £
Nigg	Donald M. Thomson, BD	1975	1986	7 Redmoss Avenue, AB1 4JR [0224] Aberdeen 871168	351	19	......	83	35	11138	1098	603	8793
North of St. Andrew	W. Gordon Haggarty, LTH, CPS	1971	1976	51 Osborne Place, AB2 4BX [0224] Aberdeen 646429	1928	104	95	120	16	63102	13061	13561	11101
Northfield	James Scott, MA, BD	1973	......	28 Byron Crescent, AB2 7EX [0224] Aberdeen 692332	626	18	100	46	10	23377	3460	2000	8646
Queen's Cross	Robert F. Brown, MA, BD, THM	1971	1984	1 St. Swithin Street, AB1 6XH [0224] Aberdeen 322549	591	44	68	63	26	73598	15310	15310	10320
Rosemount	John G. Fraser, FPHS	1952	1968	85 Argyll Place, AB2 4HU [0224] Aberdeen 634873	758	39	81	43	24	21765	1404	1404	8682
Rubislaw	Andrew G. N. Wilson, MA, BD	1977	1987	45 Rubislaw Den South, AB2 6BD [0224] Aberdeen 314878	873	79	48	86	41	66957	19350	22350	v
Rutherford	A. David M. Graham, BA, BD ¶	1971	1983	22 Osborne Place, AB2 4DA [0224] Aberdeen 648041	437	32	32	8	2	38880	4600	4600	8976
Ruthrieston—South	Hugh F. Kerr, MA, BD	1968	1985	39 Gray Street, AB1 6JD [0224] Aberdeen 586762	904	50	60	54	5	33916	6670	6670	9105
West	James L. K. Wood	1967	1981	451 Great Western Road, AB1 6NL [0224] Aberdeen 313075	657	54	38	61	38	35672	5396	5396	9873
St. Columba's Bridge of Don	Maxwell D. Craig, MA, BD. MTH	1966	1989	151 Jesmond Avenue, AB2 8UG [0224] Aberdeen 705337	558	28	......	200	30	28834	......	250	8646
St. Fittick's	Thomas Y. Bell, MA	1988	......	11 Devanha Gardens East, AB1 2UH [0224] Aberdeen 589626	665	23	46	16	......	16264	1843	1843	v
St. George's Tillydrone [E]	Stewart D. Jeffrey, BSC, BD	1962	1978	1 Gordon's Mills Road, AB2 2YU [0224] Aberdeen 491000	377	21	37	53	......	29475	......	562	*10647
St. John's for the Deaf	Vacant	......	......	—	138	11	......	......	......	716	169	200	......
St. Machar's	A. Stewart Todd, MA, BD, DD	1952	1967	18 The Chanonry, Old Aberdeen, AB2 1RQ [0224] Aberdeen 483688	835	56	30	19	......	49948	9660	9660	11652
St. Mark's	Vacant	......	......	65 Mile-end Avenue, AB2 4PU [0224] Aberdeen 632028	880	68	42	26	20	40068	13000	13000	v
St. Mary's	Michael S. M. Crawford, LTH	1966	1967	456 King Street, AB2 3DE [0224] Aberdeen 633778	907	58	55	29	24	34005	5130	5130	8784
St. Nicholas, Kirk of	J. C. Stewart, MA, BD, STM	1960	1980	48 Gray Street, AB1 6JE [0224] Aberdeen 314056	1259	67	78	16	......	43911	10906	10946	11492

Congregation	Minister			Address									
St. Nicholas, South of, Kincorth	W. E. Wilkie, LTH	1978	......	Kincorth Circle, AB1 5NX [0224] Aberdeen 872820	764	29	63	96	20	25505	3855	3855	8937
	Ann V. Lundie, DCS	......	......	Deaconess—see List H [0224] Aberdeen 898416									
St. Ninian's	Robert Tyre	1960	1976	12 Carlton Place, AB2 4BQ [0224] Aberdeen 640525	514	23	44	25	36	29045	7900	1743	9381
St. Stephn's	*Vacant*	......	......	137 Clifton Road, AB2 3RH	782	47	16	51	16	35876	3336	3336	v
Stockethill	Kenneth W. Donald, BA, BS	1982	1986	52 Ashgrove Road West, AB2 5EE [0224] Aberdeen 682617	441	13	...	11	9	15454	1108	569	8646
Summerhill	Ian A. M'Lean, BSC, BD	1981	......	36 Stronsay Drive, AB2 6JL [0224] Aberdeen 324669	308	17	...	71	27	16048	...	...	9147
Torry	Archie Stewart	1976	1981	142 Bon Accord Street, AB1 2TX [0224] Aberdeen 582900	365	20	27	39	20	21868	1576	1576	8646
Woodside	J. Gordon Mathew, MA, BD	1973	1982	322 Clifton Road, AB2 2HQ [0224] Aberdeen 484562	771	36	65	57	24	26332	3925	3951	9174
Bucksburn	William M. Alexander, BD	1971	1978	30 Inverurie Rd., Bucksburn, AB2 9LL [0224] Aberdeen 712635	788	33	45	57	18	24638	2927	2927	8901
Cults— East	Donald B. Rennie, MA	1956	1974	Cults, Aberdeen, AB1 9TD [0224] Aberdeen 867587	418	24	39	34	33	33785	5227	3049	8976
West	Thomas C. Richardson, LTH, THB	1971	1978	3 Quarry Road, Cults, Aberdeen, AB1 9EX [0224] Aberdeen 867417	821	51	61	113	71	56212	9892	9892	9891
Dyce	James F. Scott	1957	1966	144 Victoria Street, Dyce, AB2 0BE [0224] Aberdeen 722380	1798	64	66	79	......	52260	7336	7565	10440
Kingswells	*Vacant*	......	......	Lang Stracht, Aberdeen, AB1 8PL [0224] Aberdeen 740229	423	29	22	26	12	19043	1640	1790	8646
Newhills	Norman Maciver, MA, BD	1976	......	Bucksburn, Aberdeen AB2 9SS [0224] Aberdeen 712655	1083	58	110	117	74	68958	8491	8491	9873
Peterculter— Kelman Memorial	Jean B. Montgomerie, MA, BD	1973	......	3 St. Ronan's Circle, Peterculter, AB1 0NE [0224] Aberdeen 732288	434	26	...	51	33	20625	3088	1046	8796
St. Peter's	*Vacant*	......	......	Peterculter, Aberdeen, AB1 0LJ [0224] Aberdeen 732117	1011	28	42	48	......	21693	4000	4000	8892
Stoneywood	*Vacant*	......	......	80 Bankhead Road, Bucksburn, Aberdeen, AB2 9EA [0224] Aberdeen 712233	541	34	31	24	10	19478	2687	2664	8892

Minister	Ord.	App.	Ret.	Charge	Address and Tel. No.
Ballantyne, Samuel, MA, BD	1941		1982	(Rutherford)	26 Cairncry Road, Aberdeen, AB2 5DP [0224] Aberdeen 483049
Cairns, David, MA, DD	1935		1972	(University of Aberdeen)	29 Viewfield Gardens, Aberdeen, AB1 7XN [0224] Aberdeen 317324
Campbell, W. M. M., BD, CPS	1970	1986		Hospital Chaplain	43 Murray Terrace, Aberdeen, AB1 2SA [0224] Aberdeen 591174
Deans, John Bell	1951		1986	(Hospital Chaplain)	6 Annfield House, 96 Fort Street, Broughty Ferry, Dundee DD5 1DZ [0382] Dundee 736649
Dickson, John C., MA	1950		1987	(Aberdeen St. Fittick's)	56 Countesswells Road, Aberdeen, AB1 7YE [0224] Aberdeen 314488
Dupar, Kenneth W., BA, BD, PHD	1965	1984		Christ's College Aberdeen	95 Forest Avenue, Aberdeen, AB1 6NT [0224] Aberdeen 319845
Elder, John, MC, MA	1921		1965	(Cults East)	22 King's Gate, Aberdeen, AB2 6BI [0224] Aberdeen 635509
Gordon, Walter J., MA, BD, STM	1934		1974	(St. Mark's)	10 Duthie Court, Aberdeen, AB1 6NG [0224] Aberdeen 318398
Grant, A. Rae, MA, BD	1923		1966	(Cults West)	23 Airyhall Drive, Aberdeen, AB1 7QE [0224] Aberdeen 319688
Gray, John, MA, BD, PHD, DD	1939		1980	(University of Aberdeen)	Tanlaw Cottage, Hendersyde Park, Kelso, TD5 [0573] Kelso 24374
Hawthorn, Daniel, MA, BD	1965	1973		Aberdeen College of Education	42 Parkhill Ave., Dyce, Aberdeen, AB2 0FP [0224] Aberdeen 722638
Hogg, Alison M., BD	1988	1988		Hospital Chaplain's Assistant	9 Craigton Avenue, Aberdeen, AB1 7RP [0224] Aberdeen 312270
Howie, David Y., MA	1931		1972	(Ruthrieston South)	2 Seafield Drive East, Aberdeen, AB1 7UX [0224] Aberdeen 315733
Hunter, A. M., BD, PHD, DPHIL, DD	1934		1971	(University of Aberdeen)	32 Gartconnel Road, Bearsden, Glasgow, G61 3BP 041–942 3406
Hutchison, A. Scott, MA, BD, DD	1957	1986		Hospital Chaplain	Linsue, Drumoak, Aberdeenshire, AB3 3AA [033 08] Drumoak 705
Johnstone, William, MA, BD	1963	1963		University of Aberdeen	37 Rubislaw Den South, Aberdeen, AB2 6BD [0224] Aberdeen 316022
M'Connachie, Catherine E., MA, BD	1969		1978	(Assistant, St. George's, Tillydrone)	Belfield Eventide Home, Banchory, AB3 3XS [033 02] Banchory 2692
M'Ewen, James S., MA, BD, DD	1940		1977	(University of Aberdeen)	8 Westfield Terrace, Aberdeen, AB2 4RU [0224] Aberdeen 645413
Mackay, Murdoch M., MA	1941		1986	(Hospital Chaplain)	17 Hillview Ter., Cults, Aberdeen, AB1 9HJ [0224] Aberdeen 868082
Main, Alan, TD, MA, BD, STM, PHD	1963	1980		University of Aberdeen	37 Carden Place, Aberdeen, AB1 1UN [0224] Aberdeen 641100
Mirrilees, J. B., MA, BD	1937		1977	(High Hilton)	1 Beechgrove Court, Aberdeen, AB2 4YO [0224] Aberdeen 638351
Montgomery, Robert W., MA, BD	1953	1988		(Melville Carden Place)	2 Sunnybank, Logie Coldstone, Aboyne AB3 3PQ
Patterson, John H., BA, BD	1936		1976	(Dalton with Hightae)	2 Grove Cottage, Deal Road, Worth, Deal, Kent
Reid, Alan A. S., MA, BD, STM	1962	1981		University Chaplain	48 Don Street, Old Aberdeen, AB2 1UU [0224] Aberdeen 484271
Ricketts, Henry M., MA, BD	1942		1981	(Aberdeen Craigiebuckler)	306 Queen's Road, Aberdeen, AB1 8DT [0224] Aberdeen 315783
Robertson, Matthew, LTH	1968	1968		Chaplain, Army	St. Andrew's Garrison Church, Aldershot, Hants
Russell, Andrew M., MA, BD	1940		1976	(Woodside North)	3 Hill Place, Alloa, FK10 2LP [0259] Alloa 213115
Sefton, Henry R., MA, BD, STM, PHD	1957	1972		University of Aberdeen	25 Albury Place, Aberdeen, AB1 2TQ [0224] Aberdeen 572305
Skakle, George S., MA	1945		1987	(Aberdeen Powis)	30 Whitehall Terrace, Aberdeen, AB2 4RY [0224] Aberdeen 646478
Stuart, Alex. M., MA, BD	1939		1979	(Banchory Ternan West)	21 Rosewell Gardens, Aberdeen, AB2 6HZ [0224] Aberdeen 325168
Sunter, William	1970		1988	(Kingswells)	
Swinton, Alan C., MA	1953	1971		Hospital Chaplain	38 Harcourt Road, Aberdeen, AB2 4NZ [0224] Aberdeen 319340
Torrance, J. B., MA, BD	1954	1977		University of Aberdeen	46 Don Street, Aberdeen, AB2 1UU [0224] Aberdeen 481526
Walton, Ainslie, MA, MED	1954	1987		University of Aberdeen	63 High Street, Old Aberdeen, AB2 3EH [0224] Aberdeen 483925
Watt, William G.	1970		1977	(South of St. Nicholas Kincorth)	12 Eriskay Drive, Lang Stracht, AB2 6SJ [0224] Aberdeen 697014
Wood, James S., MA, DD	1932		1973	(Aberdeen South)	10 Westfield Terrace, Aberdeen, AB2 4RU [0224] Aberdeen 640640
Wylie, W. Andrew, MA	1953	1986		Industrial Chaplain	Rosebank, Sauchen, Aberdeenshire, AB3 7PA [033 03] Sauchen 320
Young, Henry J., MA, BD	1953		1980	(Edinburgh Dean)	44 Stanley Street, Aberdeen, AB1 6UR

ADDRESSES OF ABERDEEN CHURCHES

Beechgrove	Beechgrove Avenue 632102	
Craigiebuckler	Springfield Road	
Denburn	Summer Street	
Ferryhill—		
North	Ferryhill Rd. x Ferryhill Ter.	
South	Fonthill Rd. x Polmuir Road 583070	
Garthdee	Ramsay Gardens	
Gilcomston South	Union St. x Summer St. 596144	
Greyfriars	Broad Street 644719	
High Hilton	Hilton Drive	
Holburn—		
Central	Holburn Street 580967	
West	Great Western Road 596613	
John Knox	Mounthooly 633182	
Langstane Kirk	Union St. x Bon-Accord Street 582716	
Mannofield	Great Western Rd. x Craigton Road 310087	
Mastrick	Greenfern Road 694121	
Melville–Carden Place	Carden Place x Albert Street	
Middlefield	Manor Avenue	
Nigg	Kirk Road	
North Church of St. Andrew	Queen Street 643567	
Northfield	Byron Crescent	
Queen's Cross	Queen's Cross 644742	
Rosemount	Caroline Place	
Rubislaw	Queen's Cross 595477	
Rutherford	Rosemount Place	
Ruthrieston—		
South		
West		
St. Columba's	Brachead Way, Bridge of Don	
St. Fittick's	Walker Road	
St. George's	Hayton Road, Tillydrone 482204	
St. John's for the Deaf	Smithfield Road 494566	
St. Machar's	The Chanonry 485988	
St. Mark's	Rosemount Viaduct 640672	
St. Mary's	King Street	
St. Nicholas, Kirk of	Union Street 643494	
St. Nicholas, South of, Kincorth	Kincorth Circle	
St. Ninian's	Mid-Stocket Road 319519	
St. Stephen's	Powis Place	
Stockethill	Castleton Crescent 681129	
Summerhill	Stronsay Drive	
Torry	Victoria Road	
Woodside	Church Street, Woodside	

32. KINCARDINE AND DEESIDE

Meets at Banchory on the first Tuesday of February, March, November and December; and at Stonehaven, the first Tuesday of April, May, September and October and the last Tuesday of June

Clerk: Rev. J. W. S. BROWN, BTH, The Manse, Tarland, Aboyne, Aberdeenshire, AB3 4YN [033 981] Tarland 233

Charge	Minister	Ord.	Ind.	Address and Tel. No.	Com.	Eld.	W.G.	S.S.	B.C.	C.L. £	As'd £	Gi'n £	Stp. £
Aberluthnott	Alexander Robertson	1969	1987	Aberdeen Road, Laurencekirk, AB3 1AJ	367	15	17	26	.....	6337	1450	1486	v
linked with				[056 17] Laurencekirk 405									
Laurencekirk					603	22	30	29	.....	14370	2440	2440	.....
Aboyne	William D. Watt, LTH	1978	1985	St. Eunan's Road, Aboyne, AB3 5HN	420	18	42	34	13	23864	.....	360	8646
linked with				[0339] Aboyne 2447									
Dinnet					96	10	.....	6	7	2973	.....	100	.....

Charge	Minister	Ord.	Ind.	Address and Tel. No.	Com.	Eld.	W.G.	S.S.	B.C.	C.L. £ 2976	As'd £	Gi'n £ 130	Stp. £
Arbuthnott	Connie Philip, BD	1980	......	10 Kirkburn, Inverbervie, Montrose, DD10 0RT [0561] Inverbervie 62633	136	10	10	27	...	...	...	...	v
linked with													
Bervie					610	23	33	96	53	18732	1980	1980	
linked with													
Kinneff					261	10	24	9	...	4903	...	...	
Banchory-Devenick	David C. R. Simpson, BD, CPS	1983	......	Maryculter, Aberdeen, AB1 0AS [0224] Aberdeen 733120	174	11	...	15	8	7368	1110	1110	9042
linked with													
Maryculter and Cookney					404	17	...	16	...	12736	2320	1628	
Banchory Ternan East	Hamish K. Fleming, MA	1966	1986	Banchory, Kincardineshire, AB3 3YP [033 02] Banchory 2481	1480	66	99	130	55	50797	12970	14190	10500
Banchory Ternan West	George A. Chalmers, MA, BD, MLITT	1962	1986	2 Wilson Road, Banchory, AB3 3UY [033 02] Banchory 2811	933	48	87	95	20	35902	6700	6988	8862
Benholm and Johnshaven	Thomas F. Wilson, BD	1984	......	The Manse, St. Cyrus, Montrose, DD10 0BW [067 485] St. Cyrus 588	279	13	20	15	21	12286	1110	1110	9135
linked with													
Garvock St. Cyrus					409	13	38	22	...	10978	1620	1620	
Bervie	*see Arbuthnott*												
Birse and Feughside	John F. Ferguson, MA, BD	......	......	Finzean, Banchory, AB3 3PB [033 045] Feughside 237	484	31	12	17	...	11433	2040	2040	v
Braemar	J. A. Keith Angus, TD, MA	1955	1979	Crathie, Ballater, AB3 5UL [033 84] Crathie 208	138	7	20	6	...	8816	1280	1331	9372
linked with													
Crathie					204	15	15	11	...	18612	2170	2170	
Cromar	J. W. S. Brown, B TH	1960	1967	Tarland, Aberdeenshire, AB3 4YN [033 981] Tarland 233	470	19	24	13	...	13013	...	147	8898
Dinnet	*see Aboyne*												
Drumoak	D. F. Prentis, BSC, MA	1975	1988	Durris, Aberdeenshire, AB3 3BU [033 044] Crathes 557	260	11	20	27	7	9330	...	50	v
linked with													
Durris					256	11	19	17	...	6326	...	100	
Fettercairn	David Jack, L TH	1984	1988	Fettercairn, Laurencekirk, AB3 1YA [056 14] Fettercairn 203	351	...	24	31	...	10787	2430	2430	10527
linked with													
Fordoun					279	13	21	42	9	8259	1970	1970	
linked with													
Glenbervie					210	7	20	19	...	3889	1250	1250	
Finzean	*see Birse*												

Parish / Charge	Minister	Ord.	App.	Ret.									Address and Tel. No.
Fordoun	see Fettercairn												
Garvock St. Cyrus	see Benholm												
Glenbervie	see Fettercairn												
Glenmuick (Ballater)	Alastair Brown, BD	1986	......		499	25	......	40	15	24669	1850	1850	8646	Ballater, Aberdeenshire, AB3 5RQ [033 82] Ballater 510
Kincardine O'Neil linked with Lumphanan	James W. Anderson, BSC, MTH	1986	......		301	13	14	12	......	6267	......	100	8646	Lumphanan, Aberdeenshire, AB3 4QA [033 983] Lumphanan 249
					318	11	17	17	......	9875	......	......		
Kinneff	see Arbuthnott												
Laurencekirk	see Aberluthnott												
Lumphanan	see Kincardine O'Neil												
Maryculter and Cookney	see Banchory-Devenick												
Newtonhill linked with Portlethen	James D. Simpson, MA, BD	1987	....		297	8	......	95	9				v	18 Rowanbank Road, Portlethen, Aberdeen, AB3 4QP [0224] Plethen 780211
					385	11	24	97	42	9103	970	1096		
Stonehaven—Dunnottar	Vacant	......	....		1191	42	60	89	14	38243	5230	5545	9465	Stonehaven, AB3 2XL [0569] Stonehaven 62874
Fetteresso	Graham S. Finch, MA, BD	1977	1983		1157	46	......	118	36	47343	10300	10300	9840	13 Bath Street, Stonehaven, AB3 2DH [0569] Stonehaven 62876
South	Kenneth L. Petrie, MA, BD	1984	1985		485	36	56	48	36	24709	2870	2870	8784	Cameron Street, Stonehaven, AB3 2HE [0569] Stonehaven 62576
Strachan	see Birse												
Torphins	Peter R. Taylor, BD, JP	1977	1987		445	19	27	54	19	22107	1380	1380	v	Torphins, Aberdeenshire, AB3 4JS [033 982] Torphins 276

Minister	Ord.	App.	Ret.	Charge	Address and Tel. No.
Campbell, Donald, MA	1934	......	1979	(Bervie)	5 Castle Crescent, Inverbervie, DD10 0BS [056 16] Inverbervie 522
Gardiner, Andrew, A PHS	1950	......	1984	(Aboyne)	Creag Shiel, 47 Braemar Road, Ballater, AB3 5RQ [0338] Ballater 55751
Kinniburgh, Elizabeth B. F., MA, BD	1970	......	1986	(Birse with Finzean with Strachan)	7 Huntly Cottages, Aboyne, AB3 5HD [0339] Aboyne 2757
Maclean, Ewen, JP	1941	......	1983	(Fettercairn with Fordoun with Glenbervie)	2 Rustic Place, Anstruther, KY10 3EP [033 33] Anstruther 11035
MacLeod, Alexander D.	1939	......	1979	(Benholm and Johnshaven)	39 Mercury Terrace, St. Cyrus, Montrose, DD10 0AY [067 485] St. Cyrus 493
MacLeod, Kenneth	1950	......	1986	(Bourtreebush with Portlethen)	44 Fetteresso Terrace, Stonehaven, AB3 2DS [0569] Stonehaven 64008

Minister	Ord.	App.	Ret.	Charge	Address and Tel. No.
Nicholson, William	1949	.....	1986	(Banchory Ternan East *with* Durris)	33 Station Road, Banchory, AB3 3XX [033 02] *Banchory 2109*
Skinner, Silvester, MA	1941	.....	1979	(Lumphanan)	29 Silverbank Gardens, Banchory, AB3 3YZ [033 02] *Banchory 3032*
Smith, J. A. Wemyss, MA	1947	.....	1983	(Garvock St. Cyrus)	30 Greenbank Drive, Edinburgh, EH10 5RE *031—447 2205*
Smith, T. Forrest	1959	.....	1986	(Arbuthnott *with* Kinneff)	71 Urquhart Crescent, Dunfermline, KY12 8AL
Squires, J. Finlay R., MA, BD	1964	.....	1988	(Aberdeen College of Education)	16 Bath Street, Stonehaven, AB3 2DH [0569] *Stonehaven 62458*
Stuart, C. H., TD, MA	1942	.....	1982	(Echt *with* Midmar)	Rose Cottage, Raemoir Road, Banchory, AB3 4ER [033 02] *Banchory 2087*
Tierney, John P., MA	1945	.....	1985	(Peterhead West *Associate*)	3 Queenshill Drive, Aboyne, AB3 5DG [0339] *Aboyne 2741*
Tyson, Kenneth E. W.	1978	.....	1988	(Fettercairn *with* Fordoun *with* Glenbervie)	Lilac Cottage, Roundyhill, Forfar DD8 1QD
Urie, D. M. L., MA, BD, PHD	1940	.....	1980	(Kincardine O'Neil)	Kincardine O'Neil, AB3 5AB [033 984] *Kincardine O'Neil 204*

33. GORDON

Meets at Inverurie St. Andrew's on the first Tuesday of February, March, April, May, September, October, November and December, and on the fourth Tuesday of June

Clerk: Rev. IAIN U. THOMSON, MA, BD, The Manse, Skene, AB3 6XX [0224] *Aberdeen 743277*

Charge	Minister	Ord.	Ind.	Address and Tel. No.	Com.	Eld.	W.G.	S.S.	B.C.	C.L. £	As'd £	Gi'n £	Stp. £
Alford					557	20	.....	17	.....	12166	1298	1298	v
linked with													
Keig	Alfred Bowie, LTH	1974	1987	Alford, Aberdeenshire, AB3 8AD [0336] *Alford 2282*	108	9	12	8	.....	2450	384	384	v
linked with													
Tullynessle and Forbes					126	9	10	18	.....	3716	367	587	
Auchindoir and Kildrummy	*Vacant*	.....	....	Lumsden, Huntly, AB5 4JQ [046 48] *Lumsden 257*	282	13	11	25	.....	7206	.....	17	v
Barthol Chapel	William M. Murdoch, BSC, PHD, BD	1980	....		148	10	25	11	2	4095	550	550	
linked with													
Tarves				Tarves, Aberdeenshire, AB4 0JU [065 15] *Tarves 250*	651	30	53	87	16	21803	3908	3966	9921
Belhelvie	David Stuart Forsyth, MA	1948	....	Balmedie, Aberdeenshire, AB4 0YB [0358] *Balmedie 42227*	742	30	39	62	7	23831	3562	3562	9402
Blairdaff	Eric G. Milton	1963	1984		145	13	.....	12	.....	7550	678	678	9096
linked with													
Chapel of Garioch				Chapel of Garioch, Inverurie, AB5 9HE [046 76] *Pitcaple 619*	318	16	24	37	15	10824	1180	1180	
Cairnie-Glass	Allan S. Macpherson, MA	1967	1983		239	20	20	13	.....	5988	1606	1976	
linked with													
Huntly				Queen Street, Huntly, AB5 5EB [0466] *Huntly 2630*	867	34	.....	46	36	26179	3347	3347	10353

Charge		Minister	Ind.	Adm.	Address								
Chapel of Garioch	*see* Blairdaff												
Cluny		John D. Henderson, BD	1953	1982	Monymusk, Inverurie, Aberdeenshire, AB3 7HJ [046 77] Monymusk 248	256	17	19	32	.....	10378	983	983	9096
linked with Monymusk						207	10	17	19	.....	7890	793	793	
Corgarff and Strathdon		Joyce P. Collie, MA, PHD	1966	1986	Strathdon, Aberdeenshire, AB3 8UX [097 52] Strathdon 216	189	7	.....	5	.....	12864	.....	60	8646
linked with Glenbuchat Towie						187	13	12	7	7	4275	653	.....	
Culsalmond						191	13	9	10	4	4624	653	653	
linked with Daviot	Allan D. Scott, BD	1977	1984	Daviot, Inverurie, AB5 0HZ [046 75] Warle 241		204	10	.....	30	.....	6725	771	771	
Daviot						191	12	16	19	.....	5306	514	.....	
linked with Rayne						147	13	9	14	.....	4720	284	284	
Drumblade		George C. Stewart, MA	1952	1962	Deveron Road, Huntly, AB5 5DU [0466] Huntly 2702	1015	41	67	73	.....	33333	7168	7168	10413
linked with Huntly Strathbogie														
Echt		James S. Dick, MA, BTH	1988	.....	Echt, Aberdeenshire, AB3 7AB [033 06] Dunecht 533	483	21	23	70	.....	13331	1471	1471	v
linked with Midmar						191	8	.....	15	.....	5762	477	376	
Ellon		Matthew A. Rodger, BD	1978	.....	Ellon, Aberdeenshire, AB4 9AR [0358] Ellon 20476	2309	87	48	318	85	66193	15636	15636	v
		Alison J. Fazakerley, *Associate*	1988	.....	2 Chievres Road, Ellon AB4 9WG [0358] Ellon 20930									
Fintray		Albert Caie, LTH	1983	.....	Keithall, Inverurie, AB5 0LJ [0467] Inverurie 20435	115	8	23	9	.....	5580	302	302	
linked with Keithall						132	7	.....	10	.....	2563	149	120	8646
Keithall *linked with* Kinellar														
Foveran		John A. Cook, MA, BD	1986	.....	Newburgh, Aberdeenshire, AB4 0AP [035 86] Newburgh 288	206	5	.....	59	.....	5087	319	319	319
						579	20	.....	70	12	22223	1623	1623	8949
Glenbuchat Towie	*see* Corgarff													
Huntly	*see* Cairnie-Glass													
Huntly Strathbogie	*see* Drumblade													
Insch-Leslie-Premnay-Oyne		Robert S. M'Leish, LTH	1970	1984	Insch, Aberdeenshire, AB5 6JR [0464] Insch 20914	880	43	63	45	12	27943	4413	4265	10332

Charge	Minister	Ord.	Ind.	Address and Tel. No.	Com.	Eld.	W.G.	S.S.	B.C.	C.L. £	As'd £	Gi'n £	Stp. £
Inverurie—St. Andrew's	Vacant			Inverurie, Aberdeenshire, AB5 9XT [0467] Inverurie 20468	2402	82	68	106	33	47490	10791	10791	11217
West	J. Leonard Scott, MA, BD	1957	1966	Inverurie, Aberdeenshire, AB5 9YS [0467] Inverurie 20285	804	47	58	58	8	32028	6862	6862	10353
Keig	see Alford												
Keithall	see Fintray												
Kemnay	Ian M. Forbes, MA, PH D	1953	1977	Kemnay, Inverurie, AB5 9ND [0467] Kemnay 42219	800	41	33	110	70	25035	6370	6370	10353
Kinellar	see Fintray												
Kintore	Gerald B. Macallan	1954	1978	Kintore, Aberdeenshire, AB5 0UT [0467] Kintore 32219	924	41	83	107	25	28467	6467	6467	10353
Leochel Cushnie and Lynturk linked with Tough	James B. Rennie, MA	1959	1983	Leochel Cushnie, Alford, Aberdeenshire, AB3 8JU [033 64] Muir of Fowlis 239	258	15	...	10	2	7683	...	...	8646
					111	7	14	...	...	5840	...	...	
Meldrum and Bourtie	A. Grainger Stoddart,	1975	1988	Old Meldrum, Aberdeenshire, AB5 0EQ [065 12] Oldmeldrum 2250	689	34	98	91	24	38911	6304	6304	v
Methlick	E. C. P. Hood, MA	1946	1959	Methlick, Aberdeenshire, AB4 0DS [065 14] Methlick 215	488	32	48	30	8	17428	890	901	
Midmar	see Echt												
Monymusk	see Cluny												
New Machar	Ian Dryden, MA, DIP ED	1988	......	New Machar, Aberdeenshire, AB5 0RD [065 17] Newmachar 2278	558	20	32	60	...	21470	1139	1139	v
Noth	Vacant	......	......	Kennethmont, AB5 4NP [046 43] Kennethmont 244	562	32	21	68	...	14012	600	600	9147
Rayne	see Culsalmond												
Skene	I. U. Thomson, MA, BD	1970	1972	Skene, Aberdeenshire, AB3 6XX [0224] Aberdeen 743277	1503	68	67	274	54	63229	7647	7647	10353
	Gordon Kirkwood, B SC, BD *Associate*	1987	1988	Kirk Cottage, Skene, AB3 6XX [0224] Aberdeen 743407									
Tarves	see Barthol Chapel												
Tough	see Leochel Cushnie												
Tullynessle and Forbes	see Alford												

| Udny and Pitmedden | George R. Robertson, L TH | 1985 | ..... | Udny, Aberdeenshire, AB4 0RS [065 13] Udny 2052 | 599 | 27 | 32 | 60 | 9 | 28098 | 4167 | 4167 | 9432 |

Minister	Ord.	App.	Ret.	Charge	Address and Tel. No.
Andrew, John, MA, BD	1961	1972	.....	*Teacher R.E.*	Cartar's Croft, Midmar, Sauchen, AB3 7NJ [033 03] Sauchen 308
Calder, Ian H.	1985	1985	.....	*Auxiliary assigned to Huntly*	Battlehill, Huntly [0466] Huntly 3201
Claydon, William A.	1968	.....	1987	(New Machar)	Bank Terrace, Alford, AB3 8PY [0336] Alford 2016
Davidson, James M., MA	1947	.....	1989	(Inverurie St. Andrew's)	Ardlair, Montgarrie Road, Alford AB3 8LY [0336] Alford 3471
M'Auslane, T. M.	1931	.....	1972	(Gartly *with* Kennethmont)	Linden, Scott Drive, Huntly, AB5 2DB [0466] Huntly 2681
Macdonald, Roderick, TD, MA	1946	.....	1983	(Insch)	13 Western Road, Insch, AB5 6JR [0464] Insch 20332
Mackay, P. H. R., MBE, MA, PHD	1927	.....	1972	(Leslie and Waulkmill *with* Premnay)	Clola, 1 Dirleton Road, North Berwick, EH39 5BY
Mack, John C.	1985	1985	.....	*Auxiliary assigned to Insch-Leslie-Premnay-Oyne*	Auchleven, Insch, AB5 [0464] Insch 20387
Matthews, Lawrence J., BA, BD	1958	.....	1985	(Aberdeen Nigg)	Den of Largue Cottage, Forgue, Huntly, AB5 6HS 04 647 306
Milligan, Rodney	1949	.....	1985	(Culsalmond *with* Rothienorman)	Dunnydeer Park, Insch, AB5 6JR [0464] Insch 20343
Murray, James, MA	1929	.....	1974	(Newtonmore)	Newton of Affleck, Whiterashes, Newmachar, Aberdeen, AB5 0RB [065 182] Whiterashes 311
Murray, John, MA	1932	.....	1972	(Slains and Forvie)	1 Patey Road, Ellon, AB4 9WL [0358] Ellon 20541
Rushforth, Eugen W.	1943	.....	1983	(Dinnet *with* Logie Coldstone and Migvie)	9 Cromar Court, Tarland, Aboyne, AB3 4UE [033 981] Tarland 371
Shields, John M., MBE, L TH	1972	1976	.....	*Chaplain, Army*	1 RHF, Redford Barracks, Colington Road, Edinburgh
Smith, J. Donald, MA, BD, DD	1957	.....	1981	(Auchtergaven *with* Moneydie)	18 Henderson Drive, Kintore, Inverurie, AB5 0FB [046 73] Kintore 2931
Smith, Robert, MA, BD	1935	.....	1972	(Balerno)	2 Moungan, Station Road, Ellon, AB4 9AY [0358] Ellon 20679
Wallace, R. J. Stuart, MA	1947	.....	1986	(Foveran)	9 Laggan Place, Ellon, AB4 9BP [0358] Ellon 22571

34. BUCHAN

Meets at Cuminestown on the second Tuesday of February, March, April, June, September, October, November and December

Clerk: Rev. R. NEILSON, JP, BSc, BD, Hatton, Peterhead, AB4 7QQ [077 984] Hatton 229

Charge	Minister	Ord.	Ind.	Address and Tel. No.	Com.	Eld.	W.G.	S.S.	B.C.	C.L. £	As'd £	Gi'n £	Stp. £
Aberdour *linked with* Tyrie	Charles J. Birnie, MA	1969	1982	Tyrie, Fraserburgh, AB4 4DN [034 64] Memsie 325	228	13	19	17	.....	6361	.....	.....	8648
Tyrie					213	11	15	24	.....	5983	.....	167	

Charge	Minister	Ord.	Ind.	Address and Tel. No.	Com.	Eld.	W.G.	S.S.	B.C.	C.L. £	As'd £	Gi'n £	Stp. £
Auchterless	Hamish G. Smith	1965	1986	Auchterless, Turriff, AB5 8BA [088 84] Auchterless 217	380	22	27	30	...	14183	1441	1591	9159
linked with Rothienorman					237	12	20	18	...	7427	770	770	9150
Banff— St. Mary's	Austin U. Erskine ¶	1986	......	7 Colleonard Road, Banff, AB4 1DZ [026 12] Banff 2107	850	58	65	102	6	25845	3960	3960	9150
Trinity and Alvah	Harold A. M. Steven, LTH	1970	1971	Banff, AB4 1DH [026 12] Banff 2244	534	47	59	36	6	22126	3138	3138	9150
Boddam linked with Peterhead West Associate	Philippa M. B. Ott (Mrs.) BD, CPS	1986	......	31 Waterside Way, Peterhead, AB4 7GB [0779] Peterhead 72405	180	13	25	21	4	8816	...	...	8646
					334	26	60	26	7	23577	2866	2866	v
					501	25	38	58	13	18409	1277	1429	
Boyndie linked with Ordiquhill and Cornhill	George T. Poustie	1966	......	Boyndie, Banff, AB4 2JT [0261] Portsoy 43234	297	14	13	29	...	7121	...	...	8646
Crimond linked with St. Fergus	Alexander S. M. M'Ghee	1970	1985	Crimond, Fraserburgh, AB4 4YN [0346] Lonmay 32431	373	11	24	45	4	7431	...	...	8646
					231	8	20	11	11	8307	...	...	
Cruden	Rodger Neilson, BSC, BD	1972	1974	Hatton, Peterhead, AB4 7QQ [077 984] Hatton 229	687	43	57	124	7	28332	3856	3982	9102
Deer	James Wishart, BD	1986	......	Deer, Peterhead, AB4 8LN [0771] Mintlaw 23582	1115	28	33	116	...	18064	2261	2261	8739
Fordyce	Robert Lynn, BD	1984	......	Portsoy, Banff, AB4 2QB [0261] Portsoy 42272	693	40	58	75	24	30771	2932	2992	8934
Forgue-Inverkeithny linked with Ythanwells Auchaber	F. C. Collier	......	1982	Inverkeithny, Huntly, AB5 5XB [046 682] Forgue 209	287	17	18	14	...	6968	344	344	8646
					110	8	11	11	...	2646	247	247	
Fraserburgh— Old	Douglas R. Clyne, BD	1973	......	97 Saltoun Pl., Fraserburgh, AB4 5RY [0346] Fraserburgh 28536	1196	55	124	296	86	73323	13987	15295	9660
South linked with Inverallochy and Rathen East	Ronald F. Yule	1982	......	15 Victoria St., Fraserburgh, AB4 5PJ [0346] Fraserburgh 28244	540	32	50	104	10	34197	6517	6517	9660
					123	10	39	22	...	18595	354	354	
West	B. Andrew Lyon, LTH	1971	1978	23 Strichen Rd., Fraserburgh, AB4 5SA [0346] Fraserburgh 23303	976	52	93	115	42	35160	7503	7573	9150

Parish	Minister			Address									v
Fyvie	David M. M'Kay, MA, BD	1979	1987	Fyvie, Turriff, AB5 8PD [065 16] Fyvie 230	526	30	48	57	15	23457	1752	1752	v
Gamrie					245	10		13		6357			v
linked with King Edward	Alan J. Byers	1959	1988	King Edward, Banff, AB4 3NB [026 16] Eden 258	266	15	23	14		13386			
Gardenstown	Robert M. Walker, MA, BD	1978	1986	Gardenstown, Banff, AB4 3YL [026 15] Gardenstown 256	122	10		44	19	38541	2155	2155	8646
Inverallochy and Rathen East	*see Fraserburgh South*												
King Edward	*see Gamrie*												
Longside	William N. T. Hodge	1966	1978	Longside, Peterhead, AB4 7UE [077 982] Longside 224	900	37	40	70	19	20821	4500	4650	8997
Lonmay *linked with* Rathen West	G. M. Allan Fawkes, BA, BSC	1979		Lonmay, Fraserburgh, AB4 4UJ [0346] Lonmay 32227	269	16	18	49	10	9563	705	705	8646
Rathen West					152	8		17		5071	365	138	
Macduff—Doune	David J. Randall, MA, BD, THM	1971		Macduff, Banff AB4 3QL [0261] Macduff 32316	816	33		121	35	47819	4483	4483	8976
Gardner	Vacant	1973		15 Ross Street, Macduff, AB4 1NS [0261] Macduff 32432	247	16	44	40	3	18559	1262	1606	8646
Marnoch	Robert A. Jones, LTH, CA	1966	1985	Aberchirder, Huntly, AB5 5TS [046 65] Aberchirder 276	634	30	30	59	20	22636	1673	1746	8838
Maud *linked with* Savoch	W. D. Scott	1956	1970	Maud, Peterhead, AB4 8NQ [077 14] Maud 264	357	21	31	22		7694			8898
Savoch					202	9				4242			
Monquhitter *linked with* New Byth					502	27	37	31	10	11494	1453	1453	8646
New Byth	Brian S. C. Donald, LTH	1968	1979	Cuminestown, Turriff, AB5 7YD [088 83] Cuminestown 279	195	10	15	22		5493	373	373	
New Deer St. Kane's	Russel Moffat, BD, CPS	1986		Fordyce Terrace, New Deer, Turriff, AB4 8TD [077 13] New Deer 216	691	25	32	20	6	16988	1076	1076	8646
New Pitsligo	Vacant			137 High Street, New Pitsligo, Fraserburgh, AB4 4NH [077 17] New Pitsligo 256	603	18	20	52	4	19672			8646
Ordiquhill and Cornhill	*see Boyndie*												
Peterhead—Old	David S. Ross, MSC, PHD, BD	1978		49 King Street, Peterhead, AB4 6TA [0779] Peterhead 72618	983	47	81	85	28	40123	5377	5377	9150
St. Andrew's	William H. Brown	1953	1968	1 Landale Road, Peterhead, AB4 6QN [0779] Peterhead 72141	798	40		107		27014	3429	3429	8886

Charge	Minister	Ord.	Ind.	Address and Tel. No.	Com.	Eld.	W.G.	S.S.	B.C.	C.L. £	As'd £	Gi'n £	Stp. £
West Associate	*see* Boddam												
Pitsligo	*Vacant*	......	......	49 Pitsligo Street, Rosehearty, Fraserburgh, AB4 4JL [034 67] Rosehearty 237	381	21	......	83	......	13556	1655	1185	8646
linked with Sandhaven					161	10	40	40	......	6580	592	592	
Rathen West	*see* Lonmay												
Rothienorman	*see* Auchterless												
St. Fergus	*see* Crimond												
Sandhaven and Pitullie	*see* Pitsligo												
Savoch	*see* Maud												
Strichen	James L. Wilson, BD, CPS	1986	......	High Street, Strichen, Fraserburgh, AB4 4SQ [077 15] Strichen 365	630	26	31	30	15	30683	1845	1845	8754
Turriff— St. Andrew's	Donald B. C. Inglis, MA, MED, BD	1975	1983	Balmellie Road, Turriff, AB5 7DP [0888] Turriff 63240	667	35	33	56	10	25996	1951	2009	8694
St. Ninian's and Forglen	David Butters	1964	1974	Turriff, AB5 7AY [0888] Turriff 63383	1267	56	69	106	23	45753	8576	8576	9222
Tyrie	*see* Aberdour												
Ythanwells Auchaber	*see* Forgue-Inverkeithny												

Minister	Charge	Ord.	App.	Ret.	Address and Tel. No.
Geddes, Alex. S., MA, BD	(Banff St. Mary's)	1941	......	1985	65 St. Catherine Street, Banff, AB4 1JT [026 12] Banff 5892
Greig, Alexander W.	(Boyndie)	1935	......	1965	40 Airlie Gardens, Low Street, Banff, AB4 1AZ [026 12] Banff 2661
Holmes, Kenneth, BA	(Gamrie)	1940	......	1978	Cairnbeattie, 10 Westfield Rd., Turriff, AB5 7AF [088 82] Turriff 63605
M'Laren, F. Gordon, MA	(Strichen)	1937	......	1975	7 Halketts Lane, Limekilns, Dunfermline, KY11
Mitchell, A. A. S., MA, BD	(Fraserburgh Old)	1938	......	1972	33 Inver Terrace, Muirhead of Liff, Dundee, DD2 5LS
Shaw, Andrew, BSC, FRIC	(Gardenstown)	1964	......	1985	39 Bridge Street, Banff, AB4 1HD [026 12] Banff 2949
Walker, Colin D.	(Auchindoir and Kildrummy)	1977	......	1982	The Old Manse, Alvah, Banff [026 16] Eden 656
Walker, E. W., MA	(Marnoch)	1947	......	1985	Braehead, Bridge of Marnoch, Huntly, AB5 5RP [046 65] Aberchirder 800
Wark, Thomas L., LLB	(Turriff St. Andrew's)	1947	......	1982	Morven, Highfield Walk, Turriff, AB5 [088 82] Turriff 63484
Weir, Arthur A. Mullo, MA	(Forglen)	1931	......	1969	9 Milton Gardens South, Portobello, Edinburgh, EH15 3PG 031–669 6916

35. MORAY

Meets at Church Hall, Greyfriars Street, Elgin on the first Tuesday of February, March, April, May, September, October, November, December, and the fourth Tuesday of June

Clerk: Rev. JOHN T. STUART, MA, The Manse, Duffus, Elgin, IV30 2QP [0343] Hopeman 830276

Charge	Minister	Ord.	Ind.	Address and Tel. No.	Com.	Eld.	W.G.	S.S.	B.C.	C.L. £	As'd £	Gi'n £	Stp. £
Aberlour	David Anderson, MA, BD	1975	1983	Aberlour, Banffshire, AB3 9QN [034 05] Aberlour 515	653	28	55	56	10	26804	1697	989	8925
Alves and Burghead	James A. Munro, BD, DMS	1979	1987	Burghead, Elgin, Moray, IV30 2UJ [0343] Burghead 835039	299	23	16	78	14	14646	957	358	v
Bellie	David J. Ferguson	1966	1982	11 The Square, Fochabers, Moray, IV32 7DG [0343] Fochabers 820256	539	32	47	136	27	21857	5448	5448	10104
linked with Speymouth					199	11	14	......	......	7155	1195	1538	
Birnie	Gordon S. Cowie, MA, LLB,	1986	......	Birnie, Elgin, IV30 3SU [0343] Elgin 2621	318	17	47	38	6	10597	642	642	8925
linked with Pluscarden					160	13	23	21	5	6777	431	546	
Buckie— North	William Taylor, MA, MED	1984	......	14 St. Peter's Road, AB5 1DL [0542] Buckie 31328	902	58	101	89	16	40807	6530	7530	10104
South and West	Thomas N. Johnston, LTH	1972	1980	East Church Street, Buckie, AB5 1ES [0542] Buckie 32103	543	36	63	46	4	28955	2920	2635	9246
Cullen and Deskford	Alexander J. MacPherson, BD	1986	1987	Cullen, Buckie, Banffshire, AB5 2UU [0542] Cullen 40249	546	47	101	50	......	17577	2815	2815	v
Dallas					92	8	20	......	......	3417	......	......	
linked with Rafford	Peter Robertson, BSC, BD	1988	......	Nelson Road, Forres, IV36 0DR [0309] Forres 72380	122	7	20	......	......	4945	......	......	v
linked with Forres St. Leonard's					575	32	85	31	......	24816	3474	3474	
Duffus, Spynie and Hopeman	John T. Stuart, MA	1958	1984	Duffus, Elgin, IV30 2QP [0343] Hopeman 830276	551	51	77	99	......	30641	6716	6716	v
Dyke	Ann M. Poole (Mrs.), DIPED, ACE, LTH	1983	......	Brodie, Forres, IV36 0TD [030 94] Brodie 239	185	18	19	32	13	10164	1044	1044	
linked with Edinkillie					108	12	10	11	......	9973	1116	1116	8925

Charge	Minister	Ord.	Ind.	Address and Tel. No.	Com.	Eld.	W.G.	S.S.	B.C.	C.L. £	As'd £	Gi'n £	Stp. £
Elgin— High	Alistair H. Morrison, BTH, DIPYCS	1985	.....	29 Moray Street, Elgin, IV30 1JH [0343] *Elgin 2449*	885	34	57	69	.....	30551	3751	3751	9246
St. Giles'	George B. Rollo, BD	1974	1986	18 Reidhaven Street, Elgin, IV30 1QH [0343] *Elgin 7208*	1796	75	100	109	52	73461	15539	15569	11751
	Alexander Spence, MA *Associate*	1944	1986	25 Fleurs Road, Elgin, IV30 1TA									
South	Peter Diack, MA	1951	1956	2 Hay Place, Elgin, IV30 1LZ [0343] *Elgin 2545*	474	30	39	36	33	21076	3100	3316	9246
Enzie	John R. Osbeck, BD	1979	1981	70 West Church Street, Buckie, AB5 1HP [0542] *Buckie 34379*	252	18	23	15	.....	7750	853	853	8925
linked with Rathven					219	17	20	30	.....	11465	939	939	
Findochty	William B. Ross, LTH, CPS	1988	.....	20 Netherton Terrace, Findochty, Banffshire, AB5 2QD [0542] *Buckie 32545*	103	6	20	17	6	4982	.....	12	v
linked with Portknockie					139	8	34	53	.....	8012	.....	.....	
Forres— St. Laurence	William M. Reid, MA, BD	1966	1974	Pilmuir Place, Forres, IV36 0HD [0309] *Forres 72260*	834	41	102	106	70	31253	7869	7869	10104
St. Leonard's	*see Dallas*												
Grange	A. A. B. Davidson, MA, BD	1960	1963	Rothiemay, Huntly, AB5 5NE [046 681] *Rothiemay 334*	234	19	15	12	.....	7676	567	218	8898
linked with Rothiemay					255	18	24	20	.....	4757	579	978	
Keith— North, Newmill and Boharm	John T. Robertson, FPHS	1961	.....	Keith, Banffshire, AB5 3BR [054 22] *Keith 2559*	821	39	38	70	9	18524	4671	4671	10320
St. Rufus and Botriphnie	J. Angus MacLeod, MA	1957	1976	Keith, Banffshire, AB5 3BR [054 22] *Keith 2799*	1186	37	40	82	16	47166	6086	6086	10320
Kinloss and Findhorn	*Continued Vacancy*				158	14	21	23	.....	10915	.....	.....	v
Knockando, Elchies and Archiestown	*Vacant*	.....	.....	2 Seafield Square, Rothes, IV33 7AZ [034 03] *Rothes 746*	343	15	18	22	.....	6924	583	583	8925
linked with Rothes					447	15	36	37	12	14754	1296	1296	
Lossiemouth— St. Gerardine's High	Duncan Murray, BTH	1986	.....	St. Gerardine's Road, Lossiemouth, IV31 6RA [034 381] *L'mouth 3146*	492	21	62	38	6	38265	2612	2612	9246

	Minister	Ord.	App.	Ret.										Address and Tel. No.
St. James'	George L. Cordiner, BD	1973	......		421	26	59	69	22	22537	3622	3622	9246	Prospect Ter., Lossiemouth, IV31 6JS [034 381] Lossiemouth 3135
Mortlach and Cabrach	Hugh M. C. Smith, LTH	1973	1982		709	37	52	......	......	18371	3346	1500	10104	Dufftown, Keith, AB5 4AR [0340] Dufftown 20380
Pluscarden	*see* Birnie													
Portknockie	*see* Findochty													
Rafford	*see* Dallas													
Rathven	*see* Enzie													
Rothes	*see* Knockando													
Rothiemay	*see* Grange													
St. Andrews Lhanbryd and Urquhart	Vacant	......	......		763	47	19	88	11	30744	1876	1876	3976	v	St. Andrews Road, Lhanbryde, Elgin, IV30 3PU [034 384] Lhanbryde 2208
Speymouth	*see* Bellie													

Minister	Ord.	App.	Ret.	Charge	Address and Tel. No.
Duff, J. Douglas, MA., BD	1941	......	1978	(Edinkillie)	Ford Bungalow, Badabrie, Banavie, Fort William, PH33
Fraser, Donald R., MA, BD	1944	......	1985	(Kinloss and Findhorn)	Brisbane, Orchard Road, Forres, IV36 0LG [039 77] Corpach 727 [0309] Forres 72596
Forsyth, Stanley, MA	1944	......	1988	(Garmouth *with* Urquhart)	
Howieson, Thomas S.	1952	......	1974	(Rathven)	24 Orgarswick Avenue, Dymchurch, Kent, TH29 0NX
Macaulay, Alick Hugh, MA	1943	......	1981	(Bellie *with* Speymouth)	5 Duke Street, Fochabers, IV32 7DN [0343] Fochabers 820726
Macdonald, Don, FRSA	1972	......	1980	(Enzie)	15 Kendall Avenue, Stratford-upon-Avon, Warwickshire, CV37 6SG
M'Leman, James, MA, BD	1948	......	1981	(Alves *with* Burghead)	59 Pluscarden Road, Elgin, IV30 1SQ [0343] Elgin 41809
M'Millan, Robert	1948	......	1975	(Kincardine and Croick)	8 Birnie Place, Elgin, IV30 3EE [0343] Elgin 44571
Miller, W. B.	1950	......	1987	(Cawdor *with* Croy and Dalcross)	10 Kirkhill Drive, Lhanbryde, Elgin, IV30 3QW [034 384] Lhanbryde 2368
Neill, T. F.	1940	......	1975	(Dyke)	26 Hanover Court, Forres, IV36 0FA [0309] Forres 76290
Porter, John C.	1962	......	1987	(Forres St. Leonard's)	44 Birkenhillock Road, Forres, IV36 0FH [0309] Forres 73694
Prentice, Robert, MA	1940	......	1981	(Knockando, Elchies and Archiestown)	24 Birnie Road, New Elgin, Elgin, IV30 3EA [0343] Elgin 3344
Shedden, John, BD	1971	......	1986	Chaplain RAF	The Manse, Kinloss, Forres, IV36 0TX [0309] Forres 30931
Stephen, J. S., MA, BD, PHD	1942	......	1982	(Botriphine)	Rutherhill, Moss of Meft, Urquhart, Elgin, IV30 3NH
Torrie, A. R. R., MA	1948	......	1986	(Birnie *with* Pluscarden)	Cantsford, Rafford, Forres, IV36 0RU [0309] Forres 73725 [034 384] Lhanbryde 2359
Watson, George A.	1961	......	1970	(Guthrie and Rescobie)	31 Reidhaven Street, Elgin, IV30 1QH [0343] Elgin 7213
Watt, H. Forbes	1950	......	1976	(Lossiemouth St. Gerardine's High)	25 South Covesea Terrace, Lossiemouth, IV31 6NA [034 381] Lossiemouth 2975
Whiteford, Robert S., MA	1945	......	1986	(Shapinsay)	Lochinver Croft, Mosstowie, Elgin, IV30 3TT [0343] Elgin 41438

SYNOD XI—THE SOUTHERN HIGHLANDS

Meets on fourth Thursday of April alternating among the three Presbyteries—in 1982 at Spean Bridge
Correspondents: Argyll; Grampian; Ross, Sutherland and Caithness; Perth and Angus
Clerk: Rev. ROBERT J. V. LOGAN, MA, BD, 39 Southside Road, Inverness, IV2 4XA [0463] *Inverness 31140*

36. ABERNETHY

Meets at Boat of Garten on the first Tuesday of February, March, April, June, September, October, November and December
Clerk: Rev. ALBERT JENNER, The Manse, Kingussie, PH21 1HA [054 02] *Kingussie 311*

Charge	Minister	Ord.	Ind.	Address and Tel. No.	Com.	Eld.	W.G.	S.S.	B.C.	C.L. £	As'd £	Gi'n £	Stp. £
Abernethy	James A. I. MacEwan, MA, BD	1973	1980	Nethy Bridge, PH25 3DG [047 982] *Nethybridge 280*	171	14	20	43	22	13031	917	928	8646
linked with Cromdale and Advie					145	8	...	25	13	7664	761	761	
Alvie and Insh	John R. Lyall ¶	1958	1978	Kincraig, Kingussie, Inverness-shire, PH21 1NA [054 04] *Kincraig 221*	115	11	27	23	10	24362	3313	3313	8847
Boat of Garten and Kincardine	Matthew S. Stewart, LTH	1981	......	Deshar, Boat of Garten, PH24 3BU [047 983] *Boat of Garten 252*	122	13	25	28	...	11079	...	100	8646
linked with Duthil					60	6	13	21	...	4316	...	65	
Cromdale and Advie	*see Abernethy*												
Dulnain Bridge	Morris Smith, BD	1988	......	Golf Course Road, Grantown-on-Spey, PH26 3HY [0479] *Grantown-on-Spey 2084*	52	3	...	9	...	3852	352	352	v
linked with Grantown-on-Spey					363	17	46	19	...	17505	3457	3457	
Duthil	*see Boat of Garten*												
Grantown-on-Spey	*see Dulnain Bridge*												
Inveraven and Glenlivet	Christina A. Douglas, (Mrs.)	1987	......	Ballindalloch, Banffshire, AB3 9EB [080 72] *Ballindalloch 311*	200	11	...	37	...	5569	...	...	v
Kingussie	Albert Jenner	1951	1973	Kingussie, Inverness-shire, PH21 1HA [054 02] *Kingussie 311*	214	19	45	43	...	13788	1602	1602	8646
Kirkmichael and Tomintoul	D. A. Maclean, MA	1953	1985	Tomintoul, Ballindalloch, Banffshire, AB3 9HA [080 74] *Tomintoul 254*	122	4	15	...	...	6970	...	...	8646

Charge	Minister	Ord.	Ind.	...	Com.	Eld.	W.G.	S.S.	B.C.	C.L.	As'd	Gi'n	Stp.	v
Laggan *linked with* Newtonmore	Gordon S. Lennox, BD, DIP PTH	1988	...		68	6	...	...	...	3424	255	234		
					201	18	30	37	...	14543	1739	1939		8646
Rothiemurchus and Aviemore	William W. Niven, B TH	1982	...		164	11	19	32	14	20054	...	...		

Newtonmore, Inverness-shire, PH20 [054 03] Newtonmore 238

Rothiemurchus, Inverness-shire, PH22 1QH [0479] Aviemore 810280

Minister	Ord.	App.	Ret.	Charge	Address and Tel. No.
Alston, Colin M., B MUS, BD	1975	1987	...	Trinidad	31 Ellerslie Park, Port of Spain, Trinidad, WI
Boyd, James H. T., MA	1940	...	1979	(Abernethy with Cromdale and Advie)	Eynhallow, St. Bride's Avenue, Newtonmore, PH20 [054 03] N'more 580
Grant, Joseph, MC, DD	1931	...	1971	(Advie with Cromdale)	The Larches, Skye of Curr, Grantown-on-Spey, PH26 3PA [047 985] Dulnain Bridge 353
Hutchison, Alex	1931	...	1978	(Alvie and Insh)	Fronthill, Newtonmore, PH20 [054 03] Newtonmore 306
Macleod, Donald A., MA	1955	...	1987	(Inveraven and Glenlivet)	Eriskay, Kingston-on-Spey, Fochabers, IV32 7NW [0343] Fochabers 87544
Stoddart, David L.	1961	...	1987	(Laggan with Newtonmore)	3 Castle Street, Anstruther, KY10 [0333] Anstruther 310668

COMMUNION SUNDAYS

Abernethy	3 Mr., Je., Nv.	Cromdale	2 Fb., Au.	Kingussie	2 My., 1 Nv., E.
Advie	1 My., Nv.	Dulnain Bridge	2 My., 4 Oc.	Kirkmichael and Tomintoul	1 Jl., Nv. E.
Alvie and Insh	1 Ap., 2 Jl., 1 Oc., 1 Dc.	Duthil	1 Jn., Oc.	Laggan	1 Je., Oc.
Boat of Garten and Kincardine	1 My., 1 Oc.	Grantown-on-Spey	1 My., 1 Je., 1 Oc.	Newtonmore	1 My., Nv.
	2 Au.	Inveraven and Glenlivet	1 Nv.	Rothiemurchus	3 My., Nv., E. 2 My., Sp., Nv.

37. INVERNESS

Meets at Inverness, in the Dr. Black Memorial Hall, on the first Tuesday of February, March, April, May, September, October, November and December and at the Moderator's Church on the fourth Tuesday of June

Clerk: Rev. ROBERT J. V. LOGAN, MA, BD, 39 Southside Road, Inverness, IV2 4XA [0463] Inverness 231140

Correspondent for Transference of Communicants: Rev. Peter Fraser, MA, BD, 3 Fanellan, Kiltarlity, Inverness-shire, IV4 7JP [046 374] Kiltarlity 488

Charge	Minister	Ord.	Ind.	Address and Tel. No.	Com.	Eld.	W.G.	S.S.	B.C.	C.L. £	As'd £	Gi'n £	Stp. £
Ardclach *linked with* Auldearn and Dalmore	Alexander J. Shaw, MA, BD	1968	1984	Auldearn, Nairn, IV12 5SX [0667] Nairn 53180	60	7	15	...	...	4506	...	...	
					107	8	22	18	6	7171	...	187	8646

Charge	Minister	Ord.	Ind.	Address and Tel. No.	Com.	Eld.	W.G.	S.S.	B.C.	C.L. £	As'd £	Gi'n £	Stp. £
Ardersier	Garden W. M. Ritchie	1961	1971	Ardersier, Inverness, IV1 2SX [066 76] Ardersier 2224	105	8	20	65	11	9937	....	....	8748
linked with Petty					65	8	12	....	....	5692	....	....	
Auldearn and Dalmore	*see Ardclach*												
Cawdor	Ian M. Wilson	1988	......	Croy, Inverness, IV1 2PH [066 78] Croy 217	160	16	40	39	4	13444	651	651	v
linked with Croy and Dalcross	R. Graeme Dunphy, BA, BD	1988	......	21 MacLeod Road, Balloch, Inverness [0463 790] Culloden Moor 504	88	13	26	19	5	7169	503	336	
Culloden [E]	David Betts, DCS	......	......	Deacon—see List H [043] Inverness 793275	418	38	43	204	62	26018	....	....	v
Daviot and Dunlichity†	Lilian M. Bruce, BD, THM	1971	1986	Daviot, Inverness, IV1 2XQ [046 385] Daviot 242	82	5	13	11	12	8932	....	....	8646
linked with Moy, Dalarossie and Tomatin					43	4	10	18	13	6285	....	....	
Dores and Boleskine	Nicolas D. C. Archer, BA, BD	1971	1983	Foyers, Inverness, IV1 2XU [045 63] Gorthleck 206	132	8	8	13	....	16059	....	63	8646
Glenmoriston	F. Bart Buell, BA, MDIV	1980	......	Drumnadrochit, Inverness-shire, IV3 6TZ [045 62] Drumnadrochit 231	23	3	30	2	....	2103	213	213	9132
linked with Urquhart					139	11	....	14	9	35135	2611	2795	
Inverness—Crown	Robert J. V. Logan, MA, BD	1962	1970	39 Southside Road, IV2 4XA [0463] Inverness 231140	969	88	105	97	60	76060	14693	14693	10872
Dalneigh and Bonat†	Fergus A. Robertson, MA, BD	1971	1972	9 St. Mungo Road, IV3 5AS [0463] Inverness 232339	519	28	30	123	26	46504	7666	7666	9837
East†	Aonghas I. MacDonald, MA, BD	1967	1981	2 Victoria Drive, IV2 3QD [0463] Inverness 231269	369	40	47	59	19	60379	10300	10300	10017
Hilton	G. Alan S. Stirling, MA	1960	1965	4 Tomatin Road, IV2 4UR [0463] Inverness 231417	372	22	59	83	19	26655	....	....	8847
Ness Bank	Archibald T. Black, BSC	1964	1974	15 Ballifeary Road, IV3 5PJ [0463] Inverness 234653	881	66	50	163	63	60539	13667	14426	10611
St. Columba High	Alastair S. Younger, BSC, ASSC	1969	1976	3 Elm Park, IV2 3HX [0463] Inverness 232462	390	41	27	35	10	33832	8056	8183	10017

Charge / Minister			Address and Tel. No.									
St. Stephen's linked with Old High (1st Charge) — Ian F. M'Intosh, MA, THM, THD	1960	1971	24 Damfield Road, IV2 9HU [0463] Inverness 237129	366	36	27	132	22	28025	5347	5347	9837
Trinity — Norman I. MacRae, LTH	1966	.....	60 Kenneth Street, IV3 5PZ [0463] Inverness 234756	208	23	.....	28	10	34182	4624	4624	9837
West (2nd Charge) — Thomas Swanston, MA, BD, MED	1960	1971	52 Crown Drive, IV2 3QG [0463] Inverness 237420	355	31	31	95	50	41533	5444	5444	10611
Kilmorack and Erchless — A. Ayton Fairweather, AVCM	1964	1987	Beauly, Inverness-shire, IV4 7DJ [0463 378] Beauly 2260	414	51	36	37	21	49616	13035	13035	v
Kiltarlity† linked with Kirkhill — Campbell Mackinnon, BSC, BD	1982	.....	Kirkhill, Inverness, IV5 7PX [046 383] Drumchardine 662	121	12	31	25	.....	12622	.....	.....	
				81	7	14	23	.....	9070	.....	.....	8646
Moy, Dalarossie and Tomatin — see Daviot				88	8	20	26	2	7524	.....	.....	
Nairn— Old — Ian W. F. Hamilton, BD, LTH, ALCM, AVCM	1978	1986	3 Manse Road, Nairn, IV12 4RN [0667] Nairn 52203	1169	77	51	161	20	61842	13200	13200	10872
St. Ninian's — William B. Whyte, BD	1973	1975	Queen Street, Nairn, IV12 4AA [0667] Nairn 52202	455	26	44	52	15	27933	4783	4783	9390
Petty — see Ardersier												
Urquhart† — see Glenmoriston												

Minister	Ord.	App.	Ret.	Charge	Address and Tel. No.
Carrick, Mungo, MA, BD	1935	.....	1975	(Ardgour with Strontian)	5 Boarstone Place, Inverness, IV2 4XS [0463] Inverness 221466
Donn, Thomas M., MA	1932	.....	1969	(Duthil)	6 Cawdor Road, Inverness, IV2 3NR [0463] Inverness 236410
Edgar, William M. G., MA	1937	.....	1976	(Auchindoir and Kildrummy)	7 Society Street, Nairn, IV12 4PF [0667] Nairn 53676
Fraser, Peter, BA, BD	1941	.....	1980	(Glenmoriston)	3 Fanellan, Kiltarlity, Inverness-shire, IV4 7JP [046 374] Kiltarlity 488
Gilmour, Robert M., MA, BD	1942	.....	1981	(Kiltarlity)	1622 Culburnie, Kiltarlity, Inverness-shire, IV4 7JJ [046 734] Kiltarlity 229
Graham, John	1950	.....	1984	(Edinburgh St. Andrew's Clermiston)	1 Edington Road, Milton of Culcaboc, Inverness, IV2 3DB [0463] Inverness 242426
Henderson, Roderick B.	1973	.....	1982	(Kingswells)	5 Holmpark, Inverness, IV2 9XT [0463] Inverness 224022
Macaskill, Duncan	1952	.....	1974	(Lochs-in-Bernera)	71 Smithton Park, Inverness, IV1 2PB [0463] Smithton 791376
M'Ewan, John, FSCA	1967	.....	1982	(Dores and Boleskine)	46 Drumdevan Place, Inverness, IV2 4DQ [0463] Inverness 240524
Macfarlane, Donald, MA	1940	.....	1980	(Inverness East)	8 Muirfield Gardens, Inverness, IV2 4HF [0463] Inverness 231977
Newall, John A.	1934	.....	1971	(Resolis)	37 Grigor Drive, Inverness, IV2 4LS [0463] Inverness 230649
Patterson, Matthew N.	1957	.....	1985	Daviot and Dunlichity with Moy, Dalarossie and Tomatin	61 Drumfield Road, Inverness, IV2 4XY [0463] Inverness 235072
Warwick, Ivan C., MA, BD	1980	1985	.....	Chaplain, Army	1 OOH Munster BFPO 17
Wilson, John M., MA	1964	1979	.....	Adviser Religious Education	25 Crown Drive, Inverness, IV2 3QF [0463] Inverness 240855

ADDRESSES OF TOWN CHURCHES

Inverness—			
Crown	Kingsmills Road x Midmills Road 0463 238929	St. Columba High	Bank Street x Fraser Street
		St. Stephen's	Old Edinburgh Rd. x Southside Road
Dalneigh and Bona	St. Mary's Avenue	Old High	Church Street x Church Lane
East	Academy St. x Margaret St.	Trinity	Huntly Pl. x Upper Kessock Street
Hilton	Druid Rd. x Tomatin Rd.		
Ness Bank	Ness Bank x Castle Road	West	Huntly Street x Greig Street

Nairn—	
Old	Academy St. x Seabank Rd.
St. Ninian's	High Street x Queen Street

38. LOCHABER

Meets at Caol Fort William, in Kilmallie Church Hall, on the first Tuesday of each month except January, May, July and August when there is no meeting.

Clerk: Rev. ARCHIBALD RUSSELL, MA, Manse of Duror and Glencoe, Ballachulish, Argyll, PA39 4JG [085 52] Ballachulish 209

Charge	Minister	Ord.	Ind.	Address and Tel. No.	Com.	Eld.	W.G.	S.S.	B.C.	C.L. £	As'd £	Gi'n £	Stp. £
Acaracle *linked with* Ardnamurchan	Thomas Moffat	1976	1987	Acharacle, Argyll, PH36 4JU [096 785] *Salen 665*	60	4	.....	.....	6	8815	.....	.....	v
Ardgour *linked with* Strontian	James A. Carmichael, LTH	1976	....	Ardgour, Fort William, PH33 7AH [085 55] *Ardgour 230*	31	6	.....	17	.....	4341	.....	.....	
					57	9	.....	11	7	7580	.....	.....	8784
Ardnamurchan	*see Acharacle*				29	3	.....	7	3	3581	.....	.....	
Arisaig and Moidart	Thomas C. Urquhart, MA, DIPA	1953	1964	Mid Road, Arisaig, Inverness-shire, PH39 4NJ [068 75] *Arisaig 227*	31	3	.....	23	7	4722	.....	.....	8646
					53	6	.....	7	4	4867	.....	.....	
Duror *linked with* Glencoe St. Munda's	Archibald Russell, MA	1949	1979	Ballachulish, Argyll, PA39 4JG [085 52] *Ballachulish 209*	88	8	15	20	.....	12329	.....	11	8646
					87	6	23	.....	.....	18882	.....	.....	v
Fort Augustus *linked with* Glengarry	George W. Charlton	1952	1987	Fort Augustus, Inverness-shire, PH32 4BH [032 06] *Fort Augustus 210*	47	7	16	23	.....	5951	.....	200	
Fort William— Duncansburgh *linked with* Kilmonivaig	John L. Millar, MA, BD	1981	1987	Fort William, Inverness-shire, PH33 6BA [0397] *Fort William 2297*	390	29	20	35	17	23047	3991	4084	v
					90	6	11	15	12	7512	.....	.....	

Congregation	Minister			Address and Tel. No.									
MacIntosh Memorial	Alan Ramsay, MA	1967	......	Achintore Road, Fort William, PH33 6RQ [0397] Fort William 2054	332	23	20	83	13	32774	5640	5714	9675
Glencoe	see Duror												
Glengarry	see Fort Augustus												
Kilmallie	Kenneth J. MacPherson	1988	......	Corpach, Fort William, PH33 7JS [039 77] Corpach 210	412	42	50	69	12	25979	4203	4203	v
Kilmonivaig	see Fort William Duncansburgh												
Kinlochleven linked with Nether Lochaber	Klaus O. F. Buwert, LL.B, BD	1984	......	Kinlochleven, Argyll. PA40 4QW [085 54] Kinlochleven 227	152	6	......	29	......	11164	......	......	8646
					54	5	10	19	......	6527	......	23	
Mallaig and the Small Isles	R. Alan Knox, MA, LTH, AINST.AM	1965	1987	Mallaig, Inverness-shire, PH41 4RG [0687] Mallaig 2256	114	11	15	60	14	10540	......	......	v
Morvern	Alicia Ann Winning, MA, BD	1984	......	Lochaline, Morvern, by Oban, PA34 5UU [096 784] Morvern 267	72	7	13	3	3	12317	......	240	8646
Nether Lochaber	see Kinlochleven												
Strontian	see Ardgour												

Minister	Ord.	App.	Ret.	Charge	Address and Tel. No.
Anderson, David M., MSC, FBCO	1984	1984	......	Auxiliary Minister	1 Dumfries Place, Fort William, PH33 [0397] Fort William 2091
Finlayson, Duncan, MA	1943	......	1983	(Morvern)	Rhugarbh, North Shian, Appin, PA38 4BA [063 173] Appin 416
Gillies, Hugh M., MA, JP	1939	......	1980	(Fort Augustus)	4 Broadstone Park, Inverness
Kerr, James H.	1953	......	1981	(Nether Lochaber)	54 St. Michael's Drive, Cupar, Fife, KY15 5BS
MacLean, Hector A. M., MA	1937	......	1978	(Duror with Glencoe)	Gearra Beag, Duror, Argyll [063 174] Duror 215
Robertson, A. K., MA, BD, PHD	1943	......	1981	(Fort William Duncansburgh)	Ardlea, Belford Road, Fort William, PH33

COMMUNION SUNDAYS

Charge	Communion Sundays
Acharacle	P., Au., Nv.
Ardgour	1 Je., Sp., Dc., E., Au.
Ardnamurchan	1 My., Nv.
Arisaig and Moidart	2 Jn., 3 Nv.
Duror	2 My., 4 Oc.
Fort Augustus	
Fort William—Duncansburgh	1 Ap., Je., Oc.
M'Intosh Memorial	1 Mr., Je., Sp., Dc.
Glencoe	1 Ap., Oc.
Glengarry	1 Ja., Ap., Jl., Oc.
Kilmallie	3 Mr., My., Sp., 1 Dc.
Kilmonivaig	1 My., Nv.
Kinlochleven	1 Fb., Ap., Je., Oc., Dc.
Mallaig	4 My., 3 Nv.
Morvern	E 1 Jl., 4 Sp., 1 Dc.
Nether Lochaber	1 Ap., Oc.
Strontian	1 Je., Sp., Dc.

SYNOD XII—ROSS, SUTHERLAND AND CAITHNESS

Meets at Dingwall in St. Clement's Church on the third Tuesday of April
Correspondent: Southern Highlands

Clerk: Rev. R. M. MACKINNON, LTH, Kilmuir and Logie Easter Manse, Delny, Invergordon, IV18 0NW [086 284] Kildary 2280

39. ROSS

Meets at Dingwall on the first Tuesday of each month except January, May, July and August

Clerk: Rev. RODERICK MACLEAN MACKINNON, LTH, Kilmuir and Logie Easter Manse, Delny, Invergordon IV18 0NW [086 284] Kildary 2280

Charge	Minister	Ord.	Ind.	Address and Tel. No.	Com.	Eld.	W.G.	S.S.	B.C.	C.L. £	As'd £	Gi'n £	Stp. £
Alness	*Vacant*	……	……	27 Darroch Brae, Alness, Ross-shire IV17 0SD [0349] Alness 882238	116	12	24	80	15	17502	……	……	8646
Avoch	Nicholas W. M. Simpson, BA, BD	1979	1981	24 Station Crescent, Fortrose, Ross-shire, IV10 8TH [0381] Fortrose 20068	42	3	21	12	……	4625	599	599	8742
linked with Fortrose and Rosemarkie					157	15	20	56	26	20215	1605	1605	v
Contin-Strathconon	Margaret Liddell, BD, DPTH	1987	……	Contin, Strathpeffer, Ross-shire, IV14 9ES [0997] Strathpeffer 21380	50	13	……	19	12	5254	……	……	8646
Cromarty	Robert W. C. Galloway, LTH	1970	1976	Cromarty, Ross-shire, IV11 8XT [038 17] Cromarty 240	87	7	20	43	15	7823	……	……	v
Dingwall— Castle Street	Grahame M. Henderson, BD	1974	1987	Achany Road, Dingwall, Ross-shire, IV15 9JB [0349] Dingwall 63167	245	20	16	81	12	32969	7349	7649	v
St. Clement's	Gordon Holroyd, BTH, FPHS, FSASCOT	1959	1979	Castle Street, Dingwall, Ross-shire, IV15 9HU [0349] Dingwall 63379	235	21	21	85	17	24832	2270	2270	8646
Fearn and Nigg	Kenneth Macfarlane	1963	……	Fearn, Ross-shire, IV20 1XJ [086 283] Fearn 2626	149	10	78	99	14	11205	……	……	8898
Ferintosh	T. Clifford Kelly	1973	1988	Conon Bridge, Ross-shire, IV7 8BE [0349] Conon Bridge 61275	112	13	28	41	……	13064	……	……	v
Fodderty and Strathpeffer	John Buchan, BD, MTH	1968	1978	Strathpeffer, Ross-shire, IV14 9DL [0997] Strathpeffer 21398	119	10	36	38	16	13226	……	27	8646

Charge	Minister	Ord.	App.	Charge									
Fortrose and Rosemarkie	*see* Avoch												
Invergordon	David B. Scott, MA, BD,	1987	......	Cromlet Drive, Invergordon, Ross-shire, IV18 0BA [0349] Invergordon 852273	275	22	38	89	30	21211	3536	3536	v
Killearnan	Susan M. Brown (Mrs.), BD, DIPMIN¶	1985	......	Muir of Ord, Ross-shire, IV6 7SQ [0463] Muir of Ord 870234	91	11	20	16	2	10662	......	270	8646
Kilmuir and Logie Easter	Roderick Maclean Mackinnon, LTH	1968	1981	Delny, Invergordon, Ross-shire, IV18 0NW [086 284] Kildary 2280	90	7	23	21	......	11549	......	74	8646
Kiltearn	Anthony Livesley	1979	......	Evanton, Ross-shire, IV16 9UY [0349] Evanton 830472	105	9	11	49	31	14667	......	......	8646
Kinlochluichart and Strathgarve	Finlay Macdonald	1952	1969	Carsaig Cottage, Tulloch Street, Dingwall, Ross-shire, IV15 9JV [0349] Dingwall 64830	27	3	11	26	......	3262	......	......	8646
Knockbain	W. C. Campbell-Jack, BD	1980	......	Munlochy, Ross-shire, IV8 8NL [046 381] Munlochy 254	85	7	15	32	6	9156	......	......	8646
†Lochbroom and Ullapool	Philip R. Hair, BD	1980	1982	Ullapool, Ross-shire, IV26 3SX [0854] Ullapool 2050	81	5	24	38	19	13561	2078	2078	8646
Resolis and Urquhart	John M¹Leod, MA	1959	1986	Balblair, Culbokie, Conon Bridge, IV7 8LJ [034 987] Culbokie 452	80	8	14	29	......	11343	......	......	8646
Rosskeen	Andrew Y. Howe	1957	1969	Alness, Ross-shire, IV17 0XG [0349] Alness 882265	189	13	34	71	27	16820	1614	1614	8646
Tain	Douglas A. Horne, BD	1977	......	Tain, Ross-shire, IV19 1BN [0862] Tain 2064	298	13	45	118	33	27571	5101	5101	8742
Tarbat	Robert J. Mellis, BTH, CA	1982	1988	Castle Street, Portmahomack, Fearn, Ross-shire, IV20 1YE [086 287] Portmahomack 331	70	3	26	42	2	7450	......	......	v
Urray and Kilchrist	*Vacant*	......	......	Muir of Ord, Ross-shire, IV6 7TL [0463] Muir of Ord 870259	158	12	35	39	28	10756	......	......	8646

Minister	Ord.	App.	Ret.	Charge	Address and Tel. No.
Bennett, G. M. R., MA, BD	1939	......	1972	(Alness)	13 Mortonhall Park Grove, Edinburgh, EH17 8SJ 031–664 6550
Bolster, Richard F., JP	1956	......	1984	(Killearnan)	35 Tarradale Gardens, Muir of Ord, IV6 [0463] Muir of Ord 870105
Buchanan, Malcolm, MA	1936	......	1972	(Dingwall Castle Street)	Maybank, Conon Bridge, Ross-shire, IV7 8BJ [0349] Conon Bridge 61553
Campbell, William, MA	1937	......	1977	(Nigg)	22 Mayfield Wynd, Tain, Ross-shire, IV19 1LL [0862] Tain 2891
MacAlpine, A. G., MA, STM	1935	......	1975	(Tain)	Logie House, Kildary, Invergordon, IV18 0NZ [086 284] Kildary 2382

Minister	Ord.	App.	Ret.	Charge	Address and Tel. No.
Macdiarmid, Duncan, MA, JP	1927		1968	(Rosskeen)	1 Bellfield Road, North Kessock, Inverness, IV1 1XU [046 373] Kessock 324
Macdonald, Norman, MA, BD	1937		1970	(Aberdeen Trinity)	44 Alder Drive, Perth, PH1 1EU
Mackay, John, MA, JP	1941		1979	(Knockbain)	10 Tarradale Gardens, Muir of Ord, Ross-shire, IV6 7RS [0463] Muir of Ord 870808
MacKenzie, A. Ian	1945		1986	(Glenelg with Glenshiel with Kintail)	4 St.Mary's Well, Tain, IV19 1LS [0862] Tain 2305
Maclennan, William	1952		1981	(Lochbroom and Ullapool)	8 Firthview Road, Inverness, IV3 6LZ [0463] Inverness 2225253
MacLennan, Alasdair J., BD	1979	1987		Evangelism Organiser	Adjola, Urquhart Road, Dingwall, IV15 9DE [0349] Dingwall 63970
MacLeod, Donald, R..., MA	1953		1986	(Ferintosh)	1 Top Street, Conon Bridge, IV7 8BH [0349] Canon Bridge 63160
MacLeod, Finlay	1952		1978	(Avoch)	Bemeray, Station Road, Avoch, Ross-shire, IV9 8RW [0381] Fortrose 20224
Macleod, Kenneth	1934		1965	(Nigg Chapelhill)	31 Knockbreck Road, Tain, IV19 1LX [0862] Tain 2296
M'Vicar, Archy, MA	1952		1986	(Dingwall Castle Street)	13 Heatherley Crescent, Inverness, IV2 4AW [0463] Inverness 231783
Orr, William, LTH	1972		1987	(Tarbat)	Tigh-Glas, Tarbatness Road, Portmahomack, Fearn, IV20
Palit, Stephen, MA	1961		1983	(Dundonnell)	22 Drovers Way, Milton, Invergordon, IV18 0PT [086 284] Kildary 2648
Paton, Everett J.	1952		1980	(Glasgow Netherton St. Matthew's)	The Dreish, Sanquhar Road, Forres, IV36 0DG [0309] Forres 72313
Smith, Alan G., BA	1929		1976	(Logie-Easter)	3 Park Avenue, Strathpeffer, Ross-shire, IV14 [0997] Strathpeffer 21587
Sutherland, A. M., MA	1936		1976	(Resolis)	26 Drover's Way, Milton, Invergordon, IV18 0PT [086 24] Kildary 2498
Tibbs, Ivan F., MA	1943		1981	(Boat of Garten and Kirkmichael with Duthil)	
Young, William G., BD, PHD	1947		1985	(Resolis and Urquhart)	29 Ferry Brae, North Kessock, Inverness, IV1 1VH [046 373] Kessock 581

COMMUNION SUNDAYS

Alness	3 Je., 1 Nv., E.	Ferintosh	1 Mr., 2 Au.	Knockbain	4 Je., 3 Nv.
Avoch	Palm, 2 Oc.	Fodderty and Strathpeffer	l Ap., Oc., E.	Lochbroom and	3 Je.
Contin	X, E.	Fortrose and Rosemarkie	4 Ap., Nv.	Ullapool	1 Mr., Sp.
Strathconon	l Je., Nv., E.	Invergordon	3 Je., 1 Nv., l m'thly	Resolis and Urquhart	3 Fb., 3 Jl., 4 Au., Nv.
Cromarty	2 Je.	Killearnan	1 My., 3 Nv.	Rosskeen	3 Je., 1 Nv., E.
Dingwall—		Kilmuir and		Tain	4 Ja., 2 Ap., 4 Je., 4 Sp.
Castle Street	1 Fb., 3 Sp.	Logie Easter	1 Mr., Je., Oc.	Tarbat	1 Je., /1 Nv.
St. Clement's	Fb., Nv.	Kiltearn	l Ap., Nv.	Urray and Kilchrist	1 My., 3 Nv., E.
Dundonnell	4 Je.	Kinlochluichart and			
Fearn and Nigg	2 Je., l Oc., E.	Strathgarve	l Je., 4 Oc.		

40. SUTHERLAND

Meets at Lairg on the first Tuesday of March, April, June, September, November and December

Clerk: Rev. J. L. GOSKIRK, LTH, The Manse, Lairg, Sutherland, IV27 4EH [0549] Lairg 2373

Charge	Minister	Ord.	Ind.	Address and Tel. No.	Com.	Eld.	W.G.	S.S.	B.C.	C.L. £	As'd £	Gi'n £	Stp. £
Altnaharra and Farr†	John Lincoln, M PHIL, BD	1986	......	Bettyhill, by Thurso, Caithness, KW14 7SZ [064 12] Bettyhill 208	37	1	......	7	......	8127	......	......	8646
Assynt and Stoer†	Frederick R. Hurst, MA	1965	1971	Lochinver, by Lairg, Sutherland, IV27 4LH [057 14] Lochinver 342	35	3	......	27	......	8496	......	......	8748
Clyne	Ian W. M'Cree, BD	1971	1987	Golf Rd., Brora, Sutherland, KW9 6QS [0408] Brora 239	158	11	40	28	9	16692	1700	1700	v
Creich *linked with* Rosehall	Eric R. Lacey, BD	1971	1986	Bonar Bridge, Ardgay, IV24 3EB [086 32] Ardgay 256	60	5	......	38	6	6881	......	......	8646
					19	3	......	8	......	5120	6600	120	......
Dornoch Cathedral	James A. Simpson, BSC, BD, STM	1960	1976	Dornoch, Sutherland, IV25 3HN [086 2810] Dornoch 296	369	19	85	74	30	36507	6600	6908	9600
Durness† *linked with* Kinlochbervie†	William Black, BD, AMIMECHE	1968	1986	Kinlochbervie, Lairg, IV27 4RG [097 182] Kinlochbervie 287	25	3	......	10	......	3344	......	......	8646
					45	1	18	20	......	7056	......	......	......
Eddrachillis	John Selfridge, BTH, BR ED	1969	1986	Scourie, by Lairg, IV27 4TQ [0971] Scourie 2431	21	4	10	17	......	9651	......	40	8646
Golspie	Vacant	......	......	Fountain Road, Golspie, KW10 6TH [040 83] Golspie 3295	141	17	39	44	19	17697	1300	1300	8745
Kildonan and Loth, Helmsdale	John Rushton, BVMS, BD	1983	......	Helmsdale, Sutherland, KW8 6HT [043 12] Helmsdale 674	66	5	25	29	10	12332	......	150	8646
Kincardine Croick and Edderton	Frederick W. Hibbert, BA, BD	1986	......	Ardgay, Sutherland, IV24 3BG [086 32] Ardgay 285	83	5	......	27	3	12636	......	......	8646
Kinlochbervie	*see Durness*												
Lairg *linked with* Rogart	J. L. Goskirk, LTH	1968	......	Lairg, Sutherland, IV27 4EH [0549] Lairg 2373	44	8	26	47	10	7548	......	233	8748
					22	2	......	21	5	6232	......	......	......
Melness and Eriboll† *linked with* Tongue†	James A. Rettie, BTH	1981	1984	Tongue, by Lairg, Sutherland, IV27 4XL [080 05] Tongue 230	20	2	......	......	......	3071	......	......	......
					49	6	11	10	7	6482	......	24	8646
Rogart	*see Lairg*												
Rosehall	*see Creich*												
Tongue	*see Melness*												

Minister	Ord.	App.	Ret.	Charge	Address and Tel. No.
Evans, John W., MA, BD	1945	.....	1984	(Elgin High)	Mansfield, Golf Road, Dornoch, IV25 3LW [0862] Dornoch 810071
M'Clintock, Alfred, MA, BD	1940	.....	1984	(Melness and Eriboll with Tongue)	Eastwood, Tongue, by Lairg, IV27 [080 05] Tongue 339

COMMUNION SUNDAYS

Altnaharra	2 Jn., Oc.	Eddrachillis	2 My.,
Assynt and Stoer	2 Jl., 4 Oc.	Farr	/ Je., 3 Nv.
Clyne	2 Je., Nv.	Golspie	/ Je., 2 Dc., E.
Creich	3 Au., / Dc., E.	Kildonan and Loth, Helmsdale	1 Fb., My., Au., Nn.
Dornoch	3 Je., Nv., E.	Kincardine Croick	3 Mr., 1 My., / Je.,
Durness	2 Je., 4 Nv.	and Edderton	1 Au., 1 Oc.

Kinlochbervie	4 Mr., 1 Nv.
Lairg	2 Mr., 3 Je., / Oc.
Melness and Eribol	3 Je., 2 Oc.
Rogart	3 Mr., 2 Je., 1 Sp., 4 Nv.
Rosehall	1 Nv., Pentecost
Tongue	2 Je., 3 Nv.

41. CAITHNESS

Meets alternately at Wick and Thurso on the first Tuesday of February, March, May, September, November and December, and the third Tuesday of June
(February 1985 at Wick)

Clerk: Rev. MICHAEL G. MAPPIN, BA, The Manse, Watten, KW1 5YJ [095 582] Watten 220

Charge	Minister	Ord.	Ind.	Address and Tel. No.	Com.	Eld.	W.G.	S.S.	B.C.	C.L. £	As'd £	Gi'n £	Stp. £
Berriedale and Dunbeath	R. W. Blackwood, BSC, LTH	1969	.....	Ross Manse, Dunbeath, Caithness, KW6 6ED [059 33] Dunbeath 228	23	4	10	9	.....	5981	.....	.....	8748
linked with Latheron					22	2	16	17	.....	4391	.....	.....	
Bower	Michael G. Mappin, BA	1961	1970	Watten, Caithness, KW1 5YJ [095 582] Watten 220	38	3	.....	.....	.....	4620	308	308	8748
linked with Watten					63	6	16	34	.....	10260	401	468	
Canisbay	Alexander Muir, MA, BD	1982	.....	Canisbay, Wick, Caithness, KW1 4YH [095 581] John o'Groats 309	51	2	.....	21	.....	9671	.....	.....	8646
linked with Keiss					36	2	.....	25	.....	5471	.....	.....	

Congregation	Minister	Ord.	App.	Ret.	Charge — Address and Tel. No.									
Dunnet *linked with* **Olrig**	*Vacant*				Olrig, Castletown, Thurso, KW14 8TP [084 782] Castletown 221	30	1		20		2747		2	8748
						74	1		3		3930			8646
Halkirk and Westerdale	Kenneth Warner, BD, DA(EDIN), DIPTP(EDIN)	1981			Abbey Manse, Halkirk, Caithness, KW12 6UU [084 783] Halkirk 227	110	7		56	12	9456	879		
Keiss	*see Canisbay*													
Latheron	*see Berriedale*													
Lybster and Bruan	David S. Dixon, MA, BD	1976	1977		Central Manse, Lybster, Caithness, KW3 6BN [059 32] Lybster 231	47	6	19	55	4	10627			8646
Olrig	*see Dunnet*													
Reay	James S. Dewar, MA, BD	1983			Reay, Thurso, Caithness, KW14 7RE [084 781] Reay 272	53	6	19	34		12094			8646
Strathy and Halladale†	Frank D. Bardgett, MA, BD, PHD	1987			Strathy, Thurso, Caithness, KW14 7RZ [064 14] Strathy 216	32	2	25	26	1	7140			v
Thurso— St. Peter's and St. Andrew's	Donald S. Riach, MA, BL	1964	1965		46 Rose Street, Thurso, KW14 7HN [0847] Thurso 62456	218	14	40	65	7	19270	1569	1669	8760
West	Ronald Johnstone, BD	1977	1984		Thorkel Road, Thurso, KW14 7LW [0847] Thurso 62663	425	27	56	176	31	23724	2286	2286	9135
Watten	*see Bower*													
Wick— Bridge Street	A. A. Roy, MA, BD	1955			Mansefield, Miller Avenue, Wick, KW1 4DF [0955] Wick 2822	201	19	17	49		20058	1853	1853	8760
Central	*Vacant*	1961		1988	Thurso Road, Wick, KW1 5LE [0955] Wick 2851	122	14	37	25	11	20811	1458	1668	8760
Old	R. Stewart Frizzell, BD				George Street, Wick, KW1 4DE [0955] Wick 3286	274	28	51	71	20	23144	2646	2646	9159
St. Andrew's and Thrumster	William F. Wallace, BDS, BD	1968	1974		Coronation Street, Wick, KW1 5LS [0955] Wick 3166	267	15	42	140	28	27953	2256	2356	9159

Minister	Ord.	App.	Ret.	Charge
Cormack, James S.	1965	......	1988	(Wick Central)

COMMUNION SUNDAYS

Berriedale and Dunbeath	2 Mr., Je., Sp., Dc	Lybster and Bruan	3 Je., Nv., E.
Bower	1 Jl., Dc.	Olrig	2 My., 3 Oc.
Canisbay	3 Jy., 1 My., 3 Nv.	Reay	1 Ap., Sp.
Dunnet	Jl., Nv.	Strathy and Halladale	2 Jl., 4 Nv.
Halkirk	Nv., Ap., Jl.	Thurso—	
Westerdale	Ap., Oc., 4 Dc	St. Peter's & St. Andrew's	1 Fb., Ap., Je., Sp., Nv.
Keiss	1 My., 3 Nv.	West	4 Mr., Je., Nv.
Latheron	1 Jl., 2 Sp., 1 Dc., 2 Mr	Watten	1 Jl., Dc.

Wick—	
Bridge Street	/ Ap., Oc.
Central	/ Ap. Sp.
Old	4 Ap., Sp.
St. Andrew's and Thrumster	1 Mr., Je., Sp., Dc.

42. LOCHCARRON—SKYE

Meets in Kyle on the first Tuesday of each month except January, May, July and August.

Clerk: Rev. ALLAN J. MACARTHUR, BD, The Manse, Lochcarron, Ross-shire, IV54 8YD [052 02] Lochcarron 278

Charge	Minister	Ord.	Ind.	Address and Tel. No.	Com.	Eld.	W.G.	S.S.	B.C.	C.L. £	As'd £	Gi'n £	Stp. £
Applecross† linked with	Allan J. Macarthur, BD	1973	……	Lochcarron, Ross-shire, IV54 8YD [052 02] Lochcarron 278	37	5	12	15	3	8043	……	……	8898
Lochcarron and Shieldaig	Kenneth MacDonald, *Associate*	1965	1978	Applecross [052 04] Applecross 263	30	7	17	28	32	13353	……	……	
linked with Torridon and Kinlochewe					11	……	……	6	2	2764	……	……	
Bracadale*	Donald A. MacKay, LTH	1973	1981	Portnalong, Carbost, Isle of Skye, IV47 8SL [047 842] Carbost 208	26	2	……	14	……	6653	……	……	8847
Duirinish†	Michael J. Lind, LL.B, BD	1984	……	Dunvegan, Portree, Isle of Skye, IV51 9RL [047 022] Dunvegan 457	60	4	……	20	……	54778	……	……	8847
Gairloch and Dundonnell	William J. Macdonald, BD	1976	1984	Gairloch, Ross-shire IV21 2BT [0445] Gairloch 2053	74	5	……	27	14	18614	1458	690	8646
Glenelg and Kintail	Donald Beaton, MA, BD, MTH	1861	1988	Inverinate, Kyle, Ross-shire, IV40 8HE [059 981] Glenshiel 245	51	6	……	26	……	9312	……	10	v
Kilmuir and Stenscholl*	Vacant	……	……		65	14	……	33	5	13604	……	……	10347
Lochalsh and Stromeferry	Vacant	……	……		69	8	……	27	……	11537	……	……	v

Charge	Minister			Address and Tel. No.								
Lochcarron and Shieldaig	see Applecross											
Plockton and Kyle	Duncan Mackinnon	1956	1973	Kyle, Ross-shire, IV40 8DA [0599] Kyle 4294	74	7	12	57	25	15872	.....	884	8748
Portree*	John Ferguson, LTH	1973	1980	Bridge Road, Portree, Isle of Skye, IV51 9ER [0478] Portree 2019	156	19	16	74	10	22399	2750	2750	8847
Sconser and Braes												
Snizort	Donald MacLeod, LTH	1988	......	Snizort, Portree, Isle of Skye, IV51 9XE [047 032] Skeabost Bridge 260	59	5	.....	40	18	15241	.....	.....	v
Torridon and Kinlochewe	see Applecross											
Arnizort												
Stenscholl	see Kilmuir											
Culnancnoc												
Strath and Sleat*	Donald A. MacLennan	1975	1986	Broadford, Isle of Skye, IV49 9AA [047 12] Broadford 213	218	20	45	71	47	27506	4976	4976	9039
	Norman Hill, *Associate*	1984	......	Kyleakin, Isle of Skye [0509 9] Kyle 4780									

Minister	Ord.	App.	Ret.	Charge	Address and Tel. No.
Macarthur, John M. M.	1966	......	1984	(Strath and Sleat)	Willowbank, Herrapool, Broadford, Isle of Skye [047 12] Broadford 271
MacDougall, Angus	1940	......	1982	(Sleat)	The Old Manse, Kilmore Street, Isle of Skye, IV44 8RG
MacLeod, John, MA, MTH	1927	......	1972	(Lochcarron *with* Shieldaig)	2 St. John's Terrace, Edinburgh, EH12 6NW [04714] Ardvasar 238
Macpherson, Kenneth J., MA	1935	......	1984	(Duirinish)	Lionel, Port of Ness, Isle of Lewis
Matheson, James G., MA, BD, DD	1936	......	1979	(Portree)	10 Husabost, Dunvegan, Isle of Skye, IV49 [047 081] Glendale 335
Williamson, Tom, MA, BD	1941	......	1982	(Dyke *with* Edinkillie)	16 Cove, Inverasdale, Poolewe, Achnasheen, IV22 2LT 044–586 423

COMMUNION SUNDAYS

Applecross	1 Je.	Kilmuir	1 Ap., Au.	Sleat	1 Fb., Jl.
Bracadale	3 Mr., Sp.	Kintail	3 Ap., Jl.	Snizort	1 Mr., Je., 1Dc.
Duirinish	1 Ja., 2 Je., 2 Au.	Lochalsh and Stromeferry	4 Je., Sp., X.E.	Stenscholl	2 Je., 4 Oc.
Gairloch	3 Je., Nv.	Lochcarron and Shieldaig	E, 3 Je., 1 Oc.	Strath	1 Mr., Au.
Glenelg	2 Je., Nv.	Plockton and Kyle	2 My., 1 Oc.	Torridon and Kinlochewe	1 My., 2 Jl., 3 Sp.
Glenshiel	1 Jl.	Portree	E, P, X, 2 Mr., Au., 1 Nv.		

43. UIST

Meets at Lochmaddy Church, North Uist, on the fourth Wednesday of January, March, September and November, and in Leverburgh Church, Harris on the fourth Wednesday in June

Clerk: Rev. ADRIAN P. J. VARWELL, BA, BD, PHD, Griminish, Isle of Benbecula, PA88 5QA [0870] Benbecula 2180

Charge	Minister	Ord.	Ind.	Address and Tel. No.	Com.	Eld.	W.G.	S.S.	B.C.	C.L. £	As'd £	Gi'n £	Stp. £
Barra†	James B. MacLean, MTHEOL, DIP THEOL	1986	……	Cuithir, Castlebay, Isle of Barra. PA80 5XD [087 14] Castlebay 230	24	4	……	2	……	5293	……	……	8946
Benbecula†	Adrian P. J. Varwell, BA, BD, PHD	1983	……	Griminish, Isle of Benbecula, PA88 5QA [0870] Benbecula 2180	100	11	……	37	14	16193	……	……	8946
Bernera*	Vacant	……	……	Berneray, Lochmaddy, Isle of North Uist, PA82 5BD [087 67] Berneray 234	26	3	……	8	3	34401	……	……	8946
Carinish*	Vacant	……	……	Carinish, Isle of North Uist, PA82 5EJ [087 64] Locheport 219	61	11	……	22	6	11495	……	……	8847
Kilmuir and Paible*	Vacant	……	……	Paible, Isle of North Uist, PA82 5EF [087 65] Bayhead 282	40	8	……	56	7	14314	……	……	8847
Sollas	William Stewart, DCS	……	……	Deacon—see List H									
Lochmaddy and Trumisgarry*	John M. Smith	1956	1963	Lochmaddy, Isle of North Uist, PA82 5AA [087 63] Lochmaddy 363	76	10	……	22	9	13972	182	182	8847
Manish-Scarista†	Murdo Smith	1988	……	Scarista, Isle of Harris, PA85 3HT [085 985] Scarista 200	28	5	……	10	……	11023	……	……	8847
Leverburgh	John Campbell, DCS	……	……	Deacon—see List H [085 982] Leverburgh 353									
South Uist†	Vacant	……	……	Daliburgh, Lochboisdale, Isle of S. Uist, PA81 5SS [087 84] Lochboisdale 265	57	11	……	18	5	9999	……	……	v
Tarbert*	Norman Maciver, BD	1976	1988	Tarbert, Harris, Isle of Harris, PA85 3DF [0859] Harris 2231	205	17	……	41	32	37538	9747	12639	8847
Amhuinnsuidhe	Donald A. Maclean, DCS	……	……	Deacon—see List H [085 986] Scarp 201									
Scalpay	William Macrae, DCS	……	……	Deacon—see List H [085 984] Scalpay 287									

Minister	Ord.	App.	Ret.	Charge	Address and Tel. No.
Macdonald, William M.	1951	……	1972	(Kilmuir and Paible)	17 Flesherin, Point, Stornoway, PA86 0HE
MacKenzie, Colin N., MA	1947	……	1986	(Carinish)	Redbank, Creagorry, Isle of Benbecula [0870] Benbecula 2546
Macrae, D. A., MA, JP	1942	……	1988	(Tarbert)	Mission House, Moarig, Isle of Harris, PA85 [0859] Harris 2380

COMMUNION SUNDAYS

Barra		E P X
Benbecula		2 Jl., E.
Bernera		1 Fb., 2 Jl., 2 Nv.
Carinish		4 Mr., 2 Au.

Kilmuir and Paible	4 Jl., 3 Nv.
Lochmaddy and Trumisgarry	4 Je., 4 Oc.
Manish-Scarista	3 Jl., 9 Oc.

	South Uist—Iochdar	2 Mr.
	Howmore	4 Je.
Tarbert		1 Sp.
	Daliburgh	2 Mr., 3 Sp.

44. LEWIS

Meets at Stornoway, in St. Columba's Church Hall, on the second Monday of February, March, April, June, September, November and December.

Clerk: Rev. T. S. SINCLAIR, MA, LTH, Martin's Memorial Manse, Matheson Road, Stornoway, PA87 2LR [0851] Stornoway 2206

Charge	Minister	Ord.	Ind.	Address and Tel. No.	Com.	Eld.	W.G.	S.S.	B.C.	C.L. £	As'd £	Gi'n £	Stp. £
Barvas*	Hector Morrison, BSC, BD	1981	......	Barvas, Isle of Lewis, PA86 [085 184] Barva 218	104	11	......	70	20	17150	1008	1008	8847
Borve													
Carloway†	Bruce Knight Gardner, MA, BD	1988	......	Carloway, Isle of Lewis, PA86 9AU [0851 73] Carloway 255	44	1	22	7	......	15097	......	......	8847
Callanish													
Cross, Ness*	Alexander Macdonald	1957	1982	Ness, Isle of Lewis, PA86 0TB [085 181] Port-of-Ness 375	70	7	......	25	......	14964	......	......	8847
Kinloch*	Vacant	......	......	Kinloch, Isle of Lewis, PA86 9LA [085 183] Balallan 218	55	8	......	24	7	20727	......	50	8847
Knock*	James Macdonald, LTH, CPS	1984	......	Knock, Point, Isle of Lewis, PA86 9AU [0851] Garrabost 870 917	95	7	......	55	......	22143	......	560	8847
Garrabost	—	—	—	—									
Lochs-in-Bernera†	Vacant	......	......	Bernera, Isle of Lewis, PA86 9LU [0851 74] Great Bernera 210	43	7	......	13	21	6292	......	......	8847
Lochs-Crossbost*	Vacant	......	......	Lochs-Crossbost, Isle of Lewis, PA86 9NP [085 186] Crossbost 243	21	6	......	......	......	6104	......	......	8847

Charge	Minister	Ord.	Ind.	Address and Tel. No.	Com.	Eld.	W.G.	S.S.	B.C.	C.L. £	As'd £	Gi'n £	Stp. £
Park*	Donald Macaulay, OBE, JP	1968	......	Lemreway, Isle of Lewis, PA86 9RD [085 188] Gravir 257	17	4	...	...	...	4600	...	...	8847
Stornoway—High*	Roderick Morrison, MA, BD	1974	1981	Goathill Road, Stornoway, PA87 2NX [0851] Stornoway 3106	299	13	...	113	47	64717	10049	10049	8847
Martin's Memorial	T. S. Sinclair, MA, LTH	1966	1976	Matheson Rd., Stornoway, PA87 2LR [0851] Stornoway 2206	154	11	20	58	22	35726	312	312	9093
St. Columba†	David L. Wright, MA, BD	1957	1986	Lewis Street, Stornoway, PA87 2JF [0851] Stornoway 3350	156	14	25	86	26	31988	4234	4234	9093
Uig*	William Macleod	1957	1964	Miavaig, Isle of Lewis, PA86 9HW [0851 75] Timsgarry 216	82	8	...	19	12	13164	...	...	9096
Breanish													

Minister	Ord.	App.	Ret.	Charge	Address and Tel. No.
MacCuish, Angus	1944	......	1980	(Stornoway High)	54 Portrona Drive, Stornoway, PA87 2HF [0851] Stornoway 2440
Macdonald, William	1952	......	1982	(Knock)	13 Laxay, Lochs, Isle of Lewis, PA86 9PJ [085 183] Balallan 231
Macfarlane, Angus	1951	......	1979	(Uig Baile-na-cille)	30 North Street, Sandwick, PA86 0AD [0851] Stornoway 4227
Macleod, Kenneth	1955	......	1985	(Stornoway St. Columba)	2 Macdonald Road, Stile Park, Stornoway [0851] Stornoway 4058
MacRitchie, Murdo	1958	......	1969	(Acharacle)	15A New Garrabost, Isle of Lewis, PA86 0PR [0851] Garrabost 870763
MacSween, Norman	1952	......	1987	(Kinloch)	7 Balmerino Drive, Stornoway, Isle of Lewis, PA87 2TD [0851] Stornoway 3369
Morrison, Alexander	1952	......	1973	(Barvas)	Ceol Mara, Marig, Isle of Harris, PA85 3AG [0859] Harris 2267
Murray, Roderick	1957	......	1967	(Kinloch)	18 Port of Ness, Isle of Lewis, PA86 0XA [085 181] Port-of-Ness 286

COMMUNION SUNDAYS

Barvas	3 Mr., Sp.	Knock	1 Ap., Nv.	Park	2 Ap., 1 Oc.
Carloway	1 Mr., l Sp.	Lochs-in-Bernera	1 Ap., 2 Sp.	Stornoway—All Churches	3 Fb., l Au.
Cross, Ness	2 Mr., Oc.	Lochs-Crossbost	4 Mr., Sp.	Uig	3 Je., 1 Sp.
Kinloch	3 Mr., 2 Sp.				

ORKNEY, SHETLAND, AND ENGLAND

The Presbyteries of Orkney, Shetland, and England are not part of any Synod, but each has synodical powers

45. ORKNEY

Meets at Kirkwall, in East Church Hall, on the second Tuesday of January; on the first Tuesday of March, May, September, November and December; and on last Tuesday of June

Clerk: Rev. DAVID A. WILLIAMS, MA, BD, Gowanhill, 5 Hill of Heddle, Finstown, Orkney, KW17 2LH [085 676] Finstown 213

Charge	Minister	Ord.	Ind.	Address and Tel. No.	Com.	Eld.	W.G.	S.S.	B.C.	C.L. £	As'd £	Gi'n £	Stp. £
Birsay	John L. Waugh, LTH	1973	......	Birsay, Orkney, KW17 2LX [085 672] Birsay 276	176	8	24	38	......	7615	......	......	8847
Deerness	Iain J. M. M'Donald, MA, BD	1984	1985	Deerness, Orkney, KW17 2QJ [085 674] Deerness 258	128	......	11	14	9	5713	298	298	8847
linked with St. Andrew's					130	8	15	20	7	4515	298	298	
Eday	Kenneth S. Borthwick, BD	1983	1984	Stronsay, Orkney, KW17 2AF [085 76] Stronsay 311	17	3	9	5	......	2454	......	......	8946
linked with Stronsay Moncur Memorial					114	11	48	19	12	12182	......	250	
Evie					99	7	17	8	......	3280	399	339	
linked with Firth	Trevor, G. Hunt, BD	......	1986	Firth, Orkney, KW17 2EG [085 676] Finstown 328	182	8	30	21	......	6214	845	845	8892
linked with Rendall					98	4	19	8	......	6180	336	336	
Flotta and Fara	W. Graham Monteith, MA, BD, B PHIL	1974	1985	Walls, Longhope, Stromness, KW16 3PA [085 670] Longhope 325	48	3	......	8	......	3207	......	......	8946
linked with Hoy & Walls					121	10	37	19	......	4489	......	41	
Harray	R. Fraser Penny, BA, BD	1984	......	Quoyloo, Stromness, Orkney, KW16 3LX [085 684] Sandwick (O.) 506	172	11	30	26	4	20708	443	443	8847
linked with Sandwick					190	13	31	27	8	5880	399	399	
Holm	*Vacant*	......	......	Holm, Orkney, KW17 2SD [085 678] Holm 218	241	13	24	27	29	7527	......	30	v

Charge	Minister	Ord.	Ind.	Address and Tel. No.	Com.	Eld.	W.G.	S.S.	B.C.	C.L. £	As'd £	Gi'n £	Stp. £
Hoy and Walls	*see* Flotta and Fara												
Kirkwall— East	W. Brian Wilkinson, MA	1968	1987	Kirkwall, Orkney [0856] *Kirkwall 5469*	674	39	55	55	6	22559	6232	6232	v
St. Magnus Cathedral	H. W. M. Cant, MA, BD, STM	1951	1968	Berstane Road, Kirkwall, Orkney, KW15 1NA [0856] *Kirkwall 3312*	813	60	136	89	14	29060	5240	5240	9237
North Ronaldshay *linked with* Sanday	Vacant			Sanday, Orkney, KW17 2BW [085 75] *Sanday 429*	41	3				1158			v
					145	11	12	36	2	8458	365	401	
Orphir *linked with* Stenness	Thomas L. Clark, BD	1985		Stenness, Stromness, Orkney, KW16 3HH [085 676] *Finstown 331*	194	10	20	18	17	7270	289	343	8847
					129	8	19	16	6	6044			
Papa Westray *linked with* Westray	Mary G. Spowart (Mrs.), BD	1978	1986	Westray, Orkney, KW17 2DE [085 77] *Westray 357*	12	3				2035		409	8946
					80	8	30	38	6	8032			
Rendall	*see* Evie												
Rousay	Vacant			Rousay, Orkney, KW17 2PR [085 682] *Rousay 271*	68	6	10	5		2132		43	8946
Egilsay													
St. Andrew's	*see* Deerness												
Sanday	*see* North Ronaldshay												
Sandwick	*see* Harray												
Shapinsay	Ian Sutcliffe	1988		Shapinsay, Balfour, Orkney, KW17 [085 671] *Balfour 332*	121	10	27	16		5755			8946
South Ronaldshay and Burray	Morris G. McKenzie, BA, LLB	1978		St. Margaret's Hope, Orkney, KW17 2RN [085 683] *St. M. H. 288*	359	14		49	4	10113	562	100	8847
Stenness	*see* Orphir												
Stromness	Philip Earnshaw, BA, BSC, BD	1986		5 Manse Lane, Stromness, KW16 3AP [0856] *Stromness 850203*	549	22	48	73	35	29059	4197	4197	9135
Stronsay	*see* Eday												
Walls Old	*see* Flotta and Fara												
St. John's and Melsetter	.....			—									
Westray	*see* Papa Westray												

Minister	Ord.	App.	Ret.	Charge	Address and Tel. No.
Fox, Edward P. G.	1950	...	1983	(Eday with Stronsay Moncur Memorial)	Daisybank, Stronsay [08576] Stronsay 330
Mooney, Harald L., MA	1929	...	1984	(Deerness with St. Andrew's)	Cromwell Cottage, Cromwell Road, Kirkwall [0856] Kirkwall 3161
Williams, D. A., MA, BD	1944	...	1984	(Orphir with Stenness)	Gowanhill, 5 Hill of Heddle, Finstown, Orkney [085 676] Finstown 213

COMMUNION SUNDAYS

Charge	Communion Sundays	Charge	Communion Sundays
Birsay	Au., E., Dc.	Kirkwall—	
Deerness	Jl., Oc., E.	East	1 Mr., Je., Sp., Dc.
Eday	4 Ap., 1 Au., 4 Oc.	St. Magnus	1 Je., Nv., E.
Evie	3 Mr., Jc., Sp., Dc.	Orphir	1 Ap., Sp., Dc.
Firth	3 Fb., My., Au., Nv.	Papa Westray	Ap., Nv.
Flotta and Fara	My., Nv.	Rendall	3 Je., Ap., Jy., Oc.
Harray	1 Ap., Sp.	Rousay	Mr., Je., Oc.
Holm	2 Ap., Sp., Dc.	St. Andrew's	My., Oc.
		Sanday	E., Jl., Oc., X.
		Sandwick	Jl., Dc., E.
		Shapinsay	1 Fb., My., Au., Nv.
		South Ronaldshay and Burray	1 Ap., 3 Sp., Dc.
		Stenness	1 Mr., Je., Sp., Dc.
		Stromness	Fb., My., Au., Nv.
		Stronsay	3 Ap., 1 Sp.
		Walls	

46. SHETLAND

Meets at Lerwick on the first Tuesday of March, April, June, September, October, November and December

Clerk: Rev. MAGNUS CHEYNE, 30 Commercial Road, Lerwick [0595] Lerwick 3240

Charge	Minister	Ord.	Ind.	Address and Tel. No.	Com.	Eld.	W.G.	S.S.	B.C.	C.L. £	As'd £	Gi'n £	Stp. £
Burra Isle	James Hosie, MA, BD, MTH	1959	1986	Gott, Shetland, ZE2 9SB [059 584] Gott 300	55	6	10	43	...	4504	...	...	...
linked with Tingwall					215	25	29	73	2	13625	...	...	8898
Delting	Elinor J. Gordon	1988	...	Brae, Shetland, ZE2 9QJ [080 622] Brae 219	141	10	20	63	20	9455	...	...	v
linked with Nesting and Lunnasting					71	5	26	25	...	4126	...	...	...
Dunrossness	Edith F. M'Millan (Mrs.), MA, BD	1981	...	Sandwick, Shetland, ZE2 9HW [095 05] Sandwick 244	103	13	22	18	2	49419	...	...	...
linked with Sandwick, Cunningsburgh and Quarff	Arthur A. Forrester	...	...	Lay Missionary—see List H [0950] Sumburgh 60850	230	15	41	48	6	17187	...	815	8898

Charge	Minister	Ord.	Ind.	Address and Tel. No.	Com.	Eld.	W.G.	S.S.	B.C.	C.L. £	As'd £	Gi'n £	Stp. £
Fetlar	Magnus J. C. Williamson	1982	……	Mid Yell, Shetland, ZE2 9BN [0957] Mid Yell 2283	31	4	8	3	3	1327	……	……	8898
linked with Yell					227	14	47	20	……	29265	……	……	
Lerwick and Bressay	James W. Macdonald, BD	1976	1981	Lerwick, Shetland, ZE1 0ES [0595] Lerwick 2125	774	52	82	113	9	95956	9732	9732	9372
	Margaret M'Bain, DCS	……	……	Deaconess—see List H [0595] Lerwick 4312									
Nesting and Lunnasting	*see* Delting												
Northmavine	Alice H. Kirkpatrick MA, BD	1987	……	Hillswick, Shetland, ZE2 9RW [080 623] Hillswick 223	112	9	38	63	……	8441	……	……	v
Sandsting and Aithsting	John G. Miller, BED, DIPED	1983	1988	Walls, Shetland, ZE2 9PF [059 571] Walls 333	68	9	35	26	3	3056	……	……	8898
linked with Walls	Douglas Forrest	……	……	Agent—see List H	103	13	……	18	……	3403	……	……	
Sandwick, Cunningsburgh and Quarff	*see* Dunrossness												
Tingwall	*see* Burra Isle												
Unst	*Vacant*	……	……	Unst, Baltasound, Shetland, ZE2 9DZ [095 781] Baltasound 335	169	12	17	35	14	9401	……	……	8997
Walls	*see* Sandsting												
Whalsay and Skerries	Regine W. Frank, MA, BSC, BD	1988	……	North Park, Symbister, Whalsay, Shetland ZE2 9AE [080 66] Symbister 576	306	16	45	35	……	11930	……	……	8997
	James Dey	……	……	Agent—see List H [080 65] Out Skerries 244									
Yell	*see* Fetlar												

Minister	Ord.	App.	Ret.	Charge	Address and Tel. No.
Blair, James N.	1962	……	1986	Sandsting and Aithsting with Walls	2 Swinster, Sandwick, Shetland
Cheyne, Magnus	1963	1988	……	Community Minister for Shetland	30 Commercial Road, Lerwick [0595] Lerwick 3240
Ross, Kenneth, MA	1957	……	1980	Whalsay and Skerries (Northmavine)	2 Railway Cottages, Redesmouth, Bellingham, Northumberland [0660] Bellingham 20387

COMMUNION SUNDAYS

Burra Isle	1 Ap., Oc.	Nesting — My., Oc.
Cunningsburgh	1 My., Nv.	Northmavine — 3 Au., E.
Delting	Ap., Jl., Oc.	Quarff — 4 Ap., Oc.
Dunrossness	2 Je., Sp., X., E.	Sandsting and Aithsting — 3 Je., 4 Oc., 1 Nv., E.
Fetlar	2 Je., Nv.	Sandwick — 2 My., Nv.
Lerwick and Bressay	1 My., Nv.	

Tingwall	Mr., Je., Sp.
Unst	1 My., Oc.
Walls	My., Oc.
Whalsay and Skerries	Ap., Sp., X.
Yell	My., Oc.

47. ENGLAND

Meets at London, in Crown Court Church, on the second Tuesday of January and March and at St. Columba's Pont Street on the second Tuesday of June and October

Clerk: Rev. HECTOR G. ROSS, MA, 48 Copenhagen Road, Gillingham, Kent ME7 4RU [0634] Medway 571539

Charge	Minister	Ord.	Ind.	Address and Tel. No.	Com.	Eld.	W.G.	S.S.	B.C.	C.L. £	As'd £	G'i'n £	Stp. £
Corby—													
§Danesholme and Kingswood	James A. Trevorrow	1971	1987	8 Greenland Walk, Danesholme, Corby, NN18 9DH [0536] Corby 745708	....	....	....	....	....	....	....	....	....
St. Andrew's	John F. Mackie, BD	1979	1983	6 Honiton Gardens, Corby, NN18 8BW [0536] Corby 203175	642	36	50	25	11	26760	3647	1275	8685
St. Ninian's	Vacant	....	....	46 Glyndebourne Gardens, Corby [0536] Great Oakley 741179	532	29	26	36	17	18769	....	....	8646
Guernsey St. Andrew's in the Grange	George L. Lugton, MA, BD	1955	1987	The Manse, Le Villocq, Castel, Guernsey CI [0481] Guernsey 57345	172	12	....	25	6	18285	1294	1294	v
Jersey St. Columba's	Paul S. Kirby, BD	1976	1982	18 Claremont Avenue, St. Saviour, Jersey [0534] Jersey Central 30659	162	16	....	34	....	14750	....	....	....
Liverpool St. Andrew's	Vacant	....	....		85	9	18	....	....	14028	909	909	v
London— Crown Court	Kenneth G. Hughes, TD, MA, BD, PH D	1964	1986	53 Sidmouth Street, London, WC1H 8JB 01-278 5022	419	49	22	11	9	60296	9411	9411	10752
St. Columba's *linked with*	J. H. M'Indoe, MA, BD, STM	1966	1988	St. Columba's, Pont Street, London, SW1 01-584 2321	1500	62	....	40	15	144259	33927	33927	v
Newcastle St. Andrew's	W. Alex Cairns, BD *Associate*	....	....		132	14	13	....	....	12049	992	992	v

§This is an ecumenical parish sponsored by the Baptist Union, the Methodist Church, and the United Reformed Church as well as the Church of Scotland.

Minister	Ord.	App.	Ret.	Charge	Address and Tel. No.
Black, J. M., MA, BD	1963	1969	......	*Chaplain, R.A.F.*	R.A.F. College, Cranwell, Sleaford, NG34 8HB
Bowie, A. Glen, CBE, BA, BSC	1954	......	1984	*(Chaplain, R.A.F.)*	16 Weir Road, Hemingford Grey, Huntingdon, PE18 9EH *[0480] Huntingdon 63269*
Cameron, R. N.	1975	1981	......	*Chaplain, Army*	1 Royal Scots, BFPO 106
Coleman, J. A., BD	1978	1978	......	*Chaplain, R.A.F.*	28 Thorpe Place, Tattershall, Lincoln, LN4 4NU *[0526] 43174*
Craig, Gordon W., MA, BD	1972	1972	......	*Chaplain, R.N.*	*HMS Drake*, Devonport, Plymouth, PL2 2BG
Davidson-Kelly T. A., MA, BD, FSA SCOT	1975	1982	......	*Chaplain, Army*	1 Scots Guards, Hohne, BFPO 30
Davison, Charles F., MA	1947	......	1987	(Guernsey St. Andrew's in the Grange)	Maryfield, Green Lanes, St. Peter Port, Guernsey, C.I. *[0481] Guernsey 27446*
Drummond, J. S., MA	1946	......	1978	(Corby St. Ninian's)	77 Low Road, Hellesdon, Norwich
Duncan, Denis M., BD	1944	......	1986	(Editor, 'The British Weekly')	1 Cranbourne Road, London, N10 *01 883 1831*
Green, James, MA, BD, PGCE, FRAI	1951	1962	......	College of Education	31 Bainbridge Holme Road, Sunderland, Tyne and Wear *091–522 7270*
Harkness, James, OBE, QHC, MA, LB	1951	1961	......	Chaplain General	Ministry of Defence, Chaplains (Army), Bagshot Park, Surrey, GU19 5PL *[0276] Bagshot 71717*
Harvey, D. V. R., BA, MTH, FSA SCOT	1965	1968	......	*Chaplain, R.A.F.*	Command Chaplain, CSFC HQ, R.A.F., Germany, BFPO 40
Hughes, O. Tudor, MBE, BA	1934	......	1976	(Guernsey St. Andrew's in the Grange)	Bear Island House, Charnham Street, Hungerford RG17 0EP *[0488] Hungerford 83390*
Huie, David F., MA, BD, RN	1962	1968	......	*Chaplain, R.N.*	*H.M.S. Nelson*, Portsmouth, Hants, PO1 3HH
Macfarlane, Peter T., LTH	1970	1970	......	*Chaplain, Army*	Senior Chaplain, HQ 24 Infantry Brigade, Catterick, Richmond, DL10 7NP
M'Luskey, J. Fraser, MC, DD	1938	......	1986	(London St. Columba's *with* Newcastle)	14 Buckingham Terrace, Edinburgh, EH14 3AE *031-332 0935*
M'Robb, Keith M., TD, MA	1940	......	1981	(Dalserf)	26 Steele Road, Old Isleworth, Middlesex, TW7 7HN *01-892 5190*
Majcher, Philip L., BD	1982	1982	1987	*Chaplain, Army*	Scots Dragoon Guards, Tidworth, Andover, Hants
Malloch, Robert J., BD	1987	1987	......	*Chaplain, Army*	Roman Barracks, Colchester, Essex
Marnoch, Lindsay R., BA	1985	1987	......	*Chaplain, Army*	2 Scots Guards, Hounslow, London
Mills, Peter W., BD, CPS	1984	1984	......	*Chaplain, R.A.F.*	R.A.F. Locking, Weston-super-Mare, Avon, BS23 7AA
Morrice, William G., MA, BD, STM, PHD	1957	......	1975	St. John's College, Durham	69 Hallgarth Street, Durham, DH1 3AY *091-386 9699*
Munro, A. W.	1978	1978	......	*Chaplain, R.A.F.*	R.A.F. Catterick, Richmond, N. Yorks, DL10 7NP
Riggans, Walter, MA, BD	1982	......	1987	Lecturer	All Nations College, Easney, Ware, Herts, SG12 8LX
Ross, Hector G., MA	1949	......	1988	(Gillingham St. Margaret's)	48 Copenhagen Road, Gillingham, Kent, ME7 4RU *[0634] Medway 571539*
Shaw, Duncan, LTH, CPS	1984	1984	......	*Chaplain, R.A.F.*	R.A.F. Finningley, South Yorks., DN9 3NB
Stewart, Charles E., BSC, BD	1976	1976	......	*Chaplain, R.N.*	*H.M.S. Raleigh*, Torpoint, Cornwall, PL11 2PD
Torrance, Iain R., MA, BD, D PHIL	1982	1985	......	Queen's College, Birmingham	The Queen's College, Edgbaston, Birmingham, B15 2QH *[021 454 8171]*
Walker, James B., MA, BD, D PHIL	1975	......	1987	*Principal Queen's College*	71 Farquhar Road, Edgbaston, Birmingham, B15 2QP
Wallace, Donald S., QHC	1950	......	1980	*(Chaplain, R.A.F.)*	Royal Caledonian Schools, Bushey, Herts, WD2 3TS

ADDRESSES OF ENGLISH CHURCHES

Corby—		Liverpool	London—
St. Andrew's	Occupation Road		Crown Court
St. Ninian's	Beanfield	Newcastle	St. Columba's
Gillingham	Paget Street	The Western Rooms,	
		Anglican Cathedral	Crown Court, W.C.1
		Sandyford Road	Pont Street, S.W.1

48. EUROPE

Clerk: Rev. W. GERAINT EDWARDS, LL.B, BD, J W Brouwersstraat 9, 1071 1M Amsterdam, Holland. 010-31-20 662 22 21

Amsterdam	W. Geraint Edwards, LL.B, BD	1958	1980	J. W. Brouwersstraat 9, 1071 LM Amsterdam, The Netherlands 010-31-20 662 22 21
Brussels	Charles C. M'Neill, OBE, BA	1962	1984	Square du Nations 23, B1050 Brussels, Belgium 010-32-26 72 40 56
Geneva	W. D. R. Cattanach, DD	1951	1984	6 Chemin de Taverney, 1218 Grand Saconnex, Geneva 010-41-22 98 29 09
Gibraltar	D. Stuart Philip, MA	1952	1978	29 Scudhill, Gibraltar 010-350 77040
Lausanne	C. Murray Stewart, MA	1953	1985	Avenue de Rumine 26, 1005 Lausanne, Switzerland 010-41-21 23 98 28
Lisbon	Roy Hill, MA	1962	1988	Rua Tristao Vax Teixeria 120A Do Rosario 2450 Cascaie, Portugal
Malta	Colin A. Westmarland, BD	1971	1975	206 Old Bakery Street, Valetta, Malta 010-35-62 22643
Paris	Bruce Robertson MA, BD	1953	1982	10 Rue Thimonnier, 75009 Paris 010-33-14 878 4794
Rome St. Andrew's	John D. Ross, BA, DIPED	1958	1989	Via xx Settembre 7, 00187, Rome, Italy 010-39-6 475 1627
Rotterdam	J. E. Stewart Low, MA	1957	1988	Schiedamse Vest 121, 3012 BH Rotterdam, The Netherlands 010-412 4779
(Brussels)	A. J. Macleod. MA, BD	1943	1974	82 Cathcart Road, London SW10
(Genoa)	Alexander MacVicar, MBE, MA	1937	1970	c/o Faus, Arcangeli, Via Radi, 3/10 16145 Genoa, Italy
(Rome)	C. I. MacLean, MA	1957	1988	c/o WMU, 121 George Street, Edinburgh, EH2 4YN
(Rotterdam)	W. M. Isherwood, AIB	1973	1983	Avenel North, High Cross Avenue, Melrose, TD6 9SU [089 682] Melrose 3079
World Council Secretariat	David H. Philpot, MA, BD	1956	1981	28 Ch. Francois Lehmann, 1218 Grand Saconnex, Geneva, Switzerland 010-41-22 98 32 70
	James C. G. Greig, MA, BD, STM	1965	1987	Apt. 42, Rue de la Dole, 1203 Geneva 010-41-22 45 35 69
	James M. Brown, MA, BD	1982	......	Neustrasse 15, D4630 Bochum, Germany 010-49-234 133 65

49. JERUSALEM

R. C. M. Morton, BA, BD, (1960) Jerusalem St. Andrew's......1988...... Gordon C. Strachan, MA, BD, PHD (1963) Tiberias......1987

William Gardiner Scott, MA (1939–76). (Jerusalem)

List A—CHAPLAINS TO H.M. FORCES

Name	Ord.	Com.	Br'ch	Pres.	Address	
Black, J. M., MA, BD	1963	1969	R.A.F.	47	R.A.F. College, Cranwell, Sleaford, Lincs NG34 8HB	......
Blakey, Stephen A., BSc, BD	1977	1977	Army	28	B.F.P.O. 45	*1 Black Watch*
Cameron, R. N.	1975	1981	Army	47	Minden, B.F.P.O. 29	*11 Armoured B'de*
Coleman, J. A., BD	1978	1978	R.A.F.	47	R.A.F. Coningsby, Lincoln, LN4 4SY	......
Craig, Gordon T., BD	1988	1988	R.A.F.	14	Marham, King's Lynn PE33 9NP	......
Craig, Gordon W., MA, BD	1972	1972	R.N.	47	Devonport, Plymouth PL2 2BG	*H.M.S. Drake*
Dailly, J. R., BD, DipPS	1979	1979	Army	12	Redford Barracks, Edinburgh EH13 0PP	*1 K.O.S.B.*
Davidson Kelly, T. A., MA, BD, FSA Scot	1975	1982	Army	28	Hohne, B.F.P.O. 30	*1 Scots Guards*
Edwards, Michael S., MA	1982	1982	R.A.F.	16	R.A.F. Swinderby, Lincs.	......
Harkness, James, OBE, QHC, MA, LTh	1961	1961	Army	47	Chaplain General, Ministry of Defence, Chaplains (Army), Bagshot Park, Surrey GU19 5PL	......
Harvey, D. V. R., BA, MTh, FSA Scot	1965	1968	R.A.F.	47	Command Chaplain, C.S.F.C. H.Q., R.A.F., Germany, B.F.P.O. 40	*H.M.S. Nelson*
Huie, David F., MA, BD	1962	1968	R.N.	47	Portsmouth, Hants PO1 3HH	
Hynd, R. Stewart	1966	1966	Army	23	Senior Chaplain, 1 (B.R) Corps, B.F.P.O. 39	......
Jolly, Andrew, J., BD	1983	1984	Army	16	1 DWR, Northern Ireland B.F.P.O. 806	......
Keith, Donald, MA, BD	1971	1984	R.N.	16	Lochinvar Block, H.M. Naval Base, Rosyth KY11 2YA	......
M'Crum, Robert, BD	1982	1986	R.N.	17	R.N. Air Station, Culdrose, Helston, Cornwall TR12 7RH	*H.M.S Seahawk*
Macfarlane, Peter T., BA, LTh	1970	1970	Army	47	Senior Chaplain, H.Q. 24 Infantry Brigade, Catterick, Richmond DL9 3JS	......
Majcher, Philip L., BD	1982	1987	Army	47	Fallingbostel, B.F.P.O. 38	*Scots Dragoons*
Malloch, Robert J., BD	1987	1987	Army	47	St. Aidan's, Catterick, North Yorks	......
Marnoch, Lindsay R., BA	1985	1987	Army	47	Hounslow, London	*2 Scots Guards*

Name	Ord.	Service	Pres.	Address	Station
Mills, Peter W., BD, CPS	1984	R.A.F.	47	R.A.F. Wildenrath, B.F.P.O. 42	......
Munro, A. W., MA, BD	1978	R.A.F.	47	R.A.F. Catterick, Richmond, N. Yorks DL10 7NP	......
Neill, Bruce F., MA, BD, RN	1966	R.N.	24	Rosyth, Fife KY11 2XT	H.M.S. Cochrane
Rae, Scott M., BD, CPS	1976	R.N.	18	Faslane, Helensburgh G84 8HL	H.M.S. Neptune
Robertson, Matthew, LTh	1968	Army	31	St. Andrew's Garrison Church, Aldershot, Hants.	......
Scouler, Michael D., BSc, BD	1988	Army	31	Oakington Barracks, Cambridge CB4 5EJ	1 RHF
Shaw, Duncan, LTh, CPS	1984	R.A.F.	47	R.A.F. Gutersloh, B.F.P.O. 47	......
Shedden, John, BD	1971	R.A.F	35	R.A.F. Kinloss, Forres, IV36 0UH	......
Shields, John M., LTh	1972	Army	33	Glencorse Barracks, Edinburgh EH25 0NP	......
Smith, Angus, MA, LTh	1965	Army	1	Senior Chaplain, Army Headquarters Scotland, Edinburgh	......
Stewart, Charles E., BSc, BD	1976	R.N.	47	Torpoint, Cornwall PL11 2PD	H.M.S. Raleigh
Warwick, Ivan C., MA, BD	1980	Army	37	Munster, B.F.P.O. 17	1 Q.O.H.
Whitton, John P., MA, BD	1977	Army	1	H.Q. Land Forces, Episkopi, Cyprus, B.F.P.O. 53	......

A—Retired List

Name	Ord.	Rtd.	Address	Pres.
Bowie, A. Glen, CBE, BA, BSc, *R.A.F.*	1954	1984	16 Weir Road, Hemingford Grey, Huntingdon PE18 9EH	47
Ingram, J. R., *RAF*	1954	1978	48 Marlee Road, Broughty Ferry DD5 3EX	29
Wallace, Donald S. *R.A.F.*	1950	1980	Royal Caledonian Schools, Bushey, Herts WD2 3TS	47
Wright, W. G. A., MBE, MA, BD, *Army*	1940	1974	20 Lennox Street Lane, Edinburgh EH4 1PZ *031–332 8663*	1

List B—PROFESSORS AND LECTURERS

Name	Ord.	Apt.	Address	Pres.
Alexander, James S., MA, BD, BA, PhD	1966	1973	5 Strathkinness High Road, St. Andrews KY16	26
			[0334] St. Andrews 72680	
Auld, A. Graeme, MA, BD, PhD	1973	1973	3 Denham Green Terrace, Edinburgh EH5 3PG 031-552 2910	1
Cameron, James K., MA, BD, PhD, FR Hist	1953	1957	Priorscroft, 71 Hepburn Gardens, St. Andrews KY16 9LS	26
			[0334] St. Andrews 73996	
Cameron, Peter S., LLB, BD, PhD, LRAM	1984	1987	Schoolhouse, Gavinton, Duns TD11	5
Campbell, Alastair V., BD, ThD	1966	1969	34 Lockharton Avenue, Edinburgh EH14 1AZ 031-443 3250	1
Davidson, Robert, MA, BD, DD	1956	1972	357 Albert Drive, Glasgow G41 5PH 041-427 5793	16
Dupar, Kenneth W., BA, BD, PhD	1965	1984	95 Forest Avenue, Aberdeen AB1 6NT [0224] Aberdeen 319845	31
Fergusson, David A. S., MA, BD, DPhil	1984	1986	3 Caerlaverock Court, Edinburgh EH2 8UE 031-339 1726	31
Forrester, Duncan B., MA, BD, DPhil	1962	1978	25 Kingsburgh Road, Edinburgh EH12 6DZ 031-337 5646	1
Gibson, John C. L., MA, BD, DPhil	1959	1962	Cairnbank, Morton St. South, Edinburgh EH15 2NB 031-669 3635	1
Hall, G. B., BA, BD, PhD	1944	1973	2 Broomfaulds Avenue, St. Andrews KY16 8SJ	26
			[0334] St Andrews 75882	
Hamilton, David S. M., MA, BD, STM	1958	1984	2 Roselea Drive, Milngavie, Glasgow G62 8HQ 031-956 1839	16
Johnstone, William, MA, BD	1963	1963	37 Rubislaw Den South, Aberdeen AB2 6BD [0224] Aberdeen 316022	31
Lyall, David, BSc, BD, STM, PhD	1965	1987	1 Abbotsford Place, St. Andrews KY16 9HQ	26
			[0334] St. Andrews 72435	
M'Donald, J. Ian H., MA, BD, MTh, PhD, FEIS	1958	1980	23 Ravelston House Road, Edinburgh EH4 3LP 031-332 2172	1
M'Gregor, T. Stewart, MA, BD	1957	1987	19 Lonsdale Terrace, Edinburgh EH3 9HL 031-229 5332	1
M'Kane, William, MA, PhD, DLitt, DD, FBA, FRSE	1949	1967	51 Irvine Cresc., St. Andrews KY16 8LG [0334] St. Andrews 73797	26
Mackie, Steven G., MA, BD	1956	1974	South View, 59 Lade Braes, St. Andrews KY16	26
			[0334] St. Andrews 74149	
Main, Alan, TD, MA, BD, STM, PhD	1963	1980	37 Carden Place, Aberdeen AB2 1UN [0224] Aberdeen 641100	31
Martin, James D., MA, BD, PhD	1962	1969	22 Kilrymont Road, St. Andrews KY16 8DE	26
			[0334] St. Andrews 77361	
Millar, David A. R., MA	1956	1970	11 The Square, The University, Glasgow G12 8QG 041-334 8769	16
Newlands, George M., MA, BD, PhD	1970	1986	82 Highburgh Road, Glasgow G12 9EN 041-334 4712	16
O'Neill, John C., BA, BD, PhD	1960	1985	9 Lonsdale, Terrace, Edinburgh EH3 9HN 031-229 6070	1

Name	Address	Ord.	Rtd.	Pres.
Page, Ruth, MA, BD, DPhil	7 Seton Place, Edinburgh EH9 2JT 031-662 4564	1976	1979	1
Ross, Andrew C., MA, BD, STM, PhD	27 Colinton Road, Edinburgh EH10 5DR 031-447 5987	1958	1966	1
Salters, Robert B., MA, BD, PhD	119 South Street, St. Andrews KY16 9UH [0334] St. A. 73198	1966	1971	26
Sefton, Henry R., MA, BD, STM, PhD	25 Albury Place, Aberdeen AB1 2TQ [0224] Aberdeen 572305	1957	1972	31
Shanks, Norman J., MA, BD		1983	1988	16
Shaw, D. W. D., BA, BD, LLB, WS	40 North Street, St. Andrews KY16 9AQ [0334] St. Andrews 77254	1960	1979	26
Torrance, J. B., MA, BD	46 Don Street, Aberdeen AB2 1UU [0224] Aberdeen 481526	1954	1977	31
Walton, Ainslie, MA, MEd, HDipRE	63 High Street, Old Aberdeen, Aberdeen AB2 3EH	1954	1987	31
Wedderburn, A. J. M., MA, BD, PhD	[0224] Aberdeen 485925 5 Clatto Place, St. Andrews KY16 8SD [0334] St. Andrews 74923	1975	1975	26

B—Retired List

Name	Address	Ord.	Rtd.	Pres.
Anderson, Hugh, MA, BD, PhD, DD	5 Comiston Springs Avenue, Edinburgh EH10 6NT 031-447 1401	1951	1985	1
Barbour, R. A. S., MC, BD, STM, DD	Fincastle, Pitlochry PH16 5RJ [0796] Pitlochry 3209	1954	1982	27
Best, Ernest, MA, BD PhD	13 Newmill Gardens, St. Andrews KY16 8RY	1949	1982	26
Black, Matthew, MA, DD, DLitt, FBA	40 Buchanan Gardens, St. Andrews KY16 9JT [0334] St. Andrews 73315	1939	1978	26
Cairns, David, MA, DD	29 Viewfield Gardens, Aberdeen AB1 7XN [0224] Aberdeen 37324	1935	1972	31
Cheyne, Alexander C., MA, BD, BLitt, DLitt	12 Crossland Crescent, Peebles EH45 8LF [0721] Peebles 22288	1958	1986	1
Dickie, Edgar P., MC, BA, MA, DD, LLD	19 Hepburn Gardens, St. Andrews KY16 9DG	1927	1967	26
Fleming, John R., MA, BD, ThD, DD	41 Kilrymont Road, St. Andrews KY16 8DE [0334] St. Andrews 73617	1936	1977	26
Galloway, Allan D., MA, BD, STM, PhD	5 Straid Bheag, Barremman, Clynder, Helensburgh G84 0QX [043 683] Clynder 432 St. Andrews 72093	1948	1982	16
Gray, John, MA, BD, DD	113 Cluny Gardens, Edinburgh EH10 7BL 031-447 4003	1939	1978	1
Gray, John, MA, BD, PhD, DD	Tanlaw Cottage, Hendersyde Park, Kelso TD5 [0757 32] Kelso 2374	1939	1980	31
Honeyman, A. M., BD, BLitt, PhD	c/o Migdale Hospital, Bonar Bridge IV24 3AP	1936	1967	26
Hunter, A. M., MA, BD, PhD, DPhil, DD	32 Gartconnel Road, Bearsden, Glasgow G61 3BP 041-942 3406	1934	1971	31
Macdonald, John, MA, BD, STM, PhD	5 West Chapelton Drive, Bearsden G61 2DB 041-942 4872	1942	1984	—
Macdonald, Murdo Ewen, MA, BD, DD	24 Falkland Street, Glasgow G12 9PR 041-334 2087	1939	1984	16

List B—Retired List—continued

Name	Ord.	Rtd.	Address	Pres.
McEwen, James S., MA, BD, DD	1940	1977	8 Westfield Terrace, Aberdeen AB2 4RU [0224] Aberdeen 645413	31
M'Intyre, John, CVO, MA, BD, DLitt, DD, FRSE	1941	1986	22/4 Minto Street, Edinburgh EH9 1RQ 031–667 1203	1
M'Intyre, J. Ainslie, MA, BD	1963	1985	60 Bonnaughton Road, Bearsden G61 4DB 041–942 5143	16
Moir, Ian A.., MA, BD, PhD	1942	1981	56B Kirkbrae, Liberton, Edinburgh EH16 6HU 031–664 1535	FF
Porteous, Norman W., DD	1929	1968	3 Hermitage Gardens, Edinburgh EH10 6DL 031–447 4632	1
Reid, J. K. S., CBE, TD, MA, DD	1939	1976	1 Camus Park, Edinburgh EH10 6RY 031–445 2932	1
Stewart, James S., DD	1924	1966	St. Rafael's, 6 Blackford Avenue, Edinburgh EH9 2LA 031–667 3601	1
Torrance, Thomas F., MBE, DLitt, DD, DSc, DrTheol, DTheol, DrTeol, FBA, FRSE	1940	1979	37 Braid Farm Road, Edinburgh EH10 6LE 031–447 3050	1
Weir, C. J. Mullo, BD, DPhil, DD	1932	1968	4/17 Gillsland Road, Edinburgh EH10 5BW 031–228 6965	16
Whyte, James A.., MA, LLD	1945	1987	13 Hope Street, St. Andrews KY16 9WJ [0334] St. Andrews 72323	26
Wilson, Robert M'L., MA, BD, PhD, DD	1946	1983	10 Murrayfield Road, St. Andrews KY16 9AB	26
Yule, George, S. S. BA, MA	1949	1985	7 The Chanonry, Aberdeen AB2 1RN [0224] Aberdeen 491941	FF

List C—NON-PAROCHIAL APPOINTMENTS

The following List shows Ministers holding Non-Parochial Appointments wholly or mainly under the control of the Church. In terms of Act ii, 1970 as amended most, but not all, of these are entitled to a seat in Presbytery. It also includes full-time teachers of religious education.

The address given in this list refers in most cases to place of business—the home address may be found by reference to the appropriate Presbytery List.

Name	Ord.	Apt.	Appointment	Address	Pres.
Alexander, Helen J. R., BD	1981	1986	Chaplain, University of Edinburgh	Chaplaincy Centre, Bristo Street, Edinburgh EH8 9AL 031–667 1011	1

Name			Appointment	Address	
Anderson, Robert S.	1986	1987	Field Officer, WM&U	Scottish Churches House, Dunblane FK15 0AJ [0786] *Dunblane 823588*	23
Anderson, W. Crawford, LTh	1972	1980	Chaplain, Heriot-Watt University	51 Queen's Avenue, Edinburgh EH4 2DG *031–343 1277*	1
Andrew, John, MA, BD	1961	1972	Teacher, Religious Education	Cartars Croft, Midmar, Sauchen AB3 7NJ *[033 03] Sauchen 308*	33
Banks, John, BD	1968	1988	Hospital Chaplain	Ailsa Hospital, Ayr	10
Baxendale, Georgina M. (Mrs.), BD	1981	1986	Associate University Chaplain	Chaplaincy Centre, University of Glasgow, Glasgow G12	14
Bell, John L., MA, BD	1978	1988	Iona Community	416 Great Western Road, Glasgow G4 9HZ *041–334 0688*	16
Bisset, Peter T., MA, BD	1952	1974	Warden, St. Ninian's	St. Ninian's Training Centre, Crieff *[0764] Crieff 3766*	28
Blakey, Ronald S., MA, BD, MTh	1962	1981	Secretary, Assembly Council	121 George Street, Edinburgh EH2 4YN *031–225 5722*	1
Brown, R. Graeme, BA, BD	1961	1981	St. Colm's Education Centre and College	23 Inverleith Terrace, Edinburgh EH3 5AX *031–332 2230*	1
Buchan, Fiona M.	1988	1988	National Youth Adviser	121 George Street, Edinburgh EH2 4YN *031–225 3722*	1
Buchan, Isabel C. (Mrs.), BSc, BD	1975	1985	Teacher, Religious Education	Schoolhouse, Baldernock, Balmore G64 4AS	18
Campbell, John, BA, LTh	1973	1986	Area Organiser for Evangelism	3 Herries Road, Glasgow G41 4DE *041–423 3760*	
Campbell, W. M. M., BA, CPS	1970	1986	Hospital Chaplain	Royal Cornhill Hospital, Cornhill Road, Aberdeen, AB9 2ZH *[0224] Aberdeen 632411*	31
Cheyne, Magnus	1963	1986	Community Minister	30 Commercial Road, Lerwick *[0595] Lerwick 3240*	46
Clausen, Claus W., BD	....	1986	Community Minister at Hamilton Trinity	10 Allanton Lea, Hamilton ML3 8ET	17
Cumming, David P. L., MA	1957	1985	Assistant Secretary, Ministry and Mission	121 George Street, Edinburgh EH2 4YN *031–225 5722*	1
Cunningham, Alexander, MA, BD	1953	1980	Clerk, Presbytery of Glasgow	260 Bath Street, Glasgow G2 4JP *041–332 6606*	16

List C—Non-parochial Appointments—*continued*

Name	Ord.	Apt.	Appointment	Address	Pres.
Currie, Robert, MA	1955	1984	Community Minister	61 Dowanside Road, Glasgow G12 9DL 041-554 8667	16
Doyle, Ian B., MA, BD, PhD	1946	1977	Secretary, Ministry and Mission	121 George Street, Edinburgh EH2 4YN 031-225 5722	1
Duncan, James, SDA, NDA	1962	1972	Teacher, Religious Education	14 Largo Road, Lundin Links, Lower Largo KY8	26
Elliot, George, MA, BD, STM	1958	1973	Secretary, Stewardship and Finance	121 George Street, Edinburgh EH2 4YN 031-225 5722	1
Frew, Michael W., BSc, BD	1978	1987	Area Organiser for Evangelism	52 Rose Crescent, Perth PH1 1NT [0738] Perth 27722	28
Gibson, Frank S., BL, BD, STM, DSWA	1963	1972	Secretary, Social Responsibility	121 George Street, Edinburgh EH2 4YN 031-225 5722	1
Goss, Alister, J.	1975	1987	Industrial Chaplain		15
Green, James, MA, BD	1951	1962	Lecturer	Sunderland College of Education	47
Greig, James C. G., MA, BD, STM	1965	1987	World Council of Churches	150 Route de Ferney, 1211 Geneva 20	48
Haley, Derek, BD, DPS	1960	1977	Hospital Chaplain	Gartnavel Royal Hospital, Glasgow 041-334 6241	16
Hamilton, David G., MA, BD	1971	1980	Curriculum Planner, Education	121 George Street, Edinburgh EH2 4YN 031-225 5722	18
Harvey, W. John, BA, BD	1965	1988	Leader, Iona Community	2/1 99 McCulloch Street, Glasgow G41 041-429 3774	16
Hawthorn, Daniel, MA, BD	1965	1973	Lecturer in Religious Education	Aberdeen College of Education AB9 1FA	31
Hogg, Alison, M., BD	1988	1988	Hospital Chaplain's Assistant	Aberdeen City Group Hospitals [0224] Aberdeen 68188	31
Hollins, Roger M., BSc, BD, DipEd	1957	1966	Lecturer in Religious Education	Smithy Cottage, Dunure, Ayr KA7 4LH [029 250] Dunure 273	10

Name			Appointment	Address	
Hudson, Eric V., LTh	1971	1978	Religious Broadcasting	STV, Cowcaddens, Glasgow G2 *041–332 9999*	17
Hunter, G. Lindsay BD, PhD, APhS	1949	1960	Teacher, Religious Education	49 Lynn Drive, Milngavie, Glasgow G62 8HL *041–956 3040*	18
Hunter, William F.	1986	1988	Youth Officer	St. Ninian's Training Centre, Crieff *[0764] Crieff 3766*	28
Hutchison, A. Scott, MA, BD, DD	1957	1986	Hospital Chaplain	Linsue, Drumoak AB3 3AA *[033 08] Drumoak 705*	31
Jenkins, Gordon F. C., MA, BD	1968	1988	Assistant Secretary, Education	121 George Street, Edinburgh EH2 4YN *031–225 5722*	24
Johnson, Emmanuel, BA, BD	1960	1963	Missionary to Ethnic Groups in Glasgow	13 Herriet Street, Glasgow G41 *041–429 0148*	16
Johnston, John, MA, BD	1963	1987	Hospital Chaplain	Crichton Royal Hospital, Dumfries *[0387] Dumfries 55301 Ext. 256*	1
Keddie, David A., MA, BD	1966	1983	Teacher, Religious Education	52 Station Road, Bearsden, Glasgow G61 4AL *041–942 1408*	18
Laidlaw, John J., BD	1964	1973	Adviser in Religious Education	14 Dalhousie Road, Dundee DD5 2SQ *[0382] Dundee 77458*	29
Lamb, John T., BD	1978	1980	Community Minister at St. Ninians	19E Cultenshore Road, Stirling FK7 9GD *[0786] Stirling 62832*	23
Lawson, Kenneth C., MA	1963	1984	National Adult Education Adviser	St. Colm's, 23 Inverleith Terrace, Edinburgh EH3 5NX *031–343 2627*	1
Longmuir, T. Graeme, MA, BEd	1976	1984	School Chaplain	Strathallan School, Forgandenny, Perth PH2 9HP *073–881 2110*	28
M'Donald, Sandy, BA, CMIWSc	1968	1988	Secretary, Ministry and Mission	121 George Street, Edinburgh EH2 4YN *031–225 5722*	2
MacDonald, Peter J.	1986	1986	Youth Adviser	121 George Street, Edinburgh EH2 4YN	1
M'Gillivray, A. Gordon, MA, BD, STM	1951	1973	Clerk, Presbytery of Edinburgh	7 Greenfield Crescent, Balerno, Midlothian EH14 7HD *031–449 4747*	1
M'Gregor, T. Stewart, MA, BD	1957	1970	Hospital Chaplain	Edinburgh Royal Infirmary *031–229 2477*	1

List C—Non-parochial Appointments—continued

Name	Ord.	Apt.	Appointment	Address	Pres.
M'Intyre, Ailsa G., BD, DipCE	1979	1988	School Chaplain	George Heriot's School Edinburgh	1
M'Kay, Johnston R., BA, BD	1968	1987	B.B.C.	B.B.C. Queen Margaret Drive, Glasgow G12	14
Mackenzie, Ian M., MA	1967	1973	Religious Broadcasting Organiser	BBC, Queen Margaret Drive, Glasgow G12 8DG 041–339 8844	18
MacLean, Andrew T., BA, BD	1980	1985	Chaplain at Strathclyde University	Chaplaincy Centre, John Street, Glasgow G1 1JH 041–552 4400 Ext. 2442	16
M'Lean, Margaret G., BD	1978	1984	Community Minister in Annandale and Eskdale	13 High Street, Longtown [0228] Longtown 792068	7
M'Lennan Alasdair J., BD	1979	1987	Area Organiser for Evangelism	Adjola, Urquhart Road, Dingwall [0349] Dingwall 63970	39
M'Phee, Duncan C., MA, BD	1953	1978	Secretary Depute, Ministry and Mission	121 George Street, Edinburgh EH2 4YN 031–225 5722	1
Macpherson, Fergus, MA, PhD	1946	1984	British Council of Churches	2 Eaton Gate, London SW1 W8BL 01–730 9611	12
Manson, Robert L., MA	1956	1986	Hospital Chaplain's Assistant	Edinburgh Royal Infirmary 031–229 2477	1
Marshall, A. Scott	1984	1984	Community Minister at Drylaw, Muirhouse and Old Kirk	30 West Pilton Gardens, Edinburgh EH4 3QW 031–332 431	1
Matthew, Stewart G., MA, BD	1969	1979	Assistant Secretary, Education	121 George Street, Edinburgh EH2 4YN 031–225 5722	1
Melrose, J. H. Loudon, MA, BD, MEd	1955	1966	Lecturer in Religious Education	1 Laverock Avenue, Hamilton ML3 7DD [069 82] Hamilton 427958	17
Millar, David A. R., MA	1956	1982	Chaplain to Glasgow University	11 The Square, The University, Glasgow G12 8QG 041–334 8769	16
Mitchell, Andrew S., MA, DipR Ed	1965	1984	Teacher, Religious Education	105 Sinclair Street, Helensburgh G84 9HY [0463] Helensburgh 6197	18
Moodie, Alastair R., MA, BD	1971	1984	Hospital Chaplain	Crosshouse Hospital, Kilmarnock [0563] Kilmarnock 21133	11

Morrice, William G., MA, BD, STM, PhD	1957	1988	College of Education	St. John's College, Durham	47
Morrison, Mary B. (Mrs.), MA, BD	1978	1986	Area Organiser for Evangelism	2 St. Barnard's Crescent, Edinburgh EH4 1NP *031–332 6117*	1
Morton, Alasdair J., MA, BD, DipEd, FEIS	1960	1977	Secretary, Education	121 George Street, Edinburgh EH2 4YN *031–225 5722*	4
Morton, Andrew R., MA, BD	1956	1982	Depute General Secretary, World Mission and Unity	121 George Street, Edinburgh EH2 4YN *031–225 5722*	1
Morton, Gillian M. (Mrs.), MA, BD, PGCE	1983	1988	Hospital Chaplain	Borders Regional Hospital *[0896] Galashiels 4333 Ext. 1411*	4
Murison, William G.	1951	1971	Assistant Secretary, World Mission and Unity	121 George Street, Edinburgh EH2 4YN *031–225 5722*	1
Neilson, Peter, MA, BD	1975	1986	National Organiser for Evangelism	121 George Street, Edinburgh EH2 4YN *031–225 5722*	1
Ormiston, Hugh C., BSc, BD	1969	1980	Industrial Chaplain	26 Abbot's Road, Grangemouth FK3 8JF *[0324] Grangemouth 473067*	22
Orr, Norman B., BSc, ARCST	1958	1981	Industrial Chaplain	59 Elmbank Street, Glasgow G2 4PQ *041–332 4458*	16
Osborne, Alastair G., MA, BD	1973	1981	Community Minister at Ayr St. Quivox	Northfield Avenue, Ayr KA8 *[0292] Ayr 285037*	10
Pattison, Kenneth J., MA, BD, STM	1967	1984	Hospital Chaplain	Glasgow Royal Infirmary, Glasgow G4 0SF *041–552 3535*	16
Philpot, David H., MA, BD	1956	1981	World Council of Churches	150 Route de Ferney, 1211 Geneva 20	48
Rae, Robert, LTh	1968	1983	Hospital Chaplain	Dundee Acute Hospitals *[0382] Dundee 60111 Ext. 2755*	29
Reid, Alan A. S., MA, BD, STM	1962	1981	Chaplain to Aberdeen University	Chaplaincy Centre, 25 High Street, Old Aberdeen AB2 3EE *[0224] Aberdeen 40241*	…
Robertson, R. Campbell	1967	1979	Community Minister at Glasgow Anderston	Flat 12b, 30 St. Vincent Terrace, Glasgow G3 8UT *041–204 1541*	16
Ross, Donald M., MA	1953	1967	Industrial Chaplaincy Organiser	121 George Street, Edinburgh EH2 4YN *031–225 5722*	1

List C—Non-parochial Appointments—*continued*

Name	Ord.	Apt.	Appointment	Address	Pres.
Ross, Robin A., MA, BD	1977	1988	Assistant Secretary, World Mission and Unity	121 George Street, Edinburgh EH2 4YN *031–225 5722*	1
Schofield Melville, MA	1960	1988	Hospital Chaplain	Edinburgh Northern Hospitals	1
Silcox, John R., BD	1976	1984	School Chaplain	Queen Victoria School, Dunblane FK15 2JA *[0786] Dunblane 824944*	23
Smith, Ralph C. P., MA, STM	1960	1984	Director, Audio-Visual	22 Colinton Road, Edinburgh EH10 5EQ *031–447 3531*	1
Sinclair Colin A. M., BA, BD	1981	1988	Secretary, The Scripture Union	280 St. Vincent Street, Glasgow G2 5RT *041–221 0051*	16
Stein, John, MA, BD	1973	1986	Joint Warden	Carberry Tower, Musselburgh EH21 8PY *031–665 3135*	3
Stein, Margaret E. (Mrs.) DA, BD, DipRE	1984	1986	Joint Warden	Carberry Tower, Musselburgh EH21 8PY *031–665 3135*	3
Swinton, Alan C., MA	1953	1971	Hospital Chaplain	Aberdeen Royal Infirmary *[0224] Aberdeen 681818*	31
Torrance, Iain R., MA, BD, DPhil	1982	1985	Lecturer	The Queen's College, Edgbaston, Birmingham B15 2QH	47
Walker, Ian, BD, DipMS	1973	1984	Tutor at St. Colm's	23 Inverleith Terrace, Edinburgh EH3 5AX *031–332 2230*	1
Walker, James B., MA, BD, DPhil	1975	1987	College Principal	The Queen's College, Edgbaston, Birmingham B15 2QH	47
Weatherhead, J. L., MA, LLB	1960	1985	Secretary, Practice and Procedure	121 George Street, Edinburgh EH2 4YN *031–225 5722*	1
Wigglesworth, Christopher J., MBE, BSc, PhD, BD	1967	1987	General Secretary, World Mission and Unity	121 George Street, Edinburgh EH2 4YN *031–225 5722*	1
Wilkie, James L., MA, BD	1959	1984	Assistant Secretary, World Mission and Unity	121 George Street, Edinburgh EH2 4YN *031–225 5722*	1
Wilson, John M., MA	1964	1979	Adviser, Religious Education	25 Crown Drive, Inverness IV2 3QF *[0463] Inverness 40855*	37
Wylie, W. Andrew, MA	1953	1986	Industrial Chaplain	Rosebank, Sauchen AB3 7PA *[033 03] Sauchen 320*	31

List C—Retired List

Name	Ord.	Rtd.	Appointment	Address	Pres.
Aitken, E. Douglas, MA	1961	1987	(Assistant Organiser, Religious Broadcasting)	73 Scotland Drive, Dunfermline KY12 7TP [0383] *Dunfermline 26590*	24
Balfour, Thomas, MA, BD	1945	1985	(Assistant Secretary, Ministry and Mission)	12 Crosswood Crescent, Balerno EH14 7HS 031–449 3941	1
Barr, David, MA, BD	1938	1984	(Chaplain, Glasgow Royal Infirmary)	17 Victoria Park Gardens South, Glasgow G117BX 041–339 5364	16
Bell, William W. M., MA, BD	1943	1983	(Clerk, Presbytery of Paisley)	178 Titwood Road, Glasgow G41 4DD 041–423 2158	14
Bernard, Neil C., MA	1939	1976	(Africa Secretary, Overseas Council)	12 Lockerby Cottages, Edinburgh EH16 6QU 031–664 6310	1
Candlish, George, MA, BD, BSc	1935	1974	(Home Department)	....	FF
Day, Colin T., MA	1947	1984	(Warden, Carberry Tower)	20 Hadfest Road, Cousland, Dalkeith EH22 031–660 5777	3
Deans, John Bell	1951	1986	(Chaplain at Aberdeen City Hospitals)	6 Annfield House, Broughty Ferry, Dundee DD5 1DZ	31
Doig, Andrew B., DD, BD, STM	1938	1982	(Secretary, National Bible Society)	The Eildons Moulin, Pitlochry PH16 [0790] *Pitlochry 2892*	27
Duncan, Eric M., MA, BD, MLitt	1938	1972	(Teacher, Religious Education)	13B Park Terrace, Stirling FK8 2JT [0786] *Stirling 70219*	FF
Eggo, Harold C. M., TD, MA	1950	1977	(Secretary, Church and Ministry Dept.)	Milholme, East Linton EH40 3DS [062 086] *East Linton 493*	1
Fairweather, Ian C. M., MA, BD	1945	1985	(Jordanhill College of Education)	10 Hillside Road, Cardross G82 5LW [038 984] *Cardross 551*	16
Herron, Andrew, DD, LLD	1934	1981	(Clerk, Presbytery of Glasgow)	36 Darnley Road, Glasgow G41 4NE 041–423 6422	16
Kiltie, Thomas W., MA, BD	1958	1988	(Depute General Secretary, World Mission and Unity)	47 Murrayfield Gardens, Edinburgh EH12 6DH 031–337 5182	1

List C—Retired List—continued

Name	Ord.	Rtd.	Appointment	Address	Pres.
King, Alexander, DD	1924	1966	(Secretary, Overseas Council)	6 Rochester Terrace, Edinburgh EH3 5QE 031–447 3413	FF
Lyon, D. H. S., MA, BD, STM	1952	1986	(General Secretary World Mission and Unity)	30 Mansfield Road, Balerno EH14 7JZ 031–449 5031	1
Macdonald, Donald F. M., CBE, MA, LLB	1948	1985	(Secretary, Board of Practice and Procedure)	29 Auchingramont Road, Hamilton ML3 6JP	17
M'Farlan, Donald M., MA, PhD	1940	1985	(Jordanhill College of Education)	94 Southbrae Drive G13 1TZ 041–959 4370	16
Mackay, Murdoch M., MA	1941	1986	(Hospital Chaplain)	17 Hillview Terrace, Cults, Aberdeen AB1 9HJ [0224] Aberdeen 868082	31
Millar, John H., MA	1946	1986	(Teacher, Religious Education)	70 Napier Road, Glenrothes KY6 1DS [0592] Glenrothes 752927	25
Mowat, John, JP, MA	1934	1975	(Librarian, Christ's College, Aberdeen)	15 Airds Drive, Dumfries DG1 4EW [0387] Dumfries 67463	8
Orrock, Archibald A., BD	1938	1982	(Teacher, Religious Education)	3 Kilbryde Court, Dunblane FK15 9AX [0786] Dunblane 822821	23
Pogue, Victor C., BA, BD	1945	1980	(Education Research Fellow)	120 Buckstone Terrace, Edinburgh EH10 6QR 031–445 1628	24
Pritchard, J. Stanley, MA	1938	1970	(B.B.C. Religious Broadcasting)	3 Queen Margaret Road, Glasgow G20 6DP 041–946 4263	16
Raffan, Stanley J., MA, BD	1951	1987	(Chaplain, Crichton Royal Hospital)	3 Noblehill Place, Dumfries DG1 3HQ [0387] Dumfries 61952	8
Ritchie, L. A., MA, BD	1943	1982	(Chaplain to Glasgow University)	34 Baldric Road, Glasgow G13 3QJ 041–954 9277	16
Smith, Richmond, OBE, MA, BD	1952	1983	(World Alliance of Reformed Churches)	Argnish, Kippford, Dalbeattie, DG5 4LL [055 662] Kippford 624	8
Squires J. Finlay R. MA, BD	1964	1988	(Aberdeen College of Education)	16 Bath Street, Stonehaven AB3 2DH [0569] Stonehaven 62458	32
Stalker, D. M. G., MA, BD	1938	1981	(Lecturer in Biblical Studies)	Dunraven, Balerno, Midlothian EH14 7DN 031–449 3044	FF

Name	Ord.	Apt.		Address		Pres.
Towill, Edwin S., MA, BA, BD, MEd	1934	1976	(Lecturer in Religious Education)	19 Charterhall Road, Edinburgh EH9 3HS	031-667 4184	FF
Walker, Horace, MA, BD, DD	1935	1977	(Secretary, Home Board)	4/3 Belhaven Place EH10 5JN		1
Watt, J. H. Innes, MA, BD	1960	1986	(Lecturer in Religious Education)	70 Lyoncross Avenue, Barrhead G78 2TG	031-447 9666 041-881 5199	14

List D—OVERSEAS APPOINTMENTS

Name	Ord.	Apt.	Field	Location	Indigenous Church	Pres.
Aitken, William M., BA, BD	1949	1987	Zambia	Ndola	......	27
Alston, Colin M., BMus, BD	1975	1987	Americas	Trinidad	......	36
Brice, Dennis G., BSc, BD	1981	1981	Taiwan	Taipei	Presbyterian Church in Taiwan	16
Cattanach, William D. R., DD	1951	1984	Europe	Geneva	......	48
Colvin, Thomas S., BSc	1954	1988	Malawi	Blantyre	Church of Central Africa Presbyterian	...
Craig, Joan H., MTheol	1986	1986	Tanzania	Dar-es-Salaam	Presbyterian Church of East Africa	...
*Dodman, Roy A.	1987	1983	Americas	Jamaica	United Church of Jamaica and Grand Cayman	...
Dougall, Elspeth G. (Miss) MA, DipSS	1987	1987	Kenya	Kikuyu	Presbyterian Church of East Africa	...
Dougall Ian C., MA, BD	1958	1987	Kenya	Kikuyu	Presbyterian Church of East Africa	...
Edwards, W. Geraint, LLB, BD	1958	1980	Europe	Amsterdam	......	48
Elliott, Gavin J., MA, BD	1976	1982	Zambia	Lusaka	......	...
Greig, Alan, BSc, BD	1977	1984	Zambia	Ndola	United Church of Zambia	...
Hill, Roy, MA	1962	1988	Europe	Lisbon		48
Laing, William F., DSc, VRD, MA	1952	1988	Americas	Vin del Mar	......	4

*Not a Minister of the Church of Scotland

List D—Overseas Appointments—*continued*

Name	Ord.	Apt.	Field	Location	Indigenous Church	Pres.
Low, J. E. Stwart, MA	1957	1988	Europe	Rotterdam	....	48
*MacGregor, Margaret S., MA, BD, DipEd	1959	1985	North India	Calcutta	Church of India	..
MacNeill, Charles C., OBE, BA	1962	1984	Europe	Brussels	......	48
Marshall, F. J., BA	1946	1982	Bermuda	Warwick		15
Millar, Margaret R. M. (Miss), DipCE	1977	1974	Zambia	Kitwe	United Church of Zambia	..
Millar, Peter W., MA, BD, ThM	1971	1977	South India	Madras	Church of South India	49
Morton, R. Colin, M., BA, BD	1960	1988	Israel	Jerusalem St. Andrew's	......	..
Nicholson, Thomas S., BD, DPS	1982	1982	Taiwan	Taipei	Presbyterian Church in Taiwan	9
O'Leary, Thomas, BD	1983	1987	Sri Lanka	Colombo St. Andrew's	......	16
Pacitti, Stephen A., MA	1963	1977	Taiwan	Hualien	Presbyterian Church in Taiwan	48
Philip, D. Stuart, MA	1952	1978	Europe	Gibraltar	......	..
Purves, John P. S., BSc, BD	1978	1982	Jamaica	Spaldings	United Church of Jamaica and Grand Cayman	..
Rae, David L., MA, BD	1956	1957	Kolhapur	Pune	Church of North India	16
Robertson, Bruce, MA, BD	1953	1982	Europe	Paris	......	48
Ross, John D., BA	1958	1988	Europe	Rome	......	48
Ross, Kenneth R., BA, BD	1982	1988	Malawi	Zambia	Church of Central Africa Presbyterian	..
Rutherford, Brian C., BSc, BD	1977	1987	Malawi	Blantyre	Church of Central Africa Presbyterian	..
Stewart, C. Murray, MA	1953	1985	Europe	Lausanne	......	48
Strachan, C. Gordon, MA, BD, PhD	1963	1987	Israel	Tiberias	......	49
*Tamas, Bertalan	1978	1978	Europe	Budapest	Reformed Church of Hungary	..
Walker, Donald K., BD	1979	1981	Zambia	Kaluluski	United Church of Zambia	..
Westmarland, Colin A., BD	1971	1975	Europe	Malta	......	48

*Not a Minister of the Church of Scotland

List E—OVERSEAS LOCATIONS

EUROPE

AMSTERDAM

Rev. W. GERAINT EDWARDS, LLB, BD and Mrs. JEAN EDWARDS, Jan Willem Brouwersstraat 9 boven, Amsterdam, Z. *010·31·20 66 22 21.* The English Reformed Church, The Begijnhof (off the Spui). Service each Sunday 10.30 a.m.

BRUSSELS

Rev. CHARLES C. MACNEILL, OBE, BA and Mrs. ANNE MACNEILL, 23 Square des Nations B1050, Brussels, Belgium. *010·32·26 724 056.* St. Andrew's Church, Chaussee de Vleurgat 181 (off av. Louise). Service each Sunday 11 a.m.

BUDAPEST

Rev. BERTALAN TAMAS and Mrs. TAMAS, Scottish Mission, Vorosmarty utca 49/51, Budapest VI, Hungary. *010·36·12 28479.* Service first Sunday of the month 11.15 a.m.

GENEVA

Rev. WILLIAM D. R. CATTANACH, DD and Mrs. LORNA CATTANACH, 6 Ch. de Tavernay, 1218 Grand Saconnex, Geneva. *010·41·22 982 909.* The Calvin Auditoire, Place Taconnerie (beside Cathedral of St. Pierre). Service each Sunday 11 a.m.

GIBRALTAR

Rev. D. STUART PHILIP, MA and Mrs. PADDY PHILIP, 29 Scudhill, Gibraltar. *010·350 77040.* St. Andrew's Church, Governor's Parade. Service each Sunday 10.30 a.m.

LAUSANNE

Rev. C. MURRAY STEWART, MA and Mrs. MARY STEWART, The Scots Kirk, Avenue de Rumine 26, 1005 Lausanne. *010·41·21 239 828.* Service each Sunday 10.30 a.m.; 2nd and 4th 6 p.m.

LISBON

Rev. ROY HILL, MA and Mrs. PAULINE HILL, Rua Tristao Vex Tixeria, 120A Bairro, da Rosario 2750 Cascaie, Portugal. *010 351 2844 128.* St. Andrew's Church, Rua da Arriaga 13–15, Lisbon. Service each Sunday

MALTA

Rev. COLIN A. WESTMARLAND, BD, 210 Old Bakery Street, Valetta, Malta. *010·35·62 22 643.* Service each Sunday 10.30 a.m.

PARIS

Rev. BRUCE ROBERTSON, MA, BD and Mrs. EDITH ROBERTSON, 10 Rue Thimonnier, 75009 Paris. *010·33·14 878 4794.* The Scots Kirk, 17 rue Bayard, (near av. Montaigne, metro Roosevelt). Service each Sunday 10.30 a.m.

ROME

Rev. JOHN D. ROSS, BA, DipEd, and Mrs. VIOLET ROSS, St. Andrew's Church, 7 via XX Settembre, 00187 Rome. *010·39·64 751 627.* Service each Sunday 11 a.m.

List E —Overseas Locations—*continued*

ROTTERDAM

Rev. J. E. STEWAR LOW, MA and Mrs. MHAIRA LOW, The Scots Church, Schiedamse Vest 121. *010 · 4 124 779.* Service each Sunday 10.30 a.m.

AFRICA

GHANA

Miss ALEXE S. P. GRANT, MA (1986) *Teacher*, PO Box 427 Ho, Volta Region, Ghana.

Miss ANN A. REID, BSc, SRD (1988) *Nutritionist*, Agogo Hospital, PO Box 27 Agogo, Ashanti-Agin, Ghana.

ETHIOPIA

Miss BETTY J. VEITCH, RGN, SCM, DN, HV (1981) *Nurse*

KENYA

Presbyterian Church of East Africa

Rev. IAN C. DOUGALL, MA, BD (1984) and Mrs. (Rev.) ELSPETH G. DOUGALL, MA, DipSS, PCEA Pastoral Institute, PO Box 387, Kikuyu, Kenya.

Dr. GEOFFREY C. IRVINE, MB, ChB, DTM & H (1952) and Mrs. DOROTHY IRVINE, PCEA, United Kenya Club, PO Box 42220, Nairobi, Kenya.

Dr. GEOFF LACHLAN, MB, ChB, FRCS and Dr. (Mrs.) MAGGIE LACHLAN, BSc, MB, ChB, MRCP (1982) PCEA Chogoria Hospital, PO Box 35, Chogoria, Kenya.

Dr. C. M. FISCHBACHER, MB, ChB (1986) PCEA Chogoria Hospital, PO Box 35, Chogoria, Kenya.

Mr. J. F. MACLAUGHLAN, BDS (1986) PCEA Chogoria Hospital, PO Box 35, Chogoria, Kenya.

Dr. JOHN A. DORWARD, MB, ChB, MRCP, MRCPG, DRCOG (1986) and Dr. ISHBEL M. DORWARD (Mrs.) MB, ChB, DRCG, CCAP Hospital, PO Box 19, Ekwendeni, Malawi.

Missionary Associates

Mr. J. A. PHILLIPS, MB, ChB, DCH, DObst, RCOG, MCRP and Mrs. PHILLIPS, Kamuzu Central Hospital, PO Box 149, Lilongwe, Malawi.

SOUTH AFRICA

Missionary Associates

Mr. JOHN A. POOL, LRCP, LSE, LRFP&SG, AMICE, and Mrs. HELEN POOL, 28 Grimthorpe Avenue, Lincoln Meads, Pietermaritzburg, 3201, RSA.

TANZANIA

Presbyterian Church of East Africa

Rev. JOAN H. CRAIG, MTheol (1986) St. Columba's Church, PO Box 2510, Dar-es-Salaam, Tanzania.

ZAMBIA

United Church of Zambia

Rev. MARGARET R. M. MILLAR, DipCE (1974), UCZ Deaconess House, PO Box 20429, Kitwe, Zambia.

Rev. DONALD K. WALKER, BD (1981) and Mrs. JUDITH V. WALKER, United Church of Zambia, PO Box 260 279, Kaluluski, Zambia.

Rev. GAVIN J. ELLIOTT, MA, BD (1982) and Mrs. RACHEL ELLIOTT, PO Box 30079, Lusaka, Zambia.

Rev. ALAN GREIG, BSc, BD (1984) and Mrs. RUTH GREIG, BA, ALA, PO Box 20429, Kitwe, Zambia.

Rev. WILLIAM M. AITKEN, BD, DipEd (1987) and Mrs. FAITH M. AITKEN, PO Box 70408, Ndola, Zambia.

Mr. MALCOLM M'NEIL, DipYCS, DipHlthEd (1981) and Mrs. OLWEN C. A. M'NEIL, RGN, SCM, Christian Health Association of Kenya, PO Box 30690, Nairobi, Kenya.

Missionary Associates

Mrs. ELIZABETH M. MUDIE, SRN, SCM, MTD, PO Box 46464, Nairobi, Kenya.

Miss ISOBEL DICK, PO Box 46464, Nairobi, Kenya.

MALAWI

Church of Central Africa Presbyterian

Synod of Blantyre

Rev. BRIAN C. RUTHERFORD, BSc, BD (1987) and Mrs. M. JEAN RUTHERFORD, CCAP, Synod of Blantyre, PO Box 413, Blantyre, Malawi.

Rev. THOMAS S. COLVIN, BSc (1987) and Mrs. PATRICIA S. COLVIN, CCAP, PO Box 413, Blantyre, Malawi.

Rev. KENNETH R. ROSS, BA, BD (1988) and Mrs. HESTER F. ROSS, BSc, LCST, Chancellor College, University of Malawi, PO Box 280, Zomba, Malawi

Mr. A. J. DONALD MARSHALL, ARIBA, ARIAS (1987) and Mrs. ALISON MARSHALL, CCAP, Synod of Blantyre, PO Box 413, Blantyre, Malawi.

Miss BERYL S. MALLEY (1982), *Secretary*, Upper Flat, 2 Forrester Road, Edinburgh EH12 8AB (on leave prior to retirement).

Synod of Livingstonia

Dr. JOHN K. KNOWLES, MB, ChB (1978; also in Ethiopia 1976) and Mrs. HEATHER KNOWLES, CCAP Hospital, PO Box 19, Ekwendeni, Malawi.

Miss M. ANNE DAWSON, BSc, *Headmistress* (1976), PO Box 44, Embangweni, Malawi.

Miss ELIZABETH B. MANTELL, RGN, SCM (1982), *Nurse*, CCAP Hospital, PO Box 19, Ekwendeni, Malawi.

Miss HELEN M. SCOTT, BSc (1986), *Teacher*, Njase Secondary School, PO Box 630181, Choma, Zambia

Miss FIONA A. BURNETT, BSc (1988) PO Box 8200, Chisanba, Zambia.

THE CARRIBEAN

BAHAMAS

Vacant. St. Andrew's Manse, PO Box N1099, Nassau.

BERMUDA

Rev. F. J. MARSHALL, BA (1982) and Mrs. MARSHALL, The Manse, Paget West, PO Box PG88, Paget 6, Bermuda.

JAMAICA

United Church of Jamaica and Grand Cayman

Rev. JOHN P. S. PURVES, BSc, BD (1983) and Mrs. PATRICIA PURVES, Spaldings United Church, Mount Olivet Manse, PO Box 73, Spaldings, Jamaica.

Rev. ROY A. DODMAN and Mrs. JANE DODMAN, (1983), Mel Nathan Institute, 11 Burnbank Avenue, Havendale, Kingston 19, Jamaica.

Miss MARGARET FOWLER, DipComEd, St. Andrew's Scots Kirk, 58 Duke Street, Kingston, Jamaica.

TRINIDAD

Rev. COLIN M. ALSTON, BMus, BD (1987) and Mrs. CAROL-ANNE ALSTON, 50 Frederick Street, Port of Spain, Trinidad, WI.

List E—Overseas Locations—*continued*

LATIN AMERICA

CHILE

Rev. WILLIAM F. LAING, DSC, VRD, MA (1988) and Mrs. SHEILA LAING, Casilla 40, Vina del Mar, Valparaiso, Chile.

ASIA

TAIWAN

Presbyterian Church in Taiwan

Rev. STEPHEN A. PACITTI, MA (1977) and Mrs. SYLVIA PACITTI, Min Teh 1st Street 207–3, Meilun, Hualien 97046, Taiwan, ROC.

Rev. DENNIS G. BRICE, BSc, BD (1981) and Mrs. CLAUDIA D. BRICE, 4fl # 11, Hsiang, Yun Street, Taipei 10511, Taiwan, ROC.

Rev. THOMAS S. NICHOLSON, BD, DPS and Mrs. CATHERINE J. NICHOLSON, BD, 21 Hsiang Yun Jei, 2nd Floor, Taipei 105, Taiwan, ROC.

PAKISTAN

The Church of Pakistan

Mr. IAN A. MURRAY, BSc (1962) and Mrs. ISABEL MURRAY, *Teachers*, Murree Christian School, Jhika Gali, Murree Hills, Pakistan.

Mr. JOHN K. P. FERGUSON *Instructor*, (1977) and Mrs. MARGARET FERGUSON, , Christian Vocational Training Centre, PO Box 165, Baghdada, Mardan, NWFP, Pakistan.

Miss HELEN F. M°MILLAN, BSc, DipRE (1981), *Tutor*, United Bible Translation Centre, PO Box 14, Gujranwala, Pakistan.

Miss CATHERINE W. NICOL, MA (1961), *Religious Educationalist*, St. Columba Christian Girls' RTC, Barah Patthar, Sialkot 2, Pakistan.

Rev. DAVID L. RAE, MA, BD (1957), *Minister*, St. Paul's Church, Pune, and Mrs. MARGARET RAE, 1 General Bhagat Marg, Pune 411 001, Maharashtra, India.

SOUTH INDIA

Church of South India

Rev. PETER W. MILLAR, MA, BD, ThM (1977) and Mrs. DOROTHY MILLAR, *Microbiologist*, St. Mary's Parsonage, Cathedral Compound, Cathedral Road, Madras 600086, India.

Mrs. LYNDA J. SAMUEL, MA, DEP, LRAM, ABPsS (1980), *Director of Spiritual Renewal*, and Mr. R. SAMUEL, 49 Pulla Avenue, Shenoy Nagar, Madras 600030, South India

SRI LANKA

Rev. THOMAS O'LEARY, BD (1987) and Mrs. CAROLINE O'LEARY, St. Andrew's Church, 73 Kollupitiya Road, Colombo 3.

CHINA

Miss HEATHER GODDARD (1988), *Amity Foundation Teacher*, Zhejiang Teachers University, Jinhua, Zhejiang, ROC.

Dr. MARGARET E. RIDDOCH, MB, ChB, DA, FFARCS, Third Affiliated Hospital, China Medical University, Shenyang, ROC.

MIDDLE EAST AND NORTH AFRICA

ISRAEL

NOTE: Church Services are held in St. Andrew's Scots Memorial Church, Jerusalem each Sunday at 10 a.m., and at Sea of Galilee Church, Tiberias each Saturday and Sunday at 8 p.m.

Rev. R. COLIN M. MORTON, BA, BD and Mrs. CAROL MORTON (1988), St. Andrew's Scots Memorial Church, PO Box 14216, Jerusalem, Israel.

Mr. ALEXANDER M. SNEDDON (1986), *Instructor*, and Mrs. S. MARIE SNEDDON, *Teacher*, Christian Vocational Training Centre, PO Box 165, Baghdada, Mardan, NWFP, Pakistan.

Miss ELINOR S. NIVEN, MA (1988) *Librarian*, Kinnaird College for Women, 93 Jail Road, Lahore, Pakistan.

Mr. JOHN N. YOUNG, MA, PhD (1988) and Mrs. C. S. LINDSAY YOUNG, MA, PhD.

NEPAL

United Mission to Nepal

Miss CHRISTINE STONE, BA (1982), *Teacher*, PO Box 126, Kathmandu, Nepal.

Mr. CLIVE H. IRVINE, BSc (1984), *Engineer*, and Mrs. PAMELA IRVINE, PO Box 126, Kathmandu, Nepal.

Miss CATHERINE J. DICK, BA (1985), *Graphic Artist*, United Mission to Nepal, PO Box 126, Kathmandu, Nepal.

NORTH INDIA

Church of North India

Rev. MARGARET S. MACGREGOR, MA, BD, DipEd (1959), *Tutor*, Bishop's College, 224 Achanya Jagadish Chandra Bose Road, Calcutta 700 017, India.

Miss MARION N. CONACHER, RGN, SCM (1974), *Nurse*, Tilda, PO Neora, Dist. Raipur, MP 493 114, India.

Miss A. DOROTHY WALLACE, MA (1953), *Headmistress*, Nepali Girls' High School, Darjeeling 734 101, West Bengal, India.

Miss AGNES W. F. (NANCY) M'CUTCHEON, MA (1957), *Headmistress*, Mahakalguri, PO Saontalpur, Dist. Jalpaiguri, West Bengal 736 206, India.

Miss C. D. C. (SHEENA) M'CALLUM (1960), *Hostel Superintendent*, Lal Kothi, KD Pradhan Road, Kalimpong 734 301, West Bengal, India.

Miss ISHBEL M. RITCHIE, MBE, MA, MEd (1966; also in Western India 1955–65) *Headmistress*, Paljor Namgyal Girls' High School, Gangtok, Sikkim 737 101, India.

Miss DOROTHY M. CLEPHANE, BSc (1985), *Head Teacher*, Tabeetha School, PO Box 8170, Jaffa, Israel.

Miss MARY S. RITCHIE, DipCE (1985), *Teacher*, Tabeetha School, PO Box 8170, Jaffa, Israel.

Miss PAMELA J. RATTRAY, (1986), *Teacher*, Tabeetha School, PO Box 8170, Jaffa, Israel.

Mr. WALTER T. DUNLOP, ARICS (1986), *Inspector of Property* and Mrs. JENNIFER DUNLOP (1986), Tabeetha School, PO Box 8170, Jaffa, Israel.

Rev. C. GORDON STRACHAN, MA, BD, PhD (1987), *Minister/Director* and Mrs. ELSPETH STRACHAN, MA, *Administrator*, Sea of Galilee Centre, PO Box 104, Tiberias, Israel.

Miss CAROL DICKSON, DipDomSc (1987), *Domestic Bursar*, St. Andrew's Hospice, PO Box 14216, Jerusalem, Israel.

Miss EVELYN M. SIMPSON (1987), *Assistant Bursar*, St. Andrew's Hospice, PO Box 14216, Jerusalem, Israel.

Miss ELIZABETH STIRLING, DipCE (1988), *Teacher*, Tabeetha School, PO Box 8170, Jaffa, Israel.

Miss HEATHER E. HENDERSON (1988), *Cook-Caterer*, Sea of Galilee Centre, PO Box 104, Tiberias, Israel.

Miss ELIZABETH M. MALANEY, DipCE (1988), *Teacher*, Tabeetha School, PO Box 8170, Jaffa, Israel.

Miss HILARY J. A. STEWART (1988), *Assistant Administrator*, Sea of Galilee Centre, PO Box 104, Tiberias, Israel.

EGYPT

Mrs. W. MARY PAUL (1988) *Teacher*, 4 Hussen Fahmy Street, Nasr City, Cario, Egypt.

Mr. EDWARD B. THOMAS, MA (1988) *Teacher*, St. Mark's Centre, Cairo, Egypt.

SUDAN

Miss LEXA A. BOYLE, RGN, SCM, *Nurse* (1981), Government Hospital, Karima, Northern Province, Sudan.

List F—UNATTACHED MINISTERS

This List contains the names of Ministers who retain their status as Ministers of the Church of Scotland but are not wholly or mainly employed in the service of the Church. It does not contain the names of Ministers of the Church of Scotland who hold posts in other Churches. The brackets contain the name of the last charge held and the date of demitting it.

*Is believed by the Editor to hold a current "ministerial certificate" in terms of Act II 1987.

	Ord.
*Alexander, A. D., BD (Aberdeen University 1953), 60 Grove Road, West Ferry DD5 1JN	1943
Allan, William G. (Kirkcudbright St. Cuthbert's 1978)	1964
Anderson, D. W., BL (South Africa 1966), 21 Maurice Avenue, Caterham, Surrey	1959
*Arbuckle, William, MA (Glasgow Maxwell Mearns Castle 1981)	1946
Armistead, Chester D., BA, MLitt, BD (Udny and Pitmedden 1985)	1978
Baird, W. W. H. (Patna with Waterside and Lethanhill, 1979)	1972
*Barr, John, BSc, PhD, BD (Kilmacolm Old 1979), 91 Fotheringay Road, Glasgow G41 4LH	1958
Bayne, Angus L., LTh (Crossford with Kirkfieldbank 1975), 25 Victoria Road, Plumstead, Cape Town, RSA	1969
Beedie, David, MA, BD, MCIT (Forgue Inverkeithny 1981) 6 Windsor Place, Magdalen Yard Road, Dundee DD2 1BC	1962
Berrill, Peter A. D. (Glenrothes Christ's Kirk on the Green 1987)	1983
*Bertram, Thomas A. (Findochty with Portknockie 1973), 56 Avondale Avenue, East Kilbride	1972
*Birkbeck, John, MC (Aberdeen John Knox Gerrard Street 1969), 34 Airyhall Drive, Aberdeen AB1 7QB [0224]	1939
*Bjarnason, Sven (Cowdenbeath Cairns 1987), 14 Edward Street, Dunfermline KY12 0JW [0383] Dunfermline 724625	1975

	Ord.
Carnew, Leslie, BA, BD (Arrochar 1986)	1983
*Carse, George, MA, BL (Liberton Northfield 1959), 121 Liberton Brae, Edinburgh EH16 6LD 031-664 2070	1944
Chen, Gerald E. (Missionary West Indies)	1974
Chilton, R. Michael L., BD, (Corgarff and Strathdon with Glenbuchat Towie 1986)	1972
Chisholm, Henry N., DMin, Palo Duro Union Presbytery, 4820 19th Street, Lubbock, Texas 79416 (Freeport 1973)	1955
*Clarke, John B., FSAScot (Keig with Tough 1972), Knockespock, Clatt AB5 4PJ	1949
Clarke, Roger, MBE, BSc, BD (Industrial Chaplain 1984)	1966
Conlan, Brian, BSc, BD (Glenelg with Glenshiel with Kintail Associate 1980)	1971
Cook, Robert, MA, BD (Girvan South 1987)	1980
Cowan, David (Corby St. Ninian's 1988)	1971
*Cowie, John L., MA (Edinburgh Newcraighall 1976), Flat 1, 13 Glengyle Terrace, Edinburgh EH3 9LN 031-229 3212	1950
Currie, Gordon C. M. (Linlithgow St. Michael's Assistant), 43 Deanburn Park, Linlithgow [0506] Linlithgow 842722	1975
Currie, James, BSc, BD (Laggan 1974)	1960
Curtis, Arthur, H. (Prof.) Birmingham	1938
Dale, John, MA, BD (Glengarry 1967), Assistant Secretary EIS	1964
Dallison, Anthony R., BD (Livingston Old 1978), Canada	1969

Black, William B., MA, BD (Durness *with* Kinlochbervie 1981), c/o OMF, 25 Albany Drive, Glasgow G14 9JP. 1972

Blair, Lyon G., MA (Edinburgh Liberton Northfield 1975), 2 Cottage, Thirlestane, Lauder 1965

*Blount, A. Sheila BA, BD (Mrs.) (Glasgow Springburn *Associate* 1981), 34 Kenilworth Road, Bridge of Allan, Stirling FK9 4EH [0786] *B. of A.* 832118 1978

*Bowman, Norman M., MA, BD (Edinburgh St. Mary's 1964), 2 Bute Terrace, Saltcoats KA21 5BA [0294] *Saltcoats 63453* 1940

*Boyd, Kenneth M., MA, BD, PhD (International Chaplain, Edinburgh Christian Council for Overseas Students), 4A Bruntsfield Crescent, Edinburgh EH10 5HD *031-447 4144* 1971

*Bremner, William I., MA (Fauldhouse Crofthead 1949), 14 Warriston Grove, Edinburgh EH3 5NH *031-552 1351* 1937

*Bristow, W. H. G., BEd, DipRE, DipSpecEd (Chaplain, Army 1970), Lailt, Lepenstrath, Southend, Campbeltown, Argyll PA28 [058 683] *Southend 667* 1951

*Brown, Peter, MA (Kyles 1987), 24 Inchmickery Avenue, Dalgety Bay, Dunfermline KY11 5NF [0383] *Dalgety Bay 822456* 1953

Bruce, Graeme M., MA, STM (Falkirk Erskine 1972) 1962

*Buchan, Alexander, MA, BD (Kennoway 1985), Schoolhouse, Baldernock, Balmore G64 4AS *Balmore 20649* 1975

*Buchanan-Smith, Robin D., BA, ThM (Chaplain to St. Andrews University 1973), Eriska House, Ledaig, Connel, Argyll 1962

Burkinshaw, Eric, LTh (Kirtle-Eaglesfield *with* Middlebie *with* Waterbeck 1986) 1970

Cairns, Hugh C., MA, BD (Kirkcaldy Victoria Road 1966), Australia 1963

Campbell, Iain T., CA, LTh (Dunrossness 1969), 67 Warrender Park Road, Edinburgh DH9 1ES 1966

*Campbell, J. A. (*Auxiliary* Perth 1988), Kinnon Park House, Tibbermore, Perth PH1 1984

Campbell, W. C. D. (Belize 1955) 1941

*Davidson, John F., BSc (Montrose St. Andrew's 1979), 40 Craighill Gardens, Carnoustie DD7 6HX [0241] *Carnoustie 55412* 1970

Davies, C. P., MA (Gartcosh 1953), 2 Princes Gardens, Glasgow G12 9HP 1947

Dean, J. M'Bride, BD (Hamilton Gilmour Memorial and Whitehill 1970), Scarborough High School 1959

*Dickson, A. Stuart (Glasgow Calton New *with* St. Andrew's *Associate* 1988) 1953

*Doig, Archibald F. (Bargeddie 1975), 2A Barnton Park Place, Edinburgh EH4 6ET *031-336 7377* 1964

*Donald, Ronald M., LTh, BA (Dundee Menzieshill, 1977), 12 Eassie Terrace, Dundee DD2 1EJ 1969

Douglas, J. D., MA, BD, STM, PhD (Rothesay St. John's 1958), 2 Doocot Road, St. Andrews KY16 [0334] *St. Andrews 74876* 1957

Drummond, Norman W., MA, BD (Army Chaplain 1982), Loretto School, Musselburgh 1976

Dungavel, William, LTh (Dunnet with Olrig 1988), 25 Traill Street, Castletown KW14 1970

*Emslie, Calthorpe, MA, DipEd (Calderbank 1964), Craigside, Springwood Road, Peebles EH45 9ES [0721] *Peebles 20303* 1958

Falconer, Alan D., MA, BD (*Assistant* Aberdeen 1974), Bea House, 20 Pembroke Park, Dublin 4 *Dublin 684960* 1972

Ferguson, Ron (Iona Community 1988) 1972

*Ferguson, Sinclair B., MA, BD (Unst 1976), 27 Vancouver Road, Glasgow G14 9HR 1972

Findlay, Ian H. D. (Yemen 1974) 1967

*Finlayson, James Y., MA, BD, DipREd (Shotts Erskine 1963), 282 Tantallon Road, Glasgow G41 3JJ 1940

Fisher, Kenneth H., (Douglas *Associate* 1980) 1969

*Fleming, Thomas G. (Slamannan 1982), 5 Glenbervie Drive, North Broomage, Larbert FK5 4NP [0324] *Larbert 552004* 1961

Flockhart, D. Ross, BA, BD (Carberry Tower, Warden, 1966), Longwood, Humbie EH36 1956

List F—Unattached Ministers—continued

	Ord.
*Forbes, John (Glasgow Priesthill Assoc. 1988), 56 Muir Drive, Irvine KA26	1986
Forshaw, Graham M., LL.B, BD (Glasgow Calton *Assistant*, 1977), 5 Glenburnie Place, Glasgow G34 9AN	1973
*Fowler, Richard C. A., BSc, MSc, BD (Gask *with* Methven 1985), Shetland	1978
Fox, George H. (Coalsnaughton 1977), Braehead House Christian Healing Centre, Crossford, Carluke [055 586] Crossford 716	1959
Francis, James M. M., MA, BD, STM, PhD (Coldingham *with* St. Abb's 1975), 75 Hillcrest, Middle Herrington, Sunderland SR3 3NN	1972
Fraser, Ian M., MA, BD, PhD (Scottish Churches' Council), Ferndale, Gargunnock FK8 3BW	1946
*Frew, J. M., MA, BD (Glasgow Dennistoun 1953), Avalon, Bradford Road, Bath	1946
Fyfe, Walter G., MA, BD, STM (Glasgow Hall Memorial 1957), 39 Melville Street, Glasgow G41 2LJ	1955
*Galloway, Kathryn J. (Mrs.) BD, (Iona Abbey, Joint Warden 1988)	1977
Gerrard, D. H. (Buckie West 1961), RAAF, Williamtown, NSW, Australia	1942
Gibson, Ernest H. (*Assistant* Bathgate High 1979)	1978
Gibson, T., DipEd, BD (Jaffa 1964)	1960
Gisbey, John E., MA, BD (Paisley St. George's 1970)	1964
Goodheir, Albert, DLitt. (North Knapdale Tayvallich 1970)	1953
Gordon, Alasdair B., MA, LLB (Aberdeen Summerhill 1980), 2c Ashvale Court, Aberdeen AB1 6FA [0224] Aberdeen 571633	1970
Gordon, A. Isabella, BD (Manchuria 1949), 52/12 Spylaw Bank Road, Edinburgh EH13 0JG	1936
*Graham, David J., BA (Milngavie St. Paul's *Assistant* 1984)	1982
Graham, George M., MA (Paisley St. Luke's 1983)	1965
*Grainger, Harvey L., LTh (Eassie and Nevay *with* Newtyle 1981), 117 Hamilton Place, Aberdeen, AB2 4BD [0224] Aberdeen 641563	1975
Johnstone, Donald B., MA, BD (Dundee Baxter Park 1978), 22 Glenhove Road, North Carbrain, Cumbernauld	1969
Jones, Arthur J., BA (Aberdeen St. Clement's 1985)	1964
Kelly, Alistair F., BL (Edinburgh St. Morningside 1970), 22 Irvine Crescent, St. Andrews KY16 [0334] St. Andrews 72926	1961
*Kennedy, John H., MB, ChB (Glasgow St. Andrew's 1969), East Belmont Orchard, Wishaw ML2 [069 83] *Wishaw* 76084	1964
Kenny, W. M. (Fauldhouse 1973), The Steading, Lochgreen Farm, Lochgreen Road, High Bonnybridge	1960
King, A. Campbell, MA, BD, PhD (Luss 1965), Beaumont Hall, Leicester	1952
Kirk, Henry L., BA, BD, MTh (Colmonell 1980)	1978
*Lamont, Stewart J., BSc, BD (BBC 1980), 3 Doune Quadrant, Glasgow G20 6DN 041-946 3629	1972
Lapsley, R. A. N., MA (Buenos Aires 1938)	1933
Law, Iain C., BD (Urray and Kilchrist 1988)	1983
League, Robert A., BA, BD (*Edinburgh Assistant*)	1975
Lees, Frederick C., BD (Tulliallan and Kincardine 1976)	1974
*Leishman, R. Murray, MA (Hospital Chaplain 1987), 508 Lanark Road, Edinburgh EH14 5DH 031-441 2216	1957
*Liddiard, F. G. B., MA (Brechin Gardner Memorial 1971), 34 Trinity Fields Crescent, Brechin DD9 6AG [035 62] *Brechin* 2966	1957
Lind, Thomas D. (Ballantrae 1986), 3/10 Allanfield, Brunswick Park, Edinburgh EH7 031-558 1966	1965
Lister, Douglas, MA, BD (Largo and Newburn 1986), Gowanbank, Port Elphinstone, Inverurie AB5 9NN	1945
Livingstone, David, MA, BD (Greenock St. Andrew's 1963), 12 Kingussie Drive, Glasgow G44 4HY	1961
Logan, Angus, MA (Coldstream 1957), 12 Henry Street, Langholm DG13 [0541] *Langholm* 80839	1935
*Luke, Iain C., BD (*Assistant* at Edinburgh Greenside 1978), 4 Lovedale Crescent, Balerno EH14 7DP 031-449 3726	1977

1968 *Gravatt, John E., BA, MDiv (Community Minister at Paisley 1988) 15C Moorburn Place, Linwood PA3

1985 Greaves, Andrew T., BD (School Chaplain 1987)

1956 Green, George H., MA, BD (Waterside and Lethanhill 1966)
1962 *Groom, Colin J., MA (Cardenden St. Fothad's 1982), 28 Woodend Road, Cardenden KY5 0NE [0592] Cardenden 720432

1937 Guthrie, J. R., MA, BD, STM (Montrose St. George's and Trinity 1946)

1950 *Harries, David A. (Kilmodan and Colintraive 1981), Superintendent Chaplain, British Sailors' Society, PO Box 11, Ilford, Essex IG2 6NG

1974 *Hartshorn, Bryce J., (Assistant Aberdeen North of St. Andrew 1976), 52 Glasgow Road, Kirkintilloch, Glasgow G66 1BH

1974 *Haslett, Howard J., BA, BD (Assistant Edinburgh St. Giles 1973), No. 2, Edinburgh Academy, Arboretum Road, Edinburgh EH3 5PL 031-552 5737

1987 Hay, Jared W., BD, MTh, DipMin (Edinburgh Cluny Assistant 1988)

1958 Hay, Thomas A., MA, BD, STM (Dundee St. John's 1968), East Byre Cottage, Balmerino, Newport-on-Tay, Fife DD6 8SB [038 236] Gauldry 345

1953 Hearfield, B. A. (Gorebridge Stobhill 1960)
1976 Heggie, Thomas P., BSc, BD (Nairn Old 1981)
1930 Hendry, G. S., DD (Bridge of Allan Holy Trinity 1949) (Professor of Systematic Theology, Princeton, USA)

1957 Higgins, George K., MA (Oban St. Columba's Argyll Square 1977)

1964 Howie, William, MA, BD, STM (Assistant Aberdeen Northfield) 26 Morgan Road, Aberdeen AB2 5JY [0224] Aberdeen 43669

1948 *Hutton, William James, MA (Glasgow Trinity Duke Street 1968), 39 Titwood Road, Glasgow G41 2DD 041-632 1619

1963 *Ireland, Andrew, BA, BTh, DipRD (Edinburgh St. Nicholas' Sighthill 1975), 19 Glamis Gardens, Dalgety Bay, Dunfermline KY11 [0383] Dalgety Bay 82687

1946 *MacArthur, Alexander, MA (Penilee St. Andrew 1950) Luath, St. Barchan's Road, Kilbarchan PA6 2AR [050 57] Kilbarchan 2598

1970 M'Callum, Gavin, LTh (Aberdour with Tyrie 1974), High Fulwood Farm, Stewarton KA3 5JZ [056 04] Dunlop 296

1936 MacCalman, Alastair D., MA (Busby West 1974)
1965 M'Donald, Donald N. MA (Glasgow St. Columba 1987)
1959 *M'Donald, William G., MA, BD (Falkirk Graham Street with Grahamston 1975), 4 Springbank Crescent, Dunblane FK15 9AP [0786] Dunblane 823531

1954 M'Garva, R., MA, BD (Clydebank Linnvale)
1945 *M'Gregor, D. A. R., MA (Edinburgh), 14 Calside Avenue, Paisley PA2 6TD 041-889 8178

1973 M'Haffie, Fraser G., BSc, BD, CA (Assistant Edinburgh Carrick Knowe 1974), c/o 2030 Glendale Avenue, Philadelphia, Pa. USA

1947 M'Hardy, W. D., DPhil, Professor Emeritus of Hebrew, University of Oxford, 2 Ogilvie Park, Cullen, Banffshire

1939 *M'Hutchison, David, MA, DipEd, DipRE, (Hospital Chaplain 1972), 15A The Row, Lauder TD2 6TQ [057 82] Lauder 410

1986 Macintyre, Walter M., BSc, PhD (North Ronaldshay with Sanday 1987), University of Massachusets

1982 M'Lachlan, Fergus C. (Dunbarney with Forgandenny 1988)
1925 M'Lean, Neil A., MA (Falkirk Laurieston St. Columba 1944)
1963 MacLean, W. D., BD (Dailly 1965), c/o Renwick, 16 Hermitage Gardens, Edinburgh

1952 Macleod, J., MA (Kilfinichen and Kilvickeon 1964)
1986 MacLeod, Roderick N. (Assistant at Skene 1987)
1937 MacNeill, Duncan M., MA (Glendevon with Muckhart 1966)
1983 M'Millan, Stewart, BD (Whalsay and Skerries 1988), Manse of Dunrossness, Sandwick, Shetland ZE2 9HW [095 05] Sandwick 244

1963 *MacPherson, Gordon C., BD, ThM (Assistant University Chaplain 1965), 66 Langside Drive, Glasgow G43 2ST
1941 MacQueen, Alex, MA (Stair 1945), 15 Lennel Avenue, Edinburgh EH12 6DW 031-337 7346

List F—Unattached Ministers—*continued*

Ord.

MacRae, Gordon, BA (Ayr St. Quivox 1987) — 1985

M'Rae, John, LLB, BD, (Killin and Ardeonaig 1982), Red Lodge, Kilmory, Lochgilphead, Argyll PA31 8RR — 1977

M'Roberts, T. Douglas, BD (Kirkcaldy Pathhead 1978), Tangmere, Crescent Street, Halkirk, Caithness *Halkirk 513* — 1976

M'Roberts, W. (Glasgow Ruchill 1967) — 1952

*Magee, Maxwell, MA, BA (University Chaplain 1975), 18 Collingham Gardens, London SW5 0HS — 1949

*Main, Arthur W. A., BD (Kirkintilloch St. David's Memorial 1970), 10 Waterside Road, Kirkintilloch G66 3HA — 1954

Mair, John, BSc (Crimond *with* St. Fergus 1972), 8 Glenan Gardens, Helensburgh G84 8XT *[0436] Helensburgh 71744* — 1965

Makin, G. H. (Saughtree 1960), Rubislaw Park House, Aberdeen AB1 8DA — 1925

*Malloch, J. S., MBE, BL, MA, BD (Aberdeen College of Education 1965), 71 Cromwell Road, Aberdeen AB1 6UE *[0224] Aberdeen 34870* — 1938

*Marr, Alastair L., MA, BD, DipEd (Chaplain to University of Stirling 1972), 14 Rutherford Folds, Inverurie AB5 9JH *[0467] Inverurie 2375* — 1963

Martin, C. Hugh R., MA, BD, DipEd (Egypt 1988) — 1958

Martin, George M., BA, BD (Chaplain, Kamazu Academy, Malawi 1988) — 1987

Martin, James M., MA, BD (Glasgow Croftfoot 1985), 31 Aytoun Road, Glasgow G41 *041-423 6010* — 1974

Masson, John D., MA, BD, PhD (Carlisle *with* Longtown 1987) — 1984

Matheson, William, MA (Tobermory 1952), Lecturer in Celtic, University of Edinburgh, 7 Montpelier Park, Edinburgh EH10 4LU *031-229 2921* — 1943

Old, Allan M., MA (Uddingston Trinity 1970), 30 Woodfield Avenue, Colinton, Edinburgh EH13 0HX *031-441 7326* — 1946

Ord, James K. (Cumbernauld Condorrat 1968), 1 Grange Loan Gardens, Edinburgh EH9 2EB — 1963

Ostler, John H., MA, LTh (Contin Strathconon 1987) — 1975

Parker, Andrew H., BSc, BD (*Assistant* Dunfermline Abbey 1969), 34 Frostick Walk, London E2 — 1967

Paton, George (Aberdeen Stockethill 1973), 52 Northsea Court, Aberdeen *[0224] Aberdeen 492871* — 1951

Patterson, Andrew R. M., MA, BD (Mochrum 1988), 41 Main Street, Kirkinner, Newton Stewart DG8 9AN — 1985

Payne, John, BSc, BD (*Assistant* at Linlithgow St. Michael's 1986) 62 Best Street, North Fitzroy, Victoria 3068, Australia — 1985

Philip, Norris E., MA (Glenbervie 1966) — 1955

Poole, Wesley S. W., BA, BD (Carlisle 1976), 10 Blackwell, Darlington — 1960

Porter, Gair M., BD, DPS (Patna Waterside 1988) — 1986

*Reid, H. G., TD, BD (Troon St. Meddan's 1970), Gloverbank, Ceres, Fife KY15 *[033, 482] Ceres 351* — 1936

Rentoul, R. W., MA, BSc, ABPsS (Bangalore 1969), Woodhill, Ormes Lane, Tettenhall Wood, Wolverhampton WV6 8LL — 1956

Rhodes, William S., MA, MB, ChB, MRCS, LRCP, BD, STM (North India 1981), 5 Church Street, Widcombe, Bath BA2 6AZ — 1954

Riach, W. A. D., MA, PhD (Kenya 1957), Memorial University of Newfoundland, St. John's, Canada — 1943

Richmond, James, MA, BD, PhD (Holytown 1961), Dept. of Systematic Theology, University of Lancaster, Bailrigg, Lancaster LA1 4YG — 1956

May, Malcolm S., BA, BD, STM (Community House 1971), 6 Leemount Lane, Broughty Ferry, Dundee DD5 1LA [0382] 76295 — 1967

Meikle, A. C. (Whalsay 1955), Northbank, 1 Craigie Place, Perth PH2 1BB — 1950

Menzies, Stanley H., MA, BD (University Chaplain 1970) — 1958

*Mill, John Stuart, MA, BD (Edinburgh Colinton Mains 1980), 25 Craiglockhart Park, Edinburgh EH14 1ES 031-443 4921 — 1974

Millar, Jennifer M. (Mrs.) (Assistant at Mearns 1987) — 1986

Millar, Robertson (Stronsay St. John's 1931) — 1917

*Miller, James (Ordained by Presbytery of Irvine and Kilmarnock), 21 Wellpark Avenue, Kilmarnock [0563] Kilmarnock 24754 — 1979

Millican, J. A., MA (Chaplain RAF 1961) — 1945

*Mills, Archibald, MA, PhD (Department of Social Responsibility 1980), 32 High Street, South Queensferry EH30 9PP 031-331 3906 — 1953

Milne, George, BA (Rothes High 1934), 3 May Villas, Forgan Road, Dundee — 1928

Mitchell, George (Airdrie West 1984) — 1958

*Moffat, John (Dunrossness 1965), 107 Farne Road, Glasgow G44 5DR — 1938

Moir, John M., MA, BD (Glenelg 1966), Zambia — 1955

*Monteith, William N., BD, Elie, Fife (Strathallan School), West House, Elie [0333] Elie 330313 — 1970

Moore, William, MA, BD (Cawdor 1967), Senwick, Scapa Crescent, Kirkwall KW15 — 1933

*Mortimer, G. W. J., BSc, BD (Thurso West 1964), 38 Cookston Crescent, Brechin DD9 6BP [035 62] Brechin 4368 — 1961

Muirie, John, BA (London Caledonian Road 1938), 2 Endsleigh Place, London WC1 — 1931

Murdoch, J. A. H., BA, BD (Chaplain, Army 1986), Fettes College, Edinburgh — 1976

Ogilvie, Kenneth G., MA (Auchterderran 1968), 124 Comiston Drive, Edinburgh EH10 5QU 031-447 8909 — 1953

*Robertson, A. O., JP, MA, BD, STM (University Chaplain 1974), 13 Ainslie Place, Edinburgh EH3 6AS — 1953

Robertson, George (Muirkirk 1951), 11 Montague Street, Glasgow G4 9HU 041-339 1175 — 1950

*Robertson, George B., MA, BD, PhD, DipEd (Irvine Mure 1968), 15 St. Nicholas Road, Banchory AB3 — 1954

Ross, Robert J., MA, BD (Wishaw Craigneuk Belhaven 1967) — 1963

Ryrie, Alexander C., MA, BD, STM (Industrial Chaplain 1974), 19 Clarendon Crescent, Edinburgh EH4 1PU 031-332 8929 — 1956

Sangster, Roderick G., BD (Lossiemouth St. Gerardine's High 1985) — 1983

Sawyer, John F. A., MA, BD (University of Glasgow 1965), Professor of OT Language and Literature, Newcastle-upon-Tyne, 28 Brandling Place, Newcastle NE2 4RU — 1964

Scott, Donald H., BA, BD (Kilmallie 1987), General Delivery, Markdale, Ont NOC 1HO, Canada — 1983

Scott, T. H., BPhil (University Chaplain 1979), Rowanlee Cottage, Feddal Road, Braco FK15 5RE [078 688] Braco 277 — 1959

Scott-Ross, M. W. (Huts and Canteens 1971), 18A Gilstead Road, Singapore — 1951

Scouller, Hugh, BA, BD (Abernethy and Dron with Arngask 1987) — 1985

*Shand, George C., MA, BD (Assistant Edinburgh Old Kirk 1982), 3/1 West Pilton Lea, Edinburgh EH4 4ES — 1981

Shaw, W. A., BA, BD, PhD (Glenrothes St. Margaret's 1976), 29 Gillespie Road, Edinburgh EH13 0NW 031-441 3165 — 1961

Sheret, Brian S., MA, BD, DPhil (Stoneyburn 1985), 73 Fonthill Road, Aberdeen AB1 2UP — 1982

Sim, Gilbert, BD (Delting with Nesting and Lunnasting 1986), 188 High Street, Burton Latimer, Northants — 1981

Smellie, J. Laidlaw, FRSA (Cockenzie and Port Seton Old 1956), 4 Wemyss Place, Cockenzie and Port Seton EH32 0DW [0875] Port Seton 811508 — 1949

Smith, William A., LTh (Blairdaff with Monymusk 1978) — 1972

List F—Unattached Ministers—continued

*Spencer, John, MA, BD (Penicuik South 1967), 9 Findhorn Place, Edinburgh EH9 2JR 031-667 3670 — 1962

Spowart, David, MA (Grangemouth Old 1978), The Manse, Westray, Orkney KW17 2DE [085 77] Westray 357 — 1941

*Stewart, Margaret L. (Mrs.) BSc, MB, ChB, BD (Iona Community 1988), 5 Main Street, Livingston Village EH54 7AF [0506] Livingston 411396 — 1985

Stewart, W. D. S., MA, LLB, BEd (Paisley Oakshaw West 1951) — 1940

Stone, Lance B., BD, MTh (Associate at Aberdeen St. Nicholas' 1984) — 1978

Stott, Ian F. G., MA, BD (Nyasaland), Myrtle Cottage, Wrington, Bristol — 1927

Strachan, D. G., BD (Aberfeldy with Amulree and Strathbraan 1985) 30 Broomhill Terrace, Aberdeen AB1 6JN — 1978

Sutherland, Eric W. (Bonkyl and Preston 1953), 28 Warriston Crescent, Edinburgh EH3 5LB 031-556 6627 — 1947

*Taylor, John H. B, MA(Oxon), BD, DipEd (Irvine St. Andrew's 1969), 62 Woodlands Grove, Kilmarnock [0563] Kilmarnock 26698 — 1952

Taylor, Philip, LTh, DPS (Edinburgh St. Andrews Clermiston 1988) — 1983

Temple, David J., BA, BD (Aberdeen Torry 1980) — 1976

Thomas, W. Colville, BTh., DPS (Edinburgh Granton 1976), 5 Lower Granton Road, Edinburgh EH5 — 1964

Thomson, James, BD, BPhil (Stranraer Old 1983) — 1964

Timothy, H. B., BD, PhD (Wemyss St. Mary's-by-the-Sea 1949), United College, Winnipeg — 1939

*Todd, Robert, MA (Kirkfieldbank 1954), Cheviot, Roundriding Road, Dumbarton G82 2HB [0389] Dumbarton 62687 — 1945

*Tollick, Frank, BSc (Port Glasgow St. Martin's 1973), 3 Bellhouse Road, Aberdour KY3 0TL [0383] Aberdour 860 559 — 1958

*Turnbull, Julian S., BSc, BD (Dumfries Lochside 1985), 18F Forrester Park Avenue, Edinburgh EH12 9AN — 1983

*Vipont, M. A., MA (Saughtree 1951) — 1935

Waddell, James M., MA, BD (New Cumnock Arthur Memorial 1966) — 1964

Walker, David R., LLB, BD (Buenos Aires 1978), Marischal Gardens, Bucksburn, Aberdeen AB2 9BY — 1975

Walker, J. N., MA, BD (Foss and Tummel with Tenandry 1977), Fellowship of Reconciliation, 38 Kingsmead Road, Tulse Hill, London SW2 01-671 0141 — 1968

Wallace, Ronald S., BSc, MA, PhD (Lanark St. Kentigern's), 91 Comiston Drive, Edinburgh EH10 5QT 031-447 4662 — 1936

Watson, W. H., DD (Callander St. Bride's 1970), 40 Ashley Road, Aberdeen AB1 6RJ — 1933

Watt, J. G. M., MA (Glasgow Pollokshields East 1964), Scottish Marriage Guidance Council, 58 Palmerston Place, Edinburgh EH12 5AZ — 1947

Waugh, James, MA (Falkirk Camelon Trinity 1959), 50 Larbert Road, Bonnybridge FK4 1EJ [0324] Bonnybridge 812276 — 1938

Wilson, A. B. A., MA (Torryburn and Newmills 1960) — 1941

Wilson, John R., MA (Edinburgh St. Bride's 1968), Bishop Otter College of Education, Chichester — 1946

Wilson, Mark, MA, BD (Nagpur 1978), 2 Hiphen Drive, Luton, Beds LU2 9SP — 1953

Wilson, P. Douglas, LTh (Aberdeen St. Columba's Bridge of Don 1988) — 1979

Wright, Eric J., MA, BD (Glasgow St. George's Tron Associate 1983) — 1975

Wright, John H. A., MA, BD (Moulin and Pitlochry West 1973) — 1955

Wright, John P., BD (Fort William Duncansburgh 1987), 730 Crow Road, Glasgow G13 1NF 041-959 1175 — 1977

Torrance, Alan J., MA, BD, ARCM (University of Aberdeen 1984 1987)

*Trotter, R. A., MA (Indian Ecclesiastical Establishment 1931 1948), 23 Dovecot Park, Aberdour, Fife KY3 0TE [0383] *Aberdour 860373*

*Wright, Peter E., MA, BD, DipEd, DD (Muiravonside 1968 1984), 20 Wester Bankton, Murieston, Livingston EH54 9AH [0506] *Livingstone 412925*
Yates, Robin D., LTh (Cambuslang Flemington Hallside 1969 1984)

List FF—RETIRED MINISTERS

The General Assembly of 1980 passed an Act (VIII) whereby a retired Minister may, without undue formality, resign his seat in Presbytery. Such a Minister retains his full status, and, for life and doctrine, is under supervision of the Presbytery from which he resigned. The figure in square brackets represents the Presbytery in question, the figures in parentheses represent date of ordination and retiral respectively.

Anderson, G. Elliot, MA, BD (1941), Braemar (1975), 19 Falcon Avenue, Edinburgh EH10 4AL (1975), 19 Falcon *031–447 3062* [1]
Bailey, W. Grahame, MA, BD (1939), Ladykirk and Whitsome (1978), 148 Craiglea Drive, Edinburgh EH10 5PU *031–447 1633* [1]
Bisset, Douglas G., MA, JP (1926), Kingsbarns (1974), 28 Thistle Street, Carnoustie DD7 7PR [0241] *Carnoustie 52334* [26]
Bogle, Michael M., MA (1936), Banton (1975), 30 Woodburn Terrace, Edinburgh EH10 4SS *031–447 3231* [1]
Bruce, Robert W., MA (1941), Newhaven-on-Forth (1979), 8 Kirkhill Road, Edinburgh EH16 5DW *031–668 1795* [1]
Candlish, George, MA, BD, BSc (1935), Home Board (1974) [13]
Chirnside, Charles (1950), Tullibody St. Serf's (1956) [23]

Clarke, Douglas MA, (1952), Edinburgh Leith North and Bonnington (1979), 12 Silverknowes Court, Edinburgh EH4 5NS *031–336 3506* [1]
Corner, Malcolm M., MA, BD (1928), Grangemouth West (1969), 10/8 Cameron Crescent, Edinburgh EH16 5LB *031–668 1041* [1]
Cooper, George, MA, BD (1943), Kenya (1986), 69 Montpelier Park, Edinburgh EH10 4WD [1]
Couper, James M., MA, BD (1938), Kilmodan and Colintraive (1976), 16 Murray Cottages, Edinburgh EH12 7UH *031–334 0083* [1]
Craig, Eric, MA, BD (1959), Edinburgh Chalmers Lauriston (1980), 71 Nile Grove, Edinburgh EH10 4SN *031–447 7538* [1]

List FF—Retired Ministers—continued

Duncan, Eric M., MA, BD, MLitt (1938), *Teacher*, RE (1972), 13b Park Terrace, Stirling FK8 2JT [23]

Elder, David S., MA, BD (1934), Sanquhar St. Ninian's (1974), 27 Woodfield Avenue, Edinburgh EH13 0HX *031-441 1184* [1]

Ferenbach, Campbell, VRD, MA (1930), Edinburgh Liberton (1970), 3 Swanston Gardens, Edinburgh EH10 7DJ *031-445 1257* [1]

Hunter, John M'Kie (1933), Borgue (1970), Flat 6, 1 Pentland Drive, Edinburgh EH10 6PU *031-445 3295* [1]

Jones, Cyril, MA (1939), Ratho (1978), 28 Bridge Street, Newbridge EH28 8SR *031-333 2694* [1]

King, Alexander, DD (1924), Overseas Council (1966), 6 Rochester Terrace, Edinburgh EH10 5AA *031-447 3413* [1]

M'Glashan, Charles Y., CBE, DD (1937), St. Andrews Holy Trinity (1977), 26 Wellbrook Road, Bishop's Cleeve, Cheltenham GL52 4BW [1]

MacKay, James (1966), Lismore (1978), 144 Crieff Road, Perth PH1 2NY [28]

MacLeod, John, CD, MA, BD, BEd (1945), Kilmore and Kilbride Oban Old (1984), Oban, Argyll PA34 4NE *[0631] Oban 2186* [21]

Macphail, J. H. Boyd, MA (1937), Aberfoyle (1976), 3/3 St. Theresa Place, Spylaw Road, Edinburgh EH10 5UB [1]

Mathewson, R. J. Watson, MA, BD, STM (1941), Edinburgh Blackhall St. Columba (1975), 12 Learmonth Grove, Edinburgh EH4 1BP *031-332 4724* [1]

Mincher, A. K., MA, BD, DD (1935), Nigeria (1970), 17/19 Kirk Loan, Edinburgh EH12 7HD *031-334 9339* [1]

Moir, Ian A., MA, BD, PhD (University of Edinburgh 1981), 56b Kirk Brae, Edinburgh EH16 6HO *031-664 1535* [1]

Monro, George D., TD, MA (1935), Yester (1975), Flat 79, 303 Colinton Road, Edinburgh EH13 0HS *031-441 7303* [1]

Nicholson, George (1929), Karachi (1966), 14 Star Court, Pirville Circus Road, Cheltenham, Glos. [1]

Philip, Robert R., MA (1941), Rosehall (1969), 6 Hazel Hill, South Parks, Glenrothes, Fife KY6 1HF *[0592] Glenrothes 755208* [1]

Ross, John H. G., OBE, MA, BD (1940), Dundurn (1979), 43 Arden Street, Edinburgh EH9 1BS *031-447 2027* [1]

Sinclair, J. S. (1962), Newcraighall (1971), 10 Dalkeith Street, Edinburgh EH15 2HR *031-669 2046* [1]

Stalker, D. M. G., MA, BD (1938), Lecturer in Biblical Studies (1981), Dunraven, Balerno EH14 7DN *031-449 3944* [1]

Towill, Edwin S., MA, BD, MEd (1934), Lecturer in Religious Education (1976), 19 Charterhall Road, Edinburgh EH9 3HS *031-667 4184* [1]

Wallace, William (1940), Corgarff and Strathdon (1977), 5/541 Lanark Road, Edinburgh EH14 5DE *031-453 4886* [1]

Wood, Frank, MA, BD (1929), Edinburgh Morningside (1969), 59 Craiglea Drive, Edinburgh EH10 5PE *031-447 6789* [1]

Yule, George S. S., BA, MA (1949), University of Aberdeen (1985) [31]

List G—PROBATIONERS AND LICENTIATES

In terms of the relevant Act of 1985 the term "Probationer" refers exclusively to a student who, having successfully completed his course, has been licensed by a Presbytery and is serving his Probationary Year; the term "Licentiate" means (a) a Probationer as above defined whose Probationary Year has been completed and sustained, or who has been exempted from the performance of a Probationary Year; and also (b) a student who has completed his course and has been licensed by a Presbytery but has not proceeded to serve a Probationary Year.

Those whose names appear hereunder in Group I are Probationers in the above sense at the time when this List had been prepared, but by April 1987 most of them will have become Licentiates within the new meaning of that term. Those whose names appear in Group II have all the status of Licentiates; those carrying an asterisk (*) have not served a Probationary Year and are therefore not eligible to receive a Call in a vacancy; those carrying a dollar sign ($) are eligible for call but for one reason or another are not interested in proceeding to the parish ministry.

No effort has been spared in seeking to ensure that the Lists are accurate *at the time of preparation.* Anyone referring to the Lists in connection with a vacancy is, however, advised to check the up-to-date situation by reference to the Secretary of the Committee on Probationers and Transference and Admission of Ministers at 121 George Street, Edinburgh EH2 4YN (031–225 5722).

Group I—Probationers

Adams, Marjory (Lanark, July 1988)
Bain, James (Dunfermline, July 1988)
Barge, Nigel (Edinburgh, July 1988)
Bicket, Matthew S. (Glasgow, July 1988)
Black, Janette M.K. (Paisley, June 1988
Blair, Fyfe (Aberdeen, June 1988)
Boyd, Ian (Ayr, July 1988)
Bristow, Irene (Falkirk, August 1988)
Burt, David W.G. (Paisley, September 1987)
Campbell, W. Frank (Glasgow, July 1988)
Carlisle, Andrew R. (Glasgow, July 1988)
Clark, David (Jedburgh, July 1988)
Coulter, David G. (St Andrews, July 1988)
Court, David L. (Lanark, June 1988)
Craik, Sheila (Dundee, September 1988)
Davidson, James (Irvine & Kilmarnock, June 1988)
Douglas, Fiona (Hamilton, July 1988)
Duffin, Graham L. (Edinburgh, July 1988)
Elliott, Kenneth C. (Paisley, August 1988)

Fraser, Ann G. (Paisley, August 1988)
Gallacher, Jean W. (Dumbarton, July 1988)
Gosling, Frank (Stirling, June 1988)
Gregson, Elizabeth M.(Mrs) (Glasgow, July 1988)
Groves, Ian B. (Moray, June 1988)
Guy, Scott (Stirling, June 1988)
Henderson, J Mary (Edinburgh, June 1986)
Horne, Alastair M. (Lanark, June 1988)
Huggett, Judith A. (Dunfermline, July 1988)
Jack, James A.P. (Hamilton, July 1988)
Kenny, Elizabeth S.S. (Dunfermline, June 1987)
Lloyd, Ian F.B. (Aberdeen, June 1988)
M'Adam, David J. (Edinburgh, July 1988)
Macaskill, Donald (Glasgow, July 1988)
M'Callum, John (Ardrossan, September 1988)
M'Cool, Ann B. (Mrs) (Dumbarton, July 1988)
M'Culloch, Alen J.R. (Dumbarton, October 1988)
Macdonald, Mhorag (Dumbarton, July 1988)
M'Dowall, Bruce (Glasgow, July 1988)

List G—Probationers and Licentiates—*continued*

Group I—Probationers—*continued*

M'Fadzean, Iain (Paisley, August 1988)
MacKenzie, Kevin (Aberdeen, June 1988)
MacKenzie, K.I. (Aberdeen, June 1988)
MacKinnon, Charles W. (Glasgow, July 1988)
M'Lay, Alastair D. (Glasgow, July 1988)
MacLeod, Kenneth D. (Lewis, September 1988)
M'Neil, James N.R. (Aberdeen, June 1988)
Mann, John T. (England, January 1988)
Manners, Stephen (Glasgow, July 1988)
Manson, Ian A. (Edinburgh, July 1988)
Massie, Robert W. (Abedeen,June 1988)
Melville, David F. (Falkirk, July 1988)
Muir, Margaret A. (Edinburgh, July 1988)
Murphy, Victor (Edinburgh, July 1988)

Prentice, Donald K. (Moray, June 1988)
Reid, Alan (Stirling, June 1988)
Reid, Steven (Glasgow, July 1988)
Renwick, Colin O. (Dunkeld and Meigle, June 1988)
Sloan, Helen E. (Irvine and Kilmarnock, June 1988)
Stenhouse, W. Duncan (Dumfries & Kirkcudbright, July 1988)
Stott, Kenneth D. (Edinburgh, July 1988)
Strong, Colin A. (Inverness, June 1988)
Torrance, David J. (Melrose and Peebles, September 1988)
Urquhart, Neil (Ardrossan, September 1988)
Vint, Allan S. (Aberdeen, June 1988)
Watson, John M. (Paisley, August 1988)
Wells, John R. (Melrose and Peebles, September 1988)
Whiteford, John D. (Dunkeld and Meigle, June 1988)

Group II—Licentiates

$Anderson, Bryce A., MA BD STM (Aberdeen, April 1963)
*Anthony, John, MA BD (Aberdeen, October 1977)
Barrington, Charles W.H. (Edinburgh, June 1986)
Barclay, Alison M.(Mrs) MA BD DipEd (Edinburgh, July 1983)
*Baxter, W Alasdair, BA (Aberdeen, July 1983)
Bell, Matthew, BA (Hamilton, November 1975)
$Bennett, John B., BA ACMA BD (Glasgow, June 1983)
*Bissett, James F., BD (Perth, July 1978)
Blackley, Jean R.M.(Mrs), BD (Glasgow, 1983)
$Bone, John A., BSc BD STM DipEd (Ayr, April 1975)
$Brown, Brian, MA BD (Edinburgh, 1959)
Brown, Derek G., BD DipMin (Lothian, July 1986)
*Cameron, June A., BA (Glasgow, July 1978)
$Cameron, Nigel M.de S., MA BD PhD (Edinburgh, July 1977)
Cameron, Richard M. (Glasgow, July 1987)
Cranfield, Mary M. (Aberdeen, June 1986)
$Crippin, John B., BA BD (Edinburgh, July 1977)

$Little, James C., BD (Glasgow, April 1965)
*M'Coll, John (Paisley, November 1985)
$MacDonald, Duncan N., LTh (Lorn and Mull, July 1972)
*MacDonald, William D., MA (Ayr, June 1982)
*M'Kay, Angus J.M., MA BD (Glasgow, May 1971)
*M'Kay, Heather (Mrs) (Paisley, September 1985)
*M'Kenna, Edward C. (Edinburgh, June 1985)
$M'Kenzie, K. Neil, MA BD (Edinburgh, June 1969)
**M'Lachlan, I.K. (Edinburgh, July 1977)
$MacLeod, Ada V. (Mrs), MA BD (Aberdeen, June 1984)
$Marshall, Peter F., MA BD (Greenock, June 1975)
Mathers, A.R. Neal (Paisley, 1977)
Mathieson, Angus R. (Edinburgh, July 1987)
Matthews, John C. (Dumbarton, June 1986)
$Maule-Brown, Netta (Mrs), B.Com, CPS (Glasgow, 1976)
$Meiklejohn, James W., MA (Glasgow, 1939)
Michie, Lindsay M., LLB BD (Edinburgh, June 1986)

*Cunningham, James S.A., MA BD BLitt PhD (Hamilton, 1959)
*Dobbie, Gary W., MA BD (Glasgow, July 1979)
$Donald, John A., MA BD (Paisley, 1951)
$Duff, William B., MA DipEd (Glasgow, 1951)
Duncan Alastair S. (Edinburgh, July 1987)
$Dunn, James D.G., MA BD PhD (Glasgow, April 1964)
Dunphy, Rhona J.(Mrs) (Stirling, July 1987)
Earl, Jennifer M.(Mrs), MA BD (Dundee, July 1978)
$Felderhof, Marius C., BA BD MA (Kirkcaldy, October 1974)
Fletcher, G. Gray (Glasgow. July 1987)
*Fraser, Kenneth M., MA BD (Kirkcaldy, June 1969)
Garden, Margaret J. (Kincardine & Deeside, June 1986)
George, George A., BA BD (Edinburgh, July 1982)
$Gillies, Alexander Kenneth, MB ChB (Glasgow, April 1969)
$Glen, Thomas W., MA BD MEd (Glasgow, 1937)
*Grant, Frederick A., BSc (Glasgow, December 1977)
Grant, Ronald D., MA (Linlithgow & Falkirk, May 1962)
$Hall, Peter Robin, MA BD (Glasgow, April 1964)
Hannah, Angus C., MA BD (Glasgow, June 1975)
$Hannah, William M, BA BD DipEd (Glasgow, May 1969)
$Hazlett, W Ian P.
Henderson, J. Mary (Edinburgh, June 1986)
*Heron, Helen S.(Mrs), MA BD (Dundee. May 1970)
$Honeyman, Ian, MA (St Andrews, April 1965)
Hood, Adam J.J. (Lothian, July 1987)
$Hope-Smith, James (Edinburgh, April 1972)
$Houston, Joseph, MA BD PhD (Paisley, April 1964)
*Hulbert, Alastair J.M., MA BD (St Andrews, May 1968)
*Ireland, Anthony, LLB BA (Glasgow, June 1974)
$Jardine, John H., MA (Glasgow)
Johnstone Harry M.J. (West Lothian, July 1987)
Jolly, Lynn W. (Glasgow, July 1988)
$Kee, A. Alistair, MA BD STM ThD (Dumbarton, April 1961)
Keil, Alistair H., BD DipMin (Moray, December 1982)

Milton, A. Leslie (Glasgow, July 1987)
*More, John A.M., BD (Glasgow, June 1973)
$Newlands, Elizabeth (Mrs), MA BD (Edinburgh, June 1969)
$Paterson, Roderick M., MA (Deeside & Alford, June 1969)
Pyper, N.C.Sinclair (Miss) (Dundee, June 1985)
Rades, Jorg (St Andrews, June 1987)
$Reddick, Archibald F., MA (Hamilton, 1939)
*Ritchie, Stuart A., MA BD (Glasgow, June 1973)
Robertson, Blair (Edinburgh, July 1988)
$Robertson, John Graeme L., MA BD (Paisley, April 1970)
$Ross, George H., MA BD (Edinburgh, 1952)
*Scott, James H., BD (Dundee, June 1976)
$Scott, Mary-Catherine (Mrs), BA BD (Edinburgh, Dec 1979)
Scouler, Michael D. (Glasgow, July 1987)
$Shaffer, Jane A.(Mrs), MA BD (Edinburgh, July 1974)
Sinclair, David I. (Stirling, July 1987)
$Small, Alan Lindsay. MA (Edinburgh, 1962)
Smith, D Robert (Edinburgh, July 1984)
Steele, Andrew. BSc FRIC ARCST ATCL (Linlithgow and Falkirk,
    August 1966)
*Strang, John G., MA BD (Lanark, April 1970)
$Swan, James R.D., MA (Dundee, April 1960)
*Telford, William R., MA BD (Glasgow, May 1971)
$Templeton, Douglas A., BA BD PhD (Glasgow)
Underwood, Florence (Mrs), BD (Lothian, July 1986)
$Urquhart, David M., LTh (Glasgow, June 1975)
$Walker, Veronica M.(Mrs), BSc BD (Duns, June 1973)
$Watt, John W., BA PhD (Edinburgh, July 1985)
Watt, Robert J.G., BA LLB BD (Glasgow, April 1966)
*Weir, Elizabeth V.(Mrs), BSc BD (Glasgow, June 1976)
*White, Ian (Aberdeen, June 1984)
Wilson, James J. (Hamilton, June 1985)
Yates, Cleveland B., BA BD (St Andrews, June 1980)

List GG—AUXILIARY PROBATIONERS

Durno, Richard C. (Glasgow, January 1986)

Ferguson, Archibald (Dumbarton. September 1987)

List H—THE DIACONATE

The number in parentheses is that of the Presbytery within which the sphere of work is situated.

Anderson, Mrs Catherine B.; Glasgow Fernhill and Cathkin (16); 145 Galloway Drive, Rutherglen, Glasgow G73 4DG   041-631 3686

Anderson, Janet; Glasgow Ruchazie (16); 322 Gartcraig Road, Glasgow G33 2TB   041-774 5329

Austin, Graham; Easthouses, Mayfield (3); 40 Steele Avenue, Dalkeith EH22   031-663 7083

Bell, Mrs Catherine; Garthamlock and Craigend East (16); 39 Binns Road, Glasgow G33   041-774 5666

Betts, David; Culloden (37); 81 Galloway Drive, Culloden, Inverness IV12NE   [0463] Inverness 793295

Birrell, Mrs Isobel; 1 Potter's Park Crescent, Forfar, DD8 1HH   [0307] Forfar 63318

Blue, James M; Greenock St Margaret's (15); 20 Nelson Street, Greenock PA15 1QH   [0475] Greenock 20022

Brownlie, George H; Easterhouse (16); 2403 Paisley Road West, Glasgow G52 3QH   041-882 3973

Buchanan John; Rosyth (24); 85 Gill Way, Rosyth, Dunfermline KY11 2UL   [0383] Dunfermline 417825

Buchanan, Mrs Marion; Hamilton Hillhouse (17); 23 Fleming Way, Hamilton ML3 9PG   [0698] Hamilton 824235

Cameron, Margaret; Paisley Glenburn (14); 2 Rowan Gate, Paisley PA2 6RD   041-840 2479

Campbell, John; Manish Scarista (43); Mission House, Leverburgh, Isle of Harris PA83 3TS   [085 982] Leverburgh 353

Crawford, Morag; Edinburgh Drylaw (1); 118 Wester Drylaw Place, Edinburgh EH4 2TG   031-332 2253

Cunningham, Alison W.; General Secretary, The Scottish Sunday School Union; 23 Strathblane Road, Milngavie G62 8AL   041-9563131

Lyall, Ann; Glasgow Castlemilk East (16); 117 Barlia Drive, Glasgow G45 0AY   041-631 3643

M'Bain, Margaret; Lerwick and Bressay (46); 7 Navy Lane, Lerwick, Shetland   [0595] Lerwick 4312

M'Callum, Moyra, MA BD; St Colm's College (1); 23 Inverleith Terrace, Edinburgh EH3 5NX   031-332 2230

M'Cully, M. Isobel; Bonnyrigg (3); 63 Argyle Place, Bonnyrigg EH19 2PE   031-660 4673

Macdonald, Ann, BA; Glasgow Lochwood (16); 23 Auchingill Road, Glasgow G34 0LF

M'Fadzean, Maureen; East Kilbride Claremont (17); 30 Mull, St Leonard's, East Kilbride G742DX   [035 52] East Kilbride 46027

M'Kirdy, Lorraine; Uddingston Burnhead and Viewpark (17); 98 Burnhead Street, Viewpark, Uddingston G71 5RS   [0698] Uddingston 818439

Maclean, Donald A.; Tarbert (43); Mission House, Amhuinsuidhe, Isle of Harris PA85 3AS   [085 986] Scarp 201

M'Naughton, Janette; Bannockburn Ladywell (23); 13F Braehead Road, St Ninians, Stirling FK7 0ET   [0786] B'burn 810244

M'Pheat, Elspeth; Deputy Warden, Mortlich House, Churchhill, Edinburgh EH10 4BG   031-447 3239

Macpherson, James B.; Glasgow Lodging House Mission; 232 Brownside Road, Rutherglen, Glasgow G13 5BE   041-647 5173

MacQuien, Duncan; Greenock St Ninian's (15); 29 Denholm Street, Greenock PA16 8RH   [0475] Greenock 20827

Macrae, William; Tarbert (43); Mission House, Scalpay, Isle of Harris PA85   [085 984] Scalpay 287

M'Vean, Christine M.; Glasgow Carnwadric (16); 28 Cruachan Street, Glasgow G46 8LY   041-638 9035

Douglas, Marilyn; Cumbernauld Abronhill (22); 201 Almond Road, Abronill Cumbernauld G67 3LS　[0236] Cumbernauld 732136

Duff, Valerie; Columbia Seminary, 701 Columbia Drive, PO Box 520, Decatur, GA 30031, U S A

Erskine, Morag; New Erskine (14); 111 Mains Drive, Erskine PA8 041-812 6096

Evans, Mark; The People's Palace, Edinburgh EH1 1RN; 1/6 Waters Close, The Shore, Leith, Edinburgh EH6　031-225 4797

Finlayson, Ena B.; Aberdeen Middlefield (31); 13 Chapman Place, Aberdeen AB2 7DH　[0224] Aberdeen 695293

Flockhart, Andrew; Motherwell North (17); 30 Kilbrennan Drive, Motherwell ML13PN　[0698] Motherwell 51563

Gentles, Moira M; Burnside (16); 114 Langlee Avenue, Cambuslang, Glasgow G72 8SU　041-634 3839

Gillespie, Ann M.; Dumfries Lochside (8); 36 Alloway Road, Dumfries DG29LX　[0387] Dumfries 53514

Gray, Katie; Y W C A; 13 Palace Court, Bayswater, London W2 4LP

Guthrie, Jennifer; Glasgow Easterhouse (16); 2 Balcurvie Road, Glasgow G34 9QH　041-771 0823

Hanna, William; Glenrothes Christ's Kirk (25); 196 Aitken Road, Glenrothes KY7 6SG　[0592] Glenrothes 742292

Hood, Mrs Katrina; East Kilbride South (17); 6 Lister Tower, The Murray, East Kilbride G75　[035 52] East Kilbride 42720

Hughes, Helen M.; Glasgow Lansdowne (16); Flat 3B, 35 Burnbank Terrace, Glasgow G206UQ　041-339 9459

Hutchison, Mrs Maureen; Edinburgh Old Kirk (1); 23 Drylaw Crescent, Edinburgh EH42AU　031-332 8020

Johnston, Mary; Paisley St Columba Foxbar (14) 7 Mannering Road, Paisley PA20BS　[050 581] Bredilands 6227

Lamont, Fay M.; Dundee Mid Craigie (29); 5 Longtown Place, Dundee DD4 8JR　[0382] Dundee 500239

Lundie, Ann V.; Aberdeen South of St Nicholas' Kincorth (31); 20 Langdykes Road, Aberdeen AB1　[0224] Aberdeen 898416

Mair, Alex; Bridgeton St Francis in the East (16) 131 Torphin Crescent, Glasgow G326NL　041-774 8788

Malvenan, Dorothy; The Deaf Association, Dundee (29); 57 Dura Street, Dundee DD4 6TB　[0382] Dundee 41695

Martin, Jane; Dundee Chalmers Ardler (29); 12A Carnoustie Court, Ardler, Dundee DD2 3RB　[0382] Dundee 813786

Martin, Neil; Laurieston with Redding and Westquarter (22); 51 Gairloch Crescent, Falkirk FK2 9XD　[0324] Polmont 714015

Miller, Elsie M.; John Ross Memorial Church for the Deaf, Glasgow (16); 11 Fullarton Place, Coatbridge ML5 5ES　[0236] Coatbridge 26337

Morrison, Mrs Jean; Director, The Pastoral Foundation, Edinburgh (1); 45 Corslet Road, Currie EH145LZ　041-339 6859

Moyes, Sheila A.; General Secretary, Scottish Council YWCA of Great Britain, 158 Pilton Avenue, Edinburgh EH5 2JZ　031-551 1731

Mulligan, Anne; Hospital Chaplain's Assistant, Edinburgh Royal Infirmary (1); 1/6 Coxfield, Gorgie, Edinburgh EH11　031-346 7092

Munro, Patricia, BSc; Perth North (28); 29 Primrose Crescent, Perth PH1 2QG　[0738] Perth 27549

Nicol, Mrs Joyce; Hospital Chaplain's Assistant and at Kilmacolm St Columba's (15); 93 Brisbane Street, Greenock PA16 8NT　[0475] Greenock 23235

Petrie, Jacqueline G.; 3 Mill Lane, Caldecott, Market Harborough　[0536] Rockingham 770902

Pirie, George; Glasgow Castlemilk East (16); Flat 2, House 11, 142 Shawbridge Street, Glasgow G43 1NP　041-649 3280

Potts, Jean M; Edinburgh North Leith (1); 28B East Claremont Street, Edinburgh EH7 4JP　031-557 2144

Ramsden, Christine; Glasgow Gorbals (16); 184 Wolseley Street, Glasgow G5　041-429 5484

THE DIACONATE —*continued*

Rennie, Agnes M.; Edinburgh Bristo Memorial Craigmillar (1); 3/1 Craigmillar Court, Edinburgh EH16   *031-661 8475*

Rhind, Mary, MA BSc; Project Worker with Iona Community (16); 292 Berryknowes Road, Glasgow G52 2DA   *041-883 9971*

Ronald, Norma A.; Cumbernauld St Mungo's (22); 52 Hornbeam Road, Cumbernauld G67 3NQ   *[0236] Cumbernauld 721538*

Sloan, Elma C.; Secretary, Committee on Local Involvement, Dept of World Mission and Unity (1); 7 Dunedin Street, Edinburgh EH7 4JB   *031-556 3496*

Smith, Lillian, MA; Dundee Trinity (29); 6 Fintry Mains, Dundee DD4 9HF   *[0382] Dundee 500052*

Steele, Jean B.K.; Johnstone St Paul's (14); 93 George Street, Paisley PA1 2JX   *041-889 9512*

Stewart, William; Lochmaddy and Trumisgarry (43); Cnoc Sitheal, Malaclete, Sollas, Lochmaddy, Isle of North Uist PA82 5BX *[087 63] Lochportain 281*

Stewart, Mrs Una; Kelso North and Ednam *with* Sprouston (6); 10 Inch Park, Kelso TD5 7EQ   *[0573] Kelso 25065*

Stuart, Anne; Ancrum *with* Edgerston *with* Jedburgh Old (6); 7 Timpendean Cottages, Hawick Road, Jedburgh TD8 6SS *[0835] Jedburgh 3552*

Teague, Mrs Yvonne; Secretary, The Diaconate (1); 16 Rankeillor Street, Edinburgh EH 8 9HY   *031-667 7524*

Trimble, Robert A.; Kirkcaldy Templehall (25); 34 Mellerstain Road, New Liston, Kirkcaldy KY2 6UA *[0592]* Kirkcaldy 267924

Urquhart, Mrs Barbara M; Dundee Douglas and Angus (29); 26 Balmullo Square, Dundee DD4 8QL   *[0382] Dundee 450502*

White, Elizabeth; Glasgow Townhead Blochairm (16); 17 Clincarthill Road, Rutherglen, Glasgow G73 2LF   *041-647 2683*

Wilson, Matilda; Part-time Ministry with Travelling People; 12 Murdoch Terrace, Edinburgh EH11   *031-228 1475*

Macdonald, Ida; Elmtree Nursing Home, 371 Albert Drive, Glasgow G41 4NX

M'Garva, Sarah; 87 Hunter Drive, Irvine KA12 9BS

MacGregor, Sheila M; 18B Oswald Road, Edinburgh EH9 2HU

Mackenzie, Barbara N.; Abbeyfield House, 75 Colinton Road, Edinburgh EH10 5DF

M'Kenzie, Isabella; Aldersyde, 2 Crescent Road, Lundin Links, Lower Largo KY8 6AF

MacSween, Helen; Flat 17, 27A M'Queen Street, Tarbert, Isle of Harris PA85 3DH

Meek, Mrs Margaret; 13 Duntilland Avenue, Salsburgh, Shotts ML7 4NA

Mickelson, May B.; 31 Milton Road East, Edinburgh EH15 2NN

Mortimer, Aileen; 38 Sinclair Way, Knightsridge, Livingston EH54

Nicoll, Janet M.; 74 Brucefield Avenue, Dunfermline KY12 4SY

Park, Mima; 16 Lockerby Cottages, Lasswade Road, Edinburgh EH16 6QU

Phillips, Catherine W.; Flat 26, 61B St Alban's Road, Edinburgh EH9 2LS

Ramsay, Katherine M., MA; 147 Dalkeith Road, Edinburgh EH16 5HQ

Reid, Muriel C.; 62 Maxwellton Road, Calderwood, East Kilbride G74 3LX

Robertson, Annabella C.; Morlich House, Church Hill, Edinburgh EH10 4BG

Rutherford, Ellen B., MBE; 41 Duncanston, Conon Bridge, IV7 8JB

Scrimgeour, Alice M.; 265 Golfhill Drive, Glasgow G31 2PB

Smith, Mona M.L.; 50 Balmoral Place, Aberdeen AB1 6HP

Thom, Helen, BA DipEd; 84 Great King Street, Edinburgh EH3 6QU

Thomson, Ella; 91 Main Street, Kinglassie, Cardenden KY5 0YE

Webster, Elspeth H.; 82 Broomhill Avenue, Burntisland KY3

Wright, Lynda; Kilmallie (38); Iona Community, Iona Abbey, PA76 6SN [068 17] Iona 314

Retired List

Adamson, Jessie G.; 98 Barrington Drive, Glasgow G4 9ET
Aitchison, Jean B.; 43/15 Gillespie Crescent, Edinburgh EH104HX
Anderson, Mary; 33 Ryehill Terrace, Edinburgh EH6 8EN
Beaton, Jamesina; Farhills, Fort Augustus PH32 4DS
Bryden, Mrs Agnes Y.; 9 Rosewell Place, Aberdeen AB2 6HN
Campbell, Margaret M.; Tigh-an-Rudha, Port Ellen, Islay PA42
Collie, Jean; Formartindale, Udny Station, Ellon AB4 0QJ
Copland, Mrs Margaret M, MBE; 3 Craigmuschat Road, Gourock PA19 1SE
Denham, Chrissie H.; 139 Cluny Gardens, Edinburgh EH10 6BP
Drummond, Rhoda E.; Flat K, 23 Grange Road, Edinburgh EH9 2AR
Gardner, E. Dorothy; Flat 12, 15 North Church Street, Callander FK17 8EW
Gillon, Phyllis J.; 1 Queen's Road, Edinburgh EH4 2BY
Glass, Irene; 3E Falcon Road West, Edinburgh EH10 4AA
Gray, Euphemia R.; 8 Station Road, Edinburgh EH12 7AB
Grieve, Jean W.; 10 Hawthorn Avenue, Bearsden, Glasgow G613NH
Hamilton, Margaret; Morlich House, Church Hill, Edinburgh EH10 4BG
Howden, Margaret; 33A Winifred Crescent, Kirkcaldy KY2 5SX
Hutchison, Alan E. W.; 132 Lochbridge Road, North Berwick EH39 4DR
Kilgour, Margaret; Hollybush Cottage, Main Street, Saline, Dunfermline KY12 9TL
Kinloch, Elizabeth H.I.; 15 Netherburn Avenue, Glasgow G44 3UF
Laing, Jean H.; 61 Thornley Avenue, Glasgow G13 3BX
MacBeth, Edith, MBE; Queensberry Lodge, Holyrood Road, Edinburgh EH8

Weir, Minnie, MA; 4 Katrine Crescent, Kirkcaldy KY2 6RW
Welsh, Jessie R.; 40 Thomson Street, Aberdeen AB2 4QP
Whyte, Helen S., 19 Tay Road, Mastrick, Aberdeen AB2 5LA
Young, Mrs Margaret; Croston Lodge, 3A Chalmers Crescent, Edinburgh EH9 1TW

LAY MISSIONARIES

Falconer, A.J.; Glenshee (27); Glenshee Lodge, Blairgowrie PH10 7QD [025 085] Glenshee 209
Forrester, Arthur A.; Cunningsburgh (46); The Manse, Dunrossness, Shetland ZE29JH [0950] Sumburgh 60850

Retired List

Anderson, John L.: Alexander Rise, 46 Alexander Road, Glenrothes KY7 4HY
Anderson, Capt. Stephen; 70 Saughton Drive, Edinburgh EH12 5TL
Campbell, John; 28 Benside, Laxdale, Stornoway, Isle of Lewis
Campbell, Kenneth; 1 Scaldbay, Drinnishader, Isle of Harris PA85 3DX
Copeland, Roy; 18 Benford Knowe, Newarthill, Motherwell ML1 5BQ
Dunbar, William; 37 Skibo Avenue, Pitteuchar, Glenrothes KY74PY1
Elliott, Alexander, 24 Broompark View, East Calder EH53 0AD
Gilmour, William; 23 Dykes Road, Penicuik EH26 0JD
Gordon, David; 11 Blenheim Terrace, Redcar, Cleveland TS10 1QD
Isbister, James, 3 Stove Cottages, Walls, Shetland ZE2
Lamont, Donald; Old Mission House, Cul-nan-Cnoc, Portree, Isle of Skye IV51 9JD
MacDonald, Kenneth D., 40 Bayhead Street, Stornoway, Isle of Lewis

LAY MISSIONARIES—continued

Retired List—continued

Maclean, Norman; 65 New Valley, Stornoway, Isle of Lewis PA86 0DW

M'Naughtan, Mrs Winifred; 8 Kinloss Park, Cupar KY15 4EJ

Macrae, Kenneth; 16 Ladysmith Street, Ullapool IV26

Mills, Benjamin; 82 Woodside Way, Glenrothes KY7

Morrison, Angus; c/o MacLeod, Riverside House, Urgah, Tarbert, Isle of Harris PA85

Sandison, Magnus J.; 9 Murray Court, North Street, Montrose DD10 8BP

Scott, John W.; Flat 12, Kirkrigg Court, Lour Road, Forfar

Shaw, John; 2 Charleston Place, Muirtown, Invernesss

Shepherd, Denis; Mission House, Norby, Sandness, Shetland

Stephen, George; 53 Berryden Road, Peterhead AB4 6FF

Watson, James F.; Flat 3, Schaw Court, 174A Drymen Road, Bearsden, Glasgow G61

Wood, Donald C.; 31 Freeland Drive, Glasgow G53 6PG

AGENTS

Allan, Margaret R., MA BD; Edinburgh New Newcraighall and Richmond Craigmillar (1); 28 Mortonhall Park, Edinburgh EH1 8SY

Beaton, Mrgaret S.; Bridgeton St Francis in the East Church House (16); Flat F, 10 South Vesalius Street, Glasgow G32

Briggs, Ralph; Pastoral Assistant Presbytery of Lewis; Organiser for Evangelism, Uist and Lewis (44); 7 Ardmore, Lochs, Isle of Lewis PA86 9DU

Burden, Brian; Field Officer; St Ninian's Centre, 74 Main Street, Doune FK16 6BW *[0786] Dunblane 841791*

Cathcart, John; St James' Pollok (16); 152 Templeland Road, Glasgow G53

Corrie, Margaret; Priesthill and Nitshill (16); 7 Parkhouse Path, Glasgow G53

Deacons, Mary; Holy Trinity (1); 17/7 Clader Drive, Edinburgh EH11 4LT

Dey, Rev James; Outer Skerries (46); The Schoolhouse, Skerries, Shetland *[08065] Out Skerries 244*

Eldridge, Mrs Rosemary; Community Worker, International Flat, 20 Glasgow Street, Glasgow G128JP *041-334 7866*

Forrest, Douglas; Walls (46); Mission House, Foula, Shetland

Lamont, Ian; Part-time Counsellor in Evangelism; 13 The Avenue, Whitburn, Bathgate EH47 0DD

M'Gregor, Duncan; The Schoolhouse, Fair Isle, Shetland

Mann, Douglas; Field Officer, St Ninian's Centre, Crieff, Mandalay, Strathyre *[0764] Crieff 3766*

Miller, Jean; Greenock, Newark, Gibbshill (15); 1 Fox Street, Greenock PA16 8AT

Munro, Sheila; Clydebank Faifley (18); 26/3 Lennox Drive, Clydebank G81 5JU

Thomson, Mrs Jean; Dundee Mains (29); 8B Duart Road, Dundee DD3

List J—READERS

This List shows the Names and Addresses of the Readers of the Church, arranged according to Presbyteries. For particulars regarding the Office of Reader, see page 57.

* Available on this telephone during normal business hours.

† Not on Active List.

Presbytery of Edinburgh

Beasley, Ronald E., 37 Warrender Park Terrace, Edinburgh EH9 1EB
031–229 8383

Grossart, A. W., 11 Howdenhall Gardens, Edinburgh EH16 6UN
031–664 9042

Hector, Gordon M., CMG, CBE, MA, 18 Magdala Crescent, Edinburgh EH12 5BD
031–346 2317

Kelly, William A., MA, FLA, 12 Rothesay Place, Edinburgh EH3 7SL
031–225 6159

Kerrigan, Herbert A., MA, LLB, Airdene, Edinburgh Road, Dalkeith EH22
031–660 3007

Lowe, James O., 38 Mountcastle Drive North, Edinburgh EH8 7SJ
031–661 3885

Macdonald, A. S., 24 Dudley Gardens, Edinburgh EH6 4PT
031–554 3470

McLennan, A. Fraser, SSC, 100 Ravelston Dykes, Edinburgh EH12 6HB
031–337 4341

Ramsay, D. T., 11 Ladywell Gardens, Edinburgh EH12 7LQ
031–334 1977

Ross, Alexander, 3 Albert Terrace, Edinburgh EH10 5EA
031–447 1902

Smith, Alastair, 7 Falcon Avenue, Edinburgh EH10 4AL
031–229 1294

Presbytery of West Lothian

Brown, Allan, 4 Quarry Cottages, Blackridge, Bathgate EH48
[0501] Harthill 51111

Elliott, Alexander, 24 Broompark View, East Calder EH53 0DA
[0506] Mid Calder 882467

Elliott, Miss Sarah, 105 Seafield, Bathgate EH48
[0506] Bathgate 54950

Galloway, Miss Jane R., 41 Broomieknowe Drive, Deans, Livingston
[0506] Livingston 411053

Howarth, Mrs. Jean, 25 The Loan, Torphichen, Bathgate
[0506] Bathgate 630449

†Kilpatrick, Thomas, 16 Robertson Avenue, Bathgate EH48 2DR
M‘Kinnon, John, 61 Moorelands, Addiewell, West Calder EH55 8JB
Muir, Mrs. Muriel, 74 Elizabeth Drive, Boghall, Bathgate EH48
[0506] Bathgate 55673

Notman, Miss Jean S. G., 1 Church Place, Armadale EH48 2LY
[0501] Armadale 31005

Pender, Mrs. Margaret, 197 Philip Avenue, Boghall, Bathgate EH48
[0506] Bathgate 53351

†Purves, John, 41 Mid Street, Deans, Livingston EH54 8BZ
[0584] Livingston 411263

Riddell, Thomas, 160 Avontoun Park, Linlithgow EH49
[0506] Linlithgow 843251

List J—Readers—continued

Simpson, Charles, 21 Millburn Road, Bathgate EH48 2AF
[0506] Bathgate 55394

Smith, George, 15 Manse Avenue, Armadale EH48
[0501] Armadale 32025

Wilson, Thomas, Balgownie, Main Street, Dechmont, Broxburn EH52
[0506] Dechmont 811646

Presbytery of Lothian

Anderson, John W., 33 Campwood View, Mayfield, Dalkeith EH22 5QQ
031–663 2932

Binnie, Mrs. E., Raymara, 2 Douglas Road, Longniddry EH32 0LE
[0875] Longniddry 52157

Booth, S. J., 87 Reed Drive Newtongrange EH22 4SP
031–663 4635

Gibson, C. S., 27 King's Avenue, Longniddry EH32
[0875] Longniddry 53464

Hogg, David, 82 Eskhill, Penicuik EH26
Hutchison, A. E. W., 132 Lochbridge Road, North Berwick EH39
[0620] North Berwick 4077

Miller, William D., 7 Couper Avenue, North Berwick EH39 4DZ
[0620] North Berwick 3398

Nicholas, Clive H., 12 Kerr Avenue, Dalkeith EH22 3JW
031–663 6842

Ralston, Hamish, BD, Craig-ard, 19 Melbourne Road, North Berwick EH39 4LB
[0620] North Berwick 2662

Robb, Walter W., LVCM, 17 Glebe Street, Dalkeith EH22
031–663 3007

Weir, James, 3 Pankhurst Loan, Dalkeith EH22 2LP   031–663 4826

Presbytery of Melrose and Peebles

Butcher, John W., 13 Ormiston Grove, Melrose TD6
[089 682] Melrose 2339

Dalgliesh, Rowland, BSc, 9 Annerley Road, Annan DG12 6HE
[046 12] Annan 2845

Garraway, William, CEng, MIMechE, DipFEd, 36 Hospital Road, Annan DG12 5HP
[046 12] Annan 3069

M'Gillivray, Roy, Fallford Lodge, Waterbeck, Lockerbie DG13 3HE
[046 16] Waterbeck 275

MacIntosh, Iain, Orchardbank, Hallpath, Langholm DG16 0EG
[0541] Langholm 80493

Tetlow, Frank R., 1 Elmwood, Dundanion Road, Moffat DG10 9AH
[0683] Moffat 20699

Varrie, Ian A., Mansefield, Bridge Street, Lockerbie DG11 2HE
[057 62] Lockerbie 2457

Presbytery of Dumfries and Kirkcudbright

Davidson, J. Lockhart, 11 King Street, Castle Douglas DG7 1AA

Dobie, Mrs. Rachel, Glenfiddich, 2 Corbelly Hill, Dumfries DG2 7SQ
[0387] Dumfries 54806

Lewis, Frederick, MA, 18 Princess Street, Kirkcudbright DG6 4LQ
[0557] Kirkcudbright 30214

M'Kie, W. J., 23 Braeside Crescent, Castle Douglas DG7 1BW
[0556] Castle Douglas 2222

Ogilvie, D. W., MA, FSAScot., Lingerwood, Nelson Street, Dumfries DG2 9AY
[0387] Dumfries 64267

Pennington, Mrs. I. M'D., Red House, Briarbush, Penpont, Thornhill DG3 4LX
[0848] Thornhill 30772

Sinclair, W. K. M., Mount of Glenluffin, Rockcliffe, Dalbeattie DG5 4QG
[055 663] Rockcliffe 205

Watt, R. W., The Thorn, West Port, New Galloway, Castle Douglas DG7 3RJ

Presbytery of Wigtown and Stranraer

M'Clure, Miss Marion, BA, 13 Clenoch Street, Stranraer DG9 7HB
[0776] Stranraer 5144

Groves, C. Arthur, JP., 24 Hillview Crescent, Selkirk TD7
[0750] *Selkirk 21126*

Grubb, Mrs. Mary A., Lindisfarne, 35 Brownsmuir Park, Lauder TD2 6QD
[05782] *Lauder 692*

Presbytery of Duns

Deans, Mrs. M., BA, West Edge Farm, Berwick-on-Tweed TD15 1UE
[0289] *Berwick 86222*

Elphinston, Mrs. E., Edrington House, Berwick-on-Tweed TD15 1UF
[0289] *Berwick 86359*

Mathieson, Roderick, 33 Priory Hill, Coldstream TD12 4EB
[0890] *Coldstream 24903*

Smith, Leslie A., Summerhill, Beanburn, Ayton, Eyemouth TD14 5QY
[089 07] *Ayton 81320*

Presbytery of Jedburgh

Agnew, Lt.-Col. J. N., MA, Bonjedward House, Jedburgh TD8 6UE
[083 56] *Jedburgh 3464*

Clark, Mrs. Marion, Beechmount, Honeyfield Road, Jedburgh TD8 6JW
[083 56] *Jedburgh 3558*

Forbes, William S., Schoolhouse, Burnfoot, Hawick TD9 8EL
[0450] *Hawick 2357*

Steer, George H., 89 Weensland Road, Hawick TD9 9PJ
[0450] *Hawick 72859*

Thompson, Mrs. V. F., MA, Oxnam Manse, Jedburgh TD8 6RD
[083 56] *Jedburgh 2492*

Presbytery of Annandale and Eskdale

Brown, S. J., MA, 11 Well Road, Moffat

Chisholm, Dennis A. G., MA, BSc, Moss-side, Hightae, Lockerbie DG11 1JR
[0387] *Lochmaben 811803*

Macdonald, Mrs. Jean C., MA, DipRelEd, The Schoolhouse, Stoneykirk, Stranraer DG9 9JH

M'Lure, John, MA, 6 Bowling Green Road, Sandhead, Stranraer DG9 9JJ
[077 683] *Sandhead 348*

Simpson, George W., 107 George Street, Whithorn, Newton Stewart DG8 8PT
[098 85] *Whithorn 242*

Presbytery of Ayr

Kydd, Kenneth C., Old Schoolhouse, 9 Back Road, Dailly KA26 9SH
[046 581] *Dailly 462*

Mackie, R., 32 Victory Park, Girvan KA4
[0465] *Girvan 2012*

M'Nally, David, BEd, MEd, ThDip, ACP, 122 Wellbeck Crescent, Troon KA10 6AW
[0292] *Troon 312015*

Neil, T., 58 Newark Crescent, Ayr
[0292] *Alloway 45141*

Ness, E., 14 Broompark Avenue, Prestwick KA9 1LR
[0292] *Prestwick 75611*

Park, W., 1 Whitehill Way, Coylton
[029 258] *Joppa 779*

Ramage, R. Macalpine, MA, 57B St. Quivox Road, Prestwick KA9 1JF
[0292] *Prestwick 79192*

Seddon (Dr.), R. V., 1 Firth Road, Troon KA10 6TF
[0292] *Troon 313063*

Todd, S. J., 15 Firth Road, Troon KA10 6TF
[0292] *Troon 312995*

Presbytery of Irvine and Kilmarnock

Caldwell, W. Alastair, 25 Thomson Street, Kilmarnock KA3 1EQ
[0563] *Kilmarnock 21888*

Crosbie, Shona (Mrs.), 3 Woodhill Place, Kilmaurs, Kilmarnock KA3 2TL
[0563] *Kilmarnock 38758*

Findlay, Elizabeth (Mrs.), 19 Keith Place, Kilmarnock KA3 7NS
[0563] *Kilmarnock 28084*

Gunn, George, 1 Stronsay Place, Kilmarnock KA3 2JA
[0563] *Kilmarnock 29467*

List J—Readers—continued

Hunter, Joseph, 3 Duncan Drive, Irvine KA12 0HY
[0294] *Irvine 79409*
M'Lean, Donald, 1 Fouracres Drive, Kilmaurs KA3 2ND
[0563] *Kilmaurs 81475*
Scott, William, 6 Elgin Avenue, Stewarton KA3 3HJ
[0560] *Stewarton 84273*
Smith, Russell, 47 Carmel Place, Kilmaurs, Kilmarnock KA3 2QA
[0563] *Kilmaurs 38419*

Presbytery of Ardrossan

Allan, J. H., Creagh Dhubh, Golf Course Road, Whiting Bay, Arran KA27 8RE
[077 07] *Whiting Bay 462*
Barclay, Elizabeth (Mrs.), 15 Law Brae, West Kilbride KA23 9DB
Calder, Donald, 10 Drummilling Drive, West Kilbride KA23 9BE
[0294] *West Kilbride 823130*
Clarke, Samuel, Douglas Cottage, Gateside Street, West Kilbride KA23 9AZ
[0294] *West Kilbride 823282*
Nicol, Bruce, 30 Stakehill, Largs KA30 9NH
[0475] *Largs 674178*
Twomey, Douglas, 30 Burnside Road, Largs KA30 9BX
[0475] *Largs 673878*

Presbytery of Lanark

Broadley, Linda (Mrs.)
Driver, Stanley, 49 Laverockhall, Lanark ML11 7HZ
[0555] *Lanark 3801*
Farquharson, G., 6 Downie Street, Hamilton
[0698] *Hamilton 425801*
Gray, J. A., 21 Sycamore Gardens, Blackwood
[0555] *Lesmahagow 892739*
Hastings, William, Heath Field Cottage, Carlisle Road, Crawford ML12
[0322] *Crawford 612*
Jamieson, I., 29 Albany Drive, Lanark
[0555] *Lanark 4447*

Birchall, Edwin R., 11 Sunnybank Grove, Clarkston G76 7SU
041–638 4332
Calder, William, 111 Muirside Avenue, Kirkintilloch G66 3PP
041–776 5495
Callander, Thomas M. S., 31 Dalkeith Avenue, Bishopbriggs G64 2HQ
041–772 6955
Cameron, Ian, 17 Kelso Street, Glasgow G14 0LB
041–952 4997
†Campbell, James, MBE, 9 Greenbank Court, Hill Crescent, Clarkston, Glasgow G76 8DQ
041–644 2030
Corbett, Dr. Richard, 86 Kirkhill Gardens, Cambuslang G72 8EZ
041–641 3703

Farrell, W. J., 22 Battlefield Gardens, Glasgow G42 9JP
041–649 6094
Findlay, William, 36 Firpark Road, Bishopbriggs G64 1SP
041–772 7253
Gardner, Kenneth, 11F Hughenden Court, Glasgow G12
041–339 9607
Gibson, James N., 153 Peveril Avenue, Glasgow G41 3SF
041–632 4162

Gregson, Mrs. Elizabeth M., 17 Westfields, Bishopbriggs G64
041–772 8907
Harvie, Edward, 80 Otago Street, Glasgow G12 8PA
041–339 0588
Horne, William J., 27 Courthill Avenue, Glasgow G44 5AA
041–637 9774
Horner, David J., 32 Burnside Road, Rutherglen G73 4RS
041–634 2178
Knox, John, 6 Bargaran Road, Glasgow G53 5YL
041–810 3048
Lafferty, John M. M., 6 Westfields, Bishopbriggs G64
Lennie, Henry, 14 Clyde Place, Cambuslang G72 7QT
041–641 1410, 041–647 2946*
Lockhart, J. C., 56 Springfield Road, Bishopbriggs G64 1PN
041–772 1852
MacColl, Duncan N., 14 Mosspark Avenue, Glasgow G52 1JX
041–427 2395

Kerr, Sheilagh I. (Mrs.), Dunvegan, 29 Wilsontown Road, Forth
Riley, J. T. E., The Cottage, Camp Road, Symington, Biggar
[0563] Symington 345

Presbytery of Paisley

Henderson, William, 129 Braehead Road, Paisley PA2 8QG
041-884 3491
Whiteside, John, 5 Ballater Drive, Inchinnan PA4
041-812 1427

Presbytery of Greenock

Allan, J. G. B., MA, 81 Forsyth Street, Greenock PA16 8RA
[0475] Greenock 22309
Hart, J., 41 Prospecthill Street, Greenock PA15 4DN
[0475] Greenock 26687
Jamieson, J., 148 Finnart Street, Greenock PA16 8HY
[0475] Greenock 29531
M'Culloch, W. J., 22 Bank Street, Greenock PA15 4PH
[0475] Greenock 22099
M'Farlan, A., 65 Albert Road, Gourock PA19 1NJ
[0475] Gourock 34055
Manson, Mrs. E., 1 Cambridge Avenue, Gourock PA19 1XT
[0475] Gourock 32401
Marshall, Leon, Glenisla, Gryffe Road, Kilmacolm PA13 4BA
[050 587] Kilmacolm 2417
Steele, S., 5 Carwood Street, Greenock PA15 2TL
[0475] Greenock 83274
Walker, J., 85 Battery Park Avenue, Greenock PA16 7UA
[0475] Greenock 23321
Woodsend, T. E., 7 Belmont Road, Kilmacolm PA13 4LZ
[050 587] Kilmacolm 2765

Presbytery of Glasgow

†Alexander, Hugh J., 85 Hyndland Road, Glasgow G12 9JE
041-334 2372

M'Dowall, William J., 5 Elm Road, Burnside, Rutherglen G73 4JR
041-634 6093
M'Ewan, Alex, 20 Kennoway Drive, Glasgow G11 7TY
M'Farlane, Robert, 25 Avenel Road, Glasgow G13 2PB
041-954 5540

Mackinnon, John, 73 Oban Drive, Glasgow G20 6AE
M'Lachlan, David S., 77 Kingston Road, Kilsyth G65 0JG
[0236] Kilsyth 821151
M'Lean, David A., 31 Stamperland Crescent, Clarkston, Glasgow
G76 8LH
041-638 4200
M'Lean, Robert, 50 Pendicle Road, Bearsden G61 1EE
041-942 1489
M'Lellan, Duncan, 138 King's Park Avenue, Glasgow G44 4HS
041-632 8433
Middleton, W. G., 20 Rannoch Avenue, Bishopbriggs, Glasgow G64
1BU
041-772 6240
Montgomery, Hamish, 13 Avon Avenue, Kessington, Bearsden G61
2PS
041-942 3640
Nairne, Elizabeth (Mrs.), 229 Southbrae Drive, Glasgow G13 1TT
041-959 5066
Peacock, Wilson, 31 Wykeham Road, Glasgow G13 3YP
041-954 9877
Robertson, Adam, 423 Amulree Street, Glasgow G32 7SS
041-778 1563
Sands, Richard, 1 Redwood Place, Lenzie, Glasgow G66 4JQ
041-776 4428
Scott, William, BA, 41 Cardowan Drive, Stepps, Glasgow G33 6HQ
041-779 2163
Shaw, Neil D., 36 Windhill Road, Glasgow G43 2UN 041-637 8015
Shirlaw, William, 337 West George Lane, Glasgow G12
041-221 3305
Tindall, Mrs. Margaret, 2 Ashcroft Avenue, Lennoxtown, Glasgow
G65 7EN
[0360] Lennoxtown 310911
Williamson, John G., 34 King Edward Road, Glasgow G13 1QW
041-959 1300
Wilson, George A., 46 Maxwell Drive, Garrowhill, Baillieston,
Glasgow G69 6LS
041-771 3862

List J—Readers—continued

Presbytery of Hamilton

Chirnside, Peter, 141 Kylepark Drive, Uddingston G71 7DB
[0698] Uddingston 813769

Coia, Raymond, 46 Cromarty Avenue, Airdrie ML6
[0236] Airdrie 67144

Cruikshanks, William, 63 Progress Drive, Caldercruix ML6 7PU
[0236] Caldercruix 843352

Falconer, Leslie D., 48 Fraser River Tower, East Kilbride G75 8AD
[035 52] East Kilbride 30133

Haggarty, Frank, 75 Progress Drive, Caldercruix ML6 7PU
[0236] Caldercruix 842182

McAllister, George M., JP, 97 Glenburn Crescent, Viewpark, Uddingston G71 5HS
[0698] Uddingston 812460

McCumisky, Hugh, 83 Manse Road, Newmains, Wishaw ML2 9BL
[055 23] Cambusnethan 384257

McGowan, John, 211 Allanton Road, Shotts ML7 5AQ
[0501] Shotts 21529

M'Rae, James, 36 Crosshill Road, Strathaven ML10 6DS
[0357] Strathaven 20053

Muir, Robert, 33 Cairngorm Crescent, Wishaw ML2 7PS
[055 23] Wishaw 357908

Queen, Leslie, 60 Loch Assynt, East Kilbride G74 2DW
[035 52] East Kilbride 33932

Robertson, Rowan, 68 Townhead Road, Coatbridge ML5 2HU
[0236] Coatbridge 25703

Shankland, Robert, 4 Keir Crescent, Wishaw ML2 7JY
[055 23] Wishaw 379359

Smith, Alexander, 6 Coronation Street, Wishaw ML2 8LF
[069 83] Wishaw 385797

Stevenson, John, 1 Marshall Grove, Hamilton ML3 8NJ
[0698] Hamilton 428965

Wilson, John, BA, 39 Lodge Tower, Motherwell ML1 2AY
[0698] Motherwell 62962

Stewart, John Y. S., 9 Foulis Road, Inveraray PA32 8UW
[0499] Inveraray 2277

Wright, Gordon, Bealach Dearg, Craighouse, Jura, PA60 7XS

Presbytery of Dunoon

Cook, Alexander, 3 Victoria Crescent, Kirn PA23 8LN
[0369] Dunoon 2721

Fordyce, John, 34 Rothesay Court, Rothesay PA20 9BA
[0700] Rothesay 2379

Hannah, Rosemary J. (Mrs.), MTheol, Croc-an-raer House, Port Bannatyne, Rothesay PA20 0QT
[0700] Rothesay 3391

Presbytery of Lorn and Mull

Bartholomew, John, Beathaich, Calgary, Isle of Mull PA5 6QT
[008 84] Dervaig 240

Mackay, George S., Dunara, Connel, Argyll PA37 1PH
[063 71] Connel 244

†MacQuarrie, D. M., MA, Rosebank, Tobermory, Mull PA75 6PD
[0688] Tobermory 2148

†Robertson, P., MA, Dunmore, Oban PA34 4LU[063] Oban 3028

Simpson, J., Ardulin, Longsdale Road, Oban [063] Oban 62022

Waite, Garth, Lark's Nest, Easdale, Oban [085 23] Balvicar 410

Presbytery of Falkirk

Duncan, Mrs. Lorna, Richmond, 28 Solway Drive, Head of Muir, Denny FK5 5NS
[0324] Bonnybridge 813020

Jenkinson, John H., 8 Rosehall Terrace, Falkirk FK1 1PY
[0324] Falkirk 25498

Wilson, William, 115 Chatelherault Crescent, Hamilton ML3 7PL
[0698] Hamilton 421856

Presbytery of Dumbarton

Galbraith, Iain B., 358 Main Street, Alexandria G83
[0389] Alexandria 53563

Hart, R. J. M., BSc, CA, Glenmallon House, Garelochhead G84 0EZ
[0493-810] Garelochhead 293, 041-248 0820*

Kinnis, W. K. B., 64 Roman Court, Bearsden G61
041-943 0966

McKay, Ian P., 77 Falloch Road, Milngavie G62 7RR
041-956 3269

Neville, Robert, 28 Inchconnachan Drive, Balloch G82 2RZ
[0389] Alexandria 57913

Swann, Martin, Upper Ericstane, 7 West Montrose Street, Helensburgh G84 9NF
[0436] Helensburgh 2345

Woollam, R., 16 Hillfoot, Renton G82 4PP
[0389] Alexandria 52175

Young, Alex., Sandfield Cottages, Mugdock Road, Milngavie G62
041-956 1869

Presbytery of South Argyll

Campbell, Robert P. K., BL, 3 Buckingham Terrace, Great Western Road, Glasgow G12 8EB
041-334 9596

Holden, Robert, Tigh-an-Fhasgaidh, Ardrishaig, Argyll PA30
[0546] Lochgilphead 4327

McNab, Duncan Lamont, MB, ChB, Glenburn House, Ardrishaig PA30
[0546] Lochgilphead 3395

Mathisen, Ian M., Sanaigmore, Campbeltown PA28

Mitchell, James S., 4 Main Street, Port Charlotte, Islay PA48 7TX
[049 685] Port Charlotte 250

Law, D. Watson, 30A Duke Street, Denny FK6 6NP
[0324] Denny 823033

Logan, Donald, BA, DipEd, 63 Mungalhead Road, Bainsford, Falkirk FK2 7JQ
[0324] Falkirk 27960

Presbytery of Stirling

Cannon, Stephen C., MA, Ochilton, Devon Road, Dollar FK14 7EY
[025 94] Dollar 2779

Cowan, Alexander, BSc, FPS, 9 New Road, Bannockburn, Stirling FK7 8LP
[0786] Bannockburn 813460

Lindsay, John G., 21 Argyle Way, Dunblane
[0786] Dunblane 824054

Millar, Charles, 11 Catherine Road, Bannockburn
[0786] Bannockburn 811258

Presbytery of Dunfermline

Arnott, Robert G. K., 25 Sealstrand, Dalgety Bay, Dunfermline KY11 5HG
[0383] Dalgety Bay 822293

Conway, Bernard, 4 Centre Street, Kelty KY4
[0383] Kelty 830442

Dewar, James, 7 Keltyhill Avenue, Kelty KY4 0LH
[0383] Kelty 830022

Jane, Eon A., 17 Cypress Grove, Dunfermline KY12 5AF

Russell, David, 53 Blaney Crescent, Cowdenbeath KY4 9JS

Presbytery of St. Andrews

Galbraith, Mrs. Elizabeth B., 2 Burnside, Auchtermuchty KY14 7AT
[0337] Auchtermuchty 28519

Titterington, Mrs. Sigrid, Dunbog, Newburgh KY14 6JF
[0337] Newburgh 40374

List J—Readers—*continued*

Presbytery of Dunkeld and Meigle

Dutch, Alfred, MA., Katarlyn, Coupar Angus Road, Blairgowrie PH10 6JY [0250] *Blairgowrie 3371*
MacKay, W. H., 2 Carsie Road, Meikleour, Perthshire PH2 6EB [0250 83] *Meikleour 316*

Presbytery of Perth

Ashmall, Harry, Fernbank, Ferntower Road, Crieff PH7 3AL
Blair, Anne, 1A Moredun Place, Perth PH2 0DA
Buchan, J. S., 47 Dunkeld Road, Perth PH1 5RP
Duncan, G. A., Robert Douglas Memorial Home, Scone PH2 6LP
Duncan, Henry A., 6 Miller Road, Luncarty, Perth PH1 3UP [0738] *Perth 828876*

Presbytery of Dundee

Bowser, Charles N., MA, 6 Wellpark Terrace, Newport, Fife [0382] *Newport-on-Tay 542157*
Lockhart, William, Station House, Kingennie, by Broughty Ferry DD5 3NZ [082 625] *Kellas 219*
Ramsay, Thomas A., Inchkeith Place, Broughty Ferry DD5 2LT [0382] *Dundee 78915*
Simpson, Webster, 22 Laxford Lane, Broughty Ferry DD5 3HF [0382] *Dundee 78340*
Webster, Charles A., 16 Bath Street, Broughty Ferry DD5 2BY [0382] *Dundee 739520*

Presbytery of Angus

Birrell, Isobel (Mrs.), 1 Potter's Park Crescent, Forfar DD8 1HH [0307] *Forfar 63318*
Davidson, P. I., 27 Dorward Road, Montrose DD10 8SB

Wood, Eric R., MPS, 3 Garronhall, Stonehaven AB3 2HF [0569] *Stonehaven 62591*

Presbytery of Gordon

Brown, L. T., 95 Kembhill Park, Kemnay AB5 [0467] *Kemnay 43952*
Dick, Andrew, MA, New House, Strathburn Gardens, Inverurie AB5 9RY [0467] *Inverurie 20294*
Whiteley, A. M., MA, Beech Lodge, Monymusk, Sauchen AB3 7HJ [046 77] *Monymusk 229*

Presbytery of Buchan

Bain, Harry, 224 Braehead Drive, Cruden Bay AB4 7NW [0779] *Cruden Bay 813243*
Brown, Ian D., 193 West Road, Fraserburgh AB4 9NN [0346] *Fraserburgh 27727*
Brown, Mrs. Joyce, 193 West Road, Fraserburgh AB4 9NN [0346] *Fraserburgh 27727*
Byers, Mairi (Mrs.), King Edward Manse, Banff AB4 3NB [026 16] *Eden 258*
Christie, James, 2 Windy Brae, Banff AB4 1DG [026 12] *Banff 5405*
Clark, Robert, Laburnum House, Longside, Peterhead AB4 7XP [077 982] *Longside 284*
Cooper, Alfred, 23 Water Street, Strichen, Fraserburgh AB4 4ST
Davidson, James, 19 Great Stuart Street, Peterhead [0779] *Peterhead 20234*
Firth, Derek, 32 Mormond Avenue, Fraserburgh AB4 5PD [0346] *Fraserburgh 25698*
Mair, Dorothy, 7 Hamilton Road, Fraserburgh AB4 5RB [0346] *Fraserburgh 23879*

Ironside, C. T., PhD, 21 Tailyour Crescent, Montrose DD10 9BL
[0674] Montrose 3959
Leslie Melville, Ruth (Mrs.), Balgarroch, Aberlemno
[030 783] Aberlemno 219
Mitchell, Andrew Y., 6 Palmerston Street, Montrose DD10 8HR
[0674] Montrose 3141
Stevens, P. J., 7 Union Street, Montrose DD10 8PZ
[0674] Montrose 73710
Wheat, M., 4 Brougham Square, Montrose DD10 8TD
[0674] Montrose 76083
Whyte, David W., Red House, Orton, Elgin [034 88] Orton 271

Presbytery of Aberdeen

Burnet-Craigie, Angela, Linton House, Sauchen AB3 7LQ
[033 03] Sauchen 395
Douglas, Archibald, 1 Thorngrove Avenue, Aberdeen AB1 7XT
[0224] Aberdeen 310870
Gray, Peter, PhD, 165 Countesswells Road, Aberdeen AB1 7RA
[0224] Aberdeen 318172
Sinton, George P., FIMLS, 12 North Donside Road, Bridge of Don, Aberdeen AB2 8PA
[0224] Aberdeen 702273

Presbytery of Kincardine and Deeside

Bell, Peter D., BA, 63 St. Nicholas Drive, Banchory AB3 3YG
[033 02] Banchory 3661
Innes, James, 12 Formoston Park, Aboyne AB3 5HF
[0339] Aboyne 2357
Noble, John M., MA, 23 St. Nicholas Drive, Banchory AB3 3YG
[033 02] Banchory 3770
Sedgwick, Mrs. Sheila, BA, BD, BEd, Girnoc Shiel, Glengirnock, Ballater AB3 5SS
[0338] Ballater 55292
Silver, Douglas, MA, Cairnwell, Ballater Road, Aboyne AB3 5JL
[0339] Aboyne 2301

Simpson, Andrew C., 10 Wood Street, Banff AB4 1JX
[026 12] Banff 2538
Smith, Ian M. G., MA, Chomraich, Hill Street, Cruden Bay, Peterhead AB4 7NB
[0779] Cruden Bay 812698
Thomas, Geoffrey C., Upper Killyquharn, New Aberdour, Fraserburgh AB4 4LP
[034 66] New Aberdour 218

Presbytery of Moray

Buchan, William, Schoolhouse, Edenkillie, Aberlour AB3 9NN
[0345] Aberlour 232
Christie, Robert G., 41 Mar Court, Keith AB5 3DF
[054 22] Keith 2612
MacKenzie, Stuart G., Lochills Farm, Urquhart, Elgin
[034 384] Lhanbryde 2337
Whyte, David, Mains Cottage, Main Street, Urquhart, Elgin IV30 3LG
[034 384] Lhanbryde 2277

Presbytery of Inverness

Cook, A. D., 128 Laurel Avenue, Inverness IV3 5RS
[0463] Inverness 242586
Lyall, Sinclair L., 21A Crown Drive, Inverness IV2 3QF
[0463] Inverness 221765
MacLeod, J. M., MBE, JP, Dalshian, Balmacaan Road, Drumnadrochit IV3 6UR
[045 62] Drumnadrochit 340
Roberts, A. J., 33 Drumdevan Road, Inverness IV2 4DB
[0463] Inverness 222467
Weightman, A. E., 3 Dovecot Park, Culloden, Inverness IV1 2EU
[0463] Inverness 792779

List J—Readers—*continued*

Presbytery of Lochaber

MacKenzie, A. G., Innestore, Wades Road, Kinlochleven, PA40 4QT
[085 54] *Kinlochleven 260*
Mackinnon, Hugh, Mingary, Corpach, Fort William PH33 7JL
Maitland, James, St. Monance, Ardgour, Fort William PH33

Presbytery of Ross

Gilbertson, Ian, Firth View, Coulmore, N. Kessock
[046 373] *Kessock 538*
Glass, Alexander, Craigton, Tulloch Avenue, Dingwall IV15 9LH
[0349] *Dingwall 63258*
Mackintosh, Donald, Balnakyle, Munlochy IV8 8PF
[040 381] *Munlochy 242*
Trotter, Mrs. S. E., West Lodge, Swordale IV16 9XA
[0349] *Evanton 830629*
Warren, C. Peter, Wildcroft, The Braes, Ullapool IV26 2SZ
[0854] *Ullapool 2838*
Woodham, Mrs. M., Scardroy Ring Road, Dingwall IV15
[0349] *Dingwall 62116*

Presbytery of Sutherland

Betts-Brown, Andrew, 54 Muirfield Road, Brora KW9 6QY
[0408] *Brora 21610*
Burnett, Michael R., BSc, Pulrossie Farm, Dornoch, Sutherland IV25
[086 288] *Whiteface 206*
Gazey, Neville, 5 Academy Street, Brora KN9 6QE
[0408] *Brora 21607*
Mackay, Donald F., The Kennels, Suisgill Kildonan, Helmsdale KW8 6HY
[043 13] *Kinbrace 217*

Presbytery of Lochcarron-Skye

Gillies, Hector J., Culduie, Applecross, Kyle IV40 8LX

Presbytery of Uist

Taylor, Hamish, Rudha Liath, Isle of Barra
[087 15] *Northbay 383*

Presbytery of Lewis

Briggs, Ralph, 7 Achmore, Lochs
[085 186] *Crossbost 310*

Presbytery of Orkney

Doughty, Kenneth, Quoylanks, Deerness
[085 674] *Deerness 328*
Forrest, W., MA, The Schoolhouse, Stronsay KW17 2AE
Stronsay 246
Headley, Edwin, MA, Stymilders, Stenness [085 676] *Finstown 306*

Presbytery of Shetland

Jamieson Ian, Links View, Quendale, Shetland
[0950] *Sumburgh 60477*

Presbytery of England

Dick, R. F., Duneagle, Church Road, Sparkford, Somerset BA22 7JN
[0963] *40475*

Presbytery of Caithness

Morgan, R., 1 Breadalbane Crescent, Wick KW1 5AS
[0955] *Wick 2626*

Nicol, Alexander, 8 Girnigoe Street, Wick KW1 4HH

McKay, Donald, 45 Bamburgh Road, Newton Hall, Durham DH1 5NW
091-384 3141

Melville, Ian, BSc, 5 Fairlawn Avenue, London W4 5EF

Wilson, R. E. M., BSc, 34 Granville Court, Jesmond, Newcastle-upon-Tyne NE2 1TQ
091-281 0508

List K—RETIRED MISSIONARIES

The figure in parentheses represents the date of appointment; that in the margin the date of retirement. A figure in brackets [ ] represents the Presbytery of which the person is a member.

1949 Miss J. I. P. Campbell (Manchuria), 27 Cottage Homes, Thorburn Road, Edinburgh EH13 0BJ (1921)

Rev. A. Isabella Gordon, BD (Manchuria), 52/12 Spylaw Bank Road, Edinburgh EH13 0JG (1936)

1950 Miss J. M. Stewart, MB, ChB (Manchuria), The Elms, 18 Whitehouse Loan, Edinburgh EH9 2EZ (1926)

1951 Rev. Duncan Campbell, MA (Livingstonia), St. Raphael's, 6 Blackford Avenue, Edinburgh EH9 2LB (1931)

1952 Miss F. L. Davidson (Nagpur), 151 North Deeside Road, Culter, Aberdeen AB1 0RR (1929)

1953 Mr. Thomas Rankine (Blantyre), 16 Victoria Street, Alloa (1928)

1954 Mr. Richard Paterson, LCP (Blantyre), 17 Greenhill Place, Edinburgh EH10 4BR (1925)

Mrs. C. Pennington (Sheikh Othman), 43 Ainslie Street, Grimsby, Lincs. (1930)

1955 Mr. J. A. Rodger, NDA, DCA (Glas) (Blantyre), 23 Bathurst Street, Richmond, Tasmania (1924)

1956 Miss M. H. Tomory (Eastern Himalaya), 9 Plewlands Avenue, Edinburgh EH10 5JY (1924)

1957 Miss M. G. M'Millan, MB, ChB (Rajasthan), Clannoch, Bargrennan, Newton Stewart DG8 6SU (1927)

1958 Dr. R. B. Smith (Sheikh Othman), Flat G4, 21 Queen's Bay Crescent, Edinburgh EH15 2NA (1939)

1959 Rev. K. N. Paterson, MA, BD, DipEd (Western Pakistan), Glasford, Marchmont Road, Greenlaw TD10 6YQ [5] (1929)

Miss A. M. Campbell (Zambia), Cluny Lodge, 16 Cluny Drive, Edinburgh EH10 6DP (1939)

1960 Rev. David S. Elder, MA, BD (Ghana), 27 Woodfield Avenue, Edinburgh EH13 0HX [1] (1934)

Rev. John N. McDougall, MA, BD (West Pakistan), 65 Martin Avenue, Mount Albert, Auckland 3, New Zealand (1935)

Rev. J. A. R. Watt, BD (Ghana and Kenya), Greystanes, Dalginross, Comrie, Perthshire [28] (1928)

List K—Retired Missionaries—*continued*

Mr. A. Conn (Blantyre), 90 Endbutt Lane, Great Crosby, Liverpool 23 (1937)

1961   Rev. Michael M. Bogle, MA, 30 Woodburn Terrace, Edinburgh EH10 4SS [1] (1936)

1962   Rev. John R. Gray, BSc (Jamaica), Box 308, Grand Cayman, Cayman Islands, WI (1937)

  Miss E. G. Gall (Blantyre), 151 Raeburn Heights, Glenrothes, Fife KY16 1BW (1940)

1963   Very Rev. Andrew B. Doig, DD, BD, STM (Blantyre), The Eildons, Moulin, Pitlochry PH16 [27] (1938)

  Miss G. M. Patterson, BA (Eastern Himalaya), 57 Wai-Iti Crescent, Flat O, Woburn, Lower Hutt, New Zealand (1928)

1964   Miss H. M. Taylor, MBE, MA (Livingstonia), 10/22 Argyle Park Terrace, Edinburgh EH19 1JY (1933)

  Miss M. C. Fergusson (Kenya), Chequers, Atholl Road, Pitlochry 12 PH16 5DH (1937)

1965   Rev. W. H. Watson, DD (Livingstonia), 40 Ashley Road, Aberdeen AB1 6RJ (1933)

  Miss L. J. F. Cowie, MBE (South Arabia), Cliff House, Cults, Aberdeen AB1 9PS (1933)

1966   Miss M. A. B. Scott (Bengal), 27 Woodburn Terrace, Edinburgh EH10 4SS (1932)

  Miss M. L. Paterson (Livingstonia), 83 Hood Street, Drumry, Clydebank G81 2LU (1939)

  Mrs. M. M. Bogle (South Africa), 30 Woodburn Terrace, Edinburgh EH10 4SS (1934)

1967   Mr. Akanu Ibiam, MB, ChB (Calabar), c/o Christian Council of Nigeria, PO Box 434, Enugu, Nigeria, West Africa (1936)

  Rev. William Stewart, DD (Bengal), Pilgrim House, 44 Netherby Road, Edinburgh EH5 3LX [23] (1936)

Miss J. W. Robertson (Blantyre and South Africa), 9 Carlochie Place, Dundee DD4 7LY (1943)

Rev. Simeon Rathbone, 18 Ballar Avenue, Gymea, NSW 2227 Australia [7] (1943)

1971   Miss R. Gwen Dabb, MBE, MB, ChB (Blantyre), 14 Ethel Terrace, Edinburgh EH10 5NA (1943)

  Miss M. W. Douglas (Blantyre), 5/2 Spylaw Bank Road, Edinburgh EH13 0JE (1949)

  Rev. George H. Campbell (Livingstonia), 27 Avenue Street, Stewarton, Kilmarnock KA3 5AP [11] (1957)

  Rev. W. G. Murison (Santalia), 21 Hailes Gardens, Edinburgh EH13 0JL [1] (1971)

1972   Rev. A. T. H. Taylor, BD (Nigeria and Jamaica), 4 The Pleasance, Strathkinnes, Fife KY16 [26] (1938)

  Mr. C. M. Hutchison (Calabar), 75 Grampian Road, Torry, Aberdeen AB1 3ED

  Mr. G. McArthur (South Africa), 3 Craigcrook Road, Edinburgh EH4 3NQ (1956)

  Rev. C. Forrester-Paton, BD (Ghana), Acharn, Glen Road, Peebles EH45 9AY [6] (1946)

  Miss Agnes Forrest (Madras), 50C Newbattle Terrace, Edinburgh EH10 4RX

  Miss Margaret McLean (Rajasthan), Abbeville, 581 Prince Avenue, Southend-on-Sea, Essex SS0 0JH (1954)

  Miss K. M. Ramsay, MA (Bombay), 43 Falcon Avenue, Edinburgh EH10 4AL (1937)

  Miss E. L. MacKinnon (Nigeria), 142 Glencairn Street, Stevenston, Ayrshire KA20 3BU (1952)

  Rev. D. H. S. Lyon, MA, BD, STM (Nagpur), 30 Mansfield Road, Balerno EH14 7JZ [1] (1952)

1973   Rev. A. G. Somerville, MA (Nigeria), 18 Glengilp, Ardrishaig, Argyll PA30 8HF [19] (1942)

Mr. N. Leiter, BSc, MSc, (Nigeria), 12 Durham Avenue, Sneinton Dale, Nottingham NG2 4LU (1951)

Miss E. M. Scott, MA (West Pakistan), 29 Falcon Avenue, Edinburgh EH10 4AL (1933)

Miss J. M. Nicoll (Rajasthan), 74 Brucefield Avenue, Dunfermline KY11 4SY (1950)

1968 Mr. H. J. Taylor, MSc, Ph D (Assam), 3 Rochester Terrace, Edinburgh EH10 5AA

Rev. R. M. Macdonald, OBE, DD (Calabar), 14 North Church Street, Callander, Perthshire FK17 8EG [23] (1929)

1969 Rev. John R. Fleming, BD, ThD, DD (Malaysia), 41 Kilrymont Road, St. Andrews, Fife [26] (1938)

Miss J. D. Auchinachie, MA (Rajasthan), 8 House o' Hill Crescent, Edinburgh EH4 5DH (1935)

Miss D. Cooke (Malawi), 30 Linden Gardens, Tunbridge Wells, Kent (1937)

Mr. R. Fairley (Nigeria), 122 Hainton Avenue, Grimsby, S. Humberside DN32 9LQ

Mr. R. J. Tod (Nigeria), 30 Carrick Knowe Avenue, Edinburgh EH12 7BX (1953)

Miss J. E. Campbell (Malawi), 31 Falcon Avenue, Edinburgh EH10 4AL

Mr. F. Cameron, MBE, MA, BCom (Nigeria), 37 Station Road, Banchory, Kincardineshire AB3 3XX (1938)

Miss C. H. Denam (Nigeria), 139 Cluny Gardens, Edinburgh EH10 6BP (1946)

Miss M. M. Russell (Nigeria), 14 Hozier Street, Carluke ML8 5DW (1946)

1970 Rev. A. K. Mincher, BD, DD (Nigeria), 17/19 Kirk Loan, Edinburgh EH12 7HD [1] (1934)

Rev. A. M'Vicar, MBE, BD (Genoa), via Leonardo Montaldo, 24/91, 116137, Genoa, Italy [48] (1950)

Miss L. M. Smith (Madras), 6 Fintry Mains, Dundee DD4 9HF

1974 Rev. Peter M. Innes, MBE, MA (Assam), 17/14 Kirk Loan, Edinburgh EH12 7HD [30] (1952)

Mr. J. Hill (Malawi), 16 Alder Road, Bishopsmead, Tavistock, Devon (1958)

Rt. Rev. J. E. Lesslie Newbigin, CBE, DD (Madras Diocese), 15 Fox Hill, Birmingham B29 4AG (1936)

Miss Evelyn J. Stewart (Livingstonia), 94 Baronald Drive, Glasgow G12 0HY

Miss A. W. McGoff (Kolhapur), 6 Mossvale Walk, Craigend, Glasgow G33 5PF (1954)

1975 Rev. A. Donald Lamont, BSc, BD (Kenya), 36 St. Clair Terrace, Edinburgh EH10 5PS [1] (1941)

Rev. John Wilkinson, BD, MD, FRCP (Kenya), 70 Craigleith Hill Gardens, Edinburgh EH4 2JH [1] (1946)

Miss M. S. C. Burt, SRN, SCM (Kenya), 22 The Loaning, Chirnside, Duns TD11

Miss M. S. H. M'Neel (Seoni), 3F Falcon Road West, Edinburgh EH10 4AA (1938)

1976 Rev. Neil C. Bernard, MA (Calabar and Malawi), 12 Lockerby Cottages, Edinburgh EH16 6QU [1] (1930)

Rev. Alistair M. Rennie, MA, BD (Malawi), 13 Tullich Terrace, Tillicoultry FK13 6RD [23] (1939)

Rev. James L. Wilkie, MA, BD (Zambia), 7 Comely Bank Avenue, Edinburgh EH4 1EW [1] (1959)

Rev. W. M. M'Kenzie, DA (Zambia), Troqueer Road, Dumfries DG2 7DF [8] (1958)

Miss Elizabeth S. Scrimgeour, MA (Darjeeling), 73 Novar Drive, Glasgow G12 9SS (1946)

Miss Irene Glass (Delhi), 3E Falcon Road West, Edinburgh EH10 4AA (1945)

List K—Retired Missionaries—*continued*

1977   Rev. George Buchanan, OBE, MA, DD (Buenos Aires; India; Bermuda), 5788 Holland Street, Vancouver, V6N 2B1 B.C., Canada [18] (1931)

Rev. S. Paul Re'emi, DLitt (Israel), 19 Queen's Bay Crescent, Edinburgh EH15 2NA [1] (1962)

Rev. J. M. Ritchie, MA, BD (Yemen), Nazareth Hospital, EMMS PO Box 11 16100 Nazareth, Israel [23] (1974)

Rev. William G. Young, BD, PhD (Pakistan), 29 Ferry Brae, North Kessock, Inverness IV1 1YH

Miss M. H. Wilson (Nasik), 19 Ravelston Park, Edinburgh EH4 3DX (1946)

1978   Rev. John Dobos (Budapest), c/o Board of World Mission and Unity, 121 George Street, Edinburgh EH2 4YN

Rev. W. Ewing Smith, BSc (Delhi), 1 Main Street, Livingston Village EH74 7AF [2] (1962)

Rev. Mark Wilson, MA, BD (Nagpur), 2 Higham Drive, Luton, Beds. LU2 9SP (1953)

1979   Miss Winifred A. Bailey, MB, ChB (Kolhapur), 22 Mardale Crescent, Edinburgh EH10 5AG (1949)

Miss Mary I. Montgomery (Kenya), Flat 27, 2 Hawthorn Gardens, Loanhead EH20 9EE (1949)

1980   Miss Margaret Liddell (Zambia), Manse of Contin, Strathpeffer IV14 9ES (1964)

1981   Rev. William S. Rhodes, MA, MB, ChB, MRCS, LRCP, BD, STM (North India), 22 Hamilton Place, Edinburgh EH3 5AU (1954)

1982   Miss Margaret I. Reid, BSc (Malawi), 26A Angle Park Terrace, Edinburgh EH11 2JT (1964)

Miss Mary L. Archibald, BSc (Nigeria and Ghana), 47 Cleland Road, Wishaw ML2 7PH (1964)

Dr. Bryan Drever, BSc, MB, ChB (Aden, Yemen and Pakistan), 188 Addison Road, King's Heath, Birmingham (1962)

Dr. Hendrikje Kreuger (Western India), c/o Van Der Heeden, Middenweg 21, The Netherlands (1957)

Miss Moira M. Gentles, MA (Darjeeling), 114 Langlea Avenue, Cambuslang, Glasgow G72 8SV (1964)

1983   Miss Edith R. Barbour, SRN, SCM (North India), John Bishop Memorial Hospital, Anentnag, Kashmir, India

Rev. Alex. Slorach, CA, BD (Zambia), The Manse, Cranshaws, Duns TD11 3SJ [5] (1961–1966/1970–1983)

Rev. Gordon C. Morris, MA, BD (Zambia and Argentina), 42 Regent Street, Edinburgh EH5 2AY [1] (1948)

1985   Rev. Robert T. Bone (Malawi), 6 Burnbank Terrace, Kilsyth G65 0AE [16] (1960)

Mr. Ian O. Coltart, CA (North India), 161 Kirk

1986   Rev. George Cooper, BD (Kenya), 69 Montpelier Park, Edinburgh EH10 4WD [1] (1966)

1987   Miss Mary E. Rough, RGN, SCM, MTD (Blantyre), 6 Glebe Street, Dumfries DG1 2LF (1971)

1988   Miss Elizabeth Alexander (Kenya), c/o WMU 121 George Street, Edinburgh EH2 4YN

Dr. Betty Cowan (India), 2 Sunningdale Square, Kilwinning KA13 6PH

Mrs. Elsabe A. A. Irvine (Malawi), 60 Thirlestane Road, Edinburgh EH9 1AR

In writing to advertisers please mention the "Year-Book"

THE UNIVERSITIES

ST. ANDREWS—University College of St. Mary (*Founded 1539*)
St. Andrews [0334] 76161
*Principal—*D. W. D. Shaw, MA, LLB, BD
*Dean of the Faculty—*J. D. Martin, MA, BD, PhD

Chairs—		Ord.	Apt.
Divinity (1539)	D. W. D. Shaw, MA, LLB, BD 77254	1960	1979
Biblical Criticism (1539)			
Hebrew and Oriental Languages (1668†)	William M'Kane, MA, PhD, DLitt, DD, FBA, FRSE 73797	1949	1967
Ecclesiastical History (1710†)	James K. Cameron, BD, PhD, FRHistS 73996	1953	1970
Practical Theology and Christian Ethics (1934)	*Vacant*		

†Those chairs were for a time suppressed for want of funds and restored at dates given.

Lectureships—			
Divinity	*George B. Hall, BA, BD, PhD 75882	1963	1973
	M. D. Hampson, BA, DPhil, ThM 74578	...°	1977
Old Testament Language and Literature	Peter Coxon, BA, MA 74823	...°	1968
Hebrew and Old Testament	*James D. Martin, MA, BD, PhD 77361	1962	1969
	R. B. Salters, MA, BD, PhD 73198	1966	1971
Ecclesiastical History	J. S. Alexander, MA, BD, BA, PhD 72680	1966	1973
	D. W. Lovegrove, MA, BD, PhD [033 485] *Strathkinness 692*	...°	1978
New Testament Language and Literature	A. J. M. Wedderburn, MA, BD, PhD 74923	1975	1972
	R. A. Piper, BA, BD, PhD	...°	1980
Practical Theology	J. M. Keeling, BA, MA [0333] *Anstruther 311532*	1959°	1972
	Steven G. Mackie, MA, BD 74149	1956	1974
	David Lyall, BSc, BD, STM, PhD 72435	1965	1987

*Tutor in Elocution—*Mrs. Frances M. Martin, LCST, LRAM, LGSM

* Senior Lectureship.   ‡ Part-time.   ° Not Minister of Church of Scotland.

GLASGOW—University Faculty of Divinity and Trinity College
*Dean of the Faculty—*George Newlands, MA, BD, PhD
*Principal of Trinity College—*Robert Davidson, MA, BD, DD
*Clerk to the Faculty—*Patricia M. M'Gill, MA
*Clerk of Trinity College Senate—*Ian Hazlett, BA, BD, Dr theol

Chairs—		Ord.	Apt.
Divinity (1640)	George M. Newlands, MA, BD, PhD 041–334 4712	1970	1986
Old Testament Language and Literature	Robert Davidson, MA, BD, DD 041–427 5793	1956	1972

		Ord.	Apt.
Lectureships—			
Hebrew and Semitic Languages	†Robert P. Carroll, MA, PhD *041–339 0440*	...°	1969
Old Testament	Alastair G. Hunter, MSc, BD *041–632 4143*	1976	1980
Ecclesiastical History	Gavin White, BA, BD, STM, PhD *041–632 3151*	1954°	1971
	W. Ian P. Hazlett, BA, BD, Dr theol *041–423 7461*	...	1979
New Testament Language and Literature	§John K. Riches, MA *2235 20254*	1966°	1971
Biblical Studies (New Testament)	John M. G. Barclay, MA, PhD *041–954 4867*	...°	1984
Systematic Theology	§Joseph Houston, MA, BD, DPhil *041–954 7764*	...	1970
Practical Theology	David S. M. Hamilton, MA, BD, STM *041–956 1839*	1958	1984
	‡David A. R. Millar, MA *041–334 8769*	1956	1971
	Norman J. Shanks, MA, BD	1983	1989

University Librarian—Henry J. Heaney, MA, FLA
Teacher of Elocution—Dorothy Devine
Director of Field Education—Kenneth Gardner
†Reader.   ‡Part-time.   °Not Minister of the Church of Scotland.   §Senior Lecturer.

ABERDEEN—University Faculty of Divinity and Christ's College
Dean of the Faculty—W. Peter Stephens, MA, BD, DrScRel
Master of Christ's College—H. R. Sefton, MA, BD, STM, PhD
Secretary of the College Council—Alan Main, TD, MA, BD, STM, PhD
Correspondence should be addressed to King's College (AB9 2UB)

		Ord.	Apt.
Chairs—			
Systematic Theology (1620)	James B. Torrance, MA, BD *481526*	1954	1977
Practical Theology (Christ's College) (1934)	Alan Main, TD, MA, BD, STM, PhD *641100*	1963	1980
Church History (1616)	W. Peter Stephens, MA, BD, DrScRel *638107*	1960°	1986
Hebrew and Semitic Languages (1673)	William Johnstone, MA, BA, BD *316022*	1963	1980
New Testament Exegesis (1860)	I. Howard Marshall, MA, BA, BD, PhD *315259*	1962°	1979
Lectureships—			
Old Testament	Kenneth T. Aitken, BD, PhD *480967*	...°	1981
Systematic Theology	Trevor Hart, BA *483433*	1988°	1987
Church History	Henry R. Sefton, MA, BD, STM, PhD *572305*	1957	1972
New Testament Exegesis	Ruth B. Edwards (Mrs.), MA, PhD *314734*	...°	1982

		Ord.	Apt.
Teaching Fellows—			
Old Testament	‡Elizabeth M. Johnstone, BA, BLitt *316022*	...°	1984
New Testament	Max M. B. Turner, MA, PhD *494382*	1976°	1986
Practical Theology	Ainslie Walton, MA, MEd, HDipRE *485925*	1954	1987
	‡Kenneth Dupar, BA, BD, PhD *319845*	1965	1986
	‡Robert F. Brown, MA, BD, ThM *322549*	1971	1988

*Lecturer on Elocution—*R. B. Sawdon, LGSM, RSTC
°Not Minister of the Church of Scotland.　　‡ Part-time.

EDINBURGH—University Faculty of Divinity and New College
*Dean of Faculty—*Mr. D. F. Wright, MA
*Principal of New College—*Rev. Prof. D. B. Forrester, MA, BD, DPhil

		Ord.	Apt.
Chairs—			
Hebrew and Old Testament Studies (Personal Chair)	J. C. L. Gibson, MA, BD, DPhil *031–669 3635*	1959	1987
New Testament Language, Literature and Theology (1843)	John C. O'Neill, BA, BD, PhD, *031–229 6070*	1960	1985
Ecclesiastical History (1694)	Stewart J. Brown, BA, MA, PhD *031–343 1712*	...°	1988
Divinity (including Philosophy of Religion and Apologetics) (1583)	*Vacant*		
Systematic Theology (Thomas Chalmers Chair) (1843)	James P. Mackey, BA, LPh, BD, STL, DD, PhD　*031–225 9408*	1958°	1979
Christian Ethics and Practical Theology (1843)	Duncan B. Forrester, MA, BD, DPhil　　*031–337 5646*	1962	1978

Lectureships—			
Systematic Theology and Religious Studies	*Frank Whaling, MA, ThD *031–337 5119*	1962°	1973
	Ruth Page, MA, BD, DPhil *031–662 4564*	1976	1979
	David A. S. Fergusson, MA, BD, DPhil　　*031–339 1726*	1984	1986
	Bruce L. M'Cormack, BA, MA, MDiv	...°	1987
	A. Alistair Kee, MA, BD, STM, PhD　　*041–334 9992*	...°	1988
	Nicolas Wyatt, BA, BD, MTH, PhD　　*031–229 3461*	...	
Ecclesiastical History	*David F. Wright, MA *031–443 1001*	...°	1964
	*A. C. Ross, MA, BD, STM, PhD *031–447 5987*	1958	1966
	Susan Hardman Moore, MA, MAR, PhD	...	1987
Hebrew and Old Testament Studies	*A. Graeme Auld, MA, BD, PhD *031–552 2910*	1973	1973
	*A. Peter Hayman, BA, PhD *[062 081] Gifford 218*	1972°	1972

		Ord.	Apt.
New Testament Language, Literature and Theology	*David L. Mealand, MA, MLitt, PhD 031–445 3713	...	1972
	*Douglas A. Templeton, BA, BD, PhD 031–225 2013	...	1968
	Peter S. Cameron, LLB, BD, PhD, LRAM [0361] Duns 82229	1984	1987
Christian Ethics and Practical Theology	*Alastair V. Campbell, MA, BD, ThD 031–443 3250	1966	1969
	*Robin M. Gill, BD, MSocSc, PhD [089 082] 248	1969°	1972
	J. Ian H. M'Donald, MA, BD, MTh, PhD, FEIS 031–332 2172	1958	1980
	‡T. Stewart M'Gregor, MA, BD 031–229 5332	1957	1970
Fieldwork Director	George D. Wilkie, OBE, BL	1948	1986

Librarian of New College—Murray C. T. Simpson, MA, PhD, ALA, LRAM
031–225 8400

Fulton Lecturer on Elocution—Richard J. Ellis, BSc, MEd, LGSM   *031–447 4124*

*Senior Lecturer.   °Not Minister of Church of Scotland.   ‡Part-time.

MINISTERS ORDAINED FOR FIFTY YEARS AND UPWARDS

1921 John Elder, MC MA (Cults East)

1922 Daniel Blades, MA (Fala and Soutra)
Robert Robertson, MA (Collace)

1923 A.Rae Grant, MA BD (Cults West)
John P.Murray, MA (Dun)

1924 Benjamin Jones (South Africa)
Alexander King, DD (Overseas Council)
George F.MacLeod, MC DD (Glasgow Govan)
James S.Stewart, DD (University of Edinburgh)
George K. Wood, MA (Channelkirk)

1925 Hugh Erskine Fraser, MA (Roslin)
William Gray, MA (Avonbridge)
Kenneth MacFadden, MA (Hownam *with* Morebattle *with* Yetholm)
Neil A.MacLean, MA (Falkirk Laurieston St Columba)
G.H.Makin (Saughtree)

1926 Douglas G.Bisset, MA JP (Kingsbarns)
F.J.L.Maclauchlan, MC MA (Swinton)
J.Stewart Rough, MA (St Monans)
Ian G.Simpson, MA (Ceres)
Charles E.Stewart, MA (Dornock)

1927 Edgar P.Dickie, MC BA MA DD LLD (University of St Andrews)
Harry V.Gibbons (Monifieth Panmure)
John A.Hall, MA (Strathkinness)
R.M.Howieson, MA (Blairgowrie St Andrew's)
Duncan M'Diarmid, MA JP (Rosskeen)
P.H.R.Mackay, MBE MA PhD (Leslie & Waulkmill *with* Premnay)

James Morton, MA (Millport West)
John M.Rose, MA (Edinburgh West St Giles')
Ninian B. Wright, MBE DD (Kingussie)

1931 George Buchanan, OBE MA DD (Christ Church Bermuda)
John P. Crosgrove, MA (Sorbie)
Alex A.Ewing, MA BD (Ladykirk *with* Whitsome)
Joseph Grant, MC DD (Advie *with* Cromdale)
William F.Grieve, BSc (Glasgow Camphill Queen's Park)
David Y. Howie, MA (Aberdeen Ruthrieston South)
Alex Hutchison (Alvie and Insh)
Robert L.Kinnis, BD (Glasgow Baillieston Mure Memorial)
T.M.M.M'Auslane (Gartly *with* Kennethmont)
W. Murray Mackay, MA STM (Newton Mearns)
Ian R.N.Miller, MA (Madderty *with* Trinity Gask & Kinkell)
Archibald H.Minto, MA STM (Crieff St Andrew's)
John Muirie, MA (London Caledonia Road)
R. Leonard Small, OBE DD (Edinburgh St Cuthbert's)
R.A.Trotter, MA (Indian Ecclesiastical Establishment)
Arthur A.Mullo Weir, MA (Forglen)

1932 Merricks Arnott, MA (Rosneath St Modan's)
Alastair S.Calder, TD MA (Grantully and Strathtay)
Donald M.Caskie, MA HCF (Monkton and Prestwick)
Thomas M Donn, MA (Duthil)
James M.Ewing, MA (Cromarty)
John Johnston, MBE MA BD JP (Inverkeithing St Peter's)
G.Rendle Leathem, MA BD (Springfield)
John M'Kenzie, MA BCom (Glasgow Greenhead Barrowfield)
John Murray, MA (Slains and Forvie)
David A.Tosh, MA (Kirkmichael and Straloch)
C.J.Mullo Weir, MA BD DPhil DD (University of Glasgow)
James S. Wood, DD (Aberdeen South)

1928 John MacLeod, MA MTh (Lochcarron *with* Shieldaig)
William Paterson, BSc (Dundurn)
Donald H.Stewart, MA (Greenock Finnart)

1928 Michael M.Corner, MA BD (Grangemouth West)
Alec Macara, MA (Irvine Old)
William M'Craw, MA BD (Monimail)
George Milne, MA (Rothes High)

1929 A.S.Archibald, MA (Crawford)
William C.Bigwood, MA BD DD (Edinburgh St Andrew's and St George's)
John S.Dinwoodie, MA (Pittenweem)
R.M.Macdonald, OBE MA DD (Calabar)
John Macpherson, MA PhD JP (Daviot and Dunlichity)
Harald L.Mooney, MA (Deerness *with* St Andrew's)
James Murray, MA (Newtonmore)
George Nicholson (Karachi)
K.N.Paterson, MA BD DipEd (Pluscarden)
Norman W.Porteous, DD (University of Edinburgh)
Martin Shields, MA (Luss)
Alan G.Smith, BA (Logie Easter)
John A.R.Watt, MA BD (Stromness North)
James A.Williamson, CBE MA DD (Kirkurd *with* Newlands)
Frank Wood, MA BD (Edinburgh Morningside)

1930 W.M.Cunningham, MA (Cairneyhill)
D.Dewar Duncan, MA (Forfar West)
Campbell Ferenbach, VRD MA (Edinburgh Liberton)
J.Clarence Finlayson, MA (Edinburgh Grange)
G.S.Hendry, DD (Bridge of Allan Holy Trinity)
R.D.M.Johnston, MA (Ayr Sandgate)
Thomas H.Keir, DD (Melrose St Cuthbert's)
Donald M'Cuish, MA (Caddonfoot)
James F Macdonald, TD (Bendochy and Kinclaven)
John M.MacKinnon, MA (Dollar West)

1933 Philip Conacher, MA (Edinburgh John Ker Memorial)
James L.Cotter, MA BD (Dalserf)
Robert L.Crawford, MA (Annan Erskine)
John H.Duncan, MA BD (Earlston)
John M.Hunter (Borgue)
John H.A.Inglis, MA (Penpont and Keir)
R.A.N.Lapsley, MA (Buenos Aires)
D.M.Mackenzie, MA (Kinross West)
E.R.Marr, MA (Buittle)
William Martin, MA (Kenmuir Mount Vernon)
William A. Moore, MA BD (Cawdor)
J.S.Robson, MA (Army Chaplain)
W.Roy Sanderson, BD DD (Stenton *with* Whittingehame)
Roderick Smith, DD (Edinburgh Braid)
W.H.Watson, DD (Livingstonia)
Henry N. Willox, MBE MA BD (Carnwath)

1934 R.Nichol Bell, MA BD (North Berwick Abbey)
Walter M.Calderwood (Leven Forman)
Donald Campbell, MA (Bervie)
Henry Cumming, MA (Bridge of Weir Freeland)
D.Brock Doyle, MA (Bowling)
David S. Elder, MA BD (Sanquhar St Ninian's)
Hadden M.Gilmour, MA JP (Glenbuchat Towie)
Walter J.Gordon, MA BD STM (Aberdeen St Mark's)
Andrew Herron, DD LLD (Presbytery Clerk at Glasgow)
O.Tudor Hughes, MBE BA (Guernsey St Andrew's in the Grange)
A.M.Hunter, BD PhD DPhil DD (University of Aberdeen)
John G.Levack, MA BD (Prestonkirk)
Duncan A.MacCallum (Connel)
Kenneth Macleod (Nigg Chapelhill)
John Mowat, MA (Presbytery Clerk at Aberdeen)
John A.Newall (Resolis)
Thomas R.Robertson, MA BD (Broughton Glenholm and Kilbucho *with* Skirling)
Matthew Shields (Edinburgh Newington St Leonard's)

Ministers ordained for fifty years and upwards—*continued*

Robert Smith, MA (Levern and Nitshill)
John S.Thomson, MA (Covington & Thankerton *with* Libberton & Quothquan)
Edward S.Towill, MA BD MEd (Lecturer, Religious Education)
William Turner, MA BD (Gargunnock)
John Warnock, MA BD (Biggar Gillespie Moat Park *with* Elsrickle)

1935   Ian A.Auld, MA (Banchory Devenick)
Douglas Beck (Dunfermline St Ninian's)
R.W.A.Begg (Kippen)
David Cairns, MA DD (University of Aberdeen)
George Candlish, MA BD BSc (Home Board)
Mungo Carrick, MA BD (Ardgour *with* Strontian)
William M.Dempster, OBE MA STM (Paris)
J.Blair Gillon, MA (Borthwick *with* Heriot)
Alexander W.Greig (Boyndie)
John D.Jones, MA (Kirkconnel St Mark's)
Angus Logan, MA (Coldstream)
A.G.MacAlpine, MA STM (Tain)
John M'Ghie, MA (Comrie and Strowan)
James Macmillan, MA (Edinburgh Corstorphine St Anne's)
Kenneth J.Macpherson, MA (Durinish)
W.Morton Mauchline, MA BD (Largs St John's)
Alexander K.Mincher, MA BD DD (Nigeria)
George D.Monro, TD MA (Yester)
George T.H.Reid, MC MA BD DD (Aberdeen Langstane)
William Robertson, MA BD (Paisley Greenlaw)
David W.Rutherford, MC MA BD (Aberdour St Fillan's)
Robert Smith, MA VD (Balerno)
David Stevens, MA (Glenesk)
M.A.Vipont, MA (Saughtree)
Horace Walker, OBE MA BD DD (Home Board)
W.Fraser Wills, MA (Kilsyth Burns)

1937   Sidney Adamson, MA BD (Musselburgh Inveresk St Michael's)
William I.Bremner, MA (Fauldhouse Crofthead)
William Campbell, MA (Carmichael *with* Pettinain)
Ian M.W.Collins, MA BD, of Darvel Central
Andrew M.Douglas, MA (Hamilton Cadzow)
Andrew J.Easton (Dunlop)
David R.Watson, MA (Greenock St Paul's)
William M.G.Edgar, MA (Auchindoir and Kildrummy)
David G.Gray, MA BD (Dundee St Peter's)
John R.Gray, BSc (Jamaica)
Anthony J.Grubb, MA BD (Deer)
R.A.Howieson, JP MA (Newport-on-Tay St Thomas's)
Samuel Kennedy (Methven)
Frederick Levison, MA (Eccles *with* Greenlaw)
J.Victor Logan, MA (Crailing *with* Eckford)
Norman Macdonald, MA BD (Aberdeen Trinity)
Charles Y.M'Glashan, CBE DD (St Andrews Holy Trinity)
A.Taylor MacKenzie, MA BD (Auchterless)
F.Gordon M'Laren. MA (Strichen)
Hector A.M.MacLean, MA (Duror *with* Glencoe)
J.H.Boyd Macphail, MA (Aberfoyle)
Alexander MacVicar, MBE MA (Genoa)
J.B.Mirrilees, MA BD (Aberdeen High Hilton)
Robert A.Philp, BA BD (Stepps St Andrew's)
A.E.Rogerson, MA (Galashiels Ladhope St Cuthbert's)
James T.Runciman, MA (Greenock Wellpark West)
Harry C.Thomson, MA BD PhD (Glasgow Anniesland Cross)
R.V.Selby Wright, CVO TD DD FRSE JP (Edinburgh Canongate)

1938   David Barr, MA BD (Hospital Chaplain)
Alestair Bennett, TD MA (Strathkinness)

1936   Michael M.Bogle, MA (Banton)
Malcolm Buchanan, MA (Dingwall Castle Street)
Stewart Couper, MA BD (The Glens)
H.Russell Ferrie, MA (St Vigean's and Auchmithie)
John R.Fleming, MA BD ThD DD (University of St Andrews)
A.Isabella Gordon, BD (Manchuria)
John W.Goudie, MA MTh (West Kilbride Barony)
J.Hay Hamilton, MA BD (Colmonell)
A.M.Honeyman, BD BLitt PhD (University of St Andrews)
Adam Jack, MA BD (Kirkcudbright St Cuthbert's)
G.T.Jamieson, BA (Stirling Viewfield)
John A.Kitchin, MA (Perth West)
James A.Lindsay, MC MA (Burnside)
Alastair D.MacCalman (Busby West)
Norman Macdonald (Ardchattan)
R.P.Mackenzie, MA BD (Dunfermline St Leonard's)
Allan MacLeod, MA BD (Dunoon Old)
Robert C.M.Mathers, DD (Edinburgh St Matthew's)
James G.Matheson, MA BD DD (Portree)
John H Paterson (Dalton *with* Hightae)
Francis William Rae, MA BD STM DD (Dairsie *with* Kemback)
H.G.Reid, TD BD (Troon St Meddan's)
Joseph S.Ritchie, MBE MA (Haddington West)
Alexander Roberts, MA (Dunblane St Blane's)
Donald Robertson (Lochalsh and Stromeferry)
Robert M.F.Ross, FPhS (Glasgow Plantation)
W.C.B.Smith, MBE JP (Glassary)
David Steel, BD DD LLD (Linlithgow St Michael's)
Finlay J.Stewart, BA BD (Lochgelly Churchmount)
William Stewart, MA BD DD (Lecropt)
A.M.Sutherland, MA (Resolis)
Ronald S Wallace, BSc MA PhD (Lanark St Kentigern's)

John M. Bisset, MA (Glasgow Abbotsford Chalmers *with* St Ninian's Wynd)
P.F.C.Black, MA (Edzell Lethnot)
Norman Brook, MA BD (Montrose St Luke's)
Gavin S.Brown, MA BD (Falkirk Laurieston)
Donald Cameron, MA BSc JP (Blair Atholl and Struan)
James M.Couper, MA BD (Kilmodan and Colintraive)
Richard Cunningham, MA (Garvald and Morham)
Arthur H.Curtis (Professor)
Andrew B.Doig, DD BD STM (Secretary, National Bible Society)
Eric Duncan, MA BD MLitt (Teacher, Religious Education)
George B.Duncan, MA (Glasgow St George's Tron)
A.A.Fleming, BSc JP (Howgate)
Alexander Fraser, MA BD (Cumlodden and Lochfyneside)
Robert Hamilton, MA BD (Kelso Old)
David C.Henderson, CBE DD (Glamis)
Edward T.Hewitt, MA (Newmilns Loudon Old)
Peter M.Innes, MBE MA (Assam)
H.M.Jamieson, MA BD (Ashkirk *with* Lilliesleaf)
Thomas Kinloch, MA (Bannockburn Ladywell)
Robert G.Lawrie, MA (Denny Old)
R.Stewart Louden, TD DD DLitt (Edinburgh Greyfriars)
George W.H.Loudon MA BD STM (Bolton and Saltoun)
William Macartney, MA (Vienna)
W.A.M'Farlane, MA (Glasgow St Cuthbert's Queen's Cross)
A.K.Mackay (Kirkintilloch Park)
Donald G.M.Mackay, MA BD STM (Edinburgh Greenbank)
Johnston R.M'Kay, TD MA BD LLD (Greenock Finnart St Paul's)
J.M.M'Kechnie, MBE MA (Kilchrenan and Dalavich)
David N.M'Leish, MA (Fisherton)
Donald MacLeod, MA (Fairlie)
J.Fraser M'Luskey, MC DD (London St Columba *with* Newcastle)

Ministers ordained for fifty years and upwards—*continued*

Kenneth M.Macmillan (Appin)
J.S.Malloch, MBE BL MA BD (College of Education)
William Meiklejohn, MA (Rosneath St Modan's)
T.Boyd Miller (Kirkintilloch Hillhead)
A.A.S.Mitchell, MA BD (Fraserburgh Old)
John Moffat (Dunrossness)
Archibald A.Orrock, MA BD (Teacher, Religious
    Education)
J.Stanley Pritchard, MA (B B C)

Crichton Robertson, MA (Cockpen & Carrington *with*
    Lasswade)
Ronald Robertson, MA BD (Scone Old)
D.M.G.Stalker, MA BD (Lecturer, Biblical Studies)
Alexander T.H.Taylor (Dunoon St Cuthbert's)
James H.Telfer, MA (Ayr Trinity)
James Waugh, MA (Falkirk Camelon Trinity)
W.E.Williamson, BA (Cummertrees *with* Ruthwell
    and Mount Kedar)

THE UNITED REFORMED CHURCH IN THE UNITED KINGDOM

The United Reformed Church was formed on 5th October 1972 by the joining together of the Presbyterian Church of England with the Congregational Church in England and Wales. Its membership at the time of formation was approximately 200,000 with 1,950 local churches arranged in 12 Provinces and 65 Districts. Its overseas mission work in Africa, Asia and Australasia is carried out in conjunction with the Council for World Mission.

On 26th September 1981 an incorporating union took place between the United Reformed Church in England and Wales and the Reformed Association of Churches of Christ of Great Britain and Ireland.

The Church is a constituent member of the World Alliance of Reformed Churches and enjoys close relations with the Church of Scotland, the Presbyterian Church in Ireland and the Presbyterian Church of Wales, as well as with the Congregational Unions of Scotland and Ireland and the Union of Welsh Independents.

NOTA BENE.—The General Secretary will be glad to receive from Ministers the names and addresses of members or adherents of the Church of Scotland coming to reside in parts of England remote from a Church of Scotland charge and will forward them immediately to the nearest Minister; or Ministers may send names to the Secretary of the District Council within whose bounds the members will be living—names and addresses of the officers of the Synods and Districts are printed on the following pages.

The General Assembly of the United Reformed Church will meet from 1st to 4th July 1989 at York University.

Moderator (1988–89)—Revd. EDMUND A. BANYARD.

Moderator-Elect (1989–90)—Revd. C. KEITH FORECAST, MA.

General Offices of the Church—United Reformed Church House, 86 Tavistock Place, London WC1H 9RT   *01–837 7661*   Cables: Unichurch London WC1H.

General Secretary and Clerk of Assembly—Revd. Bernard G. Thorogood, MA.

Deputy General Secretary—Revd. John P. Reardon, BA.

Office and Personnel Manager—Mr. Hilary Gunn.

PERIODICAL PUBLICATION—"REFORM"

Editor—Mr. Norman Hart

THE TAVISTOCK BOOKSHOP

86 Tavistock Place, London WC1H 9RT

Manager—Mr. David Gassington

Tel: 01–837 9116 (Sales)

01–837 9028 (Accounts)

DEPARTMENTS

MINISTRIES

Central—Revd. Anthony G. Burnham, BA, Convener
Vocations—Revd. Michael B. Stolton, BD, Convener
Training—Mrs. Elizabeth Jupp, Convener
Support—Revd. Peter J. Brain, MA, BA, Convener

FAITH AND LIFE

Convener—Revd. Anthony J. Coates, MA, BA
Departmental Secretary—Revd. Terry Oakley, BA
Doctrine and Worship—Revd. Colin Gunton, Convener
Christian Education and Stewardship—Revd. William W. Mahood, BA, MTh, Convener
Children's Work—Lesley Husselbee (Mrs.) MSc, PhD, Convener
Pilots Panel—Mrs. Alma Kendall, Convener
Ministry of Healing—Revd. D. Alasdair Pratt, MA, STM, Convener
Youth—Revd. Jean Holdsworth (Mrs.), Convener

CHURCH AND SOCIETY

Convener—Dr. Mary Ede
Secretary—Revd. John P. Reardon, BA

WORLD CHURCH AND MISSION

Convener—Mrs. Rosalind E. Goodfellow, JP, BA
Secretary—Revd. Donald W. Elliott, BD, BSc, ACGI
Personnel—Revd. Raymond Adams, BA, Convener
Missionary and Ecumenical Work at Home—Revd. John F. Slow, Convener
Missionary and Ecumenical Work Abroad—Revd. Derek M. Wales, Convener
Mission and Other Faiths—Revd. F. Roger Tomes, Convener
Consultant on Jewish Matters—Revd. Ronald H. Lewis

FINANCE AND ADMINISTRATION

Chairman—Mr. Angus M. Grimmond
Secretary and Chief Accountant—Mr. Clement M. Frank, FCA
Treasurership—Mr. Desmond Davies, Convener
Maintenance of the Ministry—Revd. John D. Waller, MA, BA, FEA
Welfare and Emergencies—Revd. C. Cyril Franks, Convener
Church Buildings—Revd. Julian Macro, Convener
Retired Ministers' Housing—Revd. David L. Skidmore, Convener
Legal Advisers—Messrs. Hewitt, Woolacott and Chown
86 Station Road, Redhill, Surrey RH1 1PL

THE COLLEGES

College	*Principal*
Westminster, Cambridge *353997*	Revd. Martin H. Cressey, MA
Mansfield, Oxford *270988*	Revd. J. Charles Brock, BSc, BD, MLitt
Northern, Manchester *061–224 4381*	Revd. Dr. Robert J. McKelvey, BA, MTh, DPhil
Memorial, Aberystwyth *0792 298282*	Revd. Dr. D. Eurig Davies
Queen's, Birmingham *021–454 1527*	Revd. Dr. James B. Walker, MA, BD, DPhil
Bala/Bangor, Bangor *353402*	Revd. R. Tudur Jones, DD

PROVINCIAL MODERATORS

I—Northern

The REVD. DAVID JENKINS,, BA, BD, STM,
Office: St. James's Church, Northumberland Road, Newcastle NE1 8SG
091–232 4375
Home: 66 Kenton Road, Gosforth, Newcastle upon Tyne NE3 4NP
091–285 6994
Assistant: Mrs. C. Dixon

II—North Western

The REVD. ANTHONY G. BURNHAM, BA,
Office: Franklin Street, Patricroft, Eccles, Manchester M30 0QZ.
061–789 5583
Home: 4 Marlowe Drive, Didsbury, Manchester M20 0DE   061–445 9608

III—Mersey

The REVD. ERIC S. ALLEN, BD,
Office: (a.m. only) 63 Alton Road, Birkenhead L43 1UZ   051–653 7096
Home: 32 Westwood Road, Noctorum, Birkenhead L43 9RQ   051–652 6030
Admin. Officer: Revd. A. B. Webster, MA   051–638 2718

IV—Yorkshire

The REVD. DONALD H. HILTON, BA,
Office: 43 Hunslet Lane, Leeds LS10 1JW   0532 451267
Home: 18 Lidgett Lane, Roundhey, Leeds LS8 1PQ   0532 666627
Admin. Secy: Mr. John E. M. Gilbey, MA   0924 373847

V—East Midlands

The REVD. JOHN F. SLOW, Dip Theol,
Office: Sherwood U.R.C., Edward's Lane, Nottingham NG5 3AA
602 609241
Home: 11 Mountsorrel Drive, West Bridgford, Nottingham NG2 6LJ
0602 812974
Assistant: Mrs. C. Chaplin

VI—West Midlands

The REVD. JOHN D. WALLER, MA, BA, FCA,
Office: U.R.C. Digbeth-in-the Field, Moat Lane, Yardley,
Birmingham B26 1TW   021–783 1177
Home: 22 Ferndown Road, Solihull, West Midlands B91 2AT   021–705 3617
Admin. Officer: Mr. N. Webb   021–743 6656

VII—Eastern

The REVD. WILFRED K. GATHERCOLE, MA, BD
Office: U.R.C. Stowmarket, Suffolk IP14 1AD   0449 615130
Home: 7 Shakespeare Road, Stowmarket, Suffolk IP14 1TJ   0449 675603

VIII—South Western

The REVD. MICHAEL F. HUBBARD, MA, BA,
Office: 3 Elm Grove, Taunton, Somerset TA1 1EG   0823 275470
Home: As above
Admin. Secy.: Mrs. L. Head

IX—Wessex

The Revd. Nelson W. Bainbridge, MA,
Office: U.R.C., King's Road, Chandler's Ford, Eastleigh, Hants SO5 2EY
  0703 266548
Home: 23 Hocombe Wood Road, Chandler's Ford, Hants SO5 1PN
  0703 261510
Assistant: Mrs. S. Lambert

X—Thames North

The Revd. Michael J. Davies, FCIS,
Office: The City Temple, Holborn Viaduct, London EC1A 2DE
  01–583 8701
Home: 8 Batchworth Lane, Northwood, Middlesex HA6 3AT 092 74 27709
Admin. Officer: Mr. L. Tatton

XI—Southern

The Revd. David L. Helyar, MA,
Office: East Croydon U.R.C., Addiscombe Grove, Croydon CR0 5LP
  01–688 3730
Home: 88 Bridle Road, Shirley, Croydon, Surrey CR0 8HE 01–777 2344

XII—Wales

The Revd. John I. Morgans, BA, BD, B Litt, Ph D,
Office: City U.R.C., Windsor Place, Cardiff CF1 3BZ 0222 371102
Home: 12 Heol Dyfed, Penrhys, Rhondda CF43 3PT 0443 756754
Assistant: Mrs. G. Lawrence

DISTRICT SECRETARIES

Province I—Northern

District A—*Northumberland*
Churches 30
Members 2,076

The Rev. David A. Brown, BA,
3 River View, Morpeth,
Northumberland NE61 1JU 0670 57431

District B—*Newcastle*
Churches 38
Members 4,249

The Rev. Ann F. Jackson, MA, BD,
80 Grosvenor Road, South Shields NE33 3QE
  091–456 2052

District C—*Durham*
Churches 15
Members 1,333

Mr. Laurence A. Nicol,
49 Hipsburn Drive, Sunderland, Tyne and Wear
SR3 1TY 091–522 6489

District D—*Teesside*
Churches 19
Members 1,692

The Rev. Richard G. Helmn, BA,
10 Farington Drive, Marton, Middlesborough,
Cleveland TS7 8PH 0642 326343

District E—*Cumberland*
Churches 13
Members 1,167

The Rev. Robert R. Bance, B Sc,
South View, Duffton, Appleby, Cumbria CA16 6DF
  0930 52454

District F—*Mid Scotland*
Churches 8
Members 378

Dr. P. Arthur,
4 Corrour Road, Glasgow G42 2DT
  041–632 2431

Province II—North Western

District A—*Lancaster*
Churches 19
Members 1,582

Mr. MONTY HELMN,
3 Lindeth Road, Silverdale, Carnforth, Lancs LA5
0TT   *0524 701060*

District B—*Fylde*
Churches 23
Members 2,472

The REV. GLYN EATOCK, BA,
23 Beaufort Avenue, Bispham, Blackpool FY2 9HF
0253 52020

District C—*N.E. Lancs*
Churches 21
Members 1,356

The REV. GEOFFREY K. TOLLEY,
Highbury, Oldfield Road, Darwen, Lancs
0254 772449

District D—*North West
          Manchester*
Churches 23
Members 1,596

THE REV. B. S. JOLLY,
100 Alexandra Road, Lostock, Bolton BL6 4BG
0204 693476

District E—*North East
          Manchester*
Churches 30
Members 2,078

Mr. C. BARLOW,
5 Lyons Drive, Bury, Lancs BL8 2EA
061–764 8724

District F—*South East
          Manchester*
Churches 36
Members 3,212

DR. C. T. CALAM,
Horseshoe Cottage, Horseshoe Lane, Alderley Edge
SK9 7QP   *0625 583190*

District G—*South West
          Manchester*
Churches 16
Members 1,333

Mr. W. BLACK,
17 Winstanley Road, Sale, Manchester M33 2AG
061–962 3568

Province III—Mersey

District A—*Cheshire*
Churches 32
Members 2,036

The REV. A. F. E. WISE, MSc, D Tech,
Parkgate Road, Neston, S. Wirral L64 6QF
051–336 1275

District B—*Sefton*
Churches 17
Members 1,637

The REV. D. GLANVILLE REES, BA, BD, MA,
29 Melling Road, Southport PR9 9DU
0704 33353

District C—*Liverpool*
Churches 19
Members 1,242

The REV. (Mrs.) RUTH W. FARNWORTH,
18 Stormont Road, Liverpool L19 1QG
051–427 3479

District D—*Wirral*
Churches 23
Members 2,549

Mr. A. J. CARTER, BA,
43 Mount Road, Higher Bebington L63 5PQ
051–608 4131

District E—*St. Helen's-Wigan*
Churches 16
Members 1,244

Mr. A. C. GILLOOLEY,
10 East Mount, Orrell, Wigan WN5 8LR
0942 223110

Province IV—Yorkshire

District A—*East Yorkshire*
Churches 23
Members 1,232

Mr. G. A. LAWRENCE, MA,
32 Croftway, Selby YO8 9DD   *0757 704193*

District B—*South Yorkshire*
Churches 28
Members 1,762

Mr. J. B. SWIFT,
16 Crabtree Lane, Sheffield S5 7AY   *0742 426072*

District C—*Leeds*
Churches 23
Members 2,165

Mrs. M. HERBERT,
2 Park Crescent, Leeds LS8 1DH   *0532 661068*

District D—*Bradford*
Churches 23
Members 1,237

The REV. ALAN F. T. EVANS,
81 Denbrook Avenue, Tong Street, Bradford BD4
0QN   *0274 681112*

District E—*Wakefield &*
Dewsbury
Churches 18
Members 891

Miss M. M. HIRST,
11 Kennedy Close, Hanging Heaton, Dewsbury
WF12 7EL   *0924 465462*

District F—*Huddersfield &*
Halifax
Churches 24
Members 1,262

The REV. W. J. TAYLOR,
16 Grasmere Road, Gledholt, Huddersfield
HD1 4LJ   *0484 36400*

Province V—East Midlands

District A—*Derbyshire*
Churches 33
Members 1,494

The REV. MICHAEL T. BOND,
Stanley Mount, Alma Road, Tideswell, Buxton SK17
8ND   *0298 871498*

District B—*Leicestershire*
Churches 28
Members 1,607

Mr. D. E. JOLLEY,
36 Moat Road, Loughborough LE11 3PN
0509 212183

District C—*Lincoln*
Churches 25
Members 1,587

The REV. ERIC M'DONALD, MA,
193 Barrowby Road, Grantham, Lincs NG31 8NN
0476 73418

District D—*Northants, North*
Beds & N. Bucks
Churches 44
Members 1,821

Mr. A. W. THOMSON,
42 Churchill Way, Kettering, Northants NN15 5BZ
0536 520143

District E—*Nottinghamshire*
Churches 17
Members 1,446

The REV. ALAN C. WHITE, MA,
79 Nottingham Road, Keyworth, Nottingham NG12
5GS   *060 77 3769*

Province VI—West Midlands

District A—*Staffordshire*
Churches 37
Members 2,670

The REV. W. D. WILLIAMS,
1 Waverley Gardens, Wombourne, Staffs
0902 324037

District B—*Shropshire*
Churches 25
Members 796

The REV. A. EVANS, BD,
34 Conduit Lane, Bridgenorth WV16 5BO
074 62 3567

District C—*Worcester &*
Hereford
Churches 17
Members 1,216

Mr. P. H. TURNER, BSs, MRCS,
90 Stratford Road, Bromsgrove B60 1AT
0527 74094

District D—*Gloucester*
Churches 23
Members 1,092

Mr. A. E. M'CULLOCH,
27 Grange Park, Whitchurch, Ross-on-Wye HR9
6EA   *0600 890550*

District E—*Birmingham*
  Churches 30
  Members 3,004

The Rev. A. B. Holroyd, MA,
10 Silvermead Road, Sutton Coldfield, B73 5SR
021–354 2307

District F—*Coventry*
  Churches 25
  Members 1,820

Mr. P. Lambden,
21 Staverton Leys, Rugby CV22 5RD
0788 812927

Province VII—Eastern

District A—*Norwich*
  Churches 27
  Members 1,668

The Rev. W. H. Clement, BA,
30 Collingwood Road, Great Yarmouth, Norfolk
NR30 4LR   *0493 52010*

District B—*Ipswich &*
          Colchester
  Churches 39
  Members 1,984

The Rev. John A. Pugh,
17 Temple Road, Stowmarket, Suffolk IP14 1AT
0449 612516

District C—*Chelmsford*
  Churches 37
  Members 1,988

Mrs. D. Dean,
2 Burrswood Place, Heybridge Basin, Maldon CM9
7UQ   *621 56661*

District D—*Southend*
  Churches 21
  Members 1,854

Mr and Mrs. C. Raggett,
3 Thomas Close, Leigh on Sea S59 2XF
0702 77073

District E—*Cambridge*
  Churches 38
  Members 2,035

The Rev. Donald M'Ilhagga, MA
49 Tenterleas, St. Ives PE17 4QP   *0480 68535*

Province VIII—South West

District A—*Cornwall &*
          Plymouth
  Churches 15
  Members 925

The Rev. Bryan M. Alderson,
6 Tamar Villas, Plymstock, Plymouth PL9 7PE
0752 401294

District B—*Torbay*
  Churches 16
  Members 845

The Rev. G. E. F. Bowerman, BA,
60 Carlton Road, Torquay TQ1 1LZ   *0803 212648*

District C—*Devon, East*
  Churches 19
  Members 926

Mr. M. T. Pearce,
Ty Croeso, Offwell, Honiton EX14 3RY
040 483 304

District D—*Taunton*
  Churches 25
  Members 811

The Rev. John W. M'Minn, MA,
41 Mudford Road, Yeovil, Somerset BA21 4AE
0935 71327

District E—*North-East Wilts*
  Churches 15
  Members 705

Mr. R. G. Gray,
Broxburn, Silver Street, Minety, Wilts SN16 9QU
0666 860643

District F—*Bristol*
  Churches 37
  Members 2,840

Mrs. C. Fry,
88 Berkeley Road, Bishopton, Bristol BS7 8HG
0272 41063

District G—*North Devon* Churches 13 Members 439	The Rev. JOHN E. TICEHURST, BD, The Manse, Franklyn Avenue, Braunton, Devon EX33 2JY *0271 812574*
District H—*Mid Wilts* Churches 6 Members 128	Mr. H. O. PACKER, 17 Kenilworth Gardens, Melksham, Wilts SN12 6AE *0225 702432*
District J—*West Wilts* Churches 5 Members 264	Mrs. A. COOKE, 1 Field Close, Westbury, Wilts BA13 3AG *0373 864402*

Province IX—Wessex

District A—*Dorset* Churches 49 Members 3,260	The Rev. K. F. SOUTHERN, BA, 28 Ridgeway, Sherborne DT9 6DA *0935 814348*
District B—*Southampton* Churches 25 Members 1,835	Mrs. C. HARDWICK, 34 Randall Road, Chandler's Ford, Eastleigh S05 1AL *0703 253432*
District C—*Portsmouth* Churches 26 Members 1,424	Mr. E. REES, MA, 72 Waverley Road, Southsea, Hants PO5 2PR *0705 829430*
District D—*Guildford* Churches 27 Members 2,556	Mr. F. H. BROOMAN, CB, Tuach, Ellesmere Road, Weybridge KT13 0HS *0932 845253*
District E—*Reading & Oxford* Churches 42 Members 3,027	The Rev. D. F. WILKINS, BD, 1 Heathermount, Harmons Water, Brecknell, Berks RG12 3QF *0344 54677*

Province X—Thames North

District A—*Central &* *North London* Churches 35 Members 2,258	Mrs. M. STACY, 31 Fordington Road, London N6 4TD *01–883 3131*
District B—*West* Churches 20 Members 2,378	The Rev. K. W. MARSH, BD, 154 Joel Street, Northwood, Middlesex HA5 2PE *01–866 7034*
District C—*Chiltern* Churches 18 Members 1,271	The Rev. COLIN, FURSE, 7 Sutton Avenue, Slough SL3 7AP *0753 39300*
District D—*St. Albans* Churches 33 Members 2,888	The Rev. A. G. HAMILTON, 1 Cedar Close, Potter's Bar, Herts EN6 1EW *0707 52149*
District E—*Lea Valley* Churches 24 Members 1,316	Mrs. R. WIGGLESWORTH, 2c Grazebrook Road, London N16 0HS *01–809 0641*
District F—*Roding* Churches 29 Members 1,491	The Rev. W. J. BROWN, MA, 12 Capstan Square, Stewart Street, Cubitt Town, London E14 9EU *01–515 1658*

Province XI—Southern

District A—*Wimbledon*
  Churches 32
  Members 2,832

Miss E. STONE,
42 Woodgate, London Road, Ewell KT17 2BD
01–393 8672

District B—*Croydon*
  Churches 24
  Members 3,631

Mrs. A. MORGAN,
38 Cordrey Gardens, Coulsdon CR3 2SP
01–668 5994

District C—*Bromley*
  Churches 41
  Members 3,026

Mrs. C. WINTER,
31 The Grove, West Wickham BR4 9JT
01–777 1687

District D—*Medway*
  Churches 26
  Members 1,920

Mr. H. RING,
18 Bargrove Road, Vinters Park, Maidstone ME14
5RR   *0622 56344*

District E—*Canterbury*
  Churches 23
  Members 1,553

Mrs. J. BRADSHAW,
4 Segrave Road, Folkestone CT19 6AY
0303 54948

District F—*Sussex East*
  Churches 25
  Members 2,435

Mrs. M. R. ELLIOTT,
36 Montacute Road, Lewes BN7 1EP
0273 474 783

District G—*Sussex West*
  Churches 23
  Members 2,486

Mr. I. F. SINCLAIR,
2 Park View Terrace, Brighton BN1 5PW
0273 508780

Province XII—Wales

District A—*North Wales*
  Churches 24
  Members 1,410

The REV. J. DOUGLAS FARQHAR,
The Manse, Queensway, Shotton, Clwyd CH5 1HD
0244 812655

District B—*East Wales*
  Churches 28
  Members 761

Mrs. MARGERY DAVIES,
29 Crown Rise, Llanfrechfa Cwnbran, Gwent
036 33 61248

District C—*South Wales*
  Churches 37
  Members 2,306

Mrs. E. DAVIES,
1 Duffryn Close, Park End, Roath Park, Cardiff
0222 75209

District D—*West Wales*
  Churches 15
  Members 989

Mr. ARTHUR BALCH,
6 Pleasant View, Brynhyfryd, Swansea SA5 9HB
0792 792503

District E—*Pembrokeshire*
  Churches 24
  Members 671

The REV. DAVID FOX, B Sc,
1 Merlins Gardens, Tenby, Dyfed SA70 9AE
0834 4979

District F—*Mid Wales*
  Churches 26
  Members 674

Mrs. M. E. GRIFFITHS,
All Saints Cottage, Glasbury, Hay-on-Wye HR3 5LT
049 74 543

OTHER PRESBYTERIAN CHURCHES

THE REFORMED PRESBYTERIAN CHURCH OF SCOTLAND

Moderator—Rev. Barry Galbraith

Stated Clerk—Rev. A. Sinclair Horne, 17 George IV Bridge, Edinburgh EH1 1EE
031–220 1450

Treasurer of Synod—James Blair, Esq., Stranraer

The Joint Reformed Presbyteries of Edinburgh and Glasgow meet on first Monday of February, September and November, and on 30th May, 1989.

The Synod meets on 30th May, 1989, in Wishaw Reformed Presbyterian Church at 6.30 p.m.

The Church is in full ecclesiastical fellowship with the Reformed Presbyterian Churches of Ireland and of North America, and the Ministers of all three Churches are on a "mutual eligibility" footing.

THE FREE CHURCH OF SCOTLAND

Moderator (1988)—Rev. John A. Gillies, MA, Glasgow

Moderator Designate (1989)—Rev. K. W. R. Cameron, Thurso

Clerks—Rev. Professor Clement Graham, MA, BD
Rev. Professor John L. Mackay, MA, MLitt, BD

General Treasurer—Iain D. Gill, CA

Law Agents—Messrs. Simpson and Marwick, WS

Offices—The Mound, Edinburgh EH1 2LS *031–226 4978* and *5286*

Assembly meets 23rd May, 1989, in Assembly Hall, Johnston Terrace, Edinburgh EH1 2PU

College—The Mound, Edinburgh EH1 2LS *031–226 4978*

Principal—Rev. Professor A. C. Boyd, MA, BD

Presbyteries	*Clerks*
1. Edinburgh and Perth	Mr. Donald Jack, 20 Summerside Place, Edinburgh EH6 4NZ
2. Glasgow	Rev. Donald MacIver, BA, 9 Meadow View, Kildrum, Cumbernauld G67 2BY
3. Argyll and Lochaber	Rev. John J. Murray, Rockfield Road, Oban PA34 5PQ
4. Inverness	Rev. D. C. Meredith, Free Church Manse, Resaurie, Inverness IV1 2NH
5. Ross	Rev. Hugh M. Cartwright, MA, Ferintosh, Conon Bridge IV7 8HX
6. Caithness and Sutherland	Rev. J. H. MacLean, Free Church Manse, Lairg IV27 4AZ
7. Lochcarron	Rev. Ronald MacKenzie, Glenelg, Ross-shire IV40 8OA
8. Lewis	Rev. K. M. Ferguson, Free Church Manse, Crossbost, Lewis PA86 9NP
9. Skye and Uist	Rev. W. J. Campbell, MA, Free Church Manse, Staffin Road, Portree IV51 9HP

Foreign Missions, with centres in (*a*) Kingwilliamstown, Umtata, Butterworth, Cape Town, Southern Africa; (*b*) Lima, Cajamarca, Moyobamba, Peru; (*c*) Lakhnadon, Chhapara and Jabalpur, CP, India.

Overseas Missions: Congregations at Vancouver, Toronto, Detroit, and in Prince Edward Island.

THE FREE PRESBYTERIAN CHURCH OF SCOTLAND
The Synod meets at Inverness on Tuesday, 23rd May, 1989
Moderator
Rev. Lachlan MacLeod, 43 Denholm Street, Greenock PA16 8RH
Clerk of Synod
Rev. Donald MacLean, 13 Kingsborough Gardens, Glasgow G12 9NH   *041–339 0553*
General Treasurer
Mr. W. D. Fraser, Room 7, Seafield House, Seafield Road, Inverness IV1 1SJ

Presbyteries	Clerks
Northern	Rev. A. Murray, MA
	Free Presbyterian Manse, Lairg, Sutherland
Skye	Rev. F. MacDonald, MA
	Free Presbyterian Manse, Portree, Isle of Skye
Western	Rev. Neil Ross, BA
	Free Presbyterian Manse, Ullapool, Ross-shire
Southern	Rev. D. J. MacDonald, MA
	167 Glasgow Road, Perth PH2 0LY
Outer Isles	Rev. J. MacLeod, MA
	Free Presbyterian Manse, 16 Matheson Road, Stornoway

Theological Tutors
Rev. A. Macdonald, MA, Gairloch; Rev. J. M. MacLeod, MA, Stornoway;
Rev. D. B. MacLeod, MA, Dingwall

Foreign Mission—Zimbabwe

Overseas—Canada, Australia, New Zealand

Editor of "Free Presbyterian Magazine"
Rev. D. B. Macleod, MA, Free Presbyterian Manse, Achany Road, Dingwall
Editor of "Young People's Magazine"
Rev. Neil Ross, BA, Free Presbyterian Manse, Ullapool, Ross-shire

---

THE UNITED FREE CHURCH OF SCOTLAND
The General Assembly will meet in Glasgow, on Monday, 5th June, 1989.
Moderator—Rev. Arthur McGill Lawless, 40 Randolph Road, Glasgow G11 7LG
041–334 2773

Moderator Designate—Rev. James Cassels, MA,
3 Beresford Place, Edinburgh EH5 3SL   *031–552 4980*

Principal Clerks
Rev. J. G. McPhee, 32 Craig Road, Tayport
0382 552650

Rev. J. C. Allan BD, Erskine Manse, 116 Kinghorn Road, Burntisland
0592 873718

General Secretary—Mrs. Isabel D. Baird, United Free Church Offices
11 Newton Place, Glasgow G3 7PR   *041–332 3455*

Honorary Treasurer—Mr. J. Gray, 28 Elmore Avenue, Glasgow G44 5AD
Editor of "Stedfast"—Mr. David R. Beatty, 99 Howes Drive, Heathryfold, Aberdeen
AB2 8EH   *0224–690759*

Auditors—Messrs. Davidson and Workman, Glasgow

Presbyteries	Clerks
Lothian and Borders	Rev. Alexander Innes, MA
	31 Yewlands Crescent, Edinburgh EH16 6TB
	031–664 1705
Glasgow and the West	Rev. A. D. Scrimgeour, BD, ThM
	19 North Erskine Park, Bearsden, Glasgow
	041–942 6570
Alloa and Dunfermline	Rev. J. C. Allan, BD
	Erskine Manse, 116 Kinghorn Road, Burntisland
	0592 873718

Dundee	Rev. G. B. Bruce, LTh Millburn, Ferryden, Montrose *0674 3772*
Aberdeen and the North	Rev. T. A. B. Patterson, UF Manse, Balintore, Tain IV20 1UR *086–283 2281*

THE PRESBYTERIAN CHURCH IN IRELAND

The General Assembly will meet in The Assembly Hall, Church House, Belfast
on Monday, 5th June, 1989, at 7 o'clock, evening, and thereafter
each day in the Assembly Hall until Friday 9th June.

Moderator
Rt. Rev. A. W. Godfrey Brown, BA, PhD, DD, FRHisS, Ballycastle

Clerk of the General Assembly and General Secretary of the Church
Very Rev. T. J. Simpson, MA, LLB, DipEd, DD,
Church House, Belfast BT1 6DW   *Belfast 322284*

Presbyteries	*Clerks*
Ards	Rev. C. W. D. Kerr, MA 111 Crawfordsburn Road, Bangor, Co. Down BT19 1BJ
Armagh	Rev. J. W. Lockington, BA, BD, MTh, PhD Greenfield Manse, 72 Newry Road, Armagh BT60 1ER
Ballymena	Rev. James Gordon 120 Church Road, Glenwherry, Ballymena, Co. Antrim BT42 3EJ
Belfast North	Rev. J. M'Allister, MA 5 Lismoyne Park, Belfast BT15 5HE
Belfast South	Rev. W. A. Finlay, MA 24 Myrtlefield Park, Belfast BT9 6NE
Belfast East	Rev. Herbert Courtney, BA 20 Glendun Park, Dunmurry, Belfast BT17 9AY
Carrickfergus	Very Rev. R. V. A. Lynas, BA, DD Gardenmore Manse, Lower Cairncastle Road, Larne BT40 1PQ
Coleraine	Rev. W. I. Hunter, BSc, BTh 8 Ballywatt Road, Cloyfin, Coleraine BT52 2LT
Derry and Strabane	Rev. R. C. Graham, BA 59 Limavady Road, Londonderry BT47 1LR
Donegal	Rev. T. J. Stothers, BSc, BD MTh The Manse, St. Johnston, Lifford
Down	Rev. Samuel Armstrong 17 Downpatrick Road, Crossgar, Downpatrick BT30 9EQ
Dromore	Rev. John McCaughan, BA 8 Portulla Drive, Lisburn BT28 3JS
Dublin and Munster	Rev. W. T. McDowell, BA, BD, DD 9 Sandymount Green, Dublin 4
Foyle	Rev. William McKinney, BA 36 Woodburn Park, Londonderry BT42 1PS
Iveagh	Rev. J. H. Robinson, BSc, BD 109 Newry Street, Rathfriland BT34 5PZ
Monaghan	Rev. Walter Herron, BA The Manse, Smithborough, Co. Monaghan

Presbyteries	Clerks
Newry	Rev. S. Finlay, 156 Glasdrumman Road, Annalong, Co. Down BT34 4QL
Omagh	Rev. J. F. Murdoch, BA, BD 28A Dublin Road, Omagh, Co. Tyrone BT78 1HE
Route	Rev. H. B. Wallace, MA 211 Straid Bushmills BT57 8XB
Templepatrick	Rev. W. D. Weir, BA, BD, DipEd, 50 Killead Road, Crumlin BT29 4EN
Tyrone	Rev. R. Dickinson, MA, BD, DD 6 Magherafelt Road, Tobermore BT45 5PH

THE PRESBYTERIAN CHURCHES OF WALES

(Eglwys Bresbyteraidd Cymru)

GENERAL ASSEMBLY

Moderator (1988–89)—Rev. R. G. Alun Richards, BA, BD, 6 Maes-y-Coed, Morriston, Swansea SA6 6DS [0792] 72396

General Secretary—Rev. D. H. Owen, BSc, BD, 53 Richmond Road, Cardiff CF2 3UP [0222] *Cardiff 494913*

Treasurer (1986–91)—Mr. Alun Creunant Davies, JP, MA, Y Wern, Piercefield Road, Penparcau, Aberystwyth, Dyfed SY23 1RV [0907] *612925*

The Mission Board
Secretary—Rev. D. Andrew Jones, MA, 53 Richmond Road, Cardiff CF2 3UP [0222] *494913*

THE ASSOCIATION IN NORTH WALES

Moderator—Rev. Trefor Jones, Craig Menai, Ffordd Bangor, Caernarfon, Gwynedd LL55 1LR [0286] *3264*

Secretary—Rev. John Owen, BA, BD. Cwr y Coed, 3 Erw Goch, Ruthun, Clwyd LL15 1RR [08242] *2388*

Treasurer—Mr. Hugh Williams, 20 Ffordd Meiriadog, Old Colwyn, Colwyn Bay, Clasyd LL29 9NR [0492] *516329*

THE SOUTH WALES ASSOCIATION

Moderator—Rev. J. D. Williams, BA, BD, 78 Hoel y Gat, Penygroes, Llanelli, Dyfed SA14 7RL [0269] *844260*

Secretary—Rev. A. W. Edwards, BA, BD, Neuadd Wen, Tregaron, Dyfed SY25 6JD [097 44] *285*

Treasurer—Mr. Dan O. Griffiths, Lluest, Ffordd Llanqoedmor, Penparc, Cardigan, Dyfed SA43 2AB [0239] *612867*

THE ASSOCIATION IN THE EAST

Moderator—Rev. W. H. Whomsley, BA, 34 Coldstream Street, Llanelli, Dyfed SA15 3BH [0554] *758356*

Secretary—Rev. J. L. Dowber, 110 Llandudno Road, Penrhyn Bay, Llandudno, Gwynedd LL30 3HL [0492] *49896*

Treasurer—Mr. G. Dixey, 27 Dunstable Road, Newport, Gwent NP9 9NE [0633] *277416*

OTHER CHURCHES IN SCOTLAND

BAPTIST UNION OF SCOTLAND

President
Mr. David Sked
Craigerne, 25 The Glebe, Aberdour

Secretary
Rev. Peter H. Barber, MA, BD
14 Aytoun Road, Glasgow G41 5RT   *041–423 6169*

CONGREGATIONAL UNION OF SCOTLAND

President
Rev. J. R. Smith
82 Lansine Road, Paisley PA1 3NL   *041– 889 5010*

General Secretary
Rev. Robert Waters, MA
Church House, PO Box 189, Glasgow G1 2BX   *041–332 7667*

RELIGIOUS SOCIETY OF FRIENDS

Clerk of the General Meeting for Scotland

Alan Davies, 23 Livingston Place, Edinburgh EH9 1PD

ROMAN CATHOLIC CHURCH

Bishop's Conference in Scotland
President
Most Rev. Thomas J. Winning, DD
48 Newlands Road, Glasgow G43 2JD

Secretary
Rt. Rev. Maurice Taylor
Candida Casa, 8 Corsehill Road, Ayr KA7 2ST

SALVATION ARMY

Territorial Commander, Scotland
Colonel Dinsdale Pender, Houldsworth Street, Glasgow G3 8DU

SCOTTISH EPISCOPAL CHURCH

Primus
The Most Rev. Lawrence Edward Luscombe,
7 Shaftesbury Road, Dundee DD2 1HF

Secretary General and Treasurer
John G. Davies
21 Grosvenor Crescent, Edinburgh EH12 5EE   *031–225 6357–8*

THE SYNOD OF METHODIST CHURCH IN SCOTLAND

Chairman
Rev. Alan P. Horner, BA, BD
7 Rowanlea Drive, Giffnock, Glasgow G46 6BS   *041–633 1434*

Secretary
Rev. E. Raymond Watker
Dormarky, Glasgow Road, Kilsyth, Glasgow G65 9AE   *[0236] Kilsyth 823135*

OVERSEAS CHURCHES

The Church of Scotland is in partnership with over three hundred churches worldwide. It shares with them in membership of the World Council of Churches and the World Alliance of Reformed Churches, and with many of them it has direct partnership arrangements. The addresses of a number are given below. The Church of Scotland World Mission and Unity Year Book contains a fuller list.

Presbyterian Church in Canada
Clerk of Assembly, 50 Wynford Drive, Don Mills, Ontario

United Church of Canada
General Secretary, 85 St. Clair Avenue East, Toronto 7, Canada

Presbyterian Church (USA)
General Secredtary, 100 Witherspoon Street, Louisville,
KY 40202-1396, Kentucky, USA

Reformed Presbyterian Church in North America
General Synod, 1818 Missouri Avenue, Las Cruces, New Mexico, USA

Cumberland Presbyterian Church
General Secretary, Box 5535, Memphis 4, Tennessee, USA

Reformed Church in America
General Secretary, 475 Riverside Drive, NY 10115, New York, USA

United Church of Christ
General Secretary, 297 Park Avenue South, New York 10, USA

Uniting Church in Australia
General Secretary, P.O. Box E266, St. James, NSW 2000, Australia

Presbyterian Church of Australia in New South Wales
General Secretary, P.O. Box 100, 44 Margaret Street, Sydney, NSW 2001, Australia

Presbyterian Church of Australia in Queensland
General Secretary, Ann Street, Brisbane, Queensland 4000, Australia

Presbyterian Church of Australia in South Australia
Stated Clerk, 371 Angas Street, Adelaide, South Australia

Presbyterian Church of Australia in Victoria
Stated Clerk, 156 Collins Street, Melbourne 3000, Australia

Presbyterian Church of Australia in Western Australia
Clerk of Presbytery, P.O. Box 220, Leederville, Western Australia 6007

Presbyterian Church of New Zealand
Executive Secretary, P.O. Box 10-100, The Terrace, Wellington, New Zealand

Presbyterian Church of Southern Africa
General Secretary, P.O. Box 72057, Parkview, Johannesburg 2122, South Africa

Reformed Presbyterian Church in South Africa
General Secretary, 48 Eagle Street, Umtata, Transkei, South Africa

COMPARATIVE STATISTICS of Communicants, Elders, Baptisms, Sunday School Teachers and Scholars, and Bible Class Pupils from 1901 to 1986

FOR THE YEAR ENDING 31st DECEMBER 1987

	1901	1921	1941	1961	1983	1984	1985	1986	1987	+Increase or −Decrease
Congregations				2,212	1,748	1,765	1,758	1,745	1,727	−68
Communicants—										
Removal by Death	18,048	18,682	20,820	21,495	19,954	19,397	19,678	19,148	18,509	−639
Removals by Certificate	55,882	47,653	26,124	42,665	18,673	17,372	17,451	16,988	17,027	+39
Removals without Certificate	25,985	26,376	20,456	23,000	13,551	13,082	15,181	12,386	11,093	−1,293
Total Removals	99,915	92,711	67,400	87,160	52,178	49,851	52,310	48,522	46,629	−1,893
Admission on Profession	47,960	49,580	25,141	32,720	12,957	12,345	11,938	11,835	10,612	−1,223
Admission by Certificate	62,138	57,123	32,801	39,626	17,453	16,497	16,283	15,425	14,915	−510
Admission by Resolution				6,151	5,491	5,460	6,046	5,046	5,450	+404
Total Admissions	110,098	106,703	57,942	78,497	35,901	34,302	34,267	32,306	30,977	−1,329
Total on Rolls	1,163,594	1,277,634	1,268,839	1,292,617	902,714	887,165	870,527	854,311	838,659	−15,652
Elders	25,808	31,443	34,858	46,123	47,441	46,223	47,485	47,336	46,808	−528
Baptisms	60,444	49,026	34,627	50,387	21,276	20,390	20,069	19,830	18,794	−1,036
Sunday School Teachers and other Workers	46,506	41,279	31,188	39,527	23,447	22,505	22,148	22,009	20,799	−1,210
Sunday School Scholars	467,479	392,405	231,226	278,221	104,552	100,551	98,012	95,046	90,882	−4,164
Bible Class Pupils	141,792	126,284	48,711	71,089	37,149	35,477	34,403	32,100	30,728	−1,372

RELATIVE STATISTICS FOR SCOTLAND

	1901	1921	1941	1961	1983	1984	1985	1986
Total Population	4,472,103	4,882,497	5,007,000	5,178,490	5,150,405	5,145,722	5,136,509	5,121,303
Adults (20 years and over)	2,520,946	2,964,685	3,325,000	...	3,328,023	3,689,569	3,705,486	3,717,234
Children of school age	866,908	871,072	753,000	...	983,176	778,869	756,936	739,218
Children born	132,192	123,201	89,743	101,169	65,078	63,596	65,266	66,348

MEMBERSHIP LOSSES IN 1987

The membership decrease shown on the opposite page may be set out thus:

Remove by death	18,509	
Less Admit by profession	10,612	7,897
Remove by certificate	17,027	
Less Admit by certificate	14,915	12,112
Other removals	11,093	
Less Restorations	5,450	5,643
Total Decrease		15,652

From the above it is clear that the fall in membership is due mainly to failure to enrol new members to replace the deaths.

Those communicating at least once in the year amounted to 481,520, being 57.5% of membership (58.8% in 1986).

Infant baptisms in 1986 were 26% of births (29% in 1985).

STATISTICS ANENT MINISTRY

	1984	*1985*	*1986*	*1987*
At Home				
Charges at 31st December	1,427	1,428	1,402	1,387
Ministers serving Charges	1,348	1,299	1,290	1,264
Chaplains to H M Forces	33	33	32	32
Probationers available for Charges	12	18	10	9
Vacant Charges	79	111	112	137
Abroad				
Ordained Ministers and Chaplains	38	36	33	13
Vacancies for Ministers and Chaplains	9	9	9	2

	1985	*1986*	*1987*	*1988*
Students Completing their Courses				
New College, Edinburgh	23	20	19	21
Trinity College, Glasgow	20	27	20	32
St Mary's College, St Andrews	7	5	11	6
Christ's College, Aberdeen	11	10	9	13
	61	62	59	72

MINISTERIAL CHANGES DURING 1988

Obituary—Ministers and Licentiate

Church	Ord.	Ind.	Ref.	Church	Pres.	Date
Ainslie, Duncan	1943		1983	(Friockheim and Kinnell)	30	March 10
Anderson, George B MA	1939		1981	(Maybole Old)	10	June 7
Baillie, Andrew OBE MBE MA	1940		1984	(Colombo)	FF	September 10
Bennett, A Murdoch MA BD	1952	1960		Eaglesham Old and Carswell	16	January 30
Cameron, Ewen	1931		1971	(Millport)	10	October 2
Campbell, Archibald M MA	1939		1984	(Traquair)	28	January 2
Currie, David R MA BD PhD	1937		1974	Galashiels St Cuthbert's	4	July 21
Cumming, John W MA BD	1945		1985	(Edinburgh Palmerston Place)	1	December 30°
Dick, Robert C	1934		1970	(Edinburgh St Nicholas' Sighthill)	1	December 16°
Downie, Thomas A	1939		1981	(Edinburgh St Luke's)	1	August 25
Duff, Alexander M	1949		1977	(Symington)	17	March 14
Fairlie, A K MA	1931		1970	(Forres High)	1	February 13
Fraser, James D	1943		1983	(Inverallochy and Rathen East)	34	January 24
Gibson, John H MA	1938		1977	(Hospital Chaplain at Dumfries)	8	October 19
Greig, John S	1976		1983	(Lochalsh and Stromeferry)	28	October 12
Hamilton, C Douglas MA	1938		1974	(Glasgow Wilton)	16	January 1
Hannah, William Menzies	1938		1969	(Aberdour with Tyrie)	34	October 22°
Hendrie, George V	1961	1961		Wemyss	25	August 8
Hewitt, Edward J G	1973		1980	(Duntocher)	11	July 25
Hood, James W	1950	1961		Campbeltown Lorne Street	19	November 11°
Johnstone, R Lawrence	1944		1976	(Kirkcowan)	9	May 26
Johnstone, Walter MA	1937		1977	(Strathy and Halladale)	41	February 11
Kennedy, W Russell BA	1940		1978	(Skelmorlie and Wemyss Bay)	15	July 1
Lawson, Alexander A	1938		1970	Kilcalmonell with Skipness)	5	August 9
Logan, George R MA BD PhD	1937		1977	(Helensburgh Park)	18	April 26
M'Innes, Alasdair	1968		1981	(Ayr Sandgate St Columba Associate)	10	September 6
MacKenzie, Ian A MA	1929		1971	(Edinburgh Cairns Memorial)	FF	September 9
MacKinnon, Roderick MA	1931		1978	(Barra)	39	March 8
Maclean, Alex J OBE MA	1935		1975	(Rome)	39	June 14
Macpherson, D C	1939		1974	(New Cumnock Old)	10	November 3°
Matheson, Robert W MA	1929		1975	(St Mungo)	7	June 28
Miller, Alexander M'D JP MA	1946		1985	(Tranent)	3	July 16
Miller, Colin F MA BD DD	1937		1984	(Asst. Edinburgh Craigentinny St Christopher's)	1	January 2

Name					Pres.	Date
Mitchell, William James	1957	:	:	(Clydebank Faifley) 1973	18	February 27
Peat, John T MA	1950	:	:	(Ayton with Burnmouth) 1977	4	April 2
Pringle, Andrew	1945	:	:	(Stair) 1976	10	October 29
Ralph, Isaac	1951	1959		New Pitsligo	34	August 6
Richmond, Archibald J R MA	1944	:	:	(Penicuik St Mungo's) 1984	26	April 12
Robertson, John DipTh FSAScot	1963	:	:	(Paisley High) 1982	F	October 3
Robson, James S MA	1933	:	:	(Army Chaplain) 1962	F	October 6
Ross, Donald DD	1918	:	:	(Grantown South) 1959	36	May 12
Ross, Lewis D MA	1932	:	:	(Elchies and Archiestown) 1969	35	April 26
Sefton, George A MA BD	1927	:	:	(Fern and Careston) 1966	30	September 2
Smart, Harold B	1932	:	:	(Denny, Dunipace North with Old) 1970	23	March 18
Steel, Hector J MA	1939	:	:	(Glasford with Strathaven East) 1979	17	September 26
Tulloch, T Arthur MA	1934	:	:	(North Ronaldshay) 1978	45	February 28
Tweedlie, Ian M B Ac BD	1957	1958	:	Lugar with Old Cumnock St Ninian's	10	July 27
Waddell, Robert MA	1939	:	:	(Walkerburn) 1974	4	May 20

° 1987

Ministers who have demitted Charges

Name	Ord.	Ind.	Church	Pres.	Date
b Alston, Colin M BMus BD	1975	1980	Dulnain Bridge with Grantown on Spey	36	November 30°
d Anderson, Duncan W M BD	1978	1982	Glasgow New Cathcart	-	December 8°
a Armstrong, W Sinclair MA BD	1951	1971	Newton Stewart Penninghame St John's	9	October 31
d Burton, Keith BA MDiv PhD	1985	1985	Noth	F	August 22
a Carmichael, William BSc FLS	1972	1972	Edinburgh Restalrig	1	December 31°
a Clark, John FPhS	1949	1980	Dunblane St Blane's	23	June 30
a Cormack, James S	1965	1968	Wick Central	41	January 18
d Cowan, David	1971	1984	Corby St Ninian's	F	June 8
a Crawford, Ron L	1961	1973	Colonsay and Oronsay	21	October 31
a Crombie, Wm D MA BD	1947	1955	Glasgow Calton New with St Andrew's	16	December 31°
d Dickson, A Stuart	1963	1985	Glasgow Calton New with St Andrew's Associate	F	March 31
a Drummond, Gilbert L Th	1963	1967	Renfrew Trinity	14	February 29
a Easton Robert MA BD	1942	1956	Glasgow New Govan	16	October 31
a Ferrier, Walter M MA BD	1946	1952	North Berwick St Andrew's	3	July 31
a Frame, William H BTh	1975	1980	Newmains Coltness Memorial with Bonkle	17	August 31
a Fraser, James P	1951	1970	Strathaven Avendale Old and Drumclog	17	September 30
a Gordon, David C	1953	1982	Gigha and Cara	19	July 31
a Goring, John M MA	1955	1962	Dunfermline Gillespie Memorial	24	August 31
a Goudie, Stuart M MA BD	1951	1977	Perceton and Dreghorn	11	October 31

Name	Ord.	Ind.	Church	Pres.	Date
d Gravatt, John E. BA MDiv	1968	1983	Community Minister at Paisley	F	June 30
a Hall, Robert K	1968	1980	Carnock	24	July 31
b Harkes, George	1962	1971	Cumbernauld Old	9	March 31
b Harvey, W John BA BD	1965	1981	Glasgow Govan Old	16	June 30
b Hill, Roy MA	1962	1970	Forfar St Margaret's	48	February 29
a Irvine, Euphemia H C (Mrs) BD	1972	1972	Milton of Campsie	16	August 31
b Jenkins, Gordon F CMA BD	1968	1968	Dunfermline North	24	September 1
a Kant, Everard W FVCM	1953	1978	Kinghorn	25	April 30
a Law, Arthur ACIS	1968	1981	Kincardine in Menteith with Norrieston	23	June 30
a Lawson, Alexander H ThM ThD FPhS	1950	1956	Clydebank Kilbowie	18	October 31
d Leishman, R Murray MA	1957	1970	Hospital Chaplain, Edinburgh Royal	F	September 30°
a Lowe, Edwin MA BD	1950	1971	Caldwell	14	September 30
a Lyall, William R	1954	1954	Grangemouth Grange	22	December 30°
Macdonald Iain A	1986	1986	Iona & Ross of Mull with Kilfinichen & Kilvickeon	1	October 31°
b M'Donald, Sandy BA CMIWSc	1968	1974	Paisley St Mark's Oldhall	2	October 11
a M'Intosh, Hamish N MMA	1949	1982	Fintry	23	December 31°
a Mackie, David	1954	1981	Strachur and Strathlachlan	20	January 31
M'Lachlan, Fergus C	1982	1982	Dunbarney with Forgandenny	F	August 31
a MacLeod, Norman	1960	1978	Orwell with Portmoak	25	September 30
a MacLeod, William J DipTh	1963	1971	Kirkintilloch St David's Memorial	16	September 2
a Macrae, D A MA JP	1942	1956	Tarbert	43	April 2
a Martin, James MA BD DD	1946	1954	Glasgow High Carntyne	16	December 31°
a Monaghan, James TD MBE	1950	1966	Edinburgh Davidson's Mains	25	January 5
a Montgomery, Robert W MA BD	1953	1968	Aberdeen Melville Carden Place	31	September 30
a Munroe, Henry BA L Th LTI	1971	1971	Denny Dunipace North with Old	22	September 4
a Orr, John F MA	1949	1957	Edinburgh St John's Oxgangs	1	November 30°
d Patterson, Andrew R M MA BD	1985	1985	Mochrum	F	August 31
a Patterson, John M	1976	1976	Blackbraes and Shieldhill	22	December 31°
a Porter, Gair M BD DPS	1986	1986	Patna Waterside	F	September 6
a Porter, Richard MA	1953	1961	Glasgow Govanhill	16	June 30
a Rae, Andrew W	1951	1969	Annan St Andrew's Greenknowe Erskine	7	December 31°
a Raffan, Stanley J MA BD	1951	1977	Hospital Chaplain, Royal Crichton Dumfries	8	November 14°
f Riach, Donald S BL	1964	1965	Thurso St Peter's and St Andrew's	-	September 6
a Robson, James MA BD	1951	1957	Falkirk Camelon St John's	22	November 30°
a Ross, Hector G MA	1949	1965	Gillingham St Margaret's	47	April 3
b Ross, Kenneth R BA BD	1982	1982	Unst	-	January 10
a Sawers, Hugh BA	1968	1982	Motherwell St Andrew's	17	July 31
b Schofield, Melville F MA	1960	1967	Kilmarnock Laigh	1	February 29
a Scott, J Miller MA BD FSA(Scot) DD	1949	1985	Jerusalem	29	August 31
a Sim, James W	1950	1965	Shotts Erskine	17	September 6

b Sinclair, Colin A M BA BD	1981	1982	Ayr Newton on Ayr	16	July 31
a Skakle, George S MA	1945	1947	Aberdeen Powis	31	May 31
d Stoddart, A Grainger	1975	1982	Peterculter St Peter's	F	December 31°
a Sutherland, Alexander S	1952	1969	Symington with Craigie	10	November 30°
a Talman, Hugh MA	1943	1954	Polmont Old	22	December 31°
d Taylor, Philip L Th DPS	1983	1988	Edinburgh St Andrew's Clermiston	F	August 6
a Thomson, George F M MA	1956	1985	Dollar with Glendevon with Muckhart Associate	23	October 31
a Tyson, Kenneth E W	1978	1983	Fettercairn with Fordoun with Glenbervie	32	December 31°
a Walker, Alexander L	1955	1966	Glasgow Trinity Possil and Henry Drummond	16	June 30
d Wilson, P Douglas L Th	1979	1986	Aberdeen St Columba's Bridge of Don	-	February 29

a On grounds of age or health   b To non-parochial or overseas appointment

c Resigned from terminable appointment   d Left service of Church of Scotland   f Resigned status   ° 1987

Ministers Translated

Name	Ord.	Translated to	Previous Charge and Year of Induction		Date
Abernethy, William L Th	1979	Glenrothes St Margaret's	Airdrie Broomknoll	1979	February 18
Barr, G Russell BA BD	1979	Greenock St Luke's	Glasgow Garthamlock and Craigend East	1979	May 4
Beaton, Donald MA BD MTh	1961	Glenelg and Kintail	Kilmuir and Stenscholl	1982	April 21
Birrell, John M MA LLB BD	1974	Forfar St. Margaret's	Carluke St. Andrew's	1980	September 22
Birss, Alan D MA BD	1979	Paisley Abbey	Inverkeithing St Peter's	1982	March 2
Bowie, Adam M'Call	1976	Cavers and Kirkton with Hobkirk and Southdean	Dull and Weem with Fortingall and Glenlyon	1981	August 24
Brook, Stanley A BD	1977	Edinburgh Holy Trinity	Dundee Menzieshill	1977	January 6
Buchanan, Fergus C MA BD	1982	Milngavie St Paul's	Stevenston Ardeer	1983	April 20
Byers, Alan J	1959	Gamrie with King Edward	Boddam	1971	February 12
Cook, John W MA BD	1962	Edinburgh Portobello St Philip's Joppa	Kilmarnock Henderson	1970	February 10
Cunningham, Iain D MA BD	1980	Carluke Kirkton	Duntocher	1980	October 29°
Dick, J Ronald BD	1973	Edinburgh St John's Oxgangs	Corsock with Kirkpatrick Durham	1982	August 17
Drummond, R Hugh	1953	Balmaclellan with Kells	Pitsligo with Sandhaven	1981	September 29
Dunn, W Iain C	1983	Edinburgh Pilrig and Dalmeny Street	Cellardyke	1983	January 20
Dunsmore, Barry W MA BD	1982	Stirling St Columba's	Saltcoats Erskine	1982	February 4
Gilchrist, Ewen J BD DipMin	1982	Perth St Matthew's	Garelochhead	1982	April 27
Grant, J Gordon MA BD	1957	Edinburgh Dean	Troon Portland	1965	November 18°
Hutcheson, Norman M MA BD	1972	Dalbeattie with Urr	Kirkcaldy St Andrew's	1973	August 11
Johnston, Robert M Theol	1973	Edinburgh St Mary's with St Stephen's	Dundee Camperdown	1973	August 10
Kelly, T Clifford	1973	Ferintosh	Cargill Burrelton with Collace	1981	May 3
Lawson, Ronald G	1964	Greenock Mid	Dumbarton St Andrew's	1976	October 12

Name	Ord.	Translated to	Previous Charge and Year of Induction		Date
Lindsay, W. Douglas BD CPS	1978	Eaglesham Old and Carswell	Glasgow Partick South	1978	September 20
Logan, Thomas LTh	1971	Clydebank Abbotsford	Irvine St Andrew's	1978	August 30
Low, J E Stewart MA	1957	Rotterdam	Carnoustie Panbride	1979	July 1931
M'Cartney, Alexander C	1973	Caputh and Clunie	Cavers and Kirkton with Hawick St Mary's		
MacGillivray, Duncan	1977	Kirkmaiden with Stoneykirk	Rotterdam	1985	November 19°
M'Indoe, John H MA BD STM	1960	London St Columba's with Newcastle	Lanark St Nicholas'	1983	May 16
M'Intosh, Colin G BSc BD	1976	Dunblane Cathedral	Glasgow St John's Renfield	1971	February 12
Macintyre, Thomas MA BD	1972	Paisley Wallneuk North	Stevenston High	1976	August 18
Maciver, Norman BD	1976	Tarbert	Kilmuir and Paible	1976	August 16
M'Mullin, J Andrew MA	1960	Blackbraes and Shieldhill	Stoneywood	1976	October 28
Macnee, Iain	1975	Girvan South	Newbattle	1972	June 15
Mellis, Robert J BTh CA	1982	Tarbat	Knockando Elchies and Archiestown with Rothes	1985	May 18
Middleton, J R H LLB BD	1981	Edinburgh Davidson's Mains	Cumbernauld Kildrum	1982	March 24
Morton, R C MBA BD	1960	Jerusalem	Prestonpans Prestongrange	1981	July 13
Ness, David T LTh	1972	Ayr St Quivox	Dundonald	1973	July 14
Oxburgh, Brian H BSc BD	1980	Saltcoats St Cuthbert's South Beach	Dunnichen Letham and Kirkden	1972	June 8
Philip, Michael R	1978	Blairgowrie St Mary's South	Banton with Twechar	1980	June 29
Prentis, David F BSc BA	1975	Drumoak with Durris	Rousay	1978	January 13
Ramsay, William G	1967	Glasgow Springburn	Paisley Wallneuk North	1982	April 14
Ridland, Alistair K MA BD	1982	Dalkeith St John's and King's Park	Annbank	1981	January 7
Robertson, Alexander	1982	Aberluthnott with Laurencekirk	Glasgow Scotstoun East	1982	May 12
Shaw, Alastair N MA BD	1969	Kilmarnock Laigh	Irvine Relief	1981	November 6°
Steele, Leslie M MA BD	1982	Galashiels Old and St Paul's	Macduff Gardner	1982	October 31
Thompson, Edward J BA BD	1973	Troon Portland	Golspie	1973	February 9
Thomson, Andrew BA	1982	Renfrew Trinity	Campbeltown Lowland	1983	June 1
Thomson, John MA BD ThM	1976	Lanark St. Nicholas'	Houston and Killellan	1982	October 19
Thomson, William H	1978	Edinburgh Liberton Northfield	Glenrothes St Columba	1978	September 20
Watson, James LTh	1964	Bowden with Lilliesleaf	Wick Old	1976	December 16°
Wilkinson, W Brian MA	1968	Kirkwall East	Kilmore and Oban	1986	April 14
Wilson, Andrew G N MA BD	1968	Aberdeen Rubislaw	Bridge of Weir Freeland	1974	November 11°
Youngson, Peter	1977	Kirriemuir St Andrew's	Jura	1978	December 10°
	1961			1975	January 14

° 1987

Ministers Inducted to Parishes

Name	Parish	Date
* Allison, May M (Mrs) BD	Kirn	May 31
Anderson, Kenneth G MA BD	Abernethy and Dron with Arngask	January 14
* Bell, Thomas Y MA	Aberdeen St Fittick's	May 6
* Bonar, Alexander F L RIC	Musselburgh St Clement's and St Ninian's	July 28
* Brewster, John MA BD DipEd	East Kilbride Greenhills	April 21
Burns, John H BSc BD	Inch with Stranraer St Andrew's	March 3
* Coltart, Ian O	Wishaw Chalmers	May 31
* Couper, David S F MA BD	Alloa North	May 18
* Cranfield, Elizabeth F MA BD	Denbeath with Methilhill	June 30
Currie, Margaret F BEd BD	Airdrie St Columba's	December 17°
* Dick, James S MA BTh	Echt with Midmar	May 17
* Dryden, Ian MA DipEd	New Machar	June 23
Duncan, Graham A BEd BD	Cumbernauld Old	August 31
* Dunphy, R Graeme BA BD	Culloden	September 2
Erskine, Michael J BD	Inverkip	November 25°
Ferguson, John A BD DipMin	Kirkcaldy Old	June 16
Finlay, W Peter MA BD	Glasgow Townhead Blochairn	October 19
Forrest, Martin R BA MA BD	Glasgow Possilpark	February 4
* Frank, Regine W MA BSc BD	Whalsay and Skerries	September 3
* Frew, Rosemary (Mrs) MA BD	Largo and Newburn with Largo St David's	May 4
* Gardner, Bruce K MA BD	Carloway	October 21
* Gordon, Elinor J	Delting with Nesting and Lunnasting	August 13
Goudie, Stuart M MA BD	Dreghorn—Perceton and Dreghorn	August 27
* Gray, Kenneth N BA BD	Bridge of Weir Freeland	June 28
Hastie, George I MA BD	Cowdenbeath Cairns	May 11
* Hegarty, John	Glasgow High Carntyne	August 24
Henderson, Roy J M BD Dip Min	Alexandria St Andrew's	October 28°
* Jack, David L Th	Fettercairn with Fordoun with Glenbervie	August 4
* Kirk, William Logan MA BD MTh	Dalton with Hightae with St Mungo	March 15
Lees, Andrew P BD	Gourock Ashton	November 19°
Lennox, Gordon S BD DipPTh	Laggan with Newtonmfore	May 10
* Liddell, Margaret BD	Contin Strathconon	November 27°
* M'Alpine, Robin J BDS BD	Duntocher	June 9
* M'Cracken, Gordon A BD	Whitburn South	June 7
Macdonald, Iain A L Th	Edinburgh Burdiehouse	February 17
M'Gowan, Andrew T B BD STM	Glasgow Trinity Possil and Henry Drummond	September 15
* M'Intyre, Elizabeth J W	Darvel Irvinebank and Easton Memorial	August 18

Name	Parish	Date
* M'Kay, Violet C C BD	Glenrothes St Ninian's	May 19
* M'Kenzie, Alan BSc BD	Alloa West	July 13
* M'Leod, Alistair G	Glenrothes St Columba's	September 28
* MacLeod, Donald LTh	Snizort	September 2
* MacPherson, Kenneth J	Kilmallie	May 5
* Mitchell, David BD DipPTheo	Glasgow Colston Wellpark	June 23
* Murning, John BD	Glasgow New Cathcart	August 31
Nicol, George G BD DPhil	Inverkeithing St Peter's	September 28
Ogston, Edgar J BSc BD	Leven Scoonie Kirk	December 21°
* Page, John R BD DipMin	Dunlop	June 9
Redpath, James G BD DipPTh	Tulliallan and Kincardine	May 17
Rennie, Adrian J T BA BD	Glasgow Calton New with St Andrew's	May 12
Rew, Malcolm M BD	Edinburgh Albany Church for the Deaf	February 17
* Robertson, Peter BSc BD	Dallas with Forres St Leonard's with Rafford	June 3
* Ross, Alan C CA BD	Annan St Andrew's Greenknowe Erskine	February 16
Ross, William B LTh CPS	Findochty with Portknockie	October 7
Simpson, Gordon M MA BD	Leslie Trinity	April 20
* Smart, D Dominic BSc BD	Dundee Logie and St John's (Cross)	July 15
* Smith, Morris BD	Dulnain Bridge with Grantown on Spey	May 16
* Smith, Murdo MA BD	Manish-Scarista	September 23
Stiven, Iain K MA BD MEd	Strachur and Strathlachlan	August 16
Stoddart, A Grainger	Meldrum and Bourtie	June 8
Sutcliffe, Ian	Shapinsay	May 6
Taylor, Philip LTh DPS	Edinburgh St Andrew's Clermiston	March 24
* Thain, Graham M LLB BD	Polmont Old	June 20
* Thomson, Margaret (Mrs) BD	Saltcoats Erskine	June 28
Thomson, Martin BSc DipEd BD	Kirkcowan with Wigtown	May 18
* Wallace, Christopher BD	Balmaghie with Tarff and Twynholm	July 12
* Wallace, James K MA BD	Falkirk Camelon St John's	June 22
White, Earlsley M BA	Uddingston Park	October 30°
* Whyte, Margaret A (Mrs) BA BD	Symington with Craigie	May 31
Wilkie, James R MA MTh	Penpont Keir and Tynron	June 16
* Wilson, Ian M	Cawdor with Croy and Dalcross	May 18
* Young, Alexander W BD DipMin	Ardrossan Barony St John's	June 22

* Ordained and Inducted

° 1987

Ministers Introduced to Appointments

Name	Appointment	Date
Fazakerley, Alison	as Associate Minister at Ellon	September 22
Fields, James T	as Associate Minister at Greenock Old West Kirk	June 28
Goss, Alister J BD	as Industrial Chaplain at Inverclyde	October 7°
Hogg, Alison M BD DipMin	as Chaplain's Assistant at Aberdeen Hospitals	June 5
Johnston, John MA BD	as Hospital Chaplain at Dumfries Crichton Royal	October 1°
Johnston, Margaret H	as Associate Minister at Glasgow Maryhill Old with High	March 24
Kirkwood, Gordon BSc BD	as Associate Minister at Skene	April 12
Nicol, Douglas M	as Associate Minister at Glasgow Priesthill and Nitshill	May 18
Norman, Nancy M BA MDiv MTh	as Associate Minister at Eddlestonwith Lyne and Manor with Peebles Old	April 1
Watson, T David BSc BD	as Associate Minister at Kilmore and Oban	September 29

Ordinations

Name	Appointment	Date
Craig, Gordon T BD	as Chaplain to H M Forces (RAF)	April 5
Davidson, David W	as Auxiliary Minister at Kilarrow and Kilmeny	October 2°
Hay, Jared W	as Assistant at Edinburgh Cluny	August 30°
Scouler, Michael	as Chaplain to HM Forces	June 27

READJUSTMENT OF CONGREGATIONS

Unions

Name of United Church	Pres.	Uniting Congregations	Date
Aberdeen St Stephen's	31	Aberdeen Causewayend	Aberdeen Powis	September 1
Dalbeattie	8	Dalbeattie Craignair	Dalbeattie Park	December 9⁰
Hawick Teviot	6	Hawick St George's West	Hawick St Margaret's and Wilton South	March 22
Hobkirk and Southdean	6	Hobkirk	Southdean	March 6
Tarff and Twynholm	8	Tongland	Twynholm	March 9

Linkings

Name of Charge	Pres.	Linked with	Date	Name of Charge	Pres.	Linked with	Date
Balmaclellan	8	Kells	March 9	Hobkirk and Southdean	6	Cavers and Kirkton	March 6
Balmaghie	8	Tarff and Twynholm	March 9	Kells	8	Balmaclellan	March 8
Boddam	34	Peterhead West Associate	February 17	Kilrenny	26	Cellardyke	September 6
Boyndie	35	Cornhill and Ord	January 29	Kirkmaiden	9	Stoneykirk	February 10
Carfin	17	Newarthill	April 1	Newarthill	17	Carfin	April 1
Cavers and Kirkton	6	Hobkirk and Southdean	March 6	Peterhead W Associate	34	Boddam	February 17
Cellardyke	26	Kilrenny	September 6	Stoneykirk	9	Kirkmaiden	February 10
Cornhill and Ord	35	Boyndie	January 29	Tarff and Twynholm	8	Balmaghie	March 9
Dalbeattie	8	Urr	December 9	Urr	8	Dalbeattie	December 9

Dissolutions

Gillingham St Margaret's	April 3
Paisley St Matthew's	June 14
Perth St Paul's	June 14

THE GENERAL ASSEMBLY 1988

Summary of Decisions &c

The deliberations of the General Assembly 1988 are briefly summarised hereunder. Of necessity the phrasing has been much telescoped and reference should be made to the full text in the Blue Book. For ease of such reference the letters and figures in parentheses denote the Committee concerned and the relevant section of its deliverance. It should be noted, however, that the items have been set forth in the order in which the Committees appear on the official list and not that in which they reported to the Assembly, and that the deliverance-numbers are those in the final form as they appear in the "blue pages" of the Book in its ultimate form. A list of abbreviations will be found on page 346.

ACTS OF ASSEMBLY
I ACT anent CONGREGATIONS in an UNSATISFACTORY STATE, being a replacement for the Act of 1961. (See Blue Book, p 446)
II ACT anent the JUDICIAL COMMISSION, being a replacement for the Act of 1961 and giving finality of judgment to the Commission. (See Blue Book, p 450)
III ACT amending ACT IV 1984 anent UNIONS AND READJUSTMENTS, simplifying some of the procedure contained in the earlier Act. (See Blue Book, p 453)
V ACT amending ACT II 1970 anent MEMBERSHIP OF PRESBYTERY to the extent of including in Presbytery membership professors and lecturers in theological subjects in Universities and Colleges in the U K and to the Scottish Director of the Scripture Union. (See Blue Book, p 3)
VI ACT amending ACT V 1978 anent the PRESBYTERY OF EUROPE, by adding Lisbon to the list of included charges. (See Blue Book, p 302)

SENT TO PRESBYTERIES UNDER BARRIER ACT
ACT amending Act V 1984 anent Settlement of Ministers (see Blue Book p 231)—Replies to be in hands of Principal Clerk by 31st December 1988.
ACT anent a Young Persons Roll (see Blue Book p 390)—Replies to be in hands of Principal Clerk by 31st December 1988.

INJUNCTIONS
Annual Statistical Returns—Presbyteries to ensure the return of these not later than 15th January (PP 6).
Investment of Funds—Boards and Committees to seek advice annually from Church of Scotland Trust regarding investment of capital funds (AC 4).
Special Funds—Boards and Committees to provide the Board of Stewardship and Finance annually with full details of these (AC 5).
Property Transactions—Boards and Committees to report to the Board of Stewardship and Finance and to the Assembly Council the amount of any sales or purchases of property (AC 7).
Church and Nation Research —The Assembly Council and the Board of Stewardship and Finance to give priority to funding a research facility, taking into account related work within other Departments (CN 1).
Scottish Assembly—Committee to give urgent attention to the question of democratic control of Scottish affairs and to the means for adopting a national referendum (CN 16).
Extended Study Leave—Committee to consider how this may be given to ministers thought capable of meeting the need for more stimulating theological literature (MoM 13).
Smoking—Courts and Boards of the Church to ensure that all public areas are non-smoking and only if there is sufficient demand to set aside prescribed areas for smoking (SR 12).

Health and Healing—All employing agencies of the Church to act on the report and the Board to report to next Assembly on initial steps taken: agree to terminate membership of Church's Council on Health and Healing (SR 15).

"Not Strangers but Pilgrims"—All Presbyteries, Boards and Committees of the Church to consider the proposals and to send comments to the Board of World Mission and Unity by 31st October 1988 (WMU 13).

World Poverty—Church and Nation and World Mission and Unity to consider the advisability of producing a report on this and the contribution the Church can make to possible solutions (Sp Com 5).

REGULATIONS

Assembly Commissioners' Expenses—Approve these at : Overnight, up to £16 50; Daily out-of-pocket, £5; Mileage Allowance, up to 12p per mile (PP 5).

Corresponding Members of Assembly—President of the Woman's Guild, Editor of Life and Work, and General Treasurer added to list (PP 9).

Ministry to the Deaf—Remit thereanent transferred to Board of Ministry and Mission (PP 10).

Point of Order—When it is proposed to raise a point of order in regard to a matter of which notice has been given the proposer should in courtesy notify the Clerks (PP 11).

Availability in Vacancy—Declared that the Interim Moderator or Locum Tenens in a vacancy is not *ipso facto* debarred from receiving a call to that charge (Ov).

"Acquisition of Manses"—Direct that a copy of this Report be sent to all Presbytery Clerks, recommending that Presbyteries delegate to a standing body to approve of a proposed property (GT 4).

Church of Scotland Trust—Revised Byelaws and Regulations approved—for General Investment Fund (Blue Book, p 42), for Income Fund (p 44), and for Deposit Fund (p 46).

"Employing Agencies"—Three of these established—Personnel Committee, Social Responsibility, and Mission (S&F 8 & AC 9).

Minimum Stipend—Declared for 1988 at £9300 and a Manse, with appropriate additions in special areas and cases (MoM 3).

Principles for Future Stipend Levels—Approve statement of principles as in Blue Book, pp 156-8 (MoM 4).

Incremental Scale of Stipend—Committee to prepare a scheme to replace present Minimum Stipend structure, with a firm date for its introduction—to report to next Assembly (MoM 5).

Community Charge—Committee to introduce an increase in stipend to take account of money released to congregations by the burden of local rates on manses being lifted, with a balancing deduction on the Manse Allowance (MoM 8).

Death in Service Grant—Note with approval that this has been increased to three times the current Minimum Stipend (MoM 17, RS 3).

Furnishing Loans—Approve proposal to amalgamate the Young Ministers' Furnishing Loan Fund and the Young Ministers' Loan Fund (MoM 18).

Further Endowment—Approve revised limits—average stipend for last three years not more than £8500; total endowments to be raised not above £2500 (MoM 20).

Insured Pension Fund—Note proposal to extend this to allow members to contribute to Fund, and authorise introduction to be effective from 1st January 1989 (RS 2).

Ministry of Healing—Consultation to be held regarding the possibility of bringing this under the wing of the Mission Committee (M 8).

Pulpit Supply Fee—Regulations amended to allow ministers of other denominations to receive the full standard fee, and that the £10 fee payable to "others" should be increased to 50% of the standard fee (PTAM 2).

Lay Missionaries—Declare that all of these are eligible for recognition as holding the office of the Diaconate and authorise the recognition of all such recommended by the Mission Committee (D 4).

Commissioning Service for Diaconate—Authorise Committee to commend to Presbyteries the use of the revised order of service (D 2).

Broadcasting—Note that this Committee has been merged with that on the Media (C 9).

MATTERS OF PARTICULAR INTEREST

Greetings sent to Methodist Church on their Special Anniversary.

"Cox"—Encourage the Board to continue its work on replacing this with a new law manual (PP 12).

"The Assuaging of the Waters"—Approve the sale of this painting and agree that the proceeds be used by the Board in its care of the Assembly Hall and of the Church's portraits and paintings (PP 17).

Rev A B Cameron—Resolved not to receive his petition for restoration of status (on the ground that it was in effect an appeal against the decision of last General Assmbly) (Pet).

Congregational Income—Note that for 1987 this was £46,673,764, an increase of £3,809,749 (S&F 2).

Auditor of the Church—Mr Robert Gordon appointed for 1989 (S&F 9).

Health Service—Urge H M Government to provide an NHS funded largely out of taxation, which will be available to all without regard to ability to pay, and which will be able to meet satisfactorily all reasonable demands upon it (CN 12).

National Lottery—Deeply regret H M Government's intention to support this with the aim of providing funds for NHS, and call for further consideration (CN 13).

British Steel Corporation—Urge H M Government to rethink proposals for privatisation in the light of its likely consequences for Scotland (CN 21).

Integrity of Broadcasting—Commend the determination of BBC and IBA to defend this in face of recent pressures (CN 37).

"Songs of God's People"—Welcome its publication and commend it for popular use (PW 2).

National Covenant—Panel asked to prepare guidelines for worship to mark the 350th anniversary of its signing, and also of the Glasgow Assembly of 1638, and designate Sunday 20th November for this purpose (PW 8).

Centenary of the Diaconate—Give thanks to God for one hundred years of service to the Church by Deaconesses, Church Sisters, and Parish Sisters; congratulate the present diaconate on the anniversary, and wish them well in their future work (D 1).

Abortion—Note the Report thereon (Blue Book pp 274-282), particularly the recommendation that "the present law needs to be monitored" (SR 7). Regret that the House of Commons was prevented from taking a vote and call on H M Government to make time for such a vote (SR 8).

Sports Sponsorship—Note with dismay the growth of this by the alcohol industry and support every effort to have drink advertisements on children's sports clothes banned (SR 11).

Tabeetha School—Congratulate on its 125 years and in view of present uncertainties welcome the undertaking to review the whole situation, noting that meantime no steps will be taken to phase out the work of the secondary department (WMU 25).

Media Office—Congratulate what had been the Press Office on its 50th anniversary (C 8).

Iona—The question of the disposal of the Manse of Iona remitted to the General Trustees with powers (Pet).

RECOMMENDATIONS, &c

National Bible Society of Scotland—Congratulated on helping to make God's Word available both at home and overseas during the Year of the Bible (PP 14).

Central Fabric Fund—Reiterate support for the policy that when fabric monies are held for a congregation in excess of their likely needs surplus money should be reallocated to the Fund (GT 2).

"Necessary Buildings"—Continue existing remits and urge Presbyteries not to approve the expenditure of large sums on repairs or additions to property merely because funds are available but to look at the long-term situation (GT 3).

Glebes—Financial Boards encouraged to consider working glebes, where available, for the benefit of the Church (GT 5).

"Better Heating" Scheme—Congregations encouraged to commission a survey (GT 7).

Insurance—Trustees to take steps necessary to ensure that buildings are adequately covered against loss by fire; attention drawn to the advantage of insuring with the Church of Scotland Insurance Co Ltd (GT 8).

Whithorn—Presbyteries and Kirk Sessions asked to make the unique excavations there as widely known as possible (GT 9).

Deeds of Covenant—Congregations urged to maintain and increase this method of giving (S&F 3).

Courses on Congregational Finance—Commend these—at Carberry Tower—particularly to newly appointed Treasurers and Members of Financial Boards (S&F 7).

Finance Publications—Copies of "Stewards of God's House" to be provided for Presbytery Clerks and Business and Property Conveners; summary of this to be prepared for issue to office-bearers; "Notes for Guidance on Raising Large Sums for Church Buildings" to be provided to congregations on request (S&F 8).

Secretary of Board of Stewardship and Finance—Note the impending retiral of Rev George Elliot and authorise nomination of successor to Assembly of 1989 (S&F 10).

Primary Tasks for the Church in the 1990's—Approve work being begun on the preparation of this—report in 1989 (S&F 11).

Woman's Guild Centenary Project—Note with satisfaction the widespread interest it has engendered (WG 3).

Department of Ministry and Mission—Await further report on its reorganisation to the Assembly of 1989 (AC 9).

Poverty Among Older People—View this with grave concern as created or accentuated by new Social Security Act and urge H M Government to take steps to relieve cases of hardship (CN 2).

Poverty and Hardship—Urge Kirk Sessions to monitor in their parishes incidence of this and to communicate as appropriate with local or national government representatives and with the Church and Nation Committee (CN 3).

Prisons—Commend to the Church's prayers all who work in them and all victims of crime; call upon H M Government to establish a committee of enquiry into sentencing policy in Scotland (CN 4,7).

Victim Support Schemes—Commend these for study and action (CN 5).

Police Force—Concerned for mounting risk to which they are subject call for constant remembrance in prayer (CN 8).

Travelling People—Urge local authorities to provide sites in accordance with existing pitch targets; call upon H M Government to continue to give 100% grants for this and to re-appoint Advisory Committee re Scotland's Travelling People when present term expires in December 1988 (CN 9,10).

Christian Use of Sunday—Welcome emphasis in report on worship, nurture and leisure (CN 14).

St Andrew's Day—Encourage Kirk Sessions and members to recognise and celebrate through local events and in the flying of the saltire (CN 15).

"Scottish Housing"—Commend report for general study and Committee to make further report on its main recommendations in 1989 (CN 17).

Community Charge—Regret failure to take adequate account of ability to pay and urge H M Government to review the 20% minimum contribution and provide for progressive rebate system (CN 18). Urge complete exemption of full-time students (CN 20).

Abolition of Rates (Scotland) Act 1987—Urge H M Government to introduce amending legislation in the interest of those on low incomes (CN 19).

Maritime Policy—Invite representatives of both management and union to consult as to how best to support the call for the formation of such a policy (CN 22).

Multi-National Enterprises—Recognise these as a feature of modern commercial life, but urge those responsible to ensure that single-industry communities are effectively diversified (CN 23). Encourage Presbyteries and members to form relationships with Churches in other parts of the world where the same company is sited, thus establishing friendships and better understanding (CN 26).

Trade Union Legislation—Urge H M Government to respect the ballot principle and the right of voluntary organisations such as trade unions to maintain their own internal discipline (CN 27).

Community Programme—View with concern plans for its termination; disapprove the economics of the new Employment Training Scheme and call for a review of its provisions (CN 28).

"Asylum-seekers"—Support BCC, WCC etc in clarifying to governments the compassion of the Christian community towards these (CN 29).

Status of Refugees—Call upon H M Government to re-confirm support for 1951 U N Convention on their status, to review its own restrictive practices and persuade its European partners to introduce more liberal policies (CN 30).

Lusaka Statement—Associate themselves with this (CN 31).

Intermediate Nuclear Force Agreement—Pray that the disarmament process may become a major priority (CN 32).

"Tug-of-Love Children"—Express deep concern over plight of those unlawfully removed from Britain (CN 33).

"The Race Against Time"—Encourage all congregations in the support of and participation in this (CN 34).

Television—Encourage members to monitor output of BBC and ITV and to make representations to the broadcasting authorities (CN 35).

Public Service Broadcasting—Urge H M Government to maintain existing standards (CN 38).

Gaelic Broadcasting—Recognising that this is important to the culture of Scotland encourage radio and television to increase Gaelic output (CN 39).

Ministry, Report on—Note with interest analysis of Presbytery responses to the 1986 report, approve the revised report and commend for study throughout the Church (PD 2)

Freemasonry—In pursuance of the 1987 remit much initial study has been undertaken by the Working Party which hopes to submit a full report in 1989 (Blue Book p 124).

Supplement of Praise for Use in Public Worship—Panel to investigate the possibility of producing such and to report to next Assembly (PW 3).

"Book of Common Order"—Note progress made in its revision (PW 4).

"Pray Today"—Commend to the whole membership of the Church (PW 5).

Corporate Congregational Prayer—Panel urged to consider preparing literature giving guidance to congregations in this field (PW 6).

Book of Prayers in Gaelic—Welcome its forthcoming publication (PW 7).

Priority of Parish Ministry—While recognising the important role of the non-parochial ministry affirm the importance of serving the local congregation within the local parish (MoM 2).

Ministerial Travelling Expenses—Note investigation is being carried out (Blue Book p 158) (MoM 7).

Recruitment to the Ministry—Committee to confer with the Department of Education and to bring this matter before the whole Church for earnest and continuing prayer (MoM 16).

Jubilee of Iona Community—Congratulate the Community on their anniversary (ICB 2).

Leader of Iona Community—Welcome the appointment of Rev W John Harvey (ICB 3).

MacLeod Centre—Note with approval its building and commend its use to the whole Church (ICB 4).

Wild Goose Publications—Encourage their use throughout the Church (ICB 5).

Presbytery Development Process—Urge Presbyteries to ensure that their Mission Committee is adequately staffed for its demanding task (M 1). Urge congregations to encourage members to train in pastoral evangelism (M 2).

"Developing the Missionary Parish"—Urge Kirk Sessions to study this workpack as a first step towards local strategy for evangelism (M 3).

"Parish Review"—Urge congregations to undertake this and to report their experience to the Committee (M 4).

Rural Areas—Committee to pursue with urgency consideration of the serious problems confronting the Church in rural areas and to report to next Assembly (M 5).

Thomson House—Note with gratification its completion as an extension to St Ninian's Crieff and commend its facilities to the congregations of the Church (M 6).

Scripture Union Inter-School Camps—Note with pleasure their jubilee and commend their contribution to the Church's mission (M 7).

Lay Missionaries—Acknowledge their faithful work; congratulate the Diaconate on its centenary year and express good wishes to those Lay Missionaries who have elected to be part of the Diaconate (M 10).

Part-Time Industrial Chaplains—Thank ministers who give time and effort in this connection and encourage others to become involved (M 12).

Community Groups—Encourage Committee in creation of "real" jobs through local Groups whose main aim would be to create employment and alleviate poverty (M 13).

Computerisation—Express concern at its ethical implications and request S R T Project to prepare and publish a report next year (M 15).

Factors Governing Work of Readjustment—Note these as set forth in Blue Book pp 208,9 (U&R 2).

Dundee Overture—(anent housing for ministers retiring in the interest of readjustment) —No further action to be taken (U&R 3).

Hawick Old—Commission of seven appointed to enquire into Basis of Union, with powers to resolve the matter (Ap).

Church Extension—Encourage Presbyteries in consultation with the Committee to plan for future requirements and to initiate investigation of the increasingly urgent needs of inner city areas (CE 3)

Projects Agreed in Principle—Note projects envisaged at Condorrat, Kirkmahoe, East Kilbride and Johnstone St Paul's (CE 8).

Aberdeen Summerhill—Raised to the status of a Parish quoad sacra (CE 12).

Rev Arthur J Doherty—Received as Minister and remitted to Presbytery of Lorn and Mull to make arrangements (Pet).

Rev George B Hall—Received as Minister and remitted to Presbytery of St Andrews to make arrangements (Pet).

Rev George G Nicol—Received as Minister and remitted to Presbytery of Edinburgh to make arrangements (Pet).

Choice of Sanctuary Furnishings—Urge congregations to consider theological as well as practical considerations in such cases (AM 2).

Scottish Church Bells—Note with satisfaction that a record of these is to be compiled (AM 4).

Chaplains to H M Forces—Express thanks to chaplains for service they are rendering (CF 1). And to those in authority for encouragement received (CF 3). Note continuing need for young ministers in Army, in Territorial Army and in Cadet Units (CF 4).

Exchange of Information with the Services—Committee to consider practical ways of encouraging this and to report to next Assembly (CF 5).

Prison Chaplains—Thanked for their work and Presbyteries urged to give priority to their recruitment (PC 2,3).

Homes for Elderly—Welcome opening of two new homes for elderly people suffering from senile dementia—Cameron House, Inverness and St Margaret's Polmont (SR2).

Community Care—Note the continual changes in the area of this work and encourage extension of the work of the Board to embrace caring work for children at risk, those with alcohol and drug problems, mental handicap, and AIDS (SR 5)

Social Service Training—Commend emphasis on its provision to meet needs of staff, and instruct Board to initiate training opportunities at residential homes (SR 6).

"Life-Style Survey"—Board to help Kirk Sessions and others to appreciate its implications and to produce a study pack (SR 9).

Woman's Guild Centenary Project—Rejoice in this effort to establish the work of the Board among drug addicted prostitutes (SR 10).

Tobacco Price—Recommend to HM Government that the price of tobacco and alcohol be increased (SR 13).

Under-Age Drinking—Invite the Board to consider this question with reference to inexpensive tonic wines (SR 14).

Ecumenical Decade : Churches in Solidarity with Women—Note its launching at Easter and encourage sharing of its aims (WMU 4).

Poverty—Encourage congregations to reflect on the question raised for the Church in Scotland by the widening gap between poor and rich both in the Third World and in Brtain itself (WMU 8).

Inter-Church Process—Welcome the broader partnership which it represents (WMU 9).

Ecumenical Instrument for Britain and Ireland—Welcome its principles and its main structure —Blue Book pp 348-354 (WMU 12).

Royal Family of Abyssinia—Give thanks for release of seven members after 14 years' detention without trial, and pray for release of others (WMU 19).

Middle East—Support call by WCC and others for an international conference thereanent (WMU 22).

Church in Tiberias—Note proposal to replace this with an adaptable building within the Sea of Galilee Centre (WMU 23).

Rev James Currie—Memorial to be dedicated in the Church in Jerusalem in recognition of his ministry in the field of pilgrimage to the Holy Land (WMU 24).

Christian Aid Contact Person—Encourage every Kirk Session to make such an appointment (WMU 32).

Boys' Brigade Support—Note continuing generosity expressed in this year's gift of £41,500 for the work of the Church overseas (WMU 34).

Ecumenical Contributions—Note that the contributions directly payable to ecumenical councils by virtue of membership amount in all for 1989 to £141,760 (WMU 43).

Children and Communion —This question to be re-examined by the Board (E 5).

"Faithquest" Sunday School Programme—Note with approval the arrangements made for its expansion (E 9).

"Anchor Points"—Appprove arrangements for development of this Bible Class syllabus (E 10).

"Breakthrough in Worship"—Welcome publication of all-age learning/worship pack and of a forthcoming second pack (E 11).

Curriculum Development Unit—Board of Stewardship and Finance to consult with Board of Education regarding further funding of this (E 12).

Church Advisory Project on Mental Handicap—Note with approval achievements of one-year pilot scheme and commend to congregations the services available (E 13).

"One in a Hundred"—Acknowledge generosity of Woman's Guild in supporting this project for 1988-89 (E 14).

Scottish Agency for Adult Christian Education—Note with interest the proposal for its establishment and approve the intention to become associated with it (E 15).

Training in Leadership and Service Course—Note encouraging expansion and commend this programme to the Church (E 14). Note proposal to provide alternative training scheme for Readers by way of this course—Blue Book pp 401-3 (E19).

"Christian Teaching in Scottish Schools"—Commend the report for study within the Church by Kirk Sessions, education groups, school chaplains and R E teachers (E 20).

Offensive Material in School Text-Books—Note with concern the increasing incidence of this and remit to the Committee for appropriate action (E 21).

Non-Uniformed Youth Work— Committee to ensure there is effective dialogue with those responsible for educational curriculum (E 23).

Threat to Universities—Note with grave concern the threat, particularly to Scottish Universities, arising from present economic policies (E 24).

Student Grants—Call upon H M Government to remedy the situation arising through drop in real value of these (E 25).

School Boards—Note with approval the Committee's stance, particularly in regard to the representation of the religious interest (E 26).

Bible Examination for Students for the Ministry—Note revised format of these three examinations which students for the ministry must pass (E 28).

Field-Work Director/Co-ordinator—Note the appointment in each of the four Faculties of Divinity (E 29).

Principal of New College—Welcome and approve re-appointment of Rev Duncan B Forrester for period of four years from 1st October 1988 (E 34).

Communication—Urge all courts and committees to take full advantage of the specialised services available through the various sections of the Department of Communication (C 2).

Bookshops— Note their continued self-financing development and the steps being taken to ensure that stocks reflect the needs of the Church (C 3).

"Life and Work"—Note its strength and success (C 4), and encourage congregations to promote its circulation (C 5).

Saint Andrew Press—Note the continuing improvement in the sales of its titles (C 7).

Audio-Visual Production—Encourage widespread reference to the catalogue of material available (C 10).

Warrant Sales—Express concern that this demeaning exercise still remains to punish the inadequate (Sp Con 4).

Investment and Banking—Note and approve recommendations in the report of the Special Committee on the Ethics of Investment and Banking as in Blue Book pp 492-3 (Sp Com 2). Church and Nation to form Consultative Group on Christian Ethics and Finance including representatives from S&F and WMU to serve for three years in first instance (Sp Com 5).

THANKED

The Very Revd Duncan Shaw for carrying out the duties of Moderator with amazing energy and delightful enthusiasm.

Revd Douglas Aitken for his distinguished contribution in the field of religious broadcasting over many years with BBC.

Mr Harry Ashmall for many years of faithful service to the ecumenical movement in Scotland and on WCC Central Commttee and Executive.

Brigadier John Balharrie MBE MC TD DL for valued service as Vice-Convener of the Committee on Chaplains to H M Forces.

Mr William Black for his unique and valued contribution to editorial, production and promotional aspects of "Life and Work".

Revd Ronald S Blakey for his outstanding service to the Board of Education.

Revd John B Cairns for outstanding contribution as Convener of the Maintenance of the Ministry Committee.

Revd Maxwell Craig for the vision and imagination with which he has guided the work of the Church and Nation Committee during his period as Convener.

Revd M Leith Fisher for time given without stint to the work of Adult Christian Education as its Convener.

Revd Dr Nelson Gray for his valuable work in the field of religious television over many years with STV.

Mr Eric Hubbard for his devoted services as Clerk and Treasurer to the Widows' and Orphans' Fund.

Dr W A P Jack for valuable contribution to the work of the General Trustees.

Revd T W Kiltie on retiring on health grounds after thirteen years of distinguished service in the Overseas Department, the last ten as Deputy General Secretary.

Revd George L Lugton for the excellence and faithfulness of the work carried out by him as Secretary and Deputy of the Church and Ministry Department and latterly the Department of Ministry and Mission.

Revd Duncan M'Lachlan for the quiet authority and distinction with which he has led the Committee on Education for the Ministry as its Convener.

Revd William B R Macmillan on completing his period as Convener of the Board of Practice and Procedure, for innate wisdom, careful preparation and unquenchable good humour in the guidance given.

Dr J C G Mercer on retiring as Convener of Personnel Committee for his valued service to that Committee.

Mr David Miller for distinguished service rendered during his short-term appointment as Secretary to the Assembly Council.

Mrs Mary Millican as Chairman for the diligence of the Special Committee in the preparation of the report on Scottish Housing.

Revd Charles S Morrice for quiet and firm handling of the business of the Youth Education Committee as its Convener.

Mrs Winifred Robson for distinguished service on retiring as Vice-President of the Woman's Guild.

Revd James M Rogers for outstanding service to Overseas Council, Inter-Church Relations and Board of World Mission and Unity since its inception.

Mrs Margaret Sawers for valuable contribution to the work of the Woman's Guild as ex officio Vice-President.

Revd William G Shannon for his thought and commitment to the work of Mission in his own parish and in the Mission Committee as its Convener.

Revd Henry A Shepherd for the diligence and carefulness of all his work as Convener of the Nominations Committee.

Mr Kenneth I Sinclair for devoted service and quiet efficiency and leadership as Convener of the Retirement Scheme Committee.

ABBREVIATIONS

Ap	Appeal
AC	Assembly Council
AM	Committee on Artistic Matters
BCC	British Council of Churches
C	Board of Communications
CE	Church Extension Committee
CF	Committee on Chaplains to H M Forces
CN	Church and Nation Committee
DC	Diaconate Committee
E	Board of Education
GT	General Trustees
ICB	Iona Community Board
M	Mission Committee
MoM	Maintenance of the Ministry Committee
Ov	Overture
Pet	Petition
PCB	Prison Chaplaincy Board
PD	Panel on Doctrine
PP	Board of Practice and Procedure
PTAM	Committee on Probationers and Transference and Admission of Ministers
PW	Panel on Worship
Ref	Reference
RS	Retirement Scheme Committee
S&F	Board of Stewardship and Finance
SpCom	Special Committee
SR	Department of Social Responsibility
U&R	Committee on Unions and Readjustments
WCC	World Council of Churches
WG	Woman's Guild
WMU	Board of World Mission and Unity

INDEX OF PERSONNEL

These columns contain, in alphabetical order, the names of all Ministers (active, retired, and in other occupations) and of all Probationers and Licentiates of the Church of Scotland, and of Deacons, Deaconesses, Lay Missionaries and Agents, and of Overseas staff (active and retired).

Ministers—The figure denotes the number of the Presbytery of which the Minister is a member and the name is that of the parish or town where he or she is placed. When the place-name is in brackets the person is retired and the name is that of the last parish or appointment. In the case of the four cities the name of the charge only is given (these being Edinburgh 1, Glasgow 16, Dundee 29, and Aberdeen 31). The letters A,B, etc refer to the lists beginning on page 252.

Associate means this minister has been introduced by the Presbytery as an Associate Minister and has a seat in Presbytery.

Assistant refers to an ordained assistant who has a seat in Presbytery.

Auxiliary means the person is an ordained Auxiliary Minister (non-stipendiary), and is assigned to the parish or area indicated.

Probr means the person is a Probationer of the Church, particulars being found at page 281.

Lic'ate means the person has the status of Licentiate as defined on page 281. Particulars on p 283.

Deacon/D'ess means that person is a Deacon/Deaconess in active service, though not necessarily of the Church, or, when in parentheses, is retired. Fuller particulars in List H on page 284, which includes also a full list of retired Deaconesses.

Lay Miss'y means the person is a Lay Missionary in the active service of the Church, and, when in parentheses, retired. The name is that of the parish to which he is attached. Fuller particulars in List H (page 284) which includes also a list of retired Lay Missionaries.

Agent refers to a person in the employment of the Mission Committee. A complete list will be found in List H.

WMU means the person is an agent (other than a Minister) in the active service of the Department of World Mission and Unity. Further information will be found on reference to List E on page 267. Names of retired Overseas staff are included in these columns, and may be found in List K on page 299. To make it easier to find them in that list the year of retirement is shown.

Only the barest minimum of information necessary for identification is given in these columns. For full particulars reference should be made to the appropriate Presbytery or other List.

A

Abernethy, W., Glenrothes	25	
Adam, W. (Leuchars)	26	
Adams, M.(Miss), *Probr*	G	
Adamson, H.M., Irvine	11	
Adamson, I.T., Abernyte *Auxiliary*	29	
Adamson, J.G.(Miss) (*D'ess*)	H	
Adamson, S. (Musselburgh)	3	
Ainslie, W.J., Easterhouse *Community Minister*	16	
Aitchison, J. (Glasgow Broomhill)	16	
Aitchison, J.B.(Miss) (*D'ess*)	H	
Aitken, A.J. (Glasgow Tollcross)	16	
Aitken, A.R., Newhaven	1	
Aitken, E.D. (*B B C*)	C and 24	
Aitken, F.R., Girvan	10	
Aitken, W.B. (Kirkpatrick Irongray)	8	
Aitken, W.M., Zambia	D and 27	

Aitkenhead, S.M. (Glasgow New Cathcart)	16	
Alexander, A.D. (*University*)	F	
Alexander, D.C. (Dunscore)	7	
Alexander, D.N., Bishopton	14	
Alexander, E.(Miss) (*WMU* 1988)	K	
Alexander, E.J., St George's Tron	16	
Alexander, H.J.R.(Miss), *University Chaplain*	C and 1	
Alexander, J.N.S. (Crieff)	28	
Alexander, J.S., *University*	B and 26	
Alexander, W.M., Bucksburn	31	
Allan, A.G., Candlish	17	
Allan, J.B., Motherwell	17	
Allan, M.R.(Miss), Newcraighall *Agent*	H and 1	
Allan, W.G. (Kirkcudbright)	F	
Allen, M.A.W., Chryston	16	

Allison, M.M.(Mrs), Kirn	20	
Allsop, T.D., Beechgrove	31	
Alston, C.M., Trinidad	D and 36	
Alston, W.G., North Kelvinside	16	
Anderson, A.F., Greenside	1	
Anderson, B.A., *Lic'ate*	G	
Anderson, C.B.(Mrs), Fernhill *D'ess*	H and 16	
Anderson, C.M., Greenock	15	
Anderson, D., Aberlour	35	
Anderson, D.J.B., Gorgie	1	
Anderson, D.M., *Auxiliary*	38	
Anderson, D.W. (South Africa)	F	
Anderson, G.E. (Braemar)	FF	
Anderson, H, DD (*University*)	B and 1	
Anderson, J.(Miss), Ruchazie *D'ess*	H and 16	
Anderson, J.F., Mannofield	31	
Anderson, J.L. (*Lay Miss'y*)	H	

B

C

Cameron, J.U., Brought Ferry 29
Cameron, J.W.M., Liberton 1
Cameron, M.(Miss), Paisley
   Glenburn, *D'ess* I and 14
Cameron, N.M. de S., *Lic'ate* G
Cameron, P.S., *University* B and 5
Cameron, R.M., *Lic'ate* G
Cameron, R.N., *Chaplain*
   Army A and 47
Campbell, A.B., Kilmore 21
Campbell, A.I., Busby 16
Campbell, A.M., Motherwell 17
Campbell, A.M.(Miss) (*WMU*
   1956) K
Campbell, A.V. *University* B and 1
Campbell, C., Old Kilpatrick 18
Campbell, C., Williamwood 16
Campbell, D. (Bervie) 32
Campbell, D. (*WMU*) K
Campbell, E.C.(Mrs), Old
   Cumnock 10
Campbell, G.H., Stewarton 11
Campbell, I.T. (Dunrossness) F
Campbell, J., *Evangelism*
   Organiser C and 16
Campbell, J. (Urquhart) 24
Campbell, J. (Coatbridge) 17
Campbell, J. (*Lay Miss'y*) H
Campbell, J., Ayr 10
Campbell, J., Leverburgh
   Deacon H and 43
Campbell, J.A. (Stoneykirk) 9
Campbell, J.A., Perth *Auxiliary* 28
Campbell, J.E.(Miss) (*WMU*
   1969) F
Campbell, J.E.R.,
   Auchterderran 25
Campbell, J.I.P.(Miss) (*WMU*
   1949) K
Campbell, K., Broughty Ferry 29
Campbell, K. (*Lay Miss'y*) H
Campbell, M.M.(Miss) (*D'ess*) H
Campbell, N.G., Palmerston Place
   Assistant 1
Campbell, P.D.G. (Geneva) 23
Campbell, R. (Kirkcaldy) 25
Campbell, R.D.M., Mearns 16
Campbell, R.F., Castleton 6
Campbell, S.A.(Miss), Currie
   Associate 1
Campbell, T.G. (Arbroath) 30
Campbell, T.K. (Bothwell) 17
Campbell, T.R., Paisley 14
Campbell, W. (Nigg) 39
Campbell, W.C.D. (Belize) F
Campbell, W.F., *Probr* G
Campbell, W.M.M., *Hospital*
   Chaplain C and 31
Campbell-Jack, W.C.,
   Knockbain 39
Candlish, G. (*Home*
   Board) C and FF
Cant, H.W.M., Kirkwall 45
Cant, T.M., Paisley 14
Capewell, W.D., Beith 12
Carlisle, A.R., *Probr* G
Carmichael, D.S., Lesmahagow 13
Carmichael, J.A., Ardgour 38
Carmichael, J.J.A. (Anwoth) 8
Carmichael, R.C.M., Craignish 19
Carmichael, W. (Restalrig) 1

Carmont, R., Sandyhills 16
Carnew, L. (Arrochar) F
Carr, W.S., Largs 12
Carrick, M. (Ardgour) 37
Carrie, J.G., Queensferry 1
Carse, G. (Liberton) F
Cartlidge, G.R.G., Newton
   Mearns 16
Cartwright, A.C.D., Fogo 5
Casebow, B.C., Salisbury 1
Caseby, A. (Carlops) 26
Cashman, P.H., North Berwick 3
Caskie, D.M. (Monkton) 10
Caskie, J.C., Carnoustie 30
Cassells, A.K., Leuchars 26
Cathcart, J., St James' Pollok
   Agent H and 16
Cattanach, W.D.R., DD,
   Geneva D and 48
Chalmers, G.A., Banchory
   Ternan 32
Chalmers, J.P., Palmerston Place 1
Chalmers, M., Fairmilehead 1
Chalmers, W.R., Dunbar 3
Chaplin, D. (Falkirk) 22
Charlton, G.W., Fort Augustus 38
Chen, G.E. F
Cherry, A.J., Stamperland 16
Chestnut, A. (Greenock) 15
Cheyne, A.C., (*University*) B and 1
Cheyne, M., *Community*
   Minister 46
Chilton, R.M.L. (Corgarff) F
Chirnside, C. (Tullibody) FF
Chisholm, A.F., Braes of
   Rannoch 27
Chisholm, H.N. (Freeport) F
Chisholm, W.D. (Monifieth) 29
Christie, A.C., Ferryhill 31
Christie, R.S., Kilmarnock 11
Christman, W.J., Ayr 10
Clark, D., *Probr* G
Clark, D.W., Helensburgh 18
Clark, J. (Dunblane) 23
Clark, J.S. (Traquair) 4
Clark, T.L., Orphir 45
Clarke, D. (Leith) FF
Clarke, J.B. (Keig) F
Clarke, R. (*Industrial Chaplain*) F
Clarkson, R.G., Strathmartine 29
Clausen, C.W., Hamilton
   Community Minister C and 17
Claydon, W.A. (New Machar) 33
Clephane, D.M.(Miss), *WMU*,
   Tabeetha E
Clinkenbeard, W.W., Carrick
   Knowe 1
Clipston, S.F., Galashiels 4
Clyne, D.R., Fraserburgh 34
Coleman, J.A., *Chaplain*
   RAF A and 47
Coleman, S.H., Merrylea 16
Coley, R., Victoria Tollcross 16
Collard, J.K. Holy Trinity
   Associate 1
Collie, J.(Miss) (*D'ess*) H
Collie, J.P.(Miss), Corgarff 33
Collier, F.C., Forgue 34
Collins, I.M.W., Darvel 11
Coltart, I.A., (*WMU* 1985) K
Coltart, I.O., Wishaw 17

Colvin, S.E.F.(Mrs), Ballingry 24
Colvin, T.S., Blantyre D
Combe, N.R., Hawick 6
Conacher, M.N.(Miss), *WMU*.
   North India E
Conacher, P. (John Ker) 1
Conkey, H., Innellan 20
Conlan, B. (Glenelg *Associate*) F
Conn, A. (*WMU* 1960) K
Cook, J., Leith 1
Cook, J.A., Foveran 33
Cook, J.S., Hamilton 17
Cook, J.W., Portobello 1
Cook, R (Girvan) F
Cooke, D.(Miss) (*WMU*) K
Cooke, J.M. (Fowlis Wester) 16
Cooper, G (Kenya) FF
Cooper, M.W. (Kirkcaldy) 25
Copeland, R. (*Lay Miss'y*) H
Copland, M.M.(Mrs) (*D'ess*) H
Copp, D.M., Milngavie 18
Cordiner, G.L., Lossiemouth 35
Cordiner, J. (Savoch) 22
Cordiner, J. (Portpatrick) 9
Cormack, J.R.H.
   (Campbeltown) 19
Cormack, J.S. (Wick) 41
Corner, M.M. (Grangemouth) FF
Corrie, M.(Miss) Priesthill
   Agent H and 16
Cotter, J.L. (Dalserf) 17
Coull, M.C., Hillington Park 16
Coulter, D.G., *Probr* G
Couper, D.S.F., Alloa 23
Couper, J.M. (Kilmodan) FF
Couper, S. (The Glens) 4
Court, D.L., *Probr* G
Coutts, F., Mastrick 31
Cowan, B. (Miss) (Dr), (*WMU*
   1988) K
Cowan, D. (Corby) F
Cowan, J.S.A., Cockenzie 3
Cowell, S.G.(Miss), Culter 13
Cowie, G.S., Birnie 35
Cowie, J.A., Auchtertool 25
Cowie, J.L. (Edinburgh
   Newcraighall) F
Cowie, J.M., Hawick 6
Cowie, L.J.F., (*WMU* 1945) K
Cowie, W.C., Glasserton 9
Cowper, M.C. (East Kilbride) 17
Craig, A.J.D., Maryhill 16
Craig, E. (Edinburgh Chalmers) FF
Craig, G.W., *Chaplain*
   RN A and 47
Craig, G.T., *Chaplain*
   RAF A and 14
Craig, I.R. (Invergowrie) 29
Craig, J.H.(Miss), Dar-es-Salaam D
Craig, J.W., St Stephen's 1
Craig, M.D., St Columba's 31
Craig, N.D. (Dalbeattie) 8
Craig, R., DD (Jerusalem) 26
Craig, R.A.S., Carntyne 16
Craig, W., Cambusbarron 23
Craik, S.(Miss), *Probr* G
Cramb, E.M., Yoker 16
Cran, J. (Bishopbriggs) 16
Cranfield, E.F.(Miss), Denbeath 25
Cranfield, M.M.(Miss), *Lic'ate* G
Cranston, G., Rutherglen 16

Cranston, R.D., Denny 22
Crawford, D.F.N. (Braes of Rannoch) 25
Crawford, M.(Miss), Drylaw D'ess H and 1
Crawford, M.S.M., St Mary's 31
Crawford, R (Annan) 11
Crawford, R.L. (Colonsay) 21
Crawford, S.D., Bishopbriggs 16
Crawford, S.G.V., Calton Parkhead 16
Crichton, J., Crosshill 10
Crichton, T., Torphichen 2
Crippin, J.B., *Lic'ate* G
Cringles, G.G., Dunblane 23
Crombie, W.D. (Calton) 16
Crocker, E.(Mrs) (D'ess) H

Crosgrove, J.P., Sorbie 9
Cross, B.F., Coalburn 13
Crosthwaite, M.D., Carstairs 13
Cruickshank, N., West Kilbride 12
Cubie, J.P., Cambuslang 16
Cullen, W.T., Cowie 23
Cumming, D.P.L., Ministry & Mission *Secretary* C and 1
Cumming, H. (Bridge of Weir) 28
Cumming, W.M. (Pettinain) 13
Cunningham, A., *Presbytery Clerk* C and 16
Cunningham, A.W. (Miss), *Deaconess* H
Cunningham, I.D., Carluke 13
Cunningham, J.S.A., *Lic'ate* G
Cunningham, R. (Garvald) 1

Cunningham, W.L. (Cairneyhill) 24
Currie, D.E.P., East Kilbride 17
Currie, G.C.M. (Linlithgow *Assistant*) F
Currie, I.S., Paisley 14
Currie, J. (Laggan) F
Currie, M.F.(Miss), Airdrie 17
Currie, R., *Community Minister* C and 16
Currie, R.D., Cambuslang 16
Currie, W.T. (Glasgow Pollokshaws) 20
Curtis, A.H. F
Cuthbertson, M., Easterhouse 16
Cuthell, T.C., St Cuthbert's 1
Cutler, J.S.H., Kilmun 20

D

Dabb, R.G.(Miss) (*WMU* 1971) K
Dailly, J.R., *Chaplain Army* A and 12
Dale, J. (Glengarry) F
Dallison, A.R. (Livingston) F
Daly, R., Inchture 29
Daly, S.S, (Paisley) 14
Davidson, A.A.B., Grange 35
Davidson, D.H., Inverleith 1
Davidson, D.W., Kilarrow *Auxiliary* 19
Davidson, F.L.(Miss) (*WMU* 1952) K
Davidson, I.M.P., Stirling 23
Davidson, J., *Probr* G
Davidson, J.F. (Montrose) F
Davidson, J.W. (Inverurie) 33
Davidson, P. (Aberdeen Ferryhill) 30
Davidson, R. (Ruchazie) 16
Davidson, R, DD, *University* B and 16
Davidson-Kelly, T.A., *Chaplain Army* A and 47
Davies, C.P. (Gartcosh) F
Davies, G.W., Kilmarnock 11
Davies, J.M., Carmyle 16

Davison, C.F. (Guernsey) 47
Dawson, M.A. (Miss), *WMU* Livingstonia E
Dawson, M.S., Kilmadock 23
Day, C.T., (*Carberry Tower*) C and 3
Deacons, M.(Miss), Holy Trinity *Agent* H and 1
Dean, J.M. (Hamilton) F
Dean, R.A.F., Dennyloanhead 22
Deans, G.D.S., Dumfries 8
Deans, J.B. (*Hospital Chaplain*) C and 31
Denham, C.M.(Miss) (*D'ess*) (*WMU* 1986) H and K
Dempster, W.M. (Paris) 1
Denniston, D.W., Kennoway 25
Devlin, S. (Baldernock) 18
Dewar, J.S., Reay 40
Dey, J., Skerries *Deacon* H and 46
Diack, P., Elgin 35
Dick, A.B., Tullibody 23
Dick, C.J.(Miss), *WMU* Nepal E
Dick, D.F.S. (Cockburnspath) 3
Dick, J.H.A., Ferryhill 31
Dick, J.R., St John's Oxgangs 1
Dick, J.S., Echt 33

Dick, T., Dunkeld 27
Dickie, E.P., DD, (*University*) B and 26
Dickie, M.M., Ayr 10
Dickson, A.S. (Calton New *Associate*) F
Dickson, C.(Miss), *WMU*, Jerusalem E
Dickson, G.T., New Luce 9
Dickson, J.C. (Aberdeen St Fittick's) 31
Dickson, J.W., Lochend 1
Dillon, J., Clydebank 18
Dixon, D.S., Lybster 41
Dixon, F.D., Paisley 14
Dobbie, G.W., *Lic'ate* G
Dobos, J. (*WMU* 1978) K
Dodd, M.E.(Miss), Colinton *Assistant* 1
Dodman, R.A., Kingston D
Doherty, A.J., Fintry 23
Doig, A.B., DD (*National Bible Society*) C and 27
Doig, A.F. (Bargeddie) F
Doig, D.M. (Mid Craigie) 29
Donald, B.S.C., Monymusk 34
Donald, J.A., *Lic'ate* G

Donald, K.W., Stockethill 31
Donald, R.M. (Dundee
  Menzieshill) F
Donald, T.W., Bowden 4
Donaldson, C.V., Ormiston 3
Donaldson, D., Whitfield 29
Donaldson, G.M., Tiree 21
Donaldson, M. (Redgorton) 28
Donaldson, M., Duneaton 13
Donaldson, R.B., Kilchoman 19
Donn, T.M. (Duthil) 37
Dorward, J.A.,(Dr), *WMU*
  Malawi E
Dougall, E.G.(Mrs), Kikuyu D
Dougall, I.C., Kikuyu D
Douglas, A.B., Prestwick 10
Douglas, A.M., High Hilton 31
Douglas, A.M. (Hamilton) 17
Douglas, C.A.(Mrs), Inveraven 36
Douglas, C.R., Livingston 2
Douglas, F.(Miss), *Probr* G
Douglas, I.M., Montrose 30
Douglas, I.P., Craigiebuckler 31
Douglas, J.D. (Rothesay) F
Douglas, M.(Miss), Cumbernauld
  D'ess H and 22
Douglas, M.W.(Miss) (*WMU*
  1971) K
Douglas, P.C., Boarhills 26
Dowie, M.M., Forfar 30
Downie, A.F.M., Dun 30

Downie, A.G., Saline 24
Downie, A.S., Ardrossan 12
Doyle, D.B. (Bowling) 19
Doyle, D.W., Motherwell 17
Doyle, I.B., Ministry & Mission
  Secretary C and 1
Drake, W.F.(Mrs), St Martin's 1
Drever, B.(Dr) (*WMU* 1982) K
Drummond, A.J., Kelty 24
Drummond, G. (Renfrew) 12
Drummond, J.S. (Corby) 47
Drummond, J.W., Rutherglen 16
Drummond, N.W. (*Chaplain*) F
Drummond, R.E.(Miss) (*D'ess*) H
Drummond, R.H., Balmaclellan 8
Dryden, I., New Machar 33
Drysdale, J.H., Coupar Angus 27
Drysdale, J.P.R., Brechin 30
Duff, J.D. (Edinkillie) 35
Duff, T.M.F., Fergushill 12
Duff, V. (Miss), *D'ess* I and 17
Duff, W.B., *Lic'ate* G
Duffin, G.L., *Probr* G
Dunbar, W. (*Lay Miss'y*) H
Duncan, A.S., *Lic'ate* G
Duncan, C.A., Stow 4
Duncan, D.D. (Forfar) 30
Duncan, D.M. (*British Weekly*) 47
Duncan, E.M. (*Teacher
  RE*) C and FF
Duncan, G.A., Cumbernauld 22

Duncan, G.B. (St George's
  Tron) 16
Duncan, J., Blair Atholl 27
Duncan, J., *Teacher RE* C and 26
Duncan, J.C., Burntisland 25
Duncan, J.H. (Earlston) 4
Duncan, R.F., (Dundee
  Auxiliary) F
Dundas, T.B.S., West Calder 2
Dungavel, W. (Olrig) F
Dunlop, A.I. (St Stephen's) 1
Dunlop, A.J., Saddell 19
Dunlop, M.W.B.. (Zambia) 16
Dunlop, W.T., *WMU* Tabeetha E
Dunn, J.D.G., *Lic'ate* G
Dunn, J.F., Coatbridge 17
Dunn, W.I.C., Pilrig 1
Dunn, W.S., Motherwell 17
Dunnett, W.G. (Hutton) 5
Dunphy, R.G., Culloden 37
Dunphy, R.J.(Mrs), *Lic'ate* G
Dunsmore, B.W., Stirling 23
Dupar, K.W., *University* B and 31
DuPuy, E.J. (Creich) 3
Dutch, H.D.M., *Auxiliary* 18
Dutton, D.W., Stranraer 9
Durno, R.C., *Aux Probr* GG
Dyer, T.J. (Largo) 26

E

Eadie, W. (Tarbert) 23
Earl, J.M.(Mrs), *Lic'ate* G
Earnshaw, P., Stromness 45
Easton, A.J. (Dunlop) 11
Easton, D.J.C., Burnside 16
Easton, D.R. (Greenock) 1
Easton, I.A.G. *Teacher RE* 18
Easton, R. (New Govan) 16
Edgar, W.M.G. (Auchindoir) 37
Edie, C.B. (Stirling) 23
Edington, G.L., Tayport 26
Edmond, G.W.B. (Ecclesmachan) 2
Edwards, M.S., *Chaplain
  RAF* A and 16
Edwards, W.G.,
  Amsterdam D and 48

Eggo, H.C.M. (Church & Ministry
  Secretary) C and 3
Elder, A.B., Dumfries 8
Elder, D.S. (Sanquhar) FF
Elder, J. (Cults) 31
Elders, I.A., Broughton Place 1
Elliot, G., (Stewardship & Finance
  Secretary) C and 1
Elliott, A (*Lay Miss'y*) H
Elliott, G.J., Zambia D
Elliott, K.C., *Probr* G
Ellis, D.W., St George's Tron
  Associate 16

Ellis, W.H. (Househillwood) 16
Elston, P.K., Dalgety 24
Embleton, B.M., Reid Mem'l 1
Emslie, C. (Calderbank) F
Erskine, A.U., Banff 34
Erskine, M.(Miss), New Erskine
  D'ess H and 14
Erskine, M.J., Inverkip 15
Evans, J.W. (Elgin) 40
Evans, M., People's Palace,
  Deacon H
Ewart, W., Bishopbriggs 16
Ewing, J. (Ardrossan) 12
Ewing, J.M. (Cromarty) 5

F

Fairley, R. (*WMU* 1969) K
Fairlie, G., Cathcart 16
Fairweather, A.A., Kilmorack 37
Fairweather, I.C.M., (*College of Education*) C and 16
Falconer, A.D. (Aberdeen *Assistant*) F
Falconer, A.J., Glenshee *Lay Miss'y* H and 27
Falconer, J.B., East Kilbride Moncreiff *Associate* 17
Falconer, J.F. (Bedrule) 6
Farquhar, W.E., Dunfermline 24
Faulds, N.L., Aberlady 3
Fawkes, G.M.A., Lonmay 34
Fazakerley, A.J., Ellon *Associate* 33
Felderhof, M.C., *Lic'ate* G
Fenemore, J.H.C., Colinton 1
Fenton, R.J. (Glasgow St Kiaran's) 16
Ferenbach, C. (Liberton) FF
Ferguson, A.M., *Auxiliary* 18
Ferguson, A., *Aux Probr* GG
Ferguson, D.J., Bellie 35
Ferguson, G., Grangemouth 22
Ferguson, J., Portree 42
Ferguson, J.A., Kirkcaldy 25
Ferguson, J.B., Lenzie 16
Ferguson, J.F., Birse 32
Ferguson, J.K.P., *MWU*, Pakistan E
Ferguson, R. (*Iona Community*) F
Ferguson, S.B. (Unst) F
Ferguson, W.B., Broomill 16
Fergusson, D.A.S., *University* B and 1
Fergusson, M.C.(Miss) (*WMU* 1964) K
Ferrie, H.R. (St Vigeans) 16
Ferrier, W.M. (North Berwick) 3
Fiddes, G.R., Prestwick 10
Fields, J.T., Greenock *Associate* 15
Finch, G.S., Stonehaven 31
Findlay, H.J.W., Wishaw 17
Findlay, I.H.D. (Yemen) F
Finlay, Q., North Bute 20
Finlay, W.P., Townhead 16
Finlayson, D. (Morvern) 38

Finlayson, E.B. (Miss), *D'ess* Middlefield H and 31
Finlayson, J.C. (Grange) 1
Finlayson, J.Y. (Shotts) F
Finnie, J.I.C. (Eccles) 5
Fischbacher, C.M. (Dr), *WMU*, Kenya E
Fisher, D.N. (Glasgow Sherbrooke) 7
Fisher, I.R., Fernhill 16
Fisher, K.H. (Douglas *Associate*) F
Fisher, M.L., Falkirk 22
Fleming, A.A. (Howgate) 22
Fleming, A.F., Strathblane 23
Fleming, H.K., Banchory 32
Fleming, J.R., DD (*University*) B and 26
Fleming, T.G. (Slamannan) F
Fletcher, G.G., *Probr* G
Fletcher, J. (Lockerbie) 7
Fletcher, J.A., Blackburn 2
Fletcher, J.M. (Kincardine) 24
Flockhart, A., Motherwell *Deacon* H and 17
Flockhart, D.R. (*Carberry Tower*) F
Forbes, G.A.R., Kirkintilloch 16
Forbes, I.M., Kemnay 33
Forbes, I.M., Howe of Fife 26
Forbes, J. (Priesthill *Associate*) F
Forbes, J.W.A., Edzell 30
Ford, A.A., Airdrie 17
Formston, A. (Inch) 9
Forrest, A.(Miss) (*WMU* 1972) K
Forrest, A.B., Uphall 2
Forrest, D., Foula *Agent* H and 46
Forrest, G.W. (Whitburn) 16
Forrest, M.R., Possilpark 16
Forrester, A.A., Cunningsburgh *Lay Miss'y* H and 46
Forrester, D.B., *University* B and 1
Forrester, I.L., Inverkeilor 30
Forrester, M.R. (Mrs), St Michael's 1
Forrester-Paton, C. (Hawick) 4
Forshaw, G.M. (Glasgow Calton New *Assistant*) F
Forsyth, A.R., Leven 25
Forsyth, D.F., Belhelvie 33

Forsyth, J. (Kilchrenan) 21
Forsyth, S. (Urquhart) 35
Foster, G.W., Steeple 29
Fowler, A.J.R., Paisley 14
Fowler, M.(Miss), *WMU*, Jamaica E
Fowler, R.C.A. (Gask) F
Fox, E.P.G. (Stronsay) 45
Fox, G.D.A. (Kelso) 6
Fox, G.H. (Coalsnaughton) F
Frame, W.H. (Newmains) 17
Francis, J.M.M. (Coldingham) F
Frank, R.W.(Miss), Whalsay 46
Fraser, A. (Cumlodden) 19
Fraser, A.G.(Miss), *Probr* G
Fraser, A.M., Gartcosh 16
Fraser, D.R. (Kinloss) 35
Fraser, D.W., Monifieth 29
Fraser, H.E. (Roslin) 3
Fraser, I.C., *Community Minister* Greenock 15
Fraser, I.M. (Rosyth) F
Fraser, I.W., Dirleton 3
Fraser, J.G. (Glasgow Elder Park) 16
Fraser, J.G., Rosemount 31
Fraser, J.P. (Strathaven) 17
Fraser, J.W. (Farnell) 3
Fraser, J.W., Penicuik 3
Fraser, K.M. *Lic'ate* G
Fraser, P. (Glenmoriston) 37
Fraser, R.M. (Gordon) 5
Frater, A., Annan 7
Frew, J.M. (Glasgow Dennistoun) F
Frew, M.W., *Evangelism Organiser* C and 28
Frew, R. (Mrs), Largo 26
Frizzell, R.S., Wick 41
Froude, J.K., Kirkcaldy 25
Fuller, J.W. (Rome) 1
Fulton, D., Lamlash 12
Fulton, F.H. (Clunie) 27
Fulton, J.R. (Kirkcaldy) 25
Fulton, R.M. (Ascog) 20
Fyall, R.S., Bannockburn 23
Fyfe, W.G. (Glasgow Hall Mem'l) F

G

Gaddes, D.R., Kelso 6
Galbraith, D.O. (Muckairn) 21
Galbraith, N., Blawarthill 16
Galbraith, W.J.L., Auchtermuchty 26
Gale, R.A.A., Dunoon 20
Gall, E.G.(Miss) (*WMU*) K
Gall, R., Addiewell 2
Gallacher, J.W.(Miss), *Probr* G
Gallan, A. (Wishaw) 17
Galloway, A.D. (*University*) B and 16
Galloway, I.F., Lansdowne 16
Galloway, K.J. (Mrs) (*Iona Abbey*) C and 21
Galloway, R.W.C., Cromarty 39

Gammack, G., Mastrick *Associate* 31
Garden, M.J. (Miss), *Lic'ate* G
Gardiner, A. (Aboyne) 31
Gardner, B.K., Carloway 44
Gardner, E.D.(Miss) (*D'ess*) H
Gardner, F.J., Gourock 15
Gardner, P.M., St Cuthbert's *Assistant* G
Garrity, T.A.W., Ayr 10
Gaston, A.R.C., Dollar 23
Gatherer, J.F., Bearsden Westerton *Associate* 18
Gatt, D.W., Thornton 25
Gauld, B.G.D.D., Carnwath 13
Geddes, A.J., Langstane 31

Geddes, A.S. (Banff) 34
Geddes, T.C., Dysart 25
Gentles, M.M.(Miss), Burnside *D'ess* H K and 16
George, G.A., *Lic'ate* G
Gerrard, D.H. (Buckie) F
Gibb, T.F. (Perth) 28
Gibbons, H.V. (Monifieth) 1
Gibson, A.C., Eskdalemuir 7
Gibson, E.H. (Bathgate *Assistant*) F
Gibson, F.S., Social Responsibility *Secretary* C and 1
Gibson, H.M., St Thomas' 16
Gibson, H.M., The High 29
Gibson, I., Abercorn 1

H

Haddow, A.H., Garthdee 31
Haggarty, W.G., North of St Andrew 31
Hair, P.R., Lochbroom 39
Haley, D., *Hospital Chaplain* C and 16
Hall, G.B., *University* B and 26
Hall, J.A. (Strathkinness) 6
Hall, J.A. (Langton) 5
Hall, K.F., Alloa 23
Hall, P.R., *Lic'ate* G
Hall, R.K. (Carnock) 24
Hall, W.M., Kilmarnock 11
Hamill, R., Castle Douglas 8
Hamilton, A.R. (Cambuslang) 16
Hamilton, D.G., Education *Curriculum Officer* C and 18
Hamilton, D.S.M., *University* B and 16
Hamilton, I., Newmilns 11
Hamilton, I.W.F., Nairn 37
Hamilton, J. (Auchterhouse) 29
Hamilton, J.H. (Colmonell) 18
Hamilton, J.H. (Yoker) 16
Hamilton, M.(Miss) (*D'ess*) H
Hamilton, P.J.R. (East Kilbride) 20
Hamilton, R. (Kelso) 6
Hamilton, W. (Glasgow Dennistoun) 16
Hamilton, W.D., Greenock 15
Hamilton, W.H. (Prestwick) 10
Handley, J., Motherwell 17
Haney, H.B., John Ross Memorial 16
Hanna, W., Glenrothes *Deacon* H and 25
Hannah, A.C., *Lic'ate* G
Hannah, W., Muirkirk 10
Hannah, W.M., *Lic'ate* G
Harbison, D.J.H., Beith 12
Hardie, H.W., Blackridge 2
Hardie, J. (Douglas) 13
Hardie, R.K., Stenhouse 22
Hardy, B.G. (St Paul's) 1
Hare, M.M.W., Kilmarnock 11
Harkes, G., *Community Minister* 9
Harkness, J., *Chaplain General* A and 47
Harper, A.J.M.(Miss), Linthouse 16
Harper, D.L., Troon 10
Harries, D.A. (Kilmodan) F
Harris, J.W.F., Bearsden 18
Harris, S.M., Linlithgow 2
Hartshorn, B.J. (Aberdeen *Assistant*) F
Harvey, D.V.R., *Chaplain RAF* A and 47
Harvey, W.J., *Iona Community* C and 16
Haslett, H.J. (St Giles' *Assistant*) F
Hastie, G.I., Cowdenbeath 24
Haston, C.B., Gretna 7
Haughton, F., Kirkintilloch 16
Hawdon, J.E., Clepington 29
Hawthorn, D., *College of Education* C and 31
Hay, B.J.L., Mackerstoun 6
Hay, J.W., (Edinburgh Cluny *Assistant*) F
Hay, T.A. (Dundee St John's) F

Hay, W.J.R., Buchanan 23
Hazlett, W.I.P., *Lic'ate* G
Headden, A.F., Craiglockhart 1
Hearfield, B.A. (Gorebridge) F
Heatlie, A.J. (Candlish) 1
Heavenor, E.S.P. (Crieff) 1
Hebenton, D.J., Ayton 5
Hegarty, J.D., High Carntyne 16
Heggie, T.P., Nairn F
Helon, G.G., Barr 10
Henderson, C.M., Campbeltown 19
Henderson, C.M.(Mrs), Limekilns *Auxiliary* 24
Henderson, D.C. (Glamis) 30
Henderson, E.M.(Miss), Granton 1
Henderson, G.M. (Cults) 26
Henderson, G.M., Dingwall 39
Henderson, H.E.(Miss), *WMU, Tiberias* E
Henderson, J.D., Cluny 33
Henderson, J.M.(Miss), *Probr* G
Henderson, R.B. (Kingswells) 37
Henderson, R.J., Limekilns 24
Henderson, R.J.M., Alexandria 18
Hendry, G.S., DD (Bridge of Allan) F
Henney, W., St Andrews 26
Henry, M.N. (Perth) 28
Hepburn, C.A.(Miss), Gargunnock 23
Hepburn, J.L., Ardoch 28
Heriot, C.R., Brightons 22
Herkes, M.(Mrs), Prestonpans 3
Heron, H.S.(Mrs), *Lic'ate* G
Heron, J. (Ochiltree) 17
Herron, A, DD (*Presbytery Clerk*) C and 16
Hetherington, R.M., Barrhead 14
Hewitt, E.T. (Newmilns) 11
Hewitt, W.C., Elderslie 14
Hibbert, F.W., Kincardine 40
Higgins, G.K. (Oban) F
Higham, R.D., Gordon 5
Hill, A.T. (Prestonpans) 3
Hill, J. (*WMU* 1973) K
Hill, J.W., Corstorphine 1
Hill, N., Strath *Associate* 42
Hill, R., Lisbon D and 48
Hill, R.S. (Glenshee) 28
Hill, S. (Muiravonside) 22
Hislop, D.T. (Maryhill) 16
Hodge, W.N.T., Longside 34
Hogg, A.M.(Miss), *Hospital Chaplain* C and 31
Hogg, D., St Andrew's East 16
Hogg, T.M., Tranent 3
Hogg, W.T., Glenorchy 21
Holland, J.C. (Strone) 22
Holland, W., Lochend 8
Hollins, R.M., *College of Education* C and 10
Holmes, K. (Gamrie) 34
Holroyd, G., Dingwall 39
Holt, J., Kilmarnock 11
Honeyman, A.M. (*University*) B and 26
Honeyman, I., *Lic'ate* G
Honeyman, J. (Clatt) 22
Hood, A.J.J., *Lic'ate* G
Hood, E.C.P., Methlick 33
Hood, E.L.(Mrs), Renfrew 14

Hood, H.S.C., Anderston 16
Hood, K.(Mrs), East Kilbride *D'ess* H and 17
Hope, G.H.(Mrs), Foulden 5
Hope-Smith, J., *Lic'ate* G
Horne, A.M., *Probr* G
Horne, D.A., Tain 39
Horsburgh, G.E., Dreghorn 11
Hosain, S., Fauldhouse 2
Hosie, J., Burra Isle 46
Houston, A.M. (Tibbermore) 28
Houston, E.W.(Miss), Hurlford 11
Houston, G.R., Perth 28
Houston, H., Rhynd 28
Houston, J., *Lic'ate* G
Houston, P.M., Renfrew 14
Houston, T.C., Baillieston 16
Howat, T.H., Broughton *Auxiliary* 4
Howat, W.P. (Ayr) 10
Howe, A.Y., Rosskeen 39
Howden, M.(Miss) (*D'ess*) H
Howie, D.Y. (Ruthrieston) 31
Howie, W. (Aberdeen *Assistant*) F
Howieson, R.A. (Newport) 26
Howieson, R.M. (Blairgowrie) 27
Howieson, T.S. (Rathven) 35
Hudson, E.V., *S T V* C and 17
Hudson, H.R., Bridgeton 16
Hudson, J.H., St Peter's 29
Huggett, J.A.(Miss), *Probr* G
Hughes, A. (Dollar) 23
Hughes, H.M.(Miss) Lansdowne *D'ess* H and 16
Hughes, K.G., London 47
Hughes, O.T. (Guernsey) 47
Huie, D.F., *Chaplain RN* A and 47
Hulbert, A.J.M., *Lic'ate* G
Hume, W. (Whitburn) 2
Humphris, P.M., Mains of Fintry 29
Hunt, T.G., Evie 45
Hunter, A.M., DD (*University*) B and 31
Hunter, G. (Glasgow Scotstoun) 16
Hunter, G.L., *Teacher RE* C and 18
Hunter, J.E., Blantyre 17
Hunter, J.M. (Borgue) FF
Hunter, W.F., *Youth Officer* C and 28
Hurst, F.R., Assynt 40
Hutcheson, J.M. (Glasgow Possilpark) 16
Hutcheson, N.M., Dalbeattie 8
Hutchison, A. (Alvie) 36
Hutchison, A.E.W. (*Deacon*) H
Hutchison, A.S. (Bowden) 1
Hutchison, A.S., DD, *Hospital Chaplain* C and 31
Hutchison, C.M. (*WMU* 1972) K
Hutchison, E.(Mrs), Calton Parkhead *Auxiliary* 16
Hutchison, H., Carmunnock 16
Hutchison, J.N. (Anstruther) 26
Hutchison, M.(Mrs), Old Kirk *D'ess* H and 1
Hutchison, M.L.(Mrs), Dumfries 8
Hutton, W.J. (Glasgow Trinity Duke Street) F
Hynd, R.S., *Chaplain Army* A and 23

I

Ibiam, A.(Dr)(*WMU* 1967) K
Inglis, A (Miss), Corstorphine *Associate* 1
Inglis, C.G. (Glasgow St Bride's) 16
Inglis, D.B.C., Turriff 34
Inglis, J.H.A. (Penpont) 26
Ingram, J.R. (*Chaplain RAF*) 29
Innes, P.M. (Assam) 30
Ireland, A. (Edinburgh St Nicholas') F
Ireland, A., *Lic'ate* G
Irvine, C.M., *WMU*, Nepal E
Irvine, E.A.A.(Mrs) (*WMU* 1988) K
Irvine, E.H.C. (Milton of Campsie) 16
Irvine, G.C.(Dr), *WMU*, Kenya E
Irvine, R.W.W., Kincardine in Menteith 23
Irving, D.R., Kilbirnie 12
Irving, G. (Brydekirk) 4
Irving, R.C. (Crossmichael) 8
Irving, W.D., Penicuik 3
Isbister, J. (*Lay Miss'y*) H
Isherwood, W.M. (Rotterdam) 48
Izett, W.A.F., Law 13

J

Jack, A. (Kirkcudbright) 28
Jack, D., Fettercairn 32
Jack, J.A.P., *Probr* G
Jack, R, Bearsden 18
Jackson, J., Bonnybridge 22
James, R.F. (Lauder) 8
Jamieson, D.B., Monifieth 29
Jamieson, G.D., Barnhill 29
Jamieson, G.T. (Stirling) 23
Jamieson, H.M. (Ashkirk) 4
Jamieson, J., Balfron 23
Jamieson, R.C. (Galston) 11
Jardine, J.H, *Lic'ate* G
Jarvie, T.W., Kilmarnock 11
Jeffrey, E.W.S., Bristo Mem'l 1
Jeffrey, S.D., St George's 31
Jenkins, A.G. (Inch) 9
Jenkins, G.F.C., Education *Secretary* C and 24
Jenner, A., Kingussie 36
Jessamine, A.L., Chapelton 17
Jesson. W.J.M. (Mochrum) 9
Johnson, E., *Ethnic Groups* C and 16
Johnston, C.D., Larkhall 17
Johnston, C.L. (Auchinleck) 10
Johnston, G.B. (Grantown on Spey) 3
Johnston, J. (Inverkeithing) 24
Johnston, J., *Hospital Chaplain* C and 8
Johnston, K.L., Blairbeth 16
Johnston, M.(Miss), Paisley *D'ess* H and 14
Johnston, M.H. (Miss), Maryhill *Associate* 16
Johnston, R., St Mary's 1
Johnston, R.D.M. (Ayr) 10
Johnston, R.W.M., Temple 16
Johnston, T.N., Buckie 35
Johnston, W.B., *DD*, Colinton 1
Johnstone, B., Hamilton 17
Johnstone, D. (Glasgow Belhaven) 16
Johnstone, D.B. (Dundee Baxter Park) F
Johnstone, H.G. (Mrs), Auchterhouse 29
Johnstone, H.M.J., *Probr* G
Johnstone, R., Thurso 41
Johnstone, R.I., Kilmarnock 11
Johnstone, T.J., Coatbridge 17
Johnstone, W., *University* B and 31
Jolly, A.J., *Chaplain Army* A and 16
Jolly, J., Old Partick 16
Jolly, L.W.(Miss), *Lic'ate* G
Jones, A.J. (Aberdeen St Clement's) F
Jones, C (Ratho) FF
Jones, E.G., St Rollox 16
Jones, J.D. (Kirkconnel) 16
Jones, J.O.a-I., Mearns *Associate* 16
Jones, P.H. (Bishopbriggs) 13
Jones, R.A., Marnoch 34
Jones, W. (Kirriemuir) 30
Jones, W.G., Kirkmichael 10

K

L

M

M'Adam, D.J., *Probr* G
M'Alister, D.J.B., North Berwick 3
Macallan, G.B., Kintore 33
MacAlpine, A.G. (Tain) 39
M'Alpine, J., Newarthill
  Auxiliary 17
M'Alpine, R.H.M., Coylton 10
M'Alpine, R.J., Duntocher 18
Macara, A. (Irvine) 11
M'Areavey, W., Kelvin 16
MacArthur, A. (Penilee) F
Macarthur, A. J., Lochcarron 42
M'Arthur, F.M., Kirk o' Field 1
M'Arthur, G. (*WMU* 1972) K
M'Arthur, J. (Howood) 14
Macarthur, J.M.M. (Strath and
  Sleat) 42
Macartney, W.M. (Vienna) 27
Macaskil, D. (Lochs in Bernera) 37
Macaskill, D., *Probr* G
Macaskill, N.R., Lochgelly 24
Macaulay, A. H. (Bellie) 35
Macaulay, D., Park 44
M'Auslane, T.M.
  (Kennethmont) 33
MacBain, I.W., Coatbridge 17
M'Bain, M.(Miss), *D'ess*
  Lerwick H and 46
MacBeth, E.(Miss) (*D'ess*) H
M'Bride, G.H.H. (Perth) 28
M'Bride, J.S. (Wishaw) 17
M'Cabe, G., Airdrie 17
M'Cabe, G.E., Dalkeith 3
M'Callum, A., Kilberry 19
M'Callum, C.D.C.(Miss), *WMU*,
  North India E
M'Callum, D.A. (Connel) 21
M'Callum, G. (Aberdour) F
M'Callum, I.D. (Stirling) 23
M'Callum, J., Falkirk 22
M'Callum, J., *Probr* G
M'Callum, M.(Miss), *D'ess* (St
  Colm's College) H
M'Callum, W. (Lochryan) 9
M'Calman, A.D. (Busby) F
M'Cance, A.M., Coatbridge 17
M'Cardel, P.M. (Stewarton) 11
M'Cartney, A.C., Caputh 27
M'Caskill, G.I.L. (Monimail) 1
M'Clements, D.E., Falkirk 22
M'Clintock, A. (Tongue) 40
MacColl, J., *Lic'ate* G
MacColl, J.C., Johnstone 14
M'Conkey, D.L. (Fossoway) 28
M'Connachie, C.E. (Miss) (St
  George's *Assistant*) 31
M'Connell, R. (Hawick) 6
M'Cool, A.B.(Mrs), *Probr* G
M'Cormick, A.F., Perth 28
M'Cormick, J.A., Ardchattan 21
MacCormick, M.G.(Miss),
  Buchlyvie 23
M'Cormick, W.C. (Glasgow
  Maryhill) 13
M'Cracken, G.A., Whitburn 2
M'Craw, W. (Monimail) 26
M'Creadie, D.W., Kirkmabreck 9
M'Cree, I.W., Clyne 40
M'Crum, R, *Chaplain RN* A and 17
MacCuish, A. (Stornoway) 44

M'Cuish, D. (Caddonfoot) 4
M'Culloch, A.J.R., *Probr* G
M'Cully, M.I.(Miss), Bonnyrigg
  D'ess H and 3
M'Cutcheon, A.W.F.(Miss), *WMU*,
  North India E
M'Cutcheon, G.A.
  (Clackmannan) 23
Macdiarmid, D. (Rosskeen) 39
Macdonald, A., Cross Ness 44
Macdonald, A., Neilston 14
Macdonald, A.(Miss), Lochwood
  D'ess H and 16
M'Donald, A.D., Holburn 31
MacDonald, A.I., Inverness 37
Macdonald, D. (Enzie) 35
Macdonald, D.F.M. (*Clerk of
  Assembly*) C and 17
Macdonald, D.M. (Kippen) 1
Macdonald, D.N. (Glasgow St
  Columba) F
Macdonald, D.N., *Lic'ate* G
Macdonald, F., Kinlochluichart 39
Macdonald, F.A.J., Jordanhill 16
Macdonald, I.(Miss) (*D'ess*) H
Macdonald, I.A., Burdiehouse 1
M'Donald, I.J.M., Deerness 45
Macdonald, I.U., Tarbolton 10
Macdonald, J. (Dundee Lochee) 29
Macdonald, J. (Knock) 44
Macdonald, J. (*University*) B
Macdonald, J.A. (Thornliebank) 16
Macdonald, J.A. (Dundee
  Balgay) 29
M'Donald, J.A., Aberuthven 28
Macdonald, J.F. (Bendochy) 27
Macdonald, J.H. (Melrose) 21
M'Donald, J.I.H.,
  University B and 1
MacDonald, J.M. (Kilmarnock) 11
Macdonald, J.W., Lerwick 46
MacDonald, K., Applecross
  Associate 42
MacDonald, K.D. (*Lay Miss'y*) H
Macdonald, M.(Miss), *Probr* G
Macdonald, M.E., DD
  (*University*) B and 16
Macdonald, N. (Ardchattan) 21
Macdonald, N. (Aberdeen
  Trinity) 39
MacDonald, P.J., *Youth
  Adviser* C and 1
M'Donald, P.D. (Ratho) 13
Macdonald, R. (Insch) 33
Macdonald, R.M.
  (Nigeria) K and 23
M'Donald, S., Ministry & Mission
  Secretary C and 1
Macdonald, W. (Knock) 44
MacDonald, W.D., *Lic'ate* G
M'Donald, W.G. (Falkirk) F
Macdonald, W.J., Gairloch 42
M'Donald, W.J.G., DD, Mayfield 1
Macdonald, W.M. (Kilmuir) 43
Macdonald, W.U. (Aberdalgie) 28
Macdonnel, A.W., Haddington 3
MacDougall, A. (Sleat) 42
M'Dougall, J.N. (*WMU* 1960) K
M'Dougall, M.I.(Miss),
  Meadowside 29

Macdougall, M.M., Portobello 1
M'Dowall, B., *Probr* G
M'Dowall, R.J., Falkirk 22
M'Enhill, P., *Lic'ate* /G
M'Ewan, J. (Dores) 37
MacEwan, J.A.I., Abernethy 36
MacEwan, P.J. (Culter) 13
M'Ewen, J.S., DD
  (*University*) B and 31
MacFadden, K. (Yetholm) 6
M'Fadyen, G.J., Whiteinch 16
M'Fadzean, I., *Probr* G
M'Fadzean M.(Miss), East Kilbride
  D'ess H and 17
M'Farlan, D.M. (*College of
  Education*) C and 16
Macfarlane, A. (Uig) 44
Macfarlane, A.J.C. (Glasgow
  Newlands South) 1
Macfarlane, D. (Inverness) 37
MacFarlane, D.C., Peebles 4
Macfarlane, K., Fearn 39
Macfarlane, P.T., *Chaplain
  Army* A and 47
Macfarlane, T.G., South
  Shawlands 16
M'Farlane, W.A. (Glasgow St
  Cuthbert's) 3
Macfarlane, W.J.E. (Alexandria) 18
M'Garva, R. (Clydebank) F
M'Garva, S.(Miss) (*D'ess*) H
M'Geachie, S. (Lochgoilhead) 2
MacGhee, A.S.M., Crimond 34
M'Ghee, R, DD, Falkirk 22
M'Ghie, J. (Comrie) 28
M'Gill, T.W., Stranraer 9
M'Gillivray, A.G., *Presbytery
  Clerk* C and 1
MacGillivray, D., Kirkmaiden 9
M'Ginty, J.W., Alloway 10
M'Glashan, C.Y., DD (St
  Andrews) FF
M'Goff, A.W.(Miss) (*WMU*) K
M'Gowan, A.T.B., Trinity Possil 16
M'Gregor, A.G.C., Leith 1
M'Gregor, D., Fair Isle *Agent* H
M'Gregor, D.A.R. (Edinburgh) F
M'Gregor, D.J., Channelkirk 4
MacGregor, D.J. (Closeburn) 8
MacGregor, M.S.(Miss),
  Calcutta D
M'Gregor, R.M. (St Margaret's
  Polmadie) 16
MacGregor, S.M.(Miss) (*D'ess*) H
M'Gregor, T.S., *Hospital
  Chaplain* C and 1
MacGregor, W., Auchtergaven 28
M'Gurk, A.F., New Cumnock 10
M'Haffie, F.G. (Edinburgh
  Assistant) F
M'Haffie, R.D., Kinning Park 16
M'Hardy, R.D. F
M'Hutchison, D. (*Hospital
  Chaplain*) F
M'Ilroy, A.M. (Darvel) 11
M'Indoe, J.H., London 47
MacInnes, D., Gardner Street 16
MacInnes, J.E. (Snizort) 21
M'Intosh, C.G., Dunblane 23
M'Intosh, H (Auchterarder) 1

N

O

O'Donnell, C.T., Anwoth	8	O'Neil, J.C., *University*	B and 1	Orrock, A.A. (*Teacher*	
Offor, C.E. (Ayr)	10	Ord, J.K. (Cumbernauld)	F	*RE*)	C and 23
Ogilvie, K.G. (Auchterderran)	F	Ormiston, H.C., *Industrial*		Orrock, D.W. (Lenzie)	16
Ogilvy, O.M. (Leswalt)	9	*Chaplain*	C and 22	Osbeck, J.R., Enzie	35
Ogston, D.D., Perth	28	Orr, D.C. (Govan)	16	Osborne, A.G., *Community*	
Ogston, E.J., Leven	25	Orr, J.F. (St John's Oxgangs)	1	*Minister*	C and 10
Old, A.M. (Uddingston)	F	Orr, J.M. (Aberfoyle)	1	Ostler, J.H. (Contin Strathconon)	F
O'Leary, T., Sri Lanka	D and 9	Orr, N.B., *Industrial*		Ott, P.M.B.(Mrs), Peterhead	34
Oliver, G., Alyth	27	*Chaplain*	C and 16	Ovens, S.B., Slamannan	22
Olsen, H.C.(Miss), Windygates	25	Orr, W. (Tarbat)	39	Owen, J.J.C., Lochmaben	7
				Oxburgh, B.H., Saltcoats	12

Contact John W. Anderson, 33 Camp Wood View, Mayfield, Dalkeith EH22 5QQ (031–663 2932) for a local speaker at your Church, Guild or Fellowship.

CHURCH OF SCOTLAND

CS ⊓ TOTAL ABSTAINERS' ASSOCIATION

Or contact R. J. M. Hart, BSc, C.A., 5 St. Vincent Place, Glasgow G1 2HT for details of individual membership (from 50p minimum).

P

Pacitti, S.A., Taiwan	D and 16	Paul, A.(Miss), Motherwell	17	Porteous, A. (Greenock)	15
Pagan, J., Dumfries	8	Paul, I., Wishaw	17	Porteous, J.K., DD, Cupar	26
Page, D.J., Mid Craigie	29	Paul, W.M.(Miss), *WMU*, Egypt	E	Porteous, N.W., DD	
Page, J.R., Dunlop	11	Payne, J. (Linlithgow *Assistant*)	F	(*University*)	B and 1
Page, R.(Miss), *University*	B and 1	Peat, S.W., Leith	1	Porter, G.M. (Patna)	10
Palit, S. (Dundonnell)	39	Penman, I.D., Coldstream	5	Porter, J.C. (Forres)	35
Palmer, G.R., Ruchazie	16	Pennington, C.(Mrs) (*WMU*		Porter, R. (Glasgow Govanhill)	16
Palmer, S.W., Kilbarchan	14	1954)	K	Porter, R.H. (Glasgow Paisley	
Park, C.D., Paisley	14	Penny, R.F., Harray	45	Road)	26
Park, M.(Miss) (*D'ess*)	H	Perry, J.G.(Miss), *D'ess*	H	Potts, J.M.(Miss), North Leith	
Parker, A.H. (Dunfermline		Peterkin, W.N. (Broom)	16	*D'ess*	H and 1
Assistant)	F	Petrie, I.D., St Andrew's	29	Poustie, G.T., Boyndie	34
Paterson, A.E.L. (Musselburgh)	3	Petrie, J.G.(Miss), *D'ess*	H	Povey, J.M., Kirk of Calder	2
Paterson, D.S., Cumbernauld	22	Petrie, K.L., Stonehaven	32	Powrie, J.E., Chalmers	29
Paterson, I.M. (Eccles)	1	Pettigrew, R. (Dalbeattie)	8	Prentice, D.K., *Probr*	G
Paterson, J.H., Airdrie	17	Petty, P.W.P. (Prestwick)	26	Prentice, G., Paisley	14
Paterson, J.L., Linlithgow	2	Philip, D.S., Gibraltar	D and 48	Prentice, R. (Knockando)	35
Paterson, J.M.K., DD		Philip, G.M., Sandyford	16	Prentis, D.F., Drumoak	32
(Milngavie)	1	Philip, J., Holyrood Abbey	1	Prescott, J.H. (Kirkmabreck)	8
Paterson, J.R.H., Milngavie	18	Philip, M.R., Blairgowrie	27	Preston, T., Port Glasgow	15
Paterson, K.N. (Pluscarden)	5	Philip, N.E. (Glenbervie)	F	Price, P.O., Blantyre	17
Paterson, M.L.(Miss) (*WMU*		Philip, R.R. (Edinburgh		Pritchard, J.S. (*B B C*)	C and 16
1966)	K	Rosehall)	FF	Pryce, S.F.A., Dumfries	8
Paterson, R. (*WMU* 1954)	K	Phillips, C.W.(Miss) (*D'ess*)	H	Purves, I., Johnstone	14
Paterson, R.M., *Lic'ate*	G	Phillips, J.S. (Ayr)	10	Purves, J.P.S., Jamaica	D
Paterson, W. (Dundurn)	29	Phillips, T.M. (West Linton)	13	Purves, J.S., Drumchapel	16
Paterson, W., Craigmillar Park	1	Philp, C.(Miss), Arbuthnott	32	Purvis, D.W. (Fisherton)	10
Patience, D., Kilmaurs	11	Philp, R.A. (Stepps)	16	Pyper, J.S. (Greenock)	15
Paton, E.J. (Glasgow Netherton)	39	Philpot, D.H., *W C C*	C and 48	Pyper, N.C.S.(Miss), *Lic'ate*	G
Paton, G. (Aberdeen Stockethill)	F	Pirie, D., Lenzie	16		
Paton, I.F., Newlands	16	Pirie, G., Castlemilk East			
Paton, J.H., Killean	19	*Deacon*	H and 16		
Patterson, A.R.M. (Mochrum)	F	Pitkeathly, T.C., Bridge of Weir	14		
Patterson, G.M.(Miss) (WMU		Plate, M.A.G.(Miss), Cardenden	25		
1963)	K	Pogue, V.C. (*Education*)	C and 24		
Patterson, J.H. (Dalton)	31	Pollock, T.L., Barlanark	16		
Patterson, J.M. (Blackbraes)	22	Pollock, W., Mull *Associate*	21		
Patterson, J.W., St Andrews	26	Poole, A.M.(Mrs), Dyke	35	**Q**	
Patterson, M.N. (Daviot)	37	Poole, W.S.W. (Carlisle)	F		
Pattison, K.J., *Hospital*		Pope, D.H.N., Priesthill	16	Quigley, B.D.(Miss), New	
Chaplain	C and 16	Portchmouth, R.J., Bendochy	27	Stevenston	17

R

Rades, J., *Lic'ate*	G
Rae, A.W. (Annan)	4
Rae, D.L., Kolhapur	D and 16
Rae, F.W. ,DD (Dairsie)	26
Rae, P.C., Beath	24
Rae, R. *Hospital Chaplain*	C and 29
Rae, S.M., *Chaplain RN*	A and 18
Raeburn, A.C., Battlefield	16
Raffan, S.J. (*Hospital Chaplain*)	C and 8
Ralston, A. (Elderslie)	14
Ramsay, A., Fort William	38
Ramsay, A.M., Bargrennan	9
Ramsay, B., Aberlemno	30
Ramsay, G.M., Airlie	30
Ramsay, K.M.(Miss) (*WMU 1971*)	H and K
Ramsay, R.J., Glenisla	30
Ramsay, W.G., Springburn	16
Ramsay, W.H.W., Duddingston	1
Ramsden, C.(Miss), Gorbals *D'ess*	H and 16
Randall, D.J., Macduff	34
Rankin, J., Perth	28
Rankine, T. (*WMU 1953*)	K
Rathbone, S. (Buenos Aires)	7
Rattray, P.J.(Miss). *WMU*, Tabeetha	E
Reamonn, P., Cockburnspath	3
Reddick, A.F., *Lic'ate*	G
Redpath, J.G., Tulliallan	24
Re'emi, S.P. (Tiberias)	K and 1
Reid, A., *Probr*	G
Reid, A.A.(Miss), Douglas *Associate*	13
Reid, A.A.(Miss), *WMU*, Ghana	E
Reid, A.A.S., *University Chaplain*	C and 31
Reid, A.B., Trinity	29
Reid, A.G., Dunfermline	24
Reid, D., Largoward	26
Reid, D.T., Cleish	28
Reid, G.T.H., DD (Aberdeen Langstane)	1
Reid, H.G. (Troon)	F
Reid, I.J.M. (Kilwinning)	1
Reid, J.K.S., DD (*University*)	B and 1
Reid, M.C.(Miss), (*D'ess*)	H
Reid, M.I.(Miss) (*WMU 1982*)	K
Reid, M.R.B.C., Falkirk	22
Reid, R.J. (Mossgreen)	24
Reid, S., *Probr*	G
Reid, W.M., Forres	35
Reid, W.S., London Road	1
Rennie, A.J.T., Calton New	16
Rennie, A.M. (Kincardine and Croick)	23
Rennie, A.M.(Miss), *D'ess* Bristo M'l	I and 1
Rennie, C.A.J., Larbert	22
Rennie, D.B., Cults	31
Rennie, J.B., Leochel Cushnie	33
Rennie, J.D., Broughton	4
Rennie, W. (Maybole)	16
Renton, I.P., St Colm's	1
Renton, J.P., Paisley	14
Rentoul, R.W. (Bangalore)	F

Renwick, C.O., *Probr*	G
Rettie, J.A., Melness	40
Revel, W.T. (Glasgow St James')	12
Rew, M.M., Albany	1
Rhind, M.(Miss), Iona Community *D'ess*	H
Rhodes, W.S. (North India)	F and K
Riach, W.A.D. (Kenya)	F
Ribbons, F., Howgate	3
Richardson, T.C., Cults	31
Richmond, J. (Holytown)	F
Ricketts, H.M. (Craigiebuckler)	31
Riddell, J.A., Jedburgh	6
Riddoch, M.E.(Miss), *WMU*, China	E
Ridland, A.K. Dalkeith	3
Riggans, W., *Lecturer*	C and 47
Ritchie, A., Airdrie	17
Ritchie, B., Crieff	28
Ritchie, G.W.M., Ardersier	37
Ritchie, I.M.(Miss), *WMU*, North India	E
Ritchie, J.M. (Coalsnaughton)	K and 23
Ritchie, J.S. (Haddington)	1
Ritchie, L.A. (*University Chaplain*)	C and 16
Ritchie, M.A., Kilbrandon	21
Ritchie, M.S.(Miss), *WMU*, Tabeetha	E
Ritchie, S.A., *Lic'ate*	G
Ritchie, W.A.B., Connel	21
Ritchie, W.M., Appin	21
Robb, S.H. (Greenock)	15
Robb, W.C., Catrine	10
Roberts, A. (Dunblane)	20
Robertson, A., Eastwood	16
Robertson, A., Aberluthnott	32
Roberson, A.C.(Miss) (*D'ess*)	H
Robertson, A.J., Baldernock	18
Robertson, A.K. (Fort William)	38
Robertson, A.O. (*University Chaplain*)	F
Robertson, B., Paris	D and 48
Robertson, B., *Lic'ate*	G
Robertson, C. (Cockpen)	3
Robertson, C., Canongate	1
Robertson, D. (Lochalsh)	19
Robertson, D.K., Polbeth	2
Robertson, D.M., Auchinleck	10
Robertson, E., Armadale	2
Robertson, F.A., Inverness	37
Robertson, G. (Muirkirk)	F
Robertson, G.B. (Irvine)	F
Robertson, G.R., Udny	33
Robertson, I.H.M. (Wormit)	11
Robertson, I.M., Carriden	22
Robertson, I.W., Colvend	8
Robertson, J. (Paisley)	F
Robertson, J, Newton	3
Robertson, J.G.L., *Lic'ate*	G
Robertson, J.H., Saltcoats	12
Robertson, J.H., Thornliebank	16
Robertson, J.M., Campsie	16
Robertson, J.T., Keith	35
Roberson, J.W.(Miss) (*WMU 1970*)	K

Robertson, M., *Chaplain Army*	A and 31
Robertson, P., Dallas	35
Robertson, R. (Collace)	29
Robertson, R. (Scone)	28
Robertson, R.C., *Community Minister*	C and 16
Robertson, S.H., Gorebridge	3
Robertson, T.G.M., Edenshead	26
Robertson, T.P., Broughty Ferry	29
Robertson, T.R. (Broughton)	8
Robertson, W. (Paisley)	14
Robinson, K.S.P. (North Merchiston)	1
Robson, G.K., Balgay	29
Robson, J. (Falkirk)	22
Rodger, J.A. (*WMU 1955*)	K
Rodger, M.A., Ellon	33
Roger, A.M., Maxwell	16
Rogers, J.M., Ryehill	29
Rogerson, A.E. (Galashiels)	4
Rogerson, S.D., Baillieston	16
Rollo, G.B., Elgin	35
Ronald, N.A,(Miss), Cumbernauld *D'ess*	H and 22
Rose, J.M. (West St Giles')	1
Ross, A.C., Annan	7
Ross, A.C., *University*	B and 1
Ross, D.M., *Industrial Organiser*	C and 3
Ross, D.S., Peterhead	34
Ross, E.J., Cowdenbeath	24
Ross, G.H., *Lic'ate*	G
Ross, H.G. (Gillingham)	47
Ross, J., Kilsyth	16
Ross, J.D., Rome	D and 48
Ross, J.H.G. (Dundurn)	FF
Ross, K. (Northmavine)	46
Ross, K.R., Malawi	D
Ross, K.W., Dalmellington	10
Ross, R.A., World Mission & Unity *Secretary*	C and 1
Ross, R.J. (Wishaw)	F
Ross, R.M.F. (Plantation)	16
Ross, W.B., Findochty	35
Ross, W.J. (Dunbarney)	28
Rough, J.S. (St Monans)	26
Rough, M.E.(Miss) (*WMU 1987*)	K
Roy, A.A., Wick	41
Roy, A.J., Ogilvie	29
Roy, I.M., Stevenston	12
Roy, J. (Irvine)	11
Roy, J.A., Lochee	29
Rule, J.A., Renfrew	14
Runciman, J.T. (Greenock)	15
Rushforth, E.W. (Dinnet)	33
Rushton, J., Kildonan	40
Russell, A., Duror	38
Russell, A.C. (Aberlemno)	30
Russell, A.M. (Aberdeen Woodside)	31
Russell, J., Tillicoultry	23
Russell, K.G., Lochgelly	24
Russell, M.M.(Miss (*WMU 1969*)	K
Russell, P.R., Clydebank	18
Rutherford, B.C., Malawi	D
Rutherford, D.W. (Aberdour)	28
Rutherford, E.B. (*D'ess*)	H
Ryrie, A.C. (*Industrial Chaplain*)	F

S

Salmond, J.S., Holytown 17
Salter, F.H. (Rothiemurchus) 16
Salters, R.B., *University* B and 26
Samuel, L.J.(Mrs), *WMU, Madras* E
Samuel, R., Rothesay 20
Sanderson, A.M., Shawlands 16
Sanderson, W.R., DD (Stenton) 3
Sandilands, I.S., Black Mount 13
Sandison, M.J. (*Lay Miss'y*) H
Sangster, E.G., Blackhall 1
Sangster, G.B.C. (Nairobi *Associate*) 1
Sangster, R.G. (Lossiemouth) F
Saunders, C.M., Ayr 10
Saunders, K., Coatbridge 17
Savage, G.M.A., Dumfries 8
Sawers, E.R.H. (Cranstoun) 3
Sawers, H. (Motherwell) 17
Sawyer, J.F.A.,)University) F
Schofield, M.F., *Hospital Chaplain* C and 1
Scobie, A.J., Cardross 18
Scollay, J. (Douglas) 1
Scott, A.D., Daviot 33
Scott, D.D., Forth 13
Scott, D.H. (Kilmallie) F
Scott, D.B., Invergordon 39
Scott, E.M., Port Glasgow 15
Scott, E.M.(Miss) (*WMU* 1967) K
Scott, G.G., St David's 29
Scott, H.M., *WMU*, Zambia E
Scott, I.G., Greenbank 1
Scott, J., Aberdeen 24
Scott, J., Northfield 31
Scott, J.F., Dyce 31
Scott, J.H., *Lic'ate* G
Scott, J.L., Inverurie 33
Scott, J.M., DD (Jerusalem) 49
Scott, J.W., Durisdeer 8
Scott, L.W. (*Lay Miss'y*) H
Scott, M.A.B.(Miss) (*WMU* 1966) K
Scott, M.C.(Mrs) *Lic'ate* G
Scott, T.H., (*University Chaplain*) F
Scott, T.T., Kilmarnock 11
Scott, W.D., Maud 34
Scott, W.G. (Jerusalem) 49
Scott-Ross, M.W. F
Scoular, J.M., Kippen 23
Scoular, S., Rosyth 24
Scouler, M.D., *Lic'ate* G
Scouller, H. (Abernethy) F
Scrimgeour, A.M.(Miss) (*D'ess*) H
Scrimgeour, E.(Miss) (*WMU* 1976) K
Scroggie, J.C. (Dundee Mains) 29
Seaman, R.S., Dornock 7
Seath, T.J.G., Motherwell 17
Sefton, H.R., *University* B and 31
Selfridge, J., Edrachillis 40
Serle, W. (Drumoak) 1
Service, J.P. (Chapel of Garioch) 10
Sewell, P.M.N., Stirling 23
Sewell, R.N. (Penicuik) 3
Shackleton, W., Greenock 15
Shaffer, J.A.(Mrs), *Lic'ate* G
Shand, G.C. (Edinburgh Old Kirk *Assistant*) F

Shanks, N.J., *University* B and 16
Shannon, W.G., Moulin 27
Sharp, A., Middlefield 31
Sharp, J.C., East Kilbride 17
Shaw, A. (Gardenstown) 34
Shaw, A.J., Ardclach 37
Shaw, A.N., Kilmarnock 11
Shaw, D., Craigentinny 1
Shaw, D., Bathgate 2
Shaw, D., *Chaplain RAF* A and 47
Shaw, D.W.D., *University* B and 26
Shaw, J. (*Lay Miss'y*) H
Shaw, W.A. (Glenrothes) F
Shearer, T. (Orwell) 16
Shedden, J., *Chaplain RAF* A and 35
Shepherd, D. (*Lay Miss'y*) H
Shepherd, H.A., Balerno 1
Sheret, B.S. (Stoneyburn) F
Sherrard, H.D., Buckhaven 25
Sherrard, J.A., Glamis 30
Sherry, G.T., Menstrie 23
Shewan, F.D.F., Muirhouse 1
Shewan, M.R.R., Ratho 1
Shields, J.M., *Chaplain Army* A and 33
Shields, M. (Newington) 1
Shields, M.B. (Luss) 23
Shirlaw, R. (Gladsmuir) 3
Shirra, J. (Scone) 28
Silcox, J.R., *School Chaplain* C and 23
Sim, G. (Delting) F
Sim, J.G. (Kirkcaldy) 25
Sim, J.W. (Shotts) 17
Sim, R.L. (Paisley) 14
Simpson, D.C.R., Banchory Devenick 32
Simpson, E.M., Grangemouth 22
Simpson, E.M.(Miss), *WMU, Jerusalem* E
Simpson, E.V., Giffnock 16
Simpson, G.M., Leslie 25
Simpson, J.A., Dornoch 40
Simpson, J.D., Newtonhill 32
Simpson, J.H., Greenock 15
Simpson, N.W.M., Avoch 39
Sinclair, C.A.M., Scripture Union *Secretary* C and 16
Sinclair, D.I., *Lic'ate* G
Sinclair, J.H., Selkirk *Associate* 4
Sinclair, J.S. (Edinburgh Newcraighall) FF
Sinclair, T.S., Stornoway 44
Skakle, G.S. (Aberdeen Powis) 31
Skinner, A., Priestfield 1
Skinner, D.M., Gilmerton 1
Skinner, S. (Lumphanan) 32
Slack, J.W. (Selkirk) 4
Sloan, E.C.(Miss), *D'ess*, World Mission & Unity H
Sloan, H.E.(Miss), *Probr* G
Sloan, R.P., Perth 28
Slorach, A., Lammermuir K and 5
Small, A.L., *Lic'ate* G
Small, R.L., DD (St Cuthbert's) 1
Smart, D.D., Logie 29
Smellie, I.L. (Cockenzie) F
Smith, A., *Chaplain Army* A and 1
Smith, A.E., Johnstone 14

Smith, A.G. (Logie Easter) 39
Smith, A.M., Cumbrae 12
Smith, C.P. (Edinburgh St Bernard's) 28
Smith, D.M.B.A., Logie 23
Smith, D.R., *Lic'ate* G
Smith, F.T., Dunfermline 24
Smith, G.S., King's Park 16
Smith, H.G., Auchterless 34
Smith, H.M.C., Cabrach 35
Smith, J.A.W. (Garvock) 32
Smith, J.D., DD (Auchtergaven) 33
Smith, J.M., Lochmaddy 43
Smith, J.R. (Glasgow Barmulloch) 16
Smith, J.S.A., Drongan 10
Smith, L.(Miss), Trinity *D'ess* H and 29
Smith, L.M.(Miss) (*WMU* 1973) K
Smith, M., Dulnain Bridge 36
Smith, M., Manish Scarista 43
Smith, M.D.W.(Miss), Kirkmahoe 8
Smith, M.M.L.(Miss) (*D'ess*) H
Smith, R. (Balerno) 33
Smith, R., DD (Braid) 1
Smith, R. (Levern and Nitshill) 14
Smith, R. (*World Alliance of Reformed Churches*) C and 8
Smith, R., Denny 22
Smith, R.B.(Dr) (*WMU* 1958) K
Smith, R.C.P., *Audio Visual Director* C and 1
Smith, R.M., Barmulloch *Auxiliary* 16
Smith, R.W., Falkirk 22
Smith, T.F. (Arbuthnott) 32
Smith, W.A. (Blairdaff) F
Smith, W.C.B. (Glassary) 20
Smith, W.E., Livingston K and 2
Sneddon, A.M., *WMU*, Pakistan E
Somerville, A.G. (Glenaray) K and 19
Sommerville, D.F. (Inverchaolin) 20
Sorenson, A.K., Househillwood 16
Southwell, W.A. (Durris) 14
Speed, D.K., Aberfoyle 23
Spence, A., Elgin St Giles' *Associate* 35
Spence, C.K.O. (Craigrownie) 18
Spence, S.M.(Mrs), Kirk o' Shotts 17
Spencer, J. (Penicuik) F
Spiers, J.M., Giffnock 16
Spowart, D. (Grangemouth) F
Spowart, M.G.(Mrs), Papa Westray 45
Squires, J.F.R. (*College of Education*) C and 32
Stalker, D.M.G. (*University*) C and FF
Steel, D, DD (Linlithgow) 1
Steel, G.H.B., Alva 23
Steele, A., *Lic'ate* G
Steele, J.B.K.(Miss) Johnstone *D'ess* H and 14
Steele, L.M., Galashiels 4
Stein, J.C., Carberry Tower *Warden* C and 3

Stein, M.E.(Mrs), Carberry Tower Warden	C and 3	Stewart, J.M. (Glasgow Colston)	16	Strachan, A.E., Musselburgh	3

Stein, M.E.(Mrs), Carberry Tower Warden   C and 3
Stenhouse, W.D., *Probr*   G
Stephen, A.H. (Glasgow Kinning Park)   28
Stephen, D.M., Marchmont   1
Stephen, G. (*Lay Miss'y*)   H
Stephen, J.S. (Botriphnie)   35
Steven, H.A.M., Banff   34
Steven, K.M., East Kilbride   17
Stevens, D. (Glenesk)   30
Stevenson, A. (Greenock)   15
Stevenson, A.L., Balmerino   26
Stevenson, G.M. (Glasgow Martyrs')   16
Stevenson, J., Kirriemuir   30
Stewart, A., Torry   31
Stewart, A.T., Greenbank   16
Stewart, A.T., Cathcart   16
Stewart, C.E., *Chaplain RN*   A and 47
Stewart, C.E. (Dornock)   7
Stewart, C.M., Lausanne   D and 48
Stewart, D. (Fenwick)   20
Stewart, D., Kirkintilloch   16
Stewart, D.C., Leith   1
Stewart, D.E.(Miss), Milton of Campsie   16
Stewart, D.H. (Greenock)   15
Stewart, E.J.(Miss) (*WMU* 1974)   K
Stewart, F.J. (Lochgelly)   3
Stewart, F.M.C., Ardler   27
Stewart, G.C., Huntly   33
Stewart, G.G., Perth   28
Stewart. H.J.A.(Miss), *WMU*, Tabeetha   E
Stewart, J., Clydebank   18
Stewart, J.E.(Mrs), Kildalton   19
Stewart, J.C., East St Nicholas'   31

Stewart, J.M. (Glasgow Colston)   16
Stewart, J.M., Johnstone   7
Stewart, J.M.(Miss) (Dr) (*WMU* 1950)   K
Stewart, J.S., DD (*University*)   B and 1
Stewart, M.L.(Mrs) (*Iona Community*)   F
Stewart, M.S., Boat of Garten   36
Stewart, N.D.(Miss), Strathbungo   16
Stewart, R.J., Bothwell   17
Stewart, U.(Mrs), Kelso *D'ess*   H and 6
Stewart, W., DD (Lecropt)   K and 23
Stewart, W., Sollas *Deacon*   H and 43
Stewart, W.D.S. (Paisley)   F
Stewart, W.T., Glasford   17
Stewart, W.T.A., Barry   30
Still, W., Gilcomston   31
Stirling. A.D., Rhu   18
Stirling, E.(Miss), *WMU*, Tabeetha   E
Stirling, G.A.S., Inverness   37
Stirling, J., Stirling   23
Stitt, R.J.M., Kilwinning   12
Stiven, I.K. Strachur   20
Stobie, C.I.G. (Fyvie)   26
Stoddart, A.G., Meldrum   33
Stoddart, D.L. (Laggan)   36
Stone, C.(Miss), *WMU*, Nepal   E
Stone, L.B. (Aberdeen Associate)   F
Stone, W.V. (Langbank)   15
Storrar, W.F., Carluke   13
Stott, I.F.G. (Nyasaland)   F
Stott, K.D., *Probr*   G

Strachan, A.E., Musselburgh   3
Strachan, C.G., Tiberias   D and 49
Strachan, D.G. (Aberfeldy)   F
Strachan, I.M., Selkirk   4
Strachan, J.C. (Hobkirk)   6
Strachan, S.G., Muthill   28
Strang, J.G., *Lic'ate*   G
Strickland, A., Dairsie   26
Strong, C., Creich   26
Strong, C.A., *Probr*   G
Stuart, A.(Miss), Ancrum *D'ess*   H and 6
Stuart, A.M. (Banchory)   31
Stuart, C.H. (Echt)   32
Stuart, J., Fisherton   10
Stuart, J.T., Duffus   35
Stuart, W. (Kingswells)   31
Sutcliffe, I., Shapinsay   45
Sutherland, A.M. (Resolis)   39
Sutherland, A.S. (Symington)   10
Sutherland, D.G. (Aberdeen Causewayend)   26
Sutherland, D.I., Hutchesontown   16
Sutherland, E.W. (Bonkyl)   F
Sutherland, E.W.(Miss), Balornock   16
Sutherland, W., Bo'ness   22
Swan, A. (Greenock)   15
Swan, A.F., Buittle   8
Swan, J.R.D., *Lic'ate*   G
Swanston, T., Inverness   37
Swinburne, N., Sauchie   23
Swinton, A.C., *Hospital Chaplain*   C and 31
Symington, A.H., Bearsden   18
Symington, R.C., Killearn   23

T

Tait, A., St Enoch's   16
Tait, H.A.G., Crieff   28
Tait, J.M., Leith   1
Tait, T.W., Rattray   27
Tait, W.G., Mossgreen *Auxiliary*   24
Talman, H. (Polmont)   22
Tamas, B., Budapest   D
Taverner, G.R., Mertoun   4
Taylor, A.H.S., Brydekirk   7
Taylor, A.S., Greenock   15

Taylor, A.T., Isle of Mull   21
Taylor, A.T.H. (Dunoon)   K and 26
Taylor, D.J., Colston Milton   16
Taylor, H.G., St David's   16
Taylor, H.J. (*WMU* 1968)   K
Taylor, H.M.(Miss) (*WMU* 1964)   K
Taylor, I., Abdie   26
Taylor, J.D. (Oathlaw)   30
Taylor, J.H.B. (Irvine)   F
Taylor, J.T.H. (Glenrothes)   25

Taylor, P. (St Andrew's Clermiston)   F
Taylor, P.R., Torphins   32
Taylor, R. (Perth)   28
Taylor, T.R., Clackmannan   23
Taylor, W., Buckie   35
Taylor, W.R., Slateford   1
Teague, Y.(Mrs), Diaconate Secretary   H
Telfer, A.B., Falkirk   22

U

V

W

Waddell, J.M. (New Cumnock) F
Walker, A.C. (Baillieston) 16
Walker, A.L. (Glasgow Trinity
Possil) 16
Walker, C.D. (Auchindoir) 34
Walker, D.K., Zambia D
Walker, D.R. (Buenos Aires) F
Walker, D.S. (Makerstoun) 23
Walker, E.W. (Marnoch) 34
Walker, G.R. (Torphins) 1
Walker, H., DD, (Home Board
Secretary) C and 1
Walker, I., St Colm's *Tutor* C and 1
Walker, J.B., Queen's College,
Birmingham C and 47
Walker, J.N. (Foss) F
Walker, K.D.F., Athelstaneford 3
Walker, R.F., Strathaven 17
Walker, R.M., Gardenstown 34
Walker, R.W. (Lesmahagow) 13
Walker, V.M.(Mrs), *Lic'ate* F
Wallace, A.D.(Miss), *WMU*, North
India E
Wallace, C., Balmaghie 8
Wallace, D.S. (*Chaplain
RAF*) A and 47
Wallace, D.W., Kilmodan 20
Wallace, H.M., Mount Florida 16
Wallace, J.H., Peebles 4
Wallace, J.K., Falkirk 22
Wallace, R.J.S. (Foveran) 33
Wallace, R.S. (Lanark) F
Wallace, W. (Corgarff) FF
Wallace, W.F., Wick 41
Walton, A., *University* B and 31
Ward, A.H., Cambuslang 16
Ward, M.J., Kinfauns 28
Wardlaw, E.G.S., Bathgate 2
Wark, A.C., Larkhall 17
Wark, T.L. (Turriff) 34
Warner, K., Halkirk 41
Warnock, D., Kirkcaldy 25
Warnock, J. (Biggar) FF
Warwick, I.C., *Chaplain
Army* A and 37
Watson, D.H.A., Anstruther 26
Watson, E.R.L.(Miss), Kildonan 12
Watson, G., Hawick 6
Watson, G.A. (Guthrie) 35
Watson, J., High Bonnybridge 22
Watson, J., Bowden 4
Watson, J.B., Canonbie 7
Watson, J.F. (*Lay Miss'y*) H
Watson, J.M., *Probr* G
Watson, T.D.,Kilmore *Associate* 21
Watson, V.G.C.(Miss),
Kelvinside 16
Watson, W.H., DD (Callander) F
Watt, A.G. (St Michael's) 1
Watt, H.F. (Lossiemouth) 35
Watt, H.F., Lochwood 16
Watt, J.A.R. (Stromness) 28
Watt, J.G.M. (Pollokshields) F
Watt, J.H.I. (*College of
Education*) C and 14
Watt, J.W., *Lic'ate* G
Watt, L.G. (Abernethy) 28
Watt, R. (Aberdeen Woodside) 23

Watt, R.J.G., *Lic'ate* G
Watt, W.D., Aboyne 32
Watt, W.G. (Aberdeen S of St
Nicholas Kincorth) 31
Waugh, J. (Falkirk) F
Waugh, J.L., Birsay 45
Weatherhead, J.L., *Clerk of
Assembly* C and 1
Webster, A.F., Victoria Park 16
Webster, E.H.(Miss) (*D'ess*) H
Webster, J.G., Troon 10
Webster, P., Greenock 15
Webster, W.T. (Dean) 1
Wedderburn, A.J.M.,
University B and 26
Weir, A.A.M. (Forglen) 34
Weir, C.J.M., DD
(*University*) B and 16
Weir, D.G., Saltcoats 12
Weir, E.V.(Mrs). *Lic'ate* G
Weir, M.(Miss) (*D'ess*) H
Weir, W.M. (Limekilns) 12
Weller, T.H.B. (Grangemouth) 1
Wells, A.M., Cumbernauld
Associate 22
Wells, J.R., *Probr* G
Welsh, A., Dennistoun 16
Welsh, J.R.(Miss) (*D'ess*) H
Westmarland, C.A.,
Malta D and 48
White, A. (Aberluthnott) 30
White, B.A., Kirkcaldy 25
White, C.P., St David's 1
White, E.(Miss) Townhead
D'ess H and 16
White, E.M., Uddingston 17
White, I., *Lic'ate* G
White, R.C. (Thornhill) 8
Whiteford, D.H. (Gullane) 3
Whiteford, J.D., *Probr* G
Whiteford, R.S. (Shapinsay) 35
Whitelaw, W.D. (Bothkennar) 22
Whitley, L.A.B., Montrose 30
Whitton, J., Larkhall 17
Whitton, J.P., *Chaplain
Army* A and 1
Whyte, D.G.H. (Inverarity) 30
Whyte, G.J., Langside 16
Whyte, H.S.(Miss) (*D'ess*) H
Whyte, I.A., Coatbridge 17
Whyte, J., Broom 16
Whyte, J.A. (*University*) B and 26
Whyte, J.H. (Gourock) 15
Whyte, J.J.S. (Lochend) 24
Whyte, M.A.(Mrs) Symington 10
Whyte, N.R., Glassary 19
Whyte, W.B., Nairn 37
Wigglesworth, J.C., W M & U,
General Secretary C and 1
Wightman, J.P.E. (Girvan) 10
Wilkie, G.D. (Kirkcaldy) 1
Wilkie, J.L., World Mission &
Unity *Secretary* C and 1
Wilkie, J.R., Penpont 8
Wilkie, W.E., South of St
Nicholas' 31
Wilkinson, J. (Kenya) K and 1
Wilkinson, W.B., Kirkwall 21

Williams, D.A. (Stenness) 45
Williamson, C.R., Aberdalgie 28
Williamson, J., Garvald *Auxiliary* 3
Williamson, J.A., DD
(Newlands) 13
Williamson, M.J.C., Yell 46
Williamson, T. (Dyke) 42
Williamson, W.E. (Cummertrees) 8
Willox, H.N. (Carnwath) 18
Wills, W.F. (Kilsyth) 12
Wilson, A.B.A. (Torryburn) F
Wilson, A.G.N., Rubislaw 31
Wilson, A.J., Downfield 29
Wilson, I.M., Cawdor 37
Wilson, J., Innerleithen 4
Wilson, J.F. (Montrose) 29
Wilson, J.H., Cleland 17
Wilson, J.J., *Lic'ate* G
Wilson, J.L., Strichen 34
Wilson, J.M., *Adviser RE* C and 37
Wilson, J.M., Bolton 3
Wilson, J.P., Lanark 13
Wilson, J.R. (Edinburgh
St Bride's) F
Wilson, M.(Miss), Gorgie
D'ess H and 1
Wilson, M. (Nagpur) F
Wilson, M.H.(Miss) (*WMU
1977*) K
Wilson, P.D. (Aberdeen
St Columba's) F
Wilson, P.M.(Mrs), Howwood 14
Wilson, R., *Auxiliary* 18
Wilson, R.M., DD
(*University*) B and 26
Wilson, T.F., Benholm 32
Wilson, T.W. (Denbeath) 25
Wilson, W.S., Kirkcudbright 8
Winning, A.A.(Miss), Morvern 38
Wishart, J., Deer 34
Wood, D.C. (*Lay Miss'y*) H
Wood, F. (Morningside) FF
Wood, G.K. (Channelkirk) 24
Wood, G.M., Largs 12
Wood, J.L.K., Ruthrieston 31
Wood, J.S., DD (Aberdeen
South) 31
Wotherspoon, I.G., Portobello 1
Wotherspoon, R.C., Castlemilk 16
Wright, D.L., Stornoway 44
Wright, E.J. (St George's Tron
Assistant) F
Wright, I.A.M., Falkland 26
Wright, J.H.A. (Moulin) F
Wright, J.P. (Fort William) F
Wright, L.(Miss), Iona Community
D'ess H and 38
Wright, M., Craigrownie 18
Wright, N.B. (Kingussie) 28
Wright, P.E. (Muiravonside) F
Wright, R.V.S., DD (Canongate) 1
Wright, W.G.A. (*Chaplain
Army*) A and 1
Wylie, W., Airdrie 17
Wylie, W.A., *Industrial
Chaplain* C and 31
Wyllie, H.R., Hamilton 17
Wynne, A.T.E. Nicosia D

Y

Yates, C.B., Lic'ate	G	Young, G.A. (St Bernard's)	1	Young, W.G. (Resolis) K and 39
Yates, R.D. (Cambuslang)	F	Young, G.S., Blairgowrie	27	Younger, A.(Mrs), Garthamlock 16
Yorke, K.B., Ochiltree	10	Young, H.J. (Edinburgh Dean)	31	Younger, A.S., Inverness 37
Young, A.F.T. (Blairgowrie)	27	Young, J., Paisley	14	Youngson, P., Kirriemuir 30
Young, A.W., Ardrossan	12	Young, J.N., *WMU*, Pakistan	E	Yule, G.S.S. (*University*) B and FF
Young, D.A., Kirkmuirhill	13	Young, M.(Mrs) (*D'ess*)	H	Yule, R.F., Fraserburgh 34
Young, E.M.(Mrs), Larbert	22	Young, W.F. (Kinglassie)	25	

INDEX OF PLACES

The number at the right of the column is that of the Presbytery.

Where the name is followed by another in italics the latter represents the name under which the former appears in the Presbytery lists or the name of the parish within which it lies. A second name in parentheses but not italics is meant to differentiate between two places of the same name. The full title of a parish, when it includes more names than one, appears only once in the list, the second and subsequent names appear alone with a reference in italics to the first name where the full title will be found.

INDEX OF SUBJECTS

INDEX TO ADVERTISERS